THE LOVOZERO ALKALI MASSIF

THE LOVOZERO ALKALI MASSIF

K. A. VLASOV
M. Z. KUZ'MENKO
E. M. ES'KOVA

Translated by
D. G. FRY and K. SYERS

Edited by
S. I. TOMKEIEFF and M. H. BATTEY

OLIVER & BOYD
EDINBURGH AND LONDON

OLIVER AND BOYD LTD

Tweeddale Court
Edinburgh 1

39a Welbeck Street
London W1

This is a translation of Ловозерский щелочный массив by
К. А. Власов, М. В. Кузьменко and **Е. М. Еськова**,
published by the U.S.S.R. Academy of Sciences Press,
Moscow, 1959.

First English edition 1966

Printed in Great Britain
by Robert Cunningham and Sons Ltd, Alva, Clackmannanshire

PREFACE

THE Lovozero alkali massif has long attracted the attention of scientists; yet although a great deal of work had already been done in the region at the time when we began studying the massif, several aspects of its geology were still obscure. Nothing had been done to find out how the distribution of the main rock-forming minerals was related to that of the rare-metal minerals and inadequate attention had been given both to the pegmatites and to the mineralogy, genesis and geochemistry of the massif.

We began with the aim of producing a comprehensive account of the pegmatites; but since the alkali pegmatites are spatially and genetically closely connected with the parent rocks, it proved impossible to study them without first establishing the precise chemical and mineralogical composition of the massif as a whole.

Part I of the present monograph describes the geological structure of the massif and the chemical and mineralogical composition of the rocks in each of its constituent complexes. We have been at pains to clarify the distribution patterns of the rock-forming and of the rare-metal minerals and the interrelationship between these patterns.

Part II describes the most typical pegmatitic bodies in each of the three rock complexes in the massif, together with a number of hybrid pegmatite veins. Several hundred new pegmatitic bodies have been found and of these more than 60 of the largest were studied in detail. The more important of the pegmatitic bodies previously recorded were also investigated. By taking into account not only mineralogical composition, but also shape, size and internal structure of these bodies, we have established the relationship between the distribution of rare-metal minerals and that of the main rock-forming minerals—that is, between the internal structure and the degree of differentiation of the pegmatites. The most highly-developed pegmatitic bodies have a clearly defined zonal structure owing to a succession of well-defined mineral parageneses, each group of rock-forming minerals having a characteristic suite of rare-metal associates.

Our structural and paragenetic classification of the pegmatites is based on a large amount of data relating to both the mineralogical composition and the more general features of internal structure and mineral paragenesis.

Part III describes 108 minerals found in the massif, 70 of them additional to previous lists. Eleven are new species (nenadkevichite, karpinskyite, vinogradovite, gerasimovskite, seidozerite, belovite, kupletskite, hydrocerite, karnasurtite, beryllite and labuntsovite); several others have not previously been described in

v

connexion with the Lovozero massif (elpidite, pyrochlore, rutile, brookite, anatase, manganosteenstrupine, polylithionite, epididymite, eudidymite, leucophane, genthelvite, chabazite, allophane, chlorites, montmorillonite, sauconite, halloysite, kaolinite, nontronite, hydrogoethite, cryptomelane, vernadite, boehmite, hemimorphite, soda (natrite), jarosite, apophyllite and others).

We have paid special attention to the genetic interrelationships, distribution patterns and paragenetic associations of these particular minerals.

The discovery that the pegmatites contain lithium and beryllium minerals and relatively large amounts of gallium opens up a new avenue in the mineralogy and geochemistry of these elements in alkali massifs.

In Part IV a number of theoretical questions of the geochemistry and origin of the massif are discussed in the light of the data set out in Parts I-III. For the first time, an average chemical composition of the various rock complexes and of the massif as a whole is given, listing not only the principal and secondary elements but also a number of rare elements. Problems of the geochemistry of particular chemical elements in the massif are discussed.

The abundant data cast new light on the problem of the origin of the massif, revealing and accounting for the main factors that have determined its history.

The chemical, spectrographic, radiochemical and polarographic analyses, the differential thermal analysis and dehydration curves and the X-ray powder patterns employed were all produced at the Institute of Ore Deposit Geology, Petrography, Mineralogy and Geochemistry and the Institute of Rare-element Mineralogy, Geochemistry and Crystallochemistry of the USSR Academy of Sciences.

In the collection and interpretation of data the authors have received much assistance from L. S. Borodin, E. I. Semenov, I. P. Tikhonenkov, E. B. Khalezova and Yu. S. Slepnev, to whom their sincere thanks are due. Studies on pegmatites by these investigators have been used in the present work.

We are indebted also to M. E. Kazakova, who performed most of the chemical analyses of the highly complex rare-metal minerals and to Yu. S. Nesterova, whose rock analyses showing twenty-six chemical elements made it possible to calculate the average chemical composition of the massif.

Laboratory assistants R. I. Sokolov and A. A. Sitnin gave much help in processing the rock material.

We particularly thank Dr V. I. Gerasimovskii for undertaking the considerable task of editing this book.

A BRIEF HISTORY OF PREVIOUS RESEARCH

The Lovozero alkali massif was first described by W. Ramsay in 1887. His pioneer work on its geology and mineralogy provided the basis for the geological expedition under his leadership, which from 1890 to 1899 made a detailed study of the Lovozero and Khibiny alkali massifs.

In 1894 and 1898 Ramsay published monographs based on the 1887-1891 field and laboratory research, elucidating aspects of the geological structure and describing the principal rock types. He suggested that the Khibiny and Lovozero complexes were parts of a single large intrusive mass, of which the Khibiny tundras formed the middle (plutonic) part and the Lovozero massif the upper part. He found evidence for this in the structure of the lujavrites, which 'is either the result of flow in a deep-seated rock or, as seems more probable, has been formed in relative tranquillity through crystallization induced near the roof of the intrusive mass'. He continues: 'That the rocks have developed their gneissic structure because of the roof is proved by the fact that this structure is invariably conformable with the roof, being either almost horizontal or slightly inclined, and matching its dips and rises.' (Ramsay, 1894.)

Ramsay was the first to draw attention to the layered structure of the Lovozero massif (1894): 'The higher parts are for the most part made up of massive rocks which, because of a parallel arrangement of gneissoid lujavrite and nepheline-lujavrite layers, resemble a complex of sedimentary deposits. Similar features occur in Greenland.' He explains the layering as due to repeated intrusions of new magma: 'The recurrent alternation of layers in the upper parts can be explained on the supposition that the rocks nearest the roof were the first to solidify and were divided by cleavage planes more quickly and readily than the rest; at the same time, new portions of magma from below were constantly arriving and penetrating along these cracks.'

The new minerals discovered by Ramsay remained unstudied and unnamed, listed simply under serial numbers, until they were investigated by mineralogists of the USSR Academy of Sciences under the direction of A. E. Fersman. Ramsay's list was then extended to several times its former length.

After Ramsay, investigation of the Lovozero massif was abandoned until 1921, when a joint team from the Institute for Study of the North and the USSR Academy of Sciences, under the direction of A. E. Fersman, began systematic mineralogical and petrographical research on the Khibiny and Lovozero massifs. This work went on until 1941. The results were published in monographs by A. E. Fersman (1922-1937), O. A. Vorob'eva (1933-1951), V. I. Gerasimovskii (1934-1957), E. M. Bonshtedt (1923-1937), N. N. Gutkova (1924-1937), E. E. Kostyleva (1923-1945), A. A. Labuntsov (1925-1927), V. I. Vlodavets (1933-1937), G. T. Kravchenko (1933-1936), L. M. Alekseeva (1927), I. D. Borneman (1936-1947), V. S. Bykova (1941), T. A. Burova (1936), V. M. Kupletskii (1925-1937), V. I. Kryzhanovskii (1924), V. V. Shcherbina (1933) and P. N. Chirvinskii (1936).

Since Ramsay's time, the main contributors to our knowledge of the Lovozero massif have been O. A. Vorob'eva, V. I. Gerasimovskii and N. A. Eliseev.

Vorob'eva has described the geological structure of the massif and the petrography of all the rock complexes, worked out the fundamental petrology and put forward her theory on the origin of the massif. She explains the primary layering in terms of Bowen's postulate of 'autointrusion' (Vorob'eva, 1940), which she interprets as 'the injection of a residual foyaitic melt into a mass of parent lujavrite magma that has begun to crystallize but is not yet plastic'. Her interpretation thus has features in common with Ramsay's views on the origin of the massif.

Gerasimovskii (1935-1950) has done much work on the mineralogy of the massif and has briefly described the pegmatites, distinguishing eight types by mineralogical composition. The first to consolidate the mineralogical data, he described 66 minerals, 10 of them new. He also described the main crystallo-chemical substitutions that occur, and produced a classified geochemical survey of the principal elements.

Gerasimovskii's views on the origin of the massif differ somewhat from those of Vorob'eva. Although he, too, attributes the structure of the differentiated complex to layer-by-layer injections of a residual foyaitic-urtitic magma, along trachytic planes in lujavrites that had already begun to crystallize, he believes that the lujavrites were already in a plastic state when this occurred.

Since 1930 industrial organizations have taken a hand in studying the Lovozero massif and a number of papers on questions related to its mineral wealth have appeared, notably by I. V. Zelenkov (1940), N. K. Nefedov (1938), V. I. Vlodavets (1933), K. K. Khazanovich (1934-1936), T. E. Vul'f (1935), M. L. Zolotar' (1936), V. I. Kotel'nikov (1935), S. A. Pervushin (1935), S. D. Pokrovskii (1933-1934), E. A. Sal'e (1932-1933), L. B. Antonov (1935), V. A. Vakar (1932), A. S. Sakharov and others.

From 1935 to 1937 the structural geology of the massif was studied under the direction of N. A. Eliseev (1938) and a comprehensive geological map was compiled. Many data were thus accumulated and have been published as a series of monographs by Eliseev (1936-1953), who attributes the layered structure to crystallization-differentiation of intruded magma *in situ* and suggests that flow effects and gravitation were the main factors in determining the spatial distribution of minerals already crystallized in the moving magma. Regarding the differentiated complex as a system of zones consisting of foyaites (bottom part), lujavrites (middle part) and urtites (upper part), he explains its formation in the following way. Nepheline, separating out at the beginning of the crystallization process, was carried upwards under the influence of the horizontal movement of the magma and gravitation. Successive batches of nepheline crystals encountered concentrations of nepheline that had separated out earlier and joined on to these, with the result that urtitic layers, with 80 per cent of nepheline crystals, were formed in a medium that was still moving. These layers formed barriers preventing to some extent the upward displacement of large nepheline crystals and the penetration of volatile substances. The accumulation of volatiles under the nepheline horizons made for lower viscosity in the magma, and in these sectors movement within the crystallizing magma was facilitated, giving rise to a trachytoid structure in the lujavritic layers. In the lower part of the volatile-impoverished zone the viscosity was higher and this part solidified somewhat earlier, to form the foyaites. The abrupt contact between the lujavrites and the urtites is due to the lujavritic magmas having moved at a significantly higher speed than the nepheline barrier.

The difference in the rate of movement between the urtites and the foyaites was slight; moreover, individual crystals from the nepheline layer were able to float up to the top, with the result that we find gradual transitions between these rock types, in the form of juvites.

The limits of possible vertical displacement of the nepheline were several times less than the thickness of the upper part of the complex, with the result that several bed-like accumulations of nepheline formed simultaneously.

Research on the Lovozero massif was interrupted by the second world war and resumed only in 1946-1947. In 1947, an expedition to the Kola Peninsula under the direction of K. A. Vlasov was arranged, under the auspices of the Institute of Geological Sciences (USSR Academy of Sciences), to study the alkali pegmatites and the mineralogy and geochemistry of the massif. The results of this expedition, which worked until 1955, are set out in the present monograph.

Side by side with the work of the Kola expedition, R. M. Yashina and L. B. Tumilovich, of the same Institute, studied the composition and rock-chemistry of the differentiated complex and the chemical composition of loparite, under the direction of Vorob'eva.

Tumilovich reports (in a personal communication) that in studying the chemistry of loparite from various rock horizons she has found corroboration for V. S. Bykova's earlier contention (1941) that the chemical composition of the loparite in the differentiated complex follows a regular pattern of change with depth, the niobium content decreasing and the rare-earth content increasing. In addition, Tumilovich has established that loparite from different rocks (urtites and lujavrites) within the same three-fold group of strata (i.e. at any one horizon) varies little in chemical composition. This is an important contribution towards explaining the process of layering in the differentiated complex and the genesis of the massif itself.

R. M. Yashina has studied the quantitative mineralogical composition of all the rock varieties in the differentiated complex and indicated the main chemical trends in these rocks.

In 1948 and 1949 a team of workers from the Leningrad Mining Institute studied the Lovozero massif under the direction of N. V. Ivanov. From the data then collected, Ivanov explains the layered structure of the differentiated complex as due to repeated intrusion of alkali magma layers, with subsequent differentiation of each batch of magma into foyaites, urtites and lujavrites. The results of this research have unfortunately not been published.

ACKNOWLEDGMENTS

SPECIAL thanks are due to the Department of Education and Science (Great Britain), and to The Geochemical Society and the National Science Foundation (U.S.A.). Without their generous support, this edition could not have been published.

NOTE

KUZ'MA ALEKSEEVICH VLASOV, born in 1905, died on 29 September 1964. An obituary notice appeared in *Proceedings of the Geological Society of London*, No. 1628 [Session 1964-5], dated 31 December 1965, pp. 209-10.

CONTENTS

PART FOUR
GEOCHEMISTRY AND GENESIS

PART ONE

GEOLOGICAL STRUCTURE AND CHEMICAL-MINERALOGICAL COMPOSITION OF THE MASSIF

INTRODUCTION

THE Lovozero alkali massif, covers an area of 650 km² in the central part of the Kola peninsula. On the east and west it is washed by two large lakes, the Lovozero and the Umbozero, both with a north-south alignment (Fig. 1). To the north and to the south it is bordered by marshy depressions with many lakes, broken by low hills covered with coniferous and mixed forest. In the centre of the massif, at an altitude of 197 m, lies the great mountain lake of Seidyavr, joined to the Lovozero by the river Seidiok. The Seidyavr depression gives the massif the shape of a horse-shoe, open to the east.

Morphologically the Lovozero massif is a mountain plateau sloping gradually to the south-east, with a very strong relief owing to the abundance of cirques and to the deep valleys of the rivers flowing into the three lakes. These valleys dissect the massif into table-mountains (Fig. 2) rising 500-1000 m above the surrounding plain. The highest mountains (Sengischorr, Angvundaschorr, Alluaiv and Kedykvyrpakhk) are situated in the north-western part of the massif, the lowest (Punkaruaiv and Suoluaiv) in its south-eastern part.

The lower parts of the mountain slopes are usually covered with coarse scree; the upper parts consist of bare, rocky outcrops. Because of the strong jointing and steep slopes in the central parts of the massif rock falls are frequent. The mountain streams for the most part flow in deep, narrow courses, sometimes with vertical walls.

These mountains contain a great many semicircular cirques with vertical walls up to 400 m high, usually open towards the periphery of the massif and often containing tarns. The largest of these are the Raslaks, I and II, situated east of Alluaiv, Sengisyavr on Sengischorr and Raityavr between Strashempakhk and Engpor.

The smoothed-off mountain tops, the deep U-shaped river valleys with their vertical walls and the numerous cirques all indicate that the relief is largely the result of glacial erosion, of which there is further evidence in the ubiquitous and abundant moraine deposits.

The foothills, forming a belt of 1-2 km wide, are made up of moraine deposits covered with moss, grass and dwarf birch. Coniferous and mixed forests are found at the foot of the mountains, downstream in the river valleys and along the Seidyavr depression (Fig. 3).

The climate is harsh, with abundant rainfall and much fog. Even on warm summer days the temperature of the lake waters rarely exceeds 14-15°C.

Fig. 1. General view of the Lovozero massif from the north-west shore of Umbozero (photograph by Z. Z. Vinogradov)

Fɪɢ. 2. Plateau-like character of the mountain massif. View from Seid''yavr (photograph by Z. Z. Vinogradov)

Fɪɢ. 3. View of Lepkhe-Nel'm from Seid''yavr (photograph by Z. Z. Vinogradov)

CHAPTER ONE

GEOLOGICAL STRUCTURE OF THE MASSIF

THE Lovozero nepheline-syenite massif, a complex body formed during several phases of intrusive activity, is a classic example of a beautifully differentiated primarily layered intrusive. Its absolute age, according to Gerling (1941) is 266 million years, corresponding to the Upper Devonian or Lower Carboniferous. Structurally the massif consists of four complexes: (1) a complex of eudialytic lujavrites, (2) a differentiated complex, (3) a complex of poikilitic syenites and (4) dyke rocks.

The eudialytic lujavrite complex forms the upper part of the massif, above 400 m absolute altitude in its eastern part and above 500-800 m in the western and southern parts, and accounts for 30 per cent in volume of that part of the massif which has been studied (to a depth of 1400 m). Its thickness varies from 150 m in the eastern part to 300-500 m in the western part (see below, Fig. 5). The complex contains:

(1) eudialytic lujavrites (90 per cent of the total volume); (2) porphyritic rocks (about 10 per cent of the total); (3) eudialytic dyke lujavrites; (4) eudialytites.

The porphyritic rocks form a thick horizon at the bottom of the complex at the contact with the differentiated complex, as well as irregularly-shaped bodies and veins in the eudialytic lujavrites.

The contact between the porphyritic rocks and those of the differentiated complex is abrupt, the contact surface undulating and dipping gently (5-10°) towards the centre of the massif. The porphyritic rocks often appear to truncate certain horizons in the differentiated complex, and are in contact with various rocks in the latter.

The eudialytic dyke lujavrites have not been studied by us. According to Eliseev (1938) they sometimes occur among unlayered eudialytic lujavrites.

The differentiated complex, more than 1000 m thick, forms the bottom of the massif, accounting for 65 per cent of its total volume. The real thickness of this complex is still unknown, for a structure-testing borehole sunk to a depth of more than 500 m at the foot of Karnasurt did not strike bedrock. A typical feature of the complex is its distinctly layered structure, due to an alternation of foyaites, urtites, lujavrites and other rocks, differing from one another in their proportions of the principal rock-forming minerals.

The foyaites are essentially microcline-bearing and the urtites nephelinitic;

the lujavrites contain equal amounts of nepheline, microcline and aegirine. The other rock varieties are intermediate.

In both complexes the rocks dip towards the centre of the massif at an angle of 5-10°, seldom more, except that at the centre itself, beside Seidyavr, they dip at the same angle in the reverse direction.

About 5 per cent of the massif consists of a poikilitic nepheline-sodalite-syenite complex, the rocks of which are widely distributed in the north-eastern (Karnasurt), central (Seidyavr area) and south-eastern (Ninchurt, Suoluaiv and other mountains) parts of the massif, where they break through the eudialytic lujavrite and differentiated complexes (Fig. 5). The poikilitic syenites form irregularly-shaped bodies $1\frac{1}{2}$ to 2 km² in area, veins up to 5 m thick and 100 m long and sheet-like or lenticular bodies.

Dyke rocks, which are extremely rare, are represented by monchiquites, tinguaites, nepheline-basalts, fourchites, shonkinites and other rocks (Eliseev et al., 1938, 1939). These all form dykes, 50-150 cm thick or occasionally thicker, extensive along the strike, both in the differentiated and in the eudialytic lujavrite complex, cutting across the trachytoid and laminated structures of these rocks.

The pegmatites are ubiquitous, occurring in all the complexes as veins up to 2 m thick and 20-50 m or occasionally 200-300 m long, as irregularly-shaped stocks up to 45×75 m in area, as small schlieren of irregular, often bizarre shape, with gradual transitions to the parent rocks and as pegmatitic horizons up to 2 m thick that can be traced, with interruptions, throughout the massif.

The alkali intrusion breaks through Archaean formations and contains in its upper parts xenoliths of sedimentary and effusive Devonian rocks (Fig. 4). The largest Archaean outcrops are to be found at the foot of P'yalkimporr, Vavnbed, Flora, Kitkn'yun, Appuaiv, Angvundaschorr, Alluaiv and other mountains (Fig. 5). Owing to their poor exposure the Archaean rocks have been incompletely studied. They are represented by biotite-plagioclase gneiss, garnet-biotite gneiss, sillimanite gneiss, amphibolitic gneisses, granite gneisses with pegmatites and aplites, migmatites, amphibolites, peridotites, pyroxenites, hornblendites and amphibolitized gabbros. Of these the commonest are the granite gneisses (Eliseev, 1938).

The contact between the massif and the Archaean rocks is abrupt and intrusive. Contact-metasomatic alteration is commonest in the acid Archaean varieties—the granite gneisses and gneisses. Until recently it was believed that there was comparatively little contact alteration of the country rocks by nepheline-syenites beyond a zone a few m thick (Eliseev, 1953). Tikhonenkov, however, has recently shown that the contact alterations in the Lovozero massif cover a much wider area, the contact zone reaching a thickness of 300-400 m in some places. This zone has been most fully studied on the northern slopes of Vavnbed, where the contact plane dips outward from the massif at an angle of 75-80°. Here wedge-shaped xenolithic gneiss residuals measuring 50×200 m lie parallel to the contact, among the alkali rocks. Aegirine-lujavrites of the central, poorly-layered part of the differentiated complex are here in contact with the country rocks, represented by plagioclase gneisses.

The first indication that the aegirine-lujavrites are altered is the appearance in them of ilmenite, roughly 150-200 m from the contact. The ilmenite has to some degree been replaced by ramsayite and lamprophyllite. The degree of replacement of ilmenite by titanosilicates gradually declines with proximity to the contact and the tenor of ilmenite increases. Thirty to fifty m from the contact the trachytoid texture of the lujavrites is destroyed and they gradually give way to non-layered mesocratic aegirine-syenites characterized by taxitic structure, the sudden enrichment of particular sectors in eudialyte (sometimes up to 30 per cent), extensive development of schlieren-like pegmatoid segregations and the occurrence of minerals, such as aenigmatite, astrophyllite and sphene, that are rarely found in alkali rocks.

Nearer to the contact the mesocratic aegirine-nepheline-syenites are gradually replaced by leucocratic pegmatoid rocks and pegmatites. The total thickness of the pegmatoid zone rarely exceeds 3-5 m.

Microcline, eudialyte and plagioclase alkali-syenites (fenites) formed through the reworking of plagioclase-gneisses by alkali magma are extensively developed at the border of the intrusion. The 15 m thick belt of alkali-syenites has a zonal structure. Microcline-eudialyte-alkali-syenites with aegirine, arfvedsonite and sphene have developed in the immediate vicinity of the contact; these are followed by plagioclase-alkali-syenites which gradually turn into plagioclase-gneisses. The plagioclase-alkali-syenites, containing relicts of plagioclase grains, retain the structure of plagioclase-gneisses even while the mineralogical composition is changing.

The syenites developed at the contact are made up of two paragenetic mineral associations. One of these is typical of the enclosing plagioclase-gneisses and the other has formed through the action of an alkali magma on these gneisses. The alkali-syenites have been subjected to intensive postmagmatic reworking (albitization) by alkaline solutions passing along the weakened contact zone. The most highly albitized potassic rocks are the microcline-eudialyte-alkali-syenites converted during the final stage into albitites. Connected with the albitization process is a particular paragenetic complex of minerals (rinkolite, apophyllite, pectolite, narsarsukite, ilmenite, zircon, pyrochlore, lithium micas, fluorite and sphene) which do not usually occur or are present in very small quantities in the Lovozero rocks.

Devonian xenoliths of irregular shape covering areas of several km² occur in the north-eastern, eastern and southern parts of the massif (Flora, P'yalkimporr, Vavnbed, Appuaiv, Kitkn'yun and other mountains).

The constitution of the Palaeozoic rock complex is highly varied (Eliseev, 1937, 1953) and includes effusive, tuffaceous and sedimentary rocks: augitic rocks, essexitic rocks, and porphyritic picrites, alkali-trachytes and porphyritic phonolites together with their tuffs, ashy, argillaceous and marly shales, quartzites and sandstones. The argillaceous and ashy shales are the most widespread sediments and the augite-porphyrites the commonest effusives. On Kuamdespakhk, Ninchurt, Kuivchorr and elsewhere, the various rocks are often interlayered with fragmental effusive rock cemented by argillaceous and tuffaceous material.

Since many of the pegmatitic veins are emplaced in augite-porphyrites, and the assimilation of these rocks by the pegmatitic solution is accompanied by significant changes in its chemistry, we shall describe the augite-porphyrites in detail.

These augite-porphyrites are particularly common in the north-eastern part of the massif, comprising compact porphyritic rocks with a finely crystalline to cryptocrystalline ground mass of dark grey, almost black colour and occasional phenocrysts of light grey-green, light green or black augite. The proportion of phenocrysts varies between 1 and 5 per cent. They reach a size of 1×0.3 cm and are usually 0.3×0.1 cm in cross-section. The groundmass of the rock, which has often not completely devitrified, consists of plagioclase, augite, hornblende, biotite, chlorite and titanomagnetite. Sphene and apatite are very occasionally present in small quantities. Plagioclase usually predominates over the coloured minerals. In texture the groundmass is almost doleritic.

Augite (titanaugite) forms phenocrysts and can also be seen as small, irregularly-shaped grains in the groundmass. In both situations it may be replaced by biotite, amphibole and chlorite.

Plagioclase (andesine-labradorite) is developed chiefly in the fine-grained groundmass.

Minute flakes of biotite form intimate intergrowths with chlorite and magnetite. Coarser scaly segregations have formed where the biotite has replaced the phenocrystic augite.

Chlorite is present in appreciable amounts in the form of fine flaky segregations developed from augite.

Titanomagnetite occurs in the form of fine segregations, mainly in the groundmass. It very often forms by the alteration of coarse augite phenocrysts and is found in intimate intergrowth with biotite and chlorite. It is in turn replaced by

TABLE 1 Chemical compositions of augite porphyrites (11 per cent)

Constituent	P'yalkimporr	Flora
SiO_2	45·78	43·52
TiO_2	7·80	3·72
ZrO_2	—	0·24
Al_2O_3	8·08	9·00
Fe_2O_3	5·90	3·87
FeO	8·65	8·20
MnO	0·12	0·03
MgO	7·61	9·29
CaO	10·73	10·00
Na_2O	2·80	10·26
K_2O	1·97	1·23
H_2O^+	0·73	0·19
H_2O^-	0·24	0·10
P_2O_5	—	0·58
Total	100·41	100·23
Analyst	E. A. Sverzhinskaya	T. A. Burova
Reference	N. A. Eliseev (1953)	

sphene developing in the fissures and attacking the titanomagnetite grains at their borders, leaving relics of irregular shape.

In chemical composition the augite-porphyrites (Table 1) differ from the alkali rocks in possessing a larger tenor of calcium, magnesium, iron and titanium and a smaller aluminium, sodium and potassium content. In the heavily altered varieties of augite-porphyrite sodium is present in large amounts (Flora).

The Devonian age of the sedimentary and effusive succession has been corroborated by the discovery of a flora including *Psygmophyllum* cf., *Williamsonii* Naht., *Archaecopteris* sp., and *Rhachiopteris* sp., identified by Krishtofovich (1937) in tuffaceous shales on Flora.

The contact between the Devonian rocks and the nepheline-syenites is distinct. A trachytoid texture, very often observable in nepheline-syenites, surrounds the xenoliths, reproducing, as it were, their contours. The Devonian rocks at the contact have been greatly altered, and have often been converted into cordierite-andalusite-hornfels, micaceous-andalusite-hornfels, mica-, hornblende-diopside-, and hornblende-biotite-hornfels.

A contact between the Devonian rocks and the Archaean has been observed in only one place, on Kitkn'yun, where it has a tectonic character.

Vorob'eva, Eliseev and Gerasimovskii, all of whom have studied the sequence

TABLE 2 Stages in the formation of the Lovozero Massif

Stage	Vorob'eva (1937)	Eliseev et al. (1938)	Gerasimovskii (1944)
IV	alkali basalts, monchiquites and other young dyke rocks	Complex of young dyke rocks (monchiquites, tinguaites; more rarely nepheline basalts, shonkinites and fourchites)	Complex of young dyke rocks
III	Tawites 1a. Poikilitic and equigranular nepheline-sodalite-rocks, urtites, foyaite-aplites 1. Foyaites (ditroites) 6·4% of area of occurrence	Complex of eudialytic and porphyritic lujavrites	1c. Tawites and poikilitic sodalite-syenites 1b. Porphyritic lujavrites 1a. Eudialytic lujavrites
II	Equigranular and porphyritic aegirine-bearing (micaceous) nepheline-syenites, 1·8% of area of occurrence	Differentiated foyaite-urtite-lujavrite complex	1b. Foyaites and urtites 1a. Aegirine-lujavrites
I	1a. Complex of eudialytic lujavrites and their dyke rocks (top of massif), 49·1% of area of occurrence 1. Aegirine-lujavrites (lower part of massif), 42·7% of area of occurrence	Complex of fine-grained nepheline- and alkali-syenites, poikilitic nepheline-syenites and tawites, urtites, juvites and foyaites	Complex of equigranular and porphyritic aegirine-bearing (micaceous) nepheline-syenites, foyaites and poikilitic nepheline-syenites

of formation of the various intrusive complexes, are unanimous in concluding that four intrusive phases were involved. None of these authors has any doubt that the dyke rocks are the youngest, though all three have different opinions both about the relative ages of the first three rock complexes and about the various types of rock within each complex (Table 2).

According to Vorob'eva (1937) the lujavrites of the differentiated complex were formed during the first phase and the eudialytic lujavrites and their dyke rocks somewhat later; the second phase saw the formation of equigranular and porphyritic aegirine-(micaceous)-nepheline-syenites; the foyaites of the differentiated complex appeared during the third phase and the poikilitic nepheline-sodalite-syenites somewhat later; in the fourth phase, dyke derivatives of the alkali intrusion appeared.

In Gerasimovskii's opinion the complex of equigranular and porphyritic aegirine-nepheline-syenites and poikilitic nepheline-syenites formed during the first phase. The lujavrites of the differentiated complex and later the foyaites and urtites crystallized during the second phase. The eudialytic lujavrites and somewhat later the porphyritic lujavrites, followed by the poikilitic sodalite-syenites, were formed during the third phase. The dyke rocks were formed during the fourth phase (see Table 2).

Eliseev, arguing from a structural analysis of the Lovozero massif and the relative ages of the individual complexes, concluded that a complex of poikilitic nepheline- and sodalite-syenites and of tawites formed during the first phase. The rocks of the differentiated complex crystallized during the second phase and the eudialytic and porphyritic lujavrite complex formed during the third phase. The process concluded with the intrusion of dyke derivates of alkali magma. This interpretation is widely accepted among geologists working on the problems of the massif.

We shall pause to consider the relative ages of the differentiated complex and the eudialytic lujavrite complex.

(1) As we have already noted, porphyritic lujavrites occur at the contact between these complexes. Their contact with the differentiated complex is of an intrusive character; with the eudialytic lujavrites they have both abrupt contacts and gradual transitions.

(2) The contact between the porphyritic lujavrites and the differentiated complex forms a gently dipping, undulating, flexured surface at horizons varying from one part of the massif to another, and appears to truncate the upper horizons of the differentiated complex in some places. As a result, in some parts of the massif the porphyritic lujavrites lie on lujavrites of the zero horizon, while in others they rest on foyaites of the first three-fold group of strata in the differentiated complex. In the Ilmaiok valley, in the northern part of the massif, the porphyritic lujavrites are bedded on foyaites of the second three-fold stratal group.

(3) According to Eliseev (1953) Palaeozoic rocks, which in his opinion form the roof of the differentiated complex and the floor of the eudialytic lujavrite complex, are intercalated in the form of discontinuous wedges at the contact

between the differentiated complex and the eudialytic lujavrite complex on the southern slopes of Kueln'yun and Kuivchorr.

(4) At their contact with the differentiated complex the grain-size of the porphyritic lujavrites diminishes, and fairly frequent xenoliths of various rocks belonging to the differentiated complex can be observed (Eliseev, 1953).

These discoveries have led most investigators to believe that the eudialytic lujavrite complex is younger than the differentiated complex. The facts, however, do not seem to warrant this conclusion, first, because they relate exclusively to the porphyritic lujavrites and only indirectly to the eudialytic lujavrite complex as a whole and, secondly, because they have been insufficiently studied. Eliseev, for example, referring to the presence of xenoliths from the differentiated complex in the porphyritic lujavrites, does not describe their shapes, sizes or contact alterations. They may well not be xenoliths at all, but facies of the foyaites, lujavrites

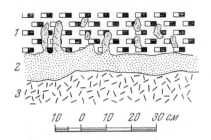

FIG. 6. Porphyritic lujavrite (1) in contact with differentiated-complex foyaites (3) on southern slope of Angvundaschorr cirque (2—albitized zone with arfvedsonite) (after N. A. Eliseev)

and urtites known to exist in the eudialytic lujavrite complex. Nor does Eliseev describe the shapes or sizes of the Palaeozoic outcrops which he indicates as occurring between the eudialytic lujavrite complex and the differentiated complex, or the contact relationships between those formations and the enclosing rocks. It is therefore debatable whether the Devonian rocks constitute the roof of the differentiated complex or are ordinary xenoliths situated at the boundary of the two complexes, particularly since xenoliths occur in both.

On the other hand, the following facts seem to indicate that the relative ages of the two complexes should be reversed:

(1) Gradual transitions between the eudialytic lujavrites and the rocks of the differentiated complex can be observed (Eliseev, 1953).

(2) At the contact with the porphyritic lujavrites the rocks of the differentiated complex have not undergone contact alteration, whereas the porphyritic lujavrites are often strongly albitized and enriched in alkali-amphibole (Fig. 6).

(3) The foyaites of the uppermost horizon in the differentiated complex, which are usually in contact with porphyritic lujavrites, are enriched in pegmatites, which form a thin discontinuous layer at the contact or occur as irregularly-shaped bodies near it.

Both complexes were probably formed at about the same time and seem to have crystallized successively from top to bottom out of a single batch of magma, the eudialytic lujavrites crystallizing first and the rocks of the differentiated complex immediately afterwards. There is evidence for this in the similarity of chemical

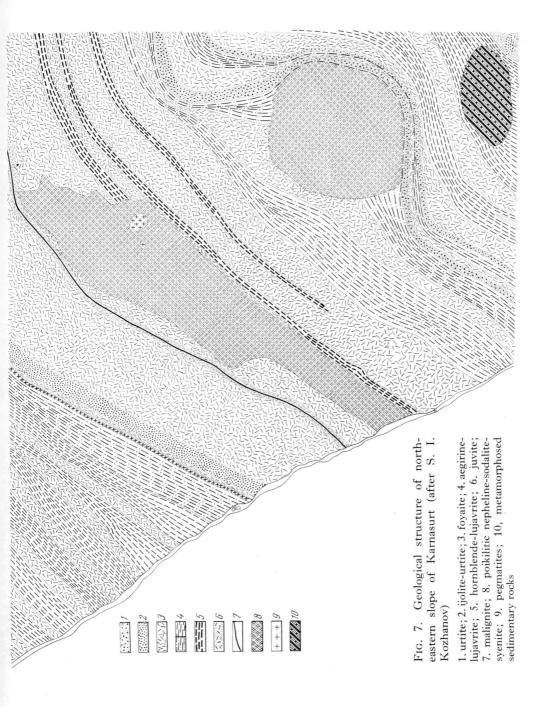

Fig. 7. Geological structure of north-eastern slope of Karnasurt (after S. I. Kozhanov)

1. urtite; 2. ijolite-urtite; 3. foyaite; 4. aegirine-lujavrite; 5. hornblende-lujavrite; 6. juvite; 7. malignite; 8. poikilitic nepheline-sodalite-syenite; 9. pegmatites; 10, metamorphosed sedimentary rocks

and mineral composition between the rocks of both complexes and the common differentiation trend of the magma. The final solution of this problem, however, calls for further research.

As regards the relative ages of the porphyritic lujavrites and the ordinary eudialytic lujavrites, both sharp intrusive contacts and gradual transitions from one to the other can be observed. According to Eliseev there are patches of eudialytic lujavrite in the porphyritic lujavrites and vice versa, the trachytoid structure in both rocks following the contours of the contact. Arguing from these relationships, and also from the similarity of the rocks in mineralogical composition, Eliseev and other authors have rightly regarded them as closely related in time of formation and as belonging to a single complex. The chemical and mineralogical similarities between the different varieties of porphyritic rocks and the eudialytic lujavrites, the gradual transitions from one to the other observable in places, and the similarity in the sequence of mineral formation, all point to crystallization from a single magma. The conformable bedding of the porphyritic horizons and the presence of gradual transitions both between them and between the different varieties of eudialytic lujavrites indicate that the eudialytic lujavrites formed first, followed by the porphyritic rocks in the course of crystallization differentiation of a single batch of magma.

Opinions differ as to the relative age of the poikilitic syenites. Vorob'eva assigns them to a late stage in the history of the massif, Eliseev to the earliest stages, while Gerasimovskii believes that some of the rocks in this complex are very young formations (the tawites and poikilitic sodalite-syenites) while others are very old rocks (the poikilitic nepheline-syenites and others).

The data collected by the present authors confirm Vorob'eva's point of view.

(1) The poikilitic syenites form intrusive bodies of irregular shape and also lenses and veins emplaced in rocks of the differentiated complex and the eudialytic lujavrite complex.

(2) Where large masses of poikilitic syenite have been intruded, the stratified arrangement of the rocks of the differentiated complex has been violently disturbed. The large intrusions of poikilitic sodalite-syenite on the north-eastern slope of Karnasurt, for example, truncate the hornblende-lujavrites of horizon VII and the aegirine-lujavrites of horizon IV (Fig. 7). Disturbance of the layering in the differentiated complex by poikilitic syenites can also be observed on Lepke-Nel'm and Kuivchorr.

(3) The lujavrites dip at low angles away from contacts with the poikilitic syenites (Fig. 8) and appear to have been moulded into domes by the intrusion of the latter. In the denuded parts of such domes trachytoid structure of the lujavrite seems to swing round the syenites, which has led Eliseev and other investigators to the erroneous conclusion that the poikilitic syenites are xenoliths within the lujavrites.

(4) Apophyses of poikilitic sodalite-syenite are to be observed in the foyaites and in xenoliths of the latter in the poikilitic syenites (Fig. 9).

(5) At the contacts with the enclosing rocks, particularly with the lujavrites,

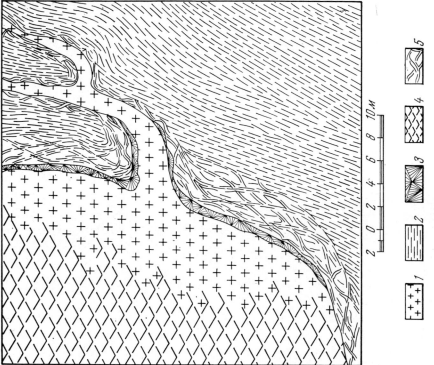

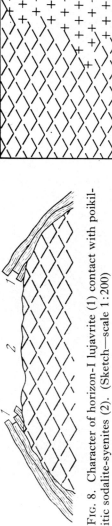

FIG. 10. Pegmatite apophyses in lujavrite

1. pegmatites; 2. lujavrite; 3. aegirine-rich margin; 4. poikilitic sodalite-syenite; 5. lujavrite with disrupted trachytoid texture

FIG. 8. Character of horizon-I lujavrite (1) contact with poikilitic sodalite-syenites (2). (Sketch—scale 1:200)

FIG. 9. Interrelationship between poikilitic sodalite-syenite (1) and foyaite (2). (Sketch—scale 1:25)

pegmatitic facies can be seen in the poikilitic syenites, differentiated from the parent rock by their coarsely granular pegmatitic texture, the absence of poikilitic texture, a high tenor of microcline, aegirine and eudialyte and also of ramsayite, murmanite, lamprophyllite and other rare-metal minerals. The pegmatitic facies pass by gradual transitions into the poikilitic syenites and have sharp contacts with the enclosing lujavrites.

(6) In places where pegmatitic facies have developed, pegmatite apophyses can be observed in the enclosing lujavrites, intruded along the parting fissures (Fig. 10).

(7) The trachytoid structure in the lujavrites has been disturbed within a zone up to half a metre thick at their contact with the poikilitic syenites. The rock in this zone is mineralogically inhomogeneous, sinuous melanocratic bands alternating with leucocratic lenses. The structure of the rocks is almost reticulate or festooned. In places where pegmatitic facies have developed in the poikilitic syenites the altered zone in the lujavrites near the contact is sometimes 1 m thick (see Fig. 10).

(8) In both the lujavrites and the foyaites at their contact with the poikilitic sodalite-syenites, processes of sodalitization, natrolitization and albitization are strongly in evidence.

All these facts indicate that the rocks of the differentiated complex have been subjected to thermal and chemical reworking at the contact with the poikilitic sodalite-syenites, under the influence of a magma rich in volatile components, especially fluorine, chlorine, sulphur, water.

As regards the large irregular bodies of finely granular and porphyritic alkali-syenites (carrying aegirine, nepheline and mica), which other authors have in many cases classified as belonging to the poikilitic syenite complex, we believe them to be xenoliths of Devonian rock, reworked by an alkali magma.

CHAPTER TWO

THE EUDIALYTIC LUJAVRITE COMPLEX

THIS complex falls into two series, the eudialytic lujavrites proper, with eudialytites, and the porphyritic rocks.

The eudialytic lujavrite group of layers consists of successive horizons of leucocratic, mesocratic and melanocratic varieties, with gradual transitions from one to another and with the mesocratic varieties predominating. Each eudialytic lujavrite variety forms horizons varying in thickness from 1-3 to 50-100 m, which frequently die out laterally or grade into a different facies. The leucocratic varieties usually preponderate in the lower part of the complex, the melanocratic varieties forming the upper part.

According to Eliseev (1938), feldspathic varieties of the eudialytic lujavrites are found in addition to the melanocratic, mesocratic and leucocratic varieties. These consist of eudialytic foyaites making up sectors of irregular shape conformably bedded with the primary banding of the eudialytic lujavrites, and passing into them by gradual transitions.

The presence of a belt 14 m thick of repeated interlayering of eudialytic lujavrite, foyaite and urtite at the bottom of the eudialytic lujavrite complex on Karnasurt (Fig. 11) indicates that differentiation is more advanced here. Most of the eudialyte is concentrated in the urtitic horizons, accounting for half the rock in places, whereas it is almost completely lacking in the lujavrites and foyaites.

Apart from the eudialytic lujavrite varieties mentioned, some investigators distinguish lamprophyllitic eudialyte-lujavrite, lamprophyllitic murmanitic eudialyte-lujavrite, and murmanitic lujavrite, the identification depending on the amount of each particular rare-metal mineral in the rock. There is appreciably less eudialyte in these rocks than in ordinary eudialytic lujavrites. The eudialyte here is accessory, whereas the lamprophyllite (up to 10 per cent) and murmanite (up to 5 per cent) assume the importance of essential rock-forming minerals in certain parts. Lamprophyllitic and murmanitic lujavrites are comparatively rare. The lamprophyllitic eudialyte and lamprophyllitic varieties gravitate towards the top of the complex, the murmanitic eudialyte and murmanitic rocks to the bottom. The lujavrite varieties mentioned make up separate horizons among normal eudialytic lujavrites and possess the characteristic feature of being impersistent along both strike and dip. Gradual transitions can be observed from one type of lujavrite (lamprophyllitic, murmanitic and eudialytic) to another.

The eudialytites form lenticular or irregularly-shaped bodies measuring

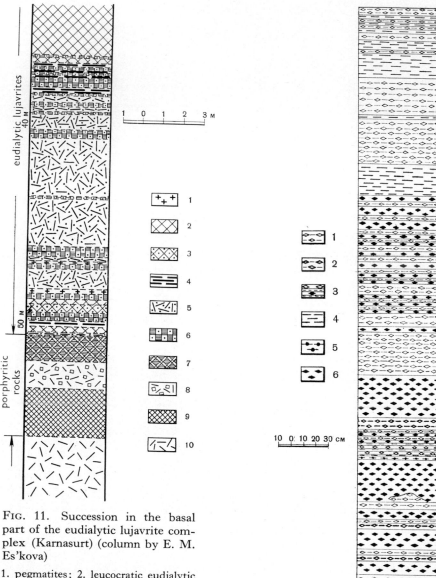

FIG. 11. Succession in the basal part of the eudialytic lujavrite complex (Karnasurt) (column by E. M. Es'kova)

1. pegmatites; 2. leucocratic eudialytic lujavrite; 3. eudialytic lujavrite with nodular structure; 4. melanocratic aegirine-lujavrite; 5. foyaite; 6. urtite; 7. porphyritic juvite; 8. porphyritic foyaite; 9. porphyritic aphanitic lujavrite; 10. foyaite of the differentiated complex

FIG. 12. Succession of rocks in the Chivruai valley eudialytic lujavrite complex (after N. A. Eliseev)

1. leucocratic eudialytic lujavrite; 2. mesocratic eudialytic lujavrite; 3. thin interstratification of eudialytic lujavrite and eudialytite; 4. aegirine-lujavrite without eudialyte; 5. aegirine-lujavrite with eudialyte; 6. eudialytite

3·5 × 50 m that lie conformably with the primary stratification of the complex, and are interbedded chiefly in the mesocratic and melanocratic eudialytic lujavrites at the top of the complex. Between the eudialytites and the enclosing rocks one finds both sharp contacts, due to an abrupt change in the mineral ratios, and also extremely gradual transitions. In both cases the eudialyte content in the enclosing rocks is found to increase.

On the slopes of Strashempakhk, facing the Suoluaiv valley, there is a thin interlayering of different varieties of eudialytic lujavrites with eudialytites (Fig. 12).

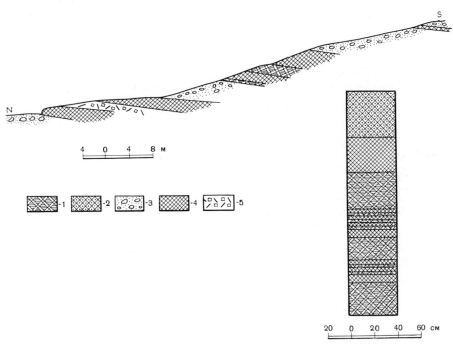

FIG. 13.   Cross-section through porphyritic juvites on northern slope of Alluaiv (after L. P. Bondarenko)

1. porphyritic juvite; 2. eudialytic lujavrite; 3. talus; 4. porphyritic lujavrite; 5. foyaite

Lenticular intercalations of eudialytites, ranging in thickness from a few millimetres to tens of centimetres, can be traced along the strike. The boundaries between these interlayers are often sharp, but gradual transitions sometimes occur (Eliseev, 1953).

The frequent close association of eudialytites with pegmatites indicates that volatile substances (emanations) have played some part in forming them. The fact that the eudialyte contains much chlorine, with which zirconium forms readily volatile compounds, points to the accumulation of large amounts of zirconium in some of the top parts of the eudialytic lujavrite complex.

The eudialytites are therefore probably facies formations of eudialytic lujavrites, crystallized from a single magma enriched in zirconium as a result of volatile transport and crystallization differentiation.

TABLE 3 Quantitative mineralogical

Rock	Nepheline	K-Na-feld-spar	Aegirine + hornblende	Eudialyte	Natrolite
Eudialytic lujavrites:					
Melanocratic	23·4-30·2	30·5-38·9	23·9-28·4	10·8-25·1	2·8-4·3
Mesocratic	19·1-22·8	39·7-43·0	19·6-23·0	7·3-12·5	5·4-7·7
Leucocratic	17·7-18·9	45·8-55·3	11·2-14·5	3·8- 8·2	6·8-9·5

Three main varieties of porphyritic rocks can be distinguished in the eudialytic lujavrite complex, porphyritic eudialytic lujavrites, porphyritic feldspathic rocks similar in composition to foyaites, and porphyritic eudialytic juvites.

The commonest of these are the porphyritic eudialytic lujavrites. They form a horizon at the bottom of the complex, 1-75 m thick, the thickness gradually increasing towards the western, south-western and southern parts of the massif. The contact between the porphyritic lujavrites and the differentiated complex is invariably sharp. A discontinuous pegmatitic horizon can often be seen along this contact. Immediately at the contact the porphyritic lujavrites lose colour as the result of very pronounced albitization, which gradually diminishes until it completely disappears about half a metre away from the contact.

Apart from this horizon, the porphyritic lujavrites form lenticular bodies and schlieren and occur also in the form of veins, intersecting the eudialytic lujavrites. The porphyritic lujavrite veins vary in thickness from a few centimetres to several metres, and the contacts between them and the country rocks are intrusive.

Porphyritic foyaites and juvites are present in rare instances in the more strongly differentiated parts of the complex. They form sheet-like bodies mainly in the north-western and western parts of the massif (Alluaiv, Angvundaschorr, Sengischorr), interbedded either at the contact between the eudialytic and the porphyritic lujavrites or among the latter. The thickness of the bodies varies from 1·5 to 3·3 m. When the porphyritic juvites are interlayered in porphyritic lujavrites the beds usually alternate (Fig. 13). The contact between the porphyritic juvites and the eudialytic lujavrites is sharp, but the transitions between all the porphyritic varieties are gradual.

THE EUDIALYTIC LUJAVRITES

Eudialytic lujavrites are greenish-grey, green and dark-green rocks, predominantly medium-grained but occasionally fine-grained, of massive, trachytoid or hypidiomorphic-granular texture. The rock consists of coarse tabular microcline crystals, mostly scattered at random but occasionally arranged parallel to one another, with the interstices filled with nepheline, finely acicular aegirine, eudialyte, mesodialite and accessory minerals. The sizes of the principal rock-forming minerals are as follows: nepheline, up to $0·4 \times 0·3 \times 0·3$ cm; feldspar up to

composition of eudialytic lujavrites (per cent)

Sodalite	Loparite	Apatite	Murmanite	Lampro-phyllite	Ramsayite	Sphene
—	0-0·05	0·05-0·2	0-0·08	0·8-1·0	0·1-0·5	0·2
0·1-0·8	0·09-0·15	0-0·1	0·1-0·2	0·5-1·4	0-0·2	0-0·1
0·7-2·5	0·1 -0·2	—	0·2-0·3	0·4-2·3	0-0·1	—

TABLE 4   Chemical compositions of eudialytic lujavrites (per cent)

Constituent	Melanocratic (Karnasurt)	Mesocratic (Karnasurt)	Leuco-cratic (Alluaiv)	Eudialytic-lampro-phyllitic (Angvunda-schorr)	Lampro-phyllitic (Angvunda-schorr)	Eudialytic-murmanitic (Punkaruaiv)
SiO_2	48·59	51·85	53·68	53·67	53·80	53·82
TiO_2	3·12	2·10	1·35	1·96	—	3·86
ZrO_2	3·45	1·39	—	—	—	0·56
$(Nb, Ta)_2O_5$	0·06	0·28	—	—	—	—
RE_2O_3	0·30	0·20	—	—	—	—
Al_2O_3	11·30	13·84	18·42	16·79	15·17	12·88
Fe_2O_3	9·38	6·06	5·91	6·57	7·11	9·80
FeO	2·02	2·47	2·57	2·53	3·09	—
MnO	1·05	0·62	0·75	0·11	1·09	0·43
MgO	1·32	2·35	0·88	1·74	1·08	0·90
CaO	3·93	3·70	2·05	2·47	1·72	1·24
SrO	0·04	not found	—	—	—	—
BaO	0·14	0·11	—	—	—	—
Na_2O	10·24	9·00	9·46	9·07	10·55	10·09
K_2O	1·86	3·60	4·92	4·14	5·09	5·26
Li_2O	0·04	0·09	not det.	not det.	not det.	—
Cs_2O	—	—	,, ,,	,, ,,	,, ,,	—
P_2O_5	0·06	0·57	—	—	—	—
V_2O_5	0·009	0·012	—	—	—	—
SO_3	0·15	0·99	—	—	—	—
S	—	—	—	—	—	—
F	not found	0·12	—	—	—	—
Cl	0·33	0·21	—	—	—	—
H_2O^+	2·86	0·96	}0·89	0·34	1·31	0·90
H_2O^-	0·26	0·02				
Total	100·51	100·54	100·88	99·39	100·01	99·74
$-O = Cl_2 + F_2$	-0·08	-0·10				
	100·43	100·44				
Analyst	Nesterova, 1949		Peterson	Bergkhell	Blanket	Kolendzyan
Reference	—		W. Ramsay (1897-1899)			*Minerals of the Khibiny and Lovozero tundras (1937)*

$2 \times 0.8 \times 0.2$ cm; aegirine, up to $1 \times 0.1 \times 0.01$ cm; minerals of the eudialyte-eucolite group, up to $0.5 \times 0.3 \times 0.2$ cm. Secondary and accessory minerals are represented by lamprophyllite, ramsayite, murmanite, loparite, sphene, apatite, and others as well as by minerals developed by replacement (albite, sodalite and natrolite).

In the eudialytic lujavrites the content of nepheline, eudialyte, sphene, apatite, ramsayite and dark minerals gradually decreases from the melanocratic to the leucocratic varieties (Table 3), while the amount of microcline, murmanite, lamprophyllite, natrolite and sodalite increases. The more advanced the differentiation of the rocks, the more pronounced is this pattern.

A typical feature of the rocks we are now describing is their high tenor of zirconium, titanium, niobium and rare earths, often many times greater than the average for the massif as a whole (Table 4). Danilova (1954), determining the fluorine content by chemical assay, found it to be 0·36 per cent in the melanocratic eudialytic lujavrites, against 0·16 per cent in the leucocratic varieties.

Separate assays on two samples of eudialytic lujavrite gave a beryllium content of 0·0015 and 0·0024 per cent respectively (analyst S. N. Fedorchuk). The nickel and copper content of these rocks, determined by the polarographic method, was 0·0003 and 0·0014 per cent, respectively (analyst O. V. Krutetskaya).

The mean tenor of the eudialytic lujavrites in radioactive elements is several times higher than the average in the earth's crust, with 5×10^{-5} gm of thorium per gram of rock and 6.8×10^{-12} gm of radium per gram. The calculated uranium content is 2×10^{-5} gm per gram (analysts S. G. Tseitlin and N. K. Zhirova).

Gallium (up to 0·01 per cent), rubidium, lead and vanadium have been identified in these rocks by spectrographic analysis.

On comparison of the chemical analyses of the different varieties of eudialytic lujavrites, the leucocratic varieties are found to contain, along with a higher concentration of silicon, aluminium and potassium, larger amounts of niobium, tantalum, lithium, phosphorus and sulphur, and smaller amounts of iron, zirconium, titanium, rare earths, fluorine and chlorine. The variation in silicon, aluminium, sodium, potassium, iron and calcium content in these rocks is due mainly to variation in the amounts of principal rock-forming minerals, primarily feldspars and aegirine. The variation in the amounts of rare elements, phosphorus and volatile substances (zirconium, titanium, niobium, tantalum, rare earths, chlorine and fluorine) is due mainly to variations in the eudialyte and mesodialyte content and, to a small extent, to variations in the amounts of minerals belonging to the lomonosovite group (murmanite and lamprophyllite).

The Eudialytites

The eudialytites are usually made up 65-75 per cent of well-formed eudialyte crystals, the interstices between these being filled with nepheline (0-15 per cent), microcline (0-12·5 per cent), arfvedsonite (0-8 per cent), acicular aegirine (3-15 per cent), murmanite, ramsayite, lamprophyllite (0-4 per cent), sodalite, albite and natrolite (0-13 per cent). Sphene, neptunite, apatite, catapleite, zircon, pyrite, pyrrhotite, chalcopyrite, molybdenite and pectolite occur in negligible amounts. The eudialytites are usually of equigranular fabric, the structure is massive, occasionally eutaxitic. These rocks differ from the eudialytic lujavrites in being dark red (owing to the high eudialyte content) more coarse-grained and having an irregular distribution of the principal minerals. They are sometimes found to be slightly trachytoid. In comparison with the eudialytic lujavrites the eudialytites typically possess a higher content of zirconium, rare earths, niobium, calcium, manganese and chlorine (Table 5) which enter into the composition of minerals of the eudialyte group. The rocks in question, determined polarographically, contain 0·006 per cent copper and the nickel content is 0·0014 per cent (analyst O. V. Krutetskaya). Separate analysis showed the thorium content to be $1·82 \times 10^{-4}$ gm per gram of rock (analysts S. G. Tseitlin and N. K. Zhirova). Beryllium (0·001 per cent), rubidium, lead, chromium, gallium (0·01 per cent) and vanadium were detected spectroscopically in the eudialytites.

TABLE 5 Chemical compositions of the Lovozero eudialytites (per cent)

Constituent	Kuftai deposit	Chivruai deposit	Vavnbed deposit (western slope)	2nd Raslak cirque
SiO_2	49·36	49·02	50·59	47·54
TiO_2	1·81	2·08	1·36	0·70
ZrO_2	6·76	7·46	8·68	6·26
$(Nb, Ta)_2O_5$	0·58	0·39	0·76	0·93
RE_2O_3	1·56	1·01	1·68	1·19
Al_2O_3	6·51	2·33	3·29	12·23
Fe_2O_3	4·04	5·57	6·08	4·53
FeO	4·08	4·69	1·46	not found
MnO	1·30	1·50	1·90	2·16
MgO	0·89	1·32	1·06	0·52
CaO	7·36	7·34	5·25	4·75
SrO	—	1·18	1·05	0·38
BaO	—	0·15	0·13	0·34
Na_2O	10·81	8·16	10·64	10·33
K_2O	1·65	1·38	1·35	2·56
Li_2O	not determined	not determined	not determined	0·04
P_2O_5	,, ,,	,, ,,	,, ,,	0·22
V_2O_5	,, ,,	,, ,,	,, ,,	not found
SO_3	,, ,,	,, ,,	,, ,,	0·15
Cl	0·65	0·52	0·34	0·73
F	0·11	0·11	0·04	not found
H_2O^+	2·35	5·02	3·96	3·43
H_2O^-	0·35	0·82	0·45	0·81
Total	100·17	100·05	100·07	99·80
$-O = Cl_2 + F_2$	−0·18	−0·15	−0·09	−0·18
	99·99	99·90	99·98	99·62
Analyst	Sverzhinskaya			Nesterova
Reference	Eliseev (1940)			—

The Porphyritic Lujavrites

These are rocks with a very compact dark grey, greenish-grey and green matrix and phenocrysts of potassium feldspar, nepheline, occasionally aegirine, arfvedsonite, eudialyte and lamprophyllite, making up 15-20 per cent and sometimes 40-50 per cent of the total volume. Sometimes, however, the number of phenocrysts is negligible. The sizes of the phenocrysts are as follows: feldspars, from 0.4×0.1 to 1.5×0.5 cm; nepheline, 0.3×0.2 cm; aegirine, from 0.4×0.1 to 1.5×0.2 cm; eudialyte, up to 0.3×0.3 cm; lamprophyllite, from 0.3×0.2 to 0.6×0.4 cm. The grain size varies between 0.1 and 0.5 mm. The groundmass is made up of nepheline, microcline, aegirine, arfvedsonite, mesodialyte, lamprophyllite, apatite, loparite, sphene, albite and other minerals.

The texture is porphyritic with a hypidiomorphic-granular or, occasionally panidiomorphic-granular groundmass and the structure trachytoid. The principal rock-forming minerals are nepheline (19.6-31.8 per cent), feldspars (24.6-41 per

TABLE 6   Chemical compositions of porphyritic lujavrites (per cent)

Constituent	Karnasurt	Mannepakhk
SiO_2	52·34	54·65
TiO_2	0·98	0·41
ZrO_2	0·18	—
$(Nb, Ta)_2O_5$	not found	—
RE_2O_3	0·06	—
Al_2O_3	16·59	17·41
Fe_2O_3	8·04	6·64
FeO	1·60	0·76
MnO	0·44	0·56
MgO	1·71	trace
CaO	2·64	1·10
SrO	0·26	—
BaO	0·07	—
Na_2O	9·09	9·14
K_2O	3·85	6·56
Li_2O	0·07	not determined
P_2O_5	0·03	—
V_2O_5	0·008	—
SO_3	0·50	—
Cl	0·18	—
F	not found	—
H_2O^+	1·68	} 2·48
H_2O^-	0·28	
Total	100·60	99·71
$-O = S$	−0·05	
	100·55	—
Analyst	Nesterova	Tseitlin
Reference	—	*Minerals of Khibiny and Lovozero tundras* (1937)

cent), aegirine (24·3-50·1 per cent) and mesodialyte (6·9-11·8 per cent); secondary and accessory minerals are represented by arfvedsonite, loparite, lamprophyllite (0·1-0·8 per cent), murmanite, sodalite (up to 5·6 per cent), natrolite (3·3-9·3 per cent) and others. In mineralogical and chemical composition (Tables 4 and 6) the porphyritic lujavrites are similar to the eudialytic lujavrites.

The chemical analysis data were supplemented by assays for fluorine and beryllium in the Karnasurt porphyritic lujavrites. The fluorine content was determined as 0·07 per cent (analyst V. V. Danilova) and the beryllium content at 0·0008 per cent (analyst S. N. Fedorchuk). Nickel was determined at 0·0006 per cent and copper 0·002 per cent by the polarographic method (analyst O. V. Krutetskaya). In addition, gallium (0·01 per cent), rubidium, tin and lead were detected spectroscopically.

The Porphyritic Juvites

Porphyritic juvites are fine-grained rocks of grey or light-grey colour with a greenish tint. The phenocrysts are nepheline and occasionally potassium feldspar, for the most part scattered randomly in the fine-grained matrix but sometimes with planar arrangement. The potassium feldspar phenocrysts vary in size from 0·2 to 0·3 cm, occasionally reaching 1 cm along the major axis. The granularity of the groundmass does not exceed 0·1-0·3 mm. The phenocrysts make up 20 to 65 per cent of the rock.

The structure is unlayered, occasionally trachytoid, owing to the orientated arrangement of the aegirine and the feldspar phenocrysts. The fine-grained groundmass is usually almost panidiomorphic-granular owing to the idiomorphism of the eudialyte and loparite in relation to the other minerals in the groundmass.

The main rock-forming minerals are nepheline (25-50 per cent), feldspar (15-40 per cent), aegirine (7-18 per cent), sodalite (9-12 per cent), eudialyte (2-10 per cent) and natrolite (5·7 per cent). Secondary and accessory minerals are represented by arfvedsonite, murmanite, lamprophyllite, lovozerite, apatite, ramsayite, cancrinite, ussingite, loparite, metaloparite and others. The porphyritic juvites are leucocratic rocks, distinguished from the porphyritic foyaites by a higher nepheline and aegirine content and from the porphyritic lujavrites by a higher sodalite and a lower aegirine content.

Apart from eudialyte and mesodialyte, which are characteristic rare-metal minerals in all the porphyritic rocks, the porphyritic juvites contain loparite. Large amounts of the latter have been found in the enclosing porphyritic lujavrites as well, although these usually do not contain that mineral. The distribution of loparite in the porphyritic juvites is uneven. In some parts it gravitates to the bottom of the layer, in others to its central part and in still others it is scattered throughout the whole layer. The murmanite and lamprophyllite content as a rule increases from the porphyritic lujavrites to the porphyritic juvites and foyaites. Porphyritic juvites with a high loparite content always contain less eudialyte and lamprophyllite. Their content of nepheline, sodalite and loparite increases towards the base, while the amount of feldspar, aegirine, eudialyte and mesodialyte decreases in that direction.

In chemical composition (Table 7) the porphyritic juvites resemble urtites and ijolitic urtites.

Compared with the porphyritic lujavrites the porphyritic juvites are poorer in silica and ferric oxide, richer in alkalis and appreciably enriched in titanium, niobium and rare earths, owing to their lower microcline and aegirine and higher nepheline and loparite content. On chemical assay the porphyritic juvites were found to contain 0·0005 per cent beryllium (analyst S. N. Fedorchuk). Strontium, chromium, gallium, vanadium, copper, nickel, barium, cobalt and lead were detected spectroscopically.

*   *   *   *

As can be seen from the above description, the characteristic feature of the eudialytic lujavrite complex is the very close genetic connexion of its members, expressed in the similarity of their chemical and mineralogical composition and the presence of gradual transitions from one to another. The formation of nephe-

TABLE 7   Chemical compositions of porphyritic
juvites (per cent)

Constituent	Angvundaschorr	Alluaiv
SiO_2	47·93	52·43
TiO_2	2·90	1·24
ZrO_2	0·40	2·28
Nb_2O_5	0·70	not determined
RE_2O_3	2·20	1·12
Al_2O_3	17·97	14·44
Fe_2O_3	4·49	5·49
FeO	1·44	1·45
MnO	0·56	0·49
MgO	0·19	2·90
CaO	1·62	2·86
Na_2O	14·90	10·36
K_2O	2·90	5·16
P_2O_5	0·03	nil
SO_3	not determined	0·10
S	,, ,,	not determined
Cl	0·43	,, ,,
H_2O^+	1·20	0·14
H_2O^-	0·50	0·10
Other	—	—
Total	100·36	100·56
$-O = Cl_2$	−0·10	
—	100·26	—
Analyst	Sverzhinskaya	Burova
Reference	Eliseev (1940)	—

line-rich rocks (porphyritic juvites) is usually followed by the formation of feldspathic rocks (porphyritic foyaites), that of leucocratic eudialytic lujavrites by
more melanocratic varieties of those rocks, and so forth.

The gradual change in quantitative mineralogical composition on transition
from one variety of eudialytic lujavrite to another and the conformable interstratification of the sequence of layers indicate that all these rocks were formed from
a single batch of magma as a result of crystallization differentiation.

The characteristic rare-metal minerals in the complex are zirconium minerals.
Niobium, rare-earth and titanium minerals occur only occasionally and in negligible quantities, but when they are present they gravitate to the leucocratic rock
types.

Four parageneses, corresponding to four stages of crystallization, can be
distinguished in the eudialytic lujavrites (Fig. 14).*

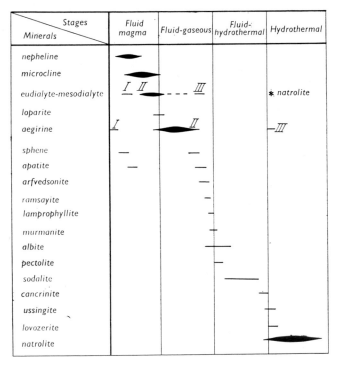

FIG. 14. Diagram of the order of crystallization in eudialytic
lujavrites

* In compiling the succession charts for mineral crystallization in the magmatic formations
(igneous rocks and pegmatites) we have used Niggli's physical-chemical charts, which are the most
appropriate for magmatic processes. The criteria used in classifying the minerals under the various
stages were: (1) the sequence of their separation as determined from the idiomorphism, replacement
effects and filling of the fissures; (2) the chemical composition; (3) the paragenetic associations.
On the basis of these criteria we find that the first fluid magma stage accounts primarily for the main
rock-forming minerals that do not contain volatile components, the second (fluid-gaseous) gives
aegirine and arfvedsonite along with rare-metal minerals containing volatile compounds, and the
third (fluid-hydrothermal) gives minerals also containing volatile components but replacing the
higher-temperature minerals of the first two stages. Hydrous minerals or minerals occurring in
close paragenetic association with them belong to the fourth (hydrothermal) stage.

The principal rock-forming minerals (nepheline and microcline), the ground-mass of mesodialyte, aegirine I and in part the sphene, apatite and loparite crystallized during the first, fluid magma stage. The crystallization of the eudialytic lujavrites began with the separation of aegirine I and small amounts of sphene and apatite included as well-formed crystals in the nepheline and microcline. After these minerals had formed the nepheline crystallized and then, apparently before the separation of nepheline had finished, the microcline began to crystallize. Nepheline inclusions in microcline crystals occur fairly frequently, those in the central parts of the crystals being fewer and having a more regular outline than those in the peripheral parts. No microcline inclusions have been found in nepheline, most of which occurs in interstices between the microcline crystals. In all probability the nepheline formed earlier than the microcline, which either enclosed nepheline grains in the course of its own development or pushed them aside.

At the end of the period of microcline formation the eudialyte began to separate, the main mass of it managing to crystallize out before the separation of aegirine II began. Well-formed crystals of eudialyte are found as inclusions in the marginal parts of the microcline crystals.

The second stage (fluid-gaseous) began with the crystallization of aegirine II. At this stage all the rare-metal minerals also crystallized: sphene, apatite, loparite, late eudialyte, ramsayite, lamprophyllite, some of the murmanite and also arfvedsonite. The aegirine II usually fills up interstices between nepheline, microcline and eudialyte segregations. Sphene and apatite, in addition to the early idiomorphic crystals, form irregularly-shaped grains that are rarely found in the peripheral parts of the aegirine II accumulations but are as a rule included in arfvedsonite, lamprophyllite and murmanite. Loparite probably crystallized earlier than part of the aegirine II and arfvedsonite, as is indicated by its inclusion as well-formed crystals in those minerals.

After the precipitation of the main mass of aegirine II, crystallization of arfvedsonite began. This for the most part filled up the interstices between minerals formed earlier, cementing them, and very often replacing aegirine II.

Next, ramsayite, lamprophyllite and murmanite separated out, filling the interstices between the main rock-forming minerals and as it were cementing the arfvedsonite, sphene and apatite segregations. Ramsayite separated out before lamprophyllite. Its grains are often bordered with, and peripherally replaced by, lamprophyllite crystals. The murmanite crystallized later than the lamprophyllite and contains idiomorphic inclusions of the latter.

The third (fluid hydrothermal) stage was marked by the crystallization of albite, pectolite, sodalite, cancrinite and ussingite. The pectolite grains have accommodated themselves to the shapes of the lamprophyllite crystals, following their contours round the periphery and being as it were cemented by sodalite. The latter has developed after nepheline, microcline, and albite and is sometimes replaced by cancrinite and ussingite. These have developed after nepheline, microcline, albite and sodalite.

In the fourth (hydrothermal) stage of eudialytic lujavrite formation fine-grained natrolite crystallized, replacing nepheline, microcline, albite, sodalite, cancrinite and ussingite. Lovozerite formed under the influence of hydrothermal solutions after mesodialyte and eudialyte, forming borders round crystals of these minerals and also interstitial grains of irregular shape.

The first stage in the formation of the eudialytites was characterized by the separation of eudialyte and negligible amounts of aegirine I and nepheline (Fig. 15). In these rocks, as in the eudialytic lujavrites, aegirine I was the earliest to separate,

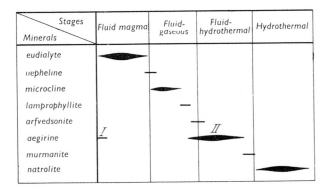

Minerals / Stages	Fluid magma	Fluid-gaseous	Fluid-hydrothermal	Hydrothermal
eudialyte				
nepheline				
microcline				
lamprophyllite				
arfvedsonite				
aegirine	I		II	
murmanite				
natrolite				

FIG. 15. Diagram of the order of crystallization of the main minerals in eudialytites

in the form of small needles included in the eudialyte. After the aegirine I, the main mass of the eudialyte separated out in the form of a few well-formed, elongate crystals.

In the second stage, the groundmass of nepheline and microcline, arfvedsonite, ramsayite and lamprophyllite crystallized, filling interstices between the eudialyte segregations and being xenomorphic in relation to them but idiomorphic in relation to aegirine II. In the third stage aegirine II and murmanite separated, cementing all the minerals enumerated above. In the fourth stage natrolitization and soda-litization of the eudialytites occurred.

The formation of the porphyritic rocks began with the separation of nepheline, orthoclase, mesodialyte, eudialyte and, very rarely, aegirine phenocrysts, usually isolated from one another in the fine-grained groundmass. Sometimes inclusions of more idiomorphic nepheline crystals, and also of eudialyte and mesodialyte, are to be found in the peripheral, but rarely in the central parts of the orthoclase phenocrysts—an indication that they crystallized earlier than the last of the orthoclase.

In the fine-grained groundmass the minerals separated out in the same order as in the eudialytic lujavrites.

Surface weathering of the eudialytic and porphyritic lujavrites has been very slight. The only alteration normally observed is that of eudialyte, mesodialyte and lovozerite into zirfesite.

CHAPTER THREE

THE DIFFERENTIATED COMPLEX

THE differentiated complex is composed of foyaites, juvites, urtites, ijolitic urtites, apatitic urtites, aegirine- and hornblende-lujavrites and malignites. The commonest are the lujavrites, foyaites and urtites. On a rough count the lujavrites (aegirine and hornblende) make up 46 per cent, the foyaites 34 per cent and the urtites about 6 per cent of the total thickness. The remaining 14 per cent is made up of transitional varieties: leucocratic lujavrites 11 per cent, juvites and other rocks 3 per cent.

It is noteworthy that the top and bottom parts of the complex are composed chiefly of leucocratic varieties—foyaites and urtites (Table 8), melanocratic varieties (lujavrites) predominating in the middle part.

All these rocks succeed one another according to a well-defined pattern. On top are foyaites; below these, urtites and lower still, lujavrites; the latter are again replaced by foyaites and so forth. The rocks in the differentiated complex are thus arranged in a series of three-component groups, comprising foyaites, urtites and lujavrites. The differentiation—in other words, the degree to which these three principal rocks form separate layers, varies in different parts of the complex. The upper part is the most differentiated, the middle is slightly differentiated and the bottom is differentiated only in parts. A good index to the degree of differentiation is the presence or absence of almost monomineralic nepheline horizons (urtites). At the top of the complex there are thick urtitic horizons in almost every three-component group; in the middle part urtites occur rather sparsely, forming layers of negligible thickness and containing large amounts of microcline and aegirine. At the bottom of the complex some of the groups appear to contain no urtitic horizons at all.

TABLE 8 Distribution of rock-types in the differentiated
complex (per cent)

Rocks	Division of the complex		
	Upper	Middle	Lower
Urtites	11	1	9
Juvites	5	—	5
Foyaites	48	10	67
Aegirine-lujavrites	24	69	16
Leucocratic aegirine-lujavrites	9	16	3
Hornblende-lujavrites	3	4	—

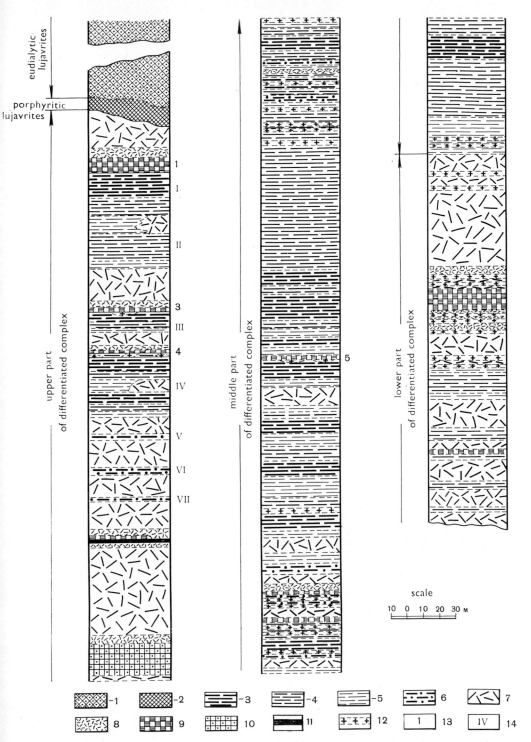

FIG. 16. Geological columnar section of north-western part of Lovozero massif (compiled by E. M. Es'kova)

1. eudialytic lujavrite; 2. porphyritic lujavrite; 3. melanocratic aegirine-lujavrite; 4. meso-cratic aegirine-lujavrite; 5. leucocratic aegirine-lujavrite; 6. hornblende-lujavrite; 7. foyaite; 8. juvite; 9. urtite; 10. ijolitic urtite; 11. malignite; 12. pegmatites (not to scale); 13. serial numbers of urtite horizons; 14. serial numbers of lujavrite horizons

Four well-developed three-component groups can be distinguished in the upper part of the complex, which is 250-375 m thick (Fig. 16). The middle part of the complex, up to 500 m thick, consists mainly of a slightly differentiated group of lujavrite layers, that accounts for nearly nine tenths of its volume; of this group, hornblende-lujavrites make up 4 per cent, leucocratic aegirine-lujavrites 16 per cent, and foyaites and urtites 10 per cent. This part of the complex is subdivided into distinct horizons of melanocratic, mesocratic and leucocratic aegirine-lujavrites with occasional foyaite, urtite and hornblende-lujavrite intercalations of small thickness. In the lower part of the complex, up to 200 m thick, there is an alternation of foyaite and lujavrite horizons. Urtites occur rarely.

This alternating pattern of different types of rock in the differentiated complex persists throughout the massif, so that the geological profile is similar in all its various zones. More than 20 foyaite horizons have been distinguished, ranging in thickness from 2 to 100 m, usually bedded between the lujavrites and the urtites, with which they are connected by gradual transitions. The transition from these foyaites to the overlying lujavrites is by way of an intermediate horizon of leucocratic lujavrites, 1-5 m thick, while the transition to the underlying urtites is through feldspathic urtites, the juvites. Where urtites are lacking in the three-component groups, the foyaites gradually give place through their leucocratic varieties, to aegirine-lujavrites above and below.

At present only 10 urtite horizons are known to exist in the differentiated complex. They vary in thickness from 0·3 to 20 m and usually lie directly above aegirine-lujavrites, with which they have clearly defined contacts; above they gradually pass into foyaites. In the absence of foyaites the urtites are bedded between two lujavrite horizons; in this case they gradually give place upwards to lujavrites, through the leucocratic varieties. In such cases the leucocratic varieties may well be rudimentary foyaites resulting from an earlier partial differentiation. At the bottom of the complex there is one thick urtite horizon (up to 15-20 m thick) bedded in the foyaites, with gradual transitions to them. Sometimes the urtitic horizons are divided into two layers with a number of lujavrite and foyaite intercalations. Discontinuous pegmatite horizons (0·05 to 2 m thick) usually occur at the contacts between the urtites and the underlying lujavrites.

The aegirine-lujavrites form thick horizons (from 3-5 up to 100 m or occasionally more), more than thirty of which have been counted in the complex. As we noted above, the lujavrites have well-defined contacts with the overlying urtites.

TABLE 9 Quantitative mineralogical

Division	Nepheline	Feldspars	Aegirine + hornblende	Natrolite	Sodalite	Loparite	Apatite
Upper	9·5-21	54·8-85	4·7-8·4	0-25·4	0-15·3	0-0·15	0-0·3
Middle	16·6-44·7	29 -51·8	8·8-14·6	0-16·9	0-6·4	0-0·5	0-3·2
Lower	15·4-23·9	55·7-67·8	4·6-9·3	0-1·8	3·8-7·5	0-0·1	0-1·8

At the immediate contact of these rocks intercalations of a rock of intermediate composition, up to 0·5 m thick, are fairly common.

The gradual transitions between the aegirine-lujavrites and underlying foyaites are effected by way of a reduction in the amount of aegirine and an increase in the feldspar content. The top of each aegirine-lujavrite horizon is usually made up of a melanocratic variety, which turns first into mesocratic and then into leucocratic varieties lower down.

In addition to the aegirine-lujavrites eight horizons of hornblende-lujavrites have been identified: three at the top of the differentiated complex and five in the middle. Those at the top are bedded in a thick group of foyaite strata above the malignite horizon and are connected with the foyaites by gradual transitions through leucocratic hornblende-lujavrites 0·5-2 m thick, the transition being more gradual at the top of the layer than at its base. In the middle of the complex the hornblende-lujavrites are interstratified either in amongst aegirine-lujavrites or at the contact of these with the foyaites, and have gradual transitions with both. The hornblende-lujavrite horizons vary in thickness from 1·5-6 m and persist along the strike in all parts of the massif.

The malignites form a single horizon of small thickness that can be traced throughout the massif in the upper part of the differentiated complex in a thick group of foyaite layers (see Fig. 16). This horizon varies from 6-15 cm in thickness, the thicker parts being in the north-west and western parts of the massif. Urtites overlie it and these gradually pass upwards into foyaites. Where the malignite tapers out (Vavnbed, Ninchurt and elsewhere) the urtites rest directly, with a sharp contact, on foyaites. Sometimes the malignite horizon is divided into two parts by a thin pegmatitic intercalation (Alluaiv, Angvundaschorr and Kuftn'yun). Below the malignite horizon and in sharp contact with it are usually juvites, passing into foyaites in some parts of the massif (Ninchurt and Sengischorr). On Vavnbed, urtites have developed below the malignite horizon.

The Foyaites

The foyaites of the differentiated complex are leucocratic feldspathic rocks. Coarse-grained and of light grey colour, they consist mainly of large variously orientated microcline laths measuring up to $2 \times 0·7 \times 0·2$ cm with the interstices

composition of the foyaites (per cent)

Mur-manite, lomono-sovite	Eudia-lyte	Lampro-phyllite	Pecto-lite	Villiaum-ite	Rinko-lite	Ussing-ite	Cancrin-ite	Others
0·25-5·1	1 -4·8	0·3-2·7	0·01-0·2	0 -3	—	0 -0·1	0 -0·3	0·2-0·3
0·1-2·5	0·6-3·9	0·5-1·8	0·2-0·7	0-1	0-0·2	0 -0·2	0·1-0·3	0·1-0·4
0·3-1·5	0·3-1·8	0·5-1·2	0·1-0·4	0·6-1·5	0-0·1	0·1-0·2	0-0·1	0·2-0·3

LAM D

filled chiefly by nepheline grains up to 0.3×0.2 cm in size and by aegirine, forming either large crystals (up to $2 \times 0.5 \times 0.1$ cm) or finely-crystalline segregations. Unlayered, or occasionally, in the transition zones to lujavrites, trachytoid, their texture is hypidiomorphic-granular (Fig. 17).

The mineralogical composition of the foyaites is extremely irregular: of the principal rock-forming minerals, feldspars vary from 29 to 85 per cent, nepheline from 9 to 45 per cent, and aegirine from 4 to 15 per cent. The commonest variety contains 60-85 per cent feldspars, 10-20 per cent nepheline and up to 5-8 per cent aegirine.

Apart from the principal rock-forming minerals, the foyaites contain arfvedsonite, lomonosovite, murmanite, eudialyte, lamprophyllite, villiaumite, ramsayite,

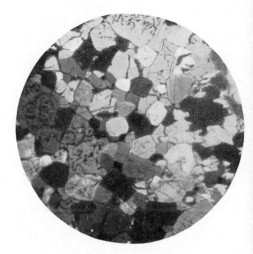

FIG. 17. Texture of foyaite. $\times 10$. Crossed nicols

FIG. 18. Texture of urtite. $\times 10$. Crossed nicols

loparite, rinkolite, molybdenite, sphalerite, galena, albite, apatite, lovchorrite, lovozerite, catapleite, sodalite, pectolite, cancrinite, neptunite, ussingite, natrolite and a number of others (Table 9).

Compared with other rocks in the complex the foyaites are rich in accessory and rare-metal minerals. Here is found the greatest variety of rare-metal minerals, which in some parts make up 5-10 per cent of the rock. There is also a wide variety of replacement minerals: albite, sodalite, hackmanite, ussingite, cancrinite and natrolite. The predominant secondary processes in the foyaites are sodalitization and albitization.

The foyaites at the top and bottom of the differentiated complex contain more feldspar and less nepheline and aegirine than those in the middle (see Table 9), which contain larger amounts of apatite and loparite. These are minerals characteristic of urtites and lujavrites and the indication is that there has been partial differentiation of the rocks in this part of the complex.

The foyaites at the top of the complex are more natrolitized and sodalitized than those in the middle and lower parts and contain more rare-metal and accessory minerals. The largest amounts of rare-metal minerals occur towards the upper surface of each foyaite horizon or in its central part; the thicker the horizon the more pronounced is this pattern.

The chemical analyses of foyaites from different parts of the differentiated complex (Table 10) show that the more advanced the differentiation process (top and bottom parts of the complex), the richer are the foyaites in silica and the poorer in alumina and calcium oxide. This is because of their high microcline and low nepheline, loparite and apatite content. The water content appreciably increases from the bottom up, because of intensified zeolitization. Compared with the juvites, the foyaites contain more silicon and potassium, and less aluminium, sodium, calcium and rare earths. This is because of the higher nepheline

TABLE 10 Chemical compositions of the foyaites and juvites (per cent)

| Constituent | Foyaites | | | | | Juvites Karnasurt, Upper division of complex |
| | Karnasurt | | | Punkaruaiv | Ninchurt | |
	Upper division of the complex	Middle division of the complex	Lower division of the complex			
SiO_2	56·09	51·55	53·88	50·80	50·12	45·14
TiO_2	0·52	0·64	0·24	1·17	0·79	0·52
ZrO_2	0·12	not det.	0·72	not det.	present	0·23
$(Nb, Ta)_2O_5$	0·16	,, ,,	not det.	,, ,,	not det.	not found
RE_2O_3	0·11	,, ,,	,, ,,	,, ,,	,, ,,	0·74
Al_2O_3	19·67	25·31	22·19	17·73	26·62	27·76
Fe_2O_3	4·12	2·45	2·48	7·53	1·95	2·78
FeO	not found	0·71	0·47	2·16	0·29	0·93
MnO	0·19	—	0·17	0·35	0·12	0·14
MgO	0·53	0·29	0·28	1·22	0·20	0·23
CaO	0·54	1·81	1·00	0·82	0·42	1·87
BaO	0·10	not det.	not det.	trace	trace	not found
SrO	0·22	,, ,,	,, ,,	not det.	not det.	0·10
Na_2O	8·53	8·88	9·70	11·36	13·16	13·79
K_2O	6·55	7·61	6·23	4·86	5·36	3·67
Li_2O	0·09	not det.	not det.	not det.	not det.	not found
P_2O_5	0·27	,, ,,	0·50	,, ,,	0·06	,, ,,
V_2O_5	not found	,, ,,	not det.	,, ,,	not det.	,, ,,
SO_3	0·23	,, ,,	0·21	,, ,,	,, ,,	0·72
S	—	,, ,,	not det.	,, ,,	nil	—
F	not found	,, ,,	,, ,,	—	—	not found
Cl	0·21	,, ,,	,, ,,	not det.	0·03	0·13
H_2O^+	1·08	0·59	0·20	,, ,,	0·90	1·24
H_2O^-	0·25	0·14	0·38	0·38	0·24	0·08
Others	—	0·32	0·98	1·57	—	—
Total	99·58	100·30	99·63	99·95	100·26	100·07
$-O = Cl_2$	−0·05					−0·03
	99·53	—	—	—	—	100·04
Analyst	Nesterova	Khalezova	Burova	Moleva		Nesterova
References		—		*Minerals of the Khibiny and Lovozero tundras* (1937)		—

TABLE 11 Radioactive element content of the foyaites (in g. per g. of rock)

Rock	Th	Ra	U
Foyaites			
Upper division of the complex	$9 \cdot 5 \times 10^{-5}$	$5 \cdot 85 \times 10^{-12}$	$1 \cdot 72 \times 10^{-5}$
Middle division of the complex	$7 \cdot 3 \times 10^{-5}$	$6 \cdot 65 \times 10^{-12}$	$1 \cdot 95 \times 10^{-5}$
Lower division of the complex	$2 \cdot 6 \times 10^{-5}$	$4 \cdot 0 \ \times 10^{-12}$	$1 \cdot 16 \times 10^{-5}$
Juvites, upper division of complex	$5 \cdot 0 \times 10^{-5}$	$2 \cdot 7 \ \times 10^{-12}$	$0 \cdot 79 \times 10^{-5}$

and loparite content in the juvites. Fluorine was detected to the extent of 0·026-0·34 per cent in foyaites from various parts of the differentiated complex (6 assays, V. V. Danilova, 1954) and beryllium in amounts of 0·0013-0·002 per cent (analyst S. N. Fedorchuk). The highest fluorine concentrations are found in foyaites from the well-differentiated parts of the complex. The foyaites of the top and bottom parts contain 0·16-0·34 per cent fluorine, those in the middle part 0·04-0·08 per cent. The foyaites at their outcrop invariably contain less fluorine, because the main fluorine-bearing mineral, villiaumite, is highly water-soluble. Table 11 shows the tenor of radioactive elements in the foyaites (analysts S. G. Tseitlin and N. K. Zhirova). These rocks contain less nickel (0·0004 per cent) and copper (0·0022 per cent) than the juvites (0·0008 per cent Ni and 0·003 per cent Cu) (analyst O. V. Krutetskaya). Spectrographic analysis (by N. V. Lizunov) showed 0·01 per cent of gallium. In addition to the above-mentioned elements, rubidium, molybdenum, lead, vanadium and tin have been detected spectrographically in the foyaites.

THE URTITES

The urtites are leucocratic nepheline-rich members of the differentiated complex. They are dark-grey, grey and greenish-grey, compact rocks of finely-granular texture and unlayered fabric, consisting of a mosaic of little grains of nepheline with small amounts of microcline and aegirine. The principal rock-forming minerals form segregations of the following sizes: nepheline, 0·2-3 mm; microcline, up to 1 cm; aegirine, up to 2 cm; and loparite, 0·2-0·5 mm. The texture is panidiomorphic-granular (Fig. 18) and in certain sectors poikilitic, owing to the inclusion, in the larger aegirine and microcline crystals, of small, well-defined nepheline segregations with tetragonal and hexagonal cross-sections and of idiomorphic crystals of loparite and apatite.

TABLE 12 Quantitative mineralogical

Division	Nepheline	Feldspars	Aegirine	Natrolite	Sodalite	Loparite
Upper	4-63·2	0-11·50	4·3-20·1	6·4-90·1	0-7·4	0-11
Middle	51·8-65·3	4-14	5·6-19·5	6·6-13·6	0·2-1·9	0-3·5
Lower	66·2-95·1	0-8·9	2·4-23·0	0-2·3	0·4-1·2	0-1·8

The mineralogical composition of the urtites varies greatly: the nepheline content, together with natrolite developed from it, ranges from 75 to 95 per cent, the microcline from fractions of one per cent up to 14 per cent, the aegirine from 2 to 20 per cent and the apatite from 0·1 to several per cent. In addition, lomonosovite, murmanite, loparite, metaloparite, villiaumite, eudialyte, lovozerite, catapleite, lamprophyllite, neptunite and rinkolite also occur (Table 12).

The urtites of the poorly-differentiated part of the complex contain large amounts of feldspar (average 10·5 per cent) and aegirine (average 14·2 per cent) as compared with the urtites of the well-differentiated upper and lower parts of the complex, where the feldspar content is 4·7-5·6 per cent and the aegirine content 3·5-5·6 per cent.

The most characteristic rare-metal minerals are loparite, rare-earth apatite and, to a small extent, eudialyte. In each horizon the greater part of the rare-metal minerals gravitates to the base. The thicker and the more mineralogically diversified the urtite horizon, the more apparent is this pattern. In the thick urtite horizons, rare-metal minerals are usually found in minute amounts in the general body of the rock, whereas in contrast there are parts near the base of the horizon which are composed almost exclusively of one or other of the rare-metal minerals. The amount of rare-metal minerals in the urtites diminishes from top to bottom of the complex.

The natrolite content also diminishes from top to bottom of the complex. In each urtitic horizon the amount of this mineral increases from the roof to the floor. In the upper part of the complex the floors of the urtitic horizons are made up almost entirely of natrolite, formed from nepheline and microcline.

The urtites and ijolitic urtites (Table 13) have characteristically a low silica content and a high alumina and soda content, corresponding to their higher nepheline content. In some varieties of the urtites there is a higher niobium, rare-earth and titanium content than in other rocks in the massif, with the highest concentrations of these elements in the floors of the urtitic horizons. In addition, a very high calcium, phosphorus and water content is found in the urtites, resulting from the high apatite and zeolite content. The urtites and ijolitic urtites from different parts of the complex all contain roughly the same amounts of radioactive elements (Table 14). In addition wet chemical analysis shows 0·0009-0·002 per cent of beryllium in the urtites (analyst S. N. Fedorchuk) and 0·05-0·13 per cent of fluorine (analyst V. V. Danilova).

The polarographic method shows 0·0014 per cent of copper (analyst O. V. Krutetskaya) and quantitative spectrographic analysis between 0·01 and 0·03 per

composition of the urtites (per cent)

Apatite	Mur-manite	Eudialyte	Lampro-phyllite	Rinkolite	Pectolite	Ussing-ite	Cancrin-ite	Others
0-2·6	0-1·4	0-6·2	0-0·5	0-0·1	0-0·9	0-0·3	0-0·1	0-1·2
0-6·8	0-0·3	0-3.6	0-0·1	—	0·1-0·2	0-0·1	0-0·5	0-0·2
0-2·8	0-0·2	0·2-0·8	0-0·05	—	0-0·5	0-0·8	0-0·6	—

TABLE 13 Chemical compositions of the urtites and ijolite-urtites (per cent)

Constituent	Urtite, lower division of complex, Karnasurt	Ijolitic urtite, Karnasurt	Urtite, Ninchurt		
SiO_2	44·40	42·75	43·76	43·68	42·43
TiO_2	0·20	0·21	0·28	0·19	0·15
ZrO_2	not determined	not determined	not determined	not determined	not determined
$(Ta, Nb)_2O_5$	,, ,,	,, ,,	,, ,,	,, ,,	,, ,,
RE_2O_3	,, ,,	,, ,,	,, ,,	,, ,,	,, ,,
Al_2O_3	28·53	29·28	27·50	28·23	26·98
Fe_2O_3	3·74	3·07	3·04	2·70	4·64
FeO	0·58	1·02	0·57	0·28	0·68
MnO	0·01	0·58	0·12	0·07	0·08
MgO	0·46	0·90	0·14	0·18	0·25
CaO	1·56	3·47	2·06	2·80	2·40
Na_2O	16·57	12·29	14·49	15·10	15·67
K_2O	3·78	5·47	3·02	3·34	3·98
P_2O_5	not determined	not determined	1·56	1·78	not determined
SO_3	,, ,,	,, ,,	not determined	not determined	,, ,,
S	,, ,,	,, ,,	—	0·06	,, ,,
F	,, ,,	0·2	—	0·04	—
Cl	,, ,,	not determined	0·03	0·07	not determined
H_2O^+	0·42	1·18	2·50	not determined	2·19
H_2O^-	nil	0·26	0·78	0·12	0·16
Other	not determined	not determined	—	0·79	—
Total	100·25	100·68	99·85	99·43	99·61
$-O=F_2$		−0·08			
	—	100·60	—	—	—
Analyst	Khalezova		Moleva	Stukalova	Vladimirova
Reference	—		Vorob'eva (1937[2])		

cent of gallium (N. V. Lizunov). Besides the elements mentioned above, lead and barium have been detected spectrographically in the urtites and ijolitic urtites.

THE AEGIRINE-LUJAVRITES

The aegirine-lujavrites are melanocratic varieties of nepheline-syenite. They are medium and fine-grained rocks made up mainly of microcline (30-55 per cent), nepheline (20-25 per cent) and aegirine (20-50 per cent). The grain sizes of the

TABLE 14 Radioactive element content of urtites (in g. per g. of rock)

Rock	Th	Ra	U
Urtite of horizon IV	$6·23 \times 10^{-4}$	$12·25 \times 10^{-12}$	$3·60 \times 10^{-5}$
Urtite of upper division of complex	$2·2 \times 10^{-5}$	$1·69 \times 10^{-12}$	$0·49 \times 10^{-5}$
Ijolitic-urtite	$1·67 \times 10^{-5}$	$1·32 \times 10^{-12}$	$0·38 \times 10^{-5}$
Urtite of middle division of complex	$3·12 \times 10^{-5}$	$2·3 \times 10^{-12}$	$0·67 \times 10^{-5}$
Analysts	Tseitlin and Zhirova		

main rock-making minerals are as follows: nepheline, up to 0·3 cm; aegirine, up to 1 cm; microcline, up to 1·5 cm.

Leucocratic, mesocratic and melanocratic varieties can be distinguished among the aegirine-lujavrites. In all varieties the microcline laths are generally parallel, imparting a trachytoid fabric to the rocks. The colour is greyish-green and dark green. The texture is hypidiomorphic-granular (Fig. 19).

In addition to the main rock-forming minerals the aegirine-lujavrites contain natrolite, sodalite, albite, loparite, apatite, murmanite, lomonosovite, eudialyte, lamprophyllite, rinkolite, lovchorrite, pectolite, ussingite, catapleite, cancrinite,

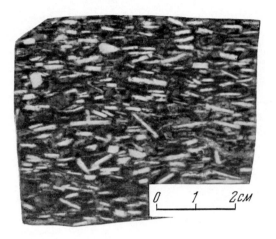

FIG. 19. Mesocratic aegirine lujav-rite. Section cut normal to trachy-toid structure

schizolite, villiaumite, sphene, ramsayite and lovozerite (Table 15). There are usually smaller amounts of rare-metal minerals in the aegirine-lujavrites at the top of the complex than in those in the middle. The maximum amounts of loparite, apatite, eudialyte and mesodialyte occur in the upper part of each horizon. The tenor of these minerals declines in inverse ratio to the feldspar content, from the top downwards, while the murmanite, lomonosovite and lamprophyllite contents increase.

The amount of natrolite in the aegirine-lujavrites increases from the lower part of the complex to the top. In each aegirine-lujavrite horizon in the differentiated parts of the complex the natrolite tenor is highest in sectors directly adjacent to urtitic horizons, but gradually diminishes from the roofs to the floors of the lujavrite layers. Sodalite is more widespread in the lujavrites of the middle part of the complex.

The silica, alumina, potash and water content increases from the melanocratic to the leucocratic aegirine-lujavrites (Table 16), while the content of titanium, niobium, zirconium, rare earths, iron, manganese, magnesium, calcium, sodium and chlorine decreases. This is due mainly to the high potassium feldspar and zeolite content and the low aegirine, loparite and apatite content in the leucocratic varieties.

Fluorine becomes more abundant as the rocks become darker, evidently

TABLE 15 Quantitative mineralogical

Division	Nepheline	Feldspars	Aegirine	Natrolite	Sodalite	Loparite	Apatite
Upper	8·4-28·4	28·4-59·7	11·8-45·3	0·8-33·4	0-2·5	0-3·9	nil
Middle	15·7-21·4	38·0-46·4	13·8-27·4	2·2- 4·7	1·8-7·0	0-1·3	0-1·3
Lower	18·3-27·5	34·6-45·3	20·3-35·1	0·3- 1·8	0·5-3·5	0·1-0·8	0-0·2

because of the rising tenor of aegirine, which contains up to 0·30 per cent fluorine, in the melanocratic varieties (Table 17, cf. Table 169).

Radioactive elements are present in roughly the same amounts in the different varieties of lujavrites in the upper and middle parts of the differentiated complex (Table 18). Some increase in the thorium content is found in the melanocratic lujavrites as compared with other varieties, owing to their high loparite content.

The beryllium content of the aegirine-lujavrites is 0·0005-0·0013 per cent,

TABLE 16 Chemical compositions of aegirine-lujavrites (per cent)

Constituent	Karnasurt					
	Melano-cratic, upper division of complex	Mesocratic				Leuco-cratic, upper division of complex
		Upper division of complex	Middle division of complex		Lower division of complex	
SiO$_2$	51·39	56·84	55·77	55·03	53·11	57·41
TiO$_2$	1·66	0·81	1·42	0·76	0·42	0·50
ZrO$_2$	0·52	0·21	0·13	not found	0·14	0·18
(Nb, Ta)$_2$O$_5$	not found	not found	not found	,, ,,	not determined	not found
RE$_2$O$_3$	0·28	0·20	0·12	,, ,,	,, ,,	,, ,,
Al$_2$O$_3$	13·96	17·22	14·41	17·01	15·63	20·85
Fe$_2$O$_3$	9·90	4·17	8·60	6·82	8·54	3·03
FeO	3·03	2·42	1·80	1·48	3·36	0·88
MnO	0·38	0·28	0·37	0·19	0·08	0·16
MgO	2·34	1·48	1·34	0·92	3·09	0·48
CaO	3·28	1·10	1·93	1·09	4·71	0·46
BaO	not found	0·13	0·05	0·07	not determined	not found
SrO	,, ,,	not found	not found	not found	,, ,,	0·22
Na$_2$O	8·95	7·28	8·07	8·97	7·01	7·07
K$_2$O	3·26	6·23	4·62	5·23	3·38	6·70
Li$_2$O	0·04	not found	0·06	0·05	not determined	0·04
P$_2$O$_5$	0·01	0·08	0·09	0·09	,, ,,	0·03
V$_2$O$_5$	0·003	0·008	0·015	0·013	,, ,,	not found
SO$_3$	0·01	not found	0·34	1·40	,, ,,	,, ,,
F	not found	trace	trace	trace	,, ,,	,, ,,
Cl	0·27	0·03	0·10	0·14	,, ,,	0·02
H$_2$O$^+$	0·24	1·42	1·18	1·22	0·12	1·82
H$_2$O$^-$	0·17	0·16	0·05	0·01	0·12	0·10
Others	—	—	—	—	—	—
Total	99·69	100·07	100·47	100·49	99·71	99·95
− O = Cl$_2$	− 0·07		− 0·02	− 0·03		
	99·62	—	100·45	100·46	—	—
Analyst	Nesterova				Khalesova	Nesterova

composition of aegirine-lujavrites (per cent)

Mur-manite	Eudialyte	Lampro-phyllite	Rinkolite	Pectolite	Ussing-ite	Cancrin-ite	Villiaum-ite	Ram-sayite
0-1·5	0·4-5·3	0-1·0	0-0·1	0-0·2	nil	nil	nil	0-0·1
0·4-3·0	0·7-4·7	0·3-2·5	0-1·1	0·1-0·4	0·1-0·3	0-0·1	0-0·5	0-0·2
0-0·3	0·3-1·2	0·2-0·5	0·05-0·2	0·1-0·2	0-0·15	0-0·1	0-0·2	0-0·5

and is characteristically highest in the melanocratic varieties (analyst S. N. Fedor-chuk). Copper has been polarographically determined at 0·001-0·002 per cent (analyst O. V. Krutetskaya) and nickel at 0·0003 per cent (in the leucocratic varieties).

Besides the above-mentioned elements, 0·003 per cent gallium and rubidium, chromium, lead and tin have been detected in the aegirine-lujavrites by spectrographic analysis.

TABLE 17 Fluorine content of aegirine-lujavrites (Karnasurt)

Rock	F (per cent)
Lujavrites of upper division of complex	
Melanocratic	0·30
Mesocratic	0·26
Leucocratic	0·05
Lujavrites of middle division of complex	
Melanocratic	0·02-0·26
Mesocratic	0·06-0·12
Leucocratic	0·07
Analyst	Danilova, 1954

HORNBLENDE-LUJAVRITES

The hornblende-lujavrites are medium-grained rocks, almost black in colour, composed mainly of microcline crystals in parallel arrangement, and interstitial

TABLE 18 Radioactive element content of aegirine-lujavrites (in g. per g. of rock)

Rock	Th	Ra	U
Lujavrites of upper division of complex:			
Melanocratic (horizon III)	$1·17 \times 10^{-4}$	$1·54 \times 10^{-12}$	$0·45 \times 10^{-5}$
Mesocratic (horizon III)	$4·65 \times 10^{-5}$	$2·4 \times 10^{-12}$	$0·70 \times 10^{-5}$
Leucocratic	$5·2 \times 10^{-5}$	$3·48 \times 10^{-12}$	$1·02 \times 10^{-5}$
Lujavrites of middle division of complex:			
Melanocratic	from $6·6 \times 10^{-5}$ to $1·12 \times 10^{-4}$	$(1·92-3·83) \times 10^{-12}$	$(0·57-1·13) \times 10^{-5}$
Mesocratic	from $1·57 \times 10^{-4}$ to $6·0 \times 10^{-5}$	$(2·38-6·65) \times 10^{-12}$	$(0·70-1·95) \times 10^{-5}$
Leucocratic	$6·96 \times 10^{-5}$	$5·8 \times 10^{-12}$	$1·72 \times 10^{-5}$
Analysts	Tseitlin and Zhirova		

TABLE 19 Quantitative mineralogical composition

Division	Nepheline	Feldspars	Aegirine	Arfved-sonite	Natrolite	Sodalite	Loparite
Upper	18·1-22·4	36·1-41·7	3·4-8·7	21·3-42·3	0·9-8·1	3·8-6·3	0-0·2
Middle	24·3-31·8	29·7-35·4	8·5-16·3	10·2-18·6	2·5-4·4	1·5-3·6	0-0.3

finely acicular hornblende, aegirine and nepheline. The lamellar microcline crystals measure $1·5 \times 0·5 \times 0·1$ cm and the nepheline grains up to $0·3 \times 0·2 \times 0·2$ cm. The structure is trachytoid (Fig. 20) and the texture hypidiomorphic-granular.

In addition to the principal rock-forming minerals, albite, eudialyte, ramsayite, murmanite, lomonosovite, loparite, lamprophyllite, sphene, apatite and others

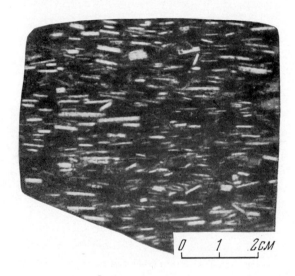

FIG. 20. Hornblende-lujavrite. Section normal to trachytoid structure

are present (Table 19). Enrichment in rare-metal minerals is observed mainly in the transition zones to foyaites, that is, in the leucocratic hornblende-lujavrites.

The hornblende-lujavrites in the middle of the complex are richer in nepheline and aegirine than those at the top and contain less feldspar and arfvedsonite. Compared with other rocks in the differentiated complex their tenor of rare-metal minerals is low.

Comparison of the chemical analyses of the hornblende- and aegirine-lujavrites (Table 20) shows that the former contain less iron and more magnesium, owing to the greater amount of arfvedsonite.

The hornblende-lujavrites at the top of the complex are slightly richer in fluorine than those in the middle (Table 21), because of their higher content of fluorine-bearing arfvedsonite and villiaumite. The fluorine content in a given hornblende-lujavrite horizon diminishes with proximity to the ground surface, because of the leaching of the villiaumite.

of hornblende-lujavrites (per cent)

Eudialyte	Murmanite	Lamprophyllite	Rinkolite-lovchorrite	Apatite	Sphene	Pectolite	Villiaumite	Ussingite	Cancrinite
0·1-2·1	0-0·3	0-0·7	—	0·0-6	0·2-0·6	0-0·2	0-0·2	—	—
0·3-1·6	0-0·4	0-0·5	0-0·4	0·2-2·5	0·1-0·4	0-0·1	—	0-0·1	0-0·2

The radioactive element content is of the same order in all the hornblende-lujavrite horizons (Table 22); this is because they all contain roughly equal amounts of loparite.

Chemical assay revealed beryllium in amounts of 0·0006-0·0008 per cent (analyst S. N. Fedochuk). Gallium (0·01 per cent) rubidium, chromium, tin, copper, rare earths, vanadium, nickel and lead were detected spectrographically.

TABLE 20 Chemical compositions of hornblende- and aegirine-lujavrites (per cent)

Constituent	Hornblende-lujavrite (Karnasurt)		Aegirine-lujavrite Angvundaschorr	
	Upper division of complex (horizon VI)	Middle division of complex		
SiO_2	54·08	52·48	54·85	53·50
TiO_2	1·04	0·72	1·44	0·86
ZrO_2	0·06	0·62	not determined	not determined
$(Nb, Ta)_2O_5$	not found	not determined	,, ,,	,, ,,
RE_2O_3	,, ,,	—	,, ,,	,, ,,
Al_2O_3	15·91	13·50	18·33	16·44
Fe_2O_3	2·86	5·10	} 6·96	8·72
FeO	4·53	2·90		1·48
MnO	0·51	0·37	0·89	0·47
MgO	4·26	2·90	1·06	1·05
CaO	1·71	2·24	1·32	1·50
SrO	not found	not determined	not determined	not determined
BaO	0·12	,, ,,	,, ,,	,, ,,
Na_2O	8·28	12·50	11·43	9·98
K_2O	5·31	5·30	3·16	4·58
Li_2O	0·04	not determined	not determined	not determined
P_2O_5	0·37	0·26	,, ,,	,, ,,
SO_3	0·17	0·14	,, ,,	,, ,,
F	trace	not determined	,, ,,	,, ,,
Cl	0·12	,, ,,	,, ,,	,, ,,
H_2O^+	0·90	0·31	} 1·06	} 1·75
H_2O^-	0·17	0·05		
Others	—	0·69	—	—
Total	100·44	100·08	100·50	100·33
$-O = Cl_2$	-0·03			
	100·41	—	—	—
Analyst	Nesterova, 1949	Burova, 1952	Bergel'	Tsiliakus
Reference	—		W. Ramsay (1897-1899)	

TABLE 21   Fluorine content of hornblende-lujavrites of Karnasurt

Occurrence	F (per cent)
Upper division of complex (horizon VI)	0·18-0·30
Middle division of complex	0·18
Analyst	Danilova, 1954

TABLE 22   Radioactive element content of hornblende-lujavrites of Karnasurt
(in g. per g. of rock)

Occurrence	Th	Ra	U
Upper division of complex:			
Horizon VI	$2·82 \times 10^{-5}$	$3·66 \times 10^{-12}$	$1·07 \times 10^{-5}$
Horizon VII	$6·36 \times 10^{-5}$	$3·5 \times 10^{-12}$	$1·02 \times 10^{-5}$
Middle division of complex	$2·9 \times 10^{-5}$	$1·96 \times 10^{-12}$	$0·57 \times 10^{-5}$
Analysts	Tseitlin and Zhirova		

THE MALIGNITES*

Malignites are medium-grained rocks, almost black in colour (Fig. 21), with generally massive, occasionally trachytoid structure, made up primarily of feldspars, nepheline and aegirine. The principal rock-forming minerals are present in segregations of the following sizes: nepheline, up to $0·2 \times 0·2 \times 0·2$ cm; feldspars, up to $0·8 \times 0·2 \times 0·1$ cm; aegirine, up to $1·5 \times 0·2 \times 0·05$ cm. The texture is hypidiogranular and, in certain parts, poikilitic, owing to the presence of nepheline and loparite inclusions in the aegirine and feldspars.

The mineralogical composition of the malignites varies, the main minerals occurring in proportions ranging from 33 to 63 per cent of nepheline *plus* zeolites, from 0·7 to 21 per cent feldspar and from 23 to 38 per cent aegirine and hornblende. In addition, loparite, murmanite, lomonosovite, eudialyte, lamprophyllite, apatite, villiaumite, sodalite, cancrinite, schizolite, sphene, neptunite, catapleite, pectolite and others are present.

The characteristic rare-metal mineral is loparite and, to a lesser extent, eudialyte and apatite. In mineralogical composition the malignites are intermediate between the urtites and lujavrites, their tenor of principal minerals depending closely on variations in the mineralogical composition of the rocks above and below: an increase in the feldspar and aegirine content in the overlying urtites, for example, corresponds with a reduction in the amounts of these minerals in the malignites.

The greatest amounts of rare-metal minerals are concentrated either at the base of the overlying urtite horizon (loparite, apatite, eudialyte) or towards the top of the malignite layer.

* Malignites were first discovered and described by N. K. Nefedov (1938; Eliseev, Nefedov, 1940).

Zeolitization and sodalitization processes are characteristic of malignites, a regular increase in the concentration of these minerals being observed, from the underlying juvites, through the malignites, to the base of the urtites. The natrolite

FIG. 21. Contact of malignite (dark) with underlying foyaites

content diminishes also as the malignite horizon is followed away from the ground surface: 230-300 m vertically below the surface the malignites contain no natrolite at all, while such minerals as villiaumite and lomonosovite are then present, but these are never in association with natrolite.

The chemical composition of the malignites (per cent) is as follows: SiO_2, 34·98 to 40·54; TiO_2, 10·40 to 11·58; Al_2O_3, 7·35 to 11·20; Fe_2O_3, 9·10 to 10·78; FeO, 1·07 to 1·41; MnO, 0·12 to 0·26; MgO, 0·00 to 1·73; CaO, 2·54 to 6·04; SrO, 0·99; Na_2O, 7·94 to 11·42; K_2O, 1·29 to 2·17; P_2O_5, 0·15 to 0·52; Cl, 0·02 to 0·05; H_2O, 1·14. In addition, the niobium, tantalum and rare-earth content in these rocks is high by comparison with other rocks. As well as the components mentioned above, fluorine has been detected to the amount of 0·30 per cent (analyst V. V. Danilova) and beryllium to 0·0004 per cent (analyst S. N. Fedorchuk). Copper was polarographically determined at 0·025 per cent (analyst O. V. Krutet-

skaya) and gallium (0·008 per cent) lead and vanadium by quantitative spectrographic analysis.

*   *   *   *

The most typical feature of the differentiated complex is its very pronounced
layered structure, owing to the repetition of three-component groups of foyaite,
urtite and lujavrite. Individual horizons of the rocks making up these three-
component groups vary in thickness, as do the groups themselves. An increase
in the thickness of one rock horizon usually corresponds to an increase in that of
the others. Gradual transitions may occur between separate horizons within a
group and between the different groups.

The fact that the principal rock-forming minerals (nepheline, microcline and
aegirine) are separated in varying degrees in space and time accounts for the great
variety of the rocks in this complex. A clear distribution pattern can be observed
in the principal rock-forming and rare-metal minerals in each three-component
group and in the complex as a whole: there is a regular and repeated recurrence
of maximum and minimum concentrations of these minerals within a given type
of rock and a gradual variation in the proportions of these minerals on transition
from one rock to another.

The characteristic elements of the minerals in the differentiated complex are
niobium, rare-earths, titanium and zirconium, the zirconium minerals being
present in significantly smaller quantities here than in the rocks of the eudialytic
lujavrite complex. Each rock variety has its own definite association of rare-metal
minerals—for example, loparite and apatite are characteristic of the urtites;
lomonosovite, murmanite lamprophyllite and eudialyte of the foyaites. The
lujavrites show a characteristic mixed rare-metal mineralization.

A high tenor of rare-metal minerals generally coincides with the more differentiated parts of the complex. It is well established that the more completely the
three-component groups have divided into foyaite, urtite and lujavrite horizons,
the more concentrated, other conditions being equal, are the rare-metal minerals
in particular parts of these horizons.

Four groups of minerals can be provisionally identified in the rocks of this
complex, differing in time of origin and evidently corresponding to four main
stages in the formation of the complex (Fig. 22).

In the first stage, nepheline, microcline, loparite, apatite and aegirine I were
formed, aegirine I being the first to crystallize. The nepheline and microcline
crystallized at different times in different rocks. In the lujavrites, for example,
they appeared almost simultaneously. The presence of nepheline inclusions in
the peripheral and occasionally in the central parts of the microcline crystals
indicates that part of the nepheline formed rather earlier than the microcline.
The number of these inclusions in the microcline of the aegirine-lujavrites is
found to increase in the direction of the urtitic horizons. The rest of the nepheline
usually occurs in interstices between parallel crystals of microcline. Loparite and
apatite formed at the end of the crystallization of microcline and are usually found

at the boundaries between nepheline grains and microcline crystals or in the peripheral parts of the latter.

In the foyaites the microcline crystallized before the nepheline. The nepheline grains are usually irregularly-shaped and as a rule adapted to the contours of the

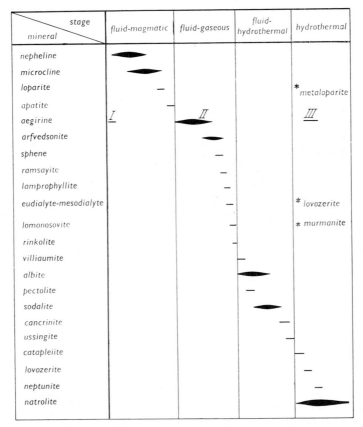

mineral \ stage	fluid-magmatic	fluid-gaseous	fluid-hydrothermal	hydrothermal
nepheline	◄►			
microcline	◄►			
loparite	—			*metaloparite
apatite	—			
aegirine	I	II		III
arfvedsonite		◄►		
sphene		—		
ramsayite		—		
lamprophyllite		—		
eudialyte-mesodialyte		—		*lovozerite
lomonosovite		—		*murmanite
rinkolite		—		
villiaumite			—	
albite			◄►	
pectolite			—	
sodalite			◄►	
cancrinite				—
ussingite				—
catapleiite				—
lovozerite				—
neptunite				—
natrolite				◄►

FIG. 22. Diagram of order of crystallization in rocks of the differentiated complex

microcline. Loparite and apatite separated out later; their crystals are found in interstices between nepheline and microcline and are usually included in aegirine II.

In the urtites the nepheline crystallized before the microcline, and loparite and apatite seem to have separated at the same time as the nepheline. Their idiomorphic crystals are either embedded in the nepheline or lie at the boundaries of its grains. Some of the apatite seems to have crystallized earlier than the loparite, since inclusions of apatite crystals can sometimes be found in the loparite. The main body of the apatite, however, was probably formed at the same time as the loparite or a little later, being usually moulded upon loparite, accommodating itself to the shapes of the loparite segregations.

In the second stage, aegirine II and the titanium, zirconium and niobium minerals crystallized (ramsayite, lamprophyllite, eudialyte, mesodialyte, lomonosovite and others). This stage began with the separation of aegirine II and arfvedsonite, which fill up the interstices between the microcline and the nepheline. Replacement of aegirine II by arfvedsonite is observed. In the hornblende-lujavrites arfvedsonite separated rather earlier than in the other rocks and occupies the position of aegirine II in them. This is because the rocks concerned replace the aegirine-lujavrites and are developing under conditions of unusually high volatile concentration, so that arfvedsonite forms in place of aegirine. The total amount of arfvedsonite and aegirine in the hornblende-lujavrites is equal to the aegirine content in the aegirine-lujavrites.

After the arfvedsonite separated, ramsayite seems to have crystallized; it contains arfvedsonite inclusions and fairly often replaces arfvedsonite peripherally. More often, it fills up the spaces between arfvedsonite segregations, accommodating itself to the shapes of the arfvedsonite. Lamprophyllite fills up the interstices between arfvedsonite and ramsayite and partially replaces them. Eudialyte and mesodialyte usually occupy with interstices between segregations of ramsayite, arfvedsonite, lamprophyllite and other minerals. Grains of members of the eudialyte group of minerals, however, are sometimes included in lamprophyllite. Lomonosovite cements, as it were, the grains of eudialyte, ramsayite and lamprophyllite and sometimes replaces the last two. In the foyaites, where the lomonosovite content is higher, it is found intergrown with microcline. It appears to be the highest-temperature mineral in these rocks. Rinkolite and lovchorrite crystallized after lomonosovite, and fill up spaces between all the above-named minerals.

In the third stage, the high-temperature minerals containing volatile substances (F, Cl, CO_2, SO_3 and OH) crystallized: villiaumite, pectolite, albite, sodalite, cancrinite and ussingite. Albite developed by replacement of microcline. Sodalite replaces nepheline, microcline and albite, and fills up interstices between loparite, lomonosovite, lamprophyllite, eudialyte, villiaumite and pectolite. Cancrinite and ussingite formed later. The former replaces nepheline and microcline and develops at the expense of sodalite; the latter replaces microcline and sodalite. The sulphides seem to have crystallized at this stage.

The fourth stage is characterized by the appearance of hydrous mineral associations, in which natrolite (replacing nepheline), microcline, albite, sodalite, cancrinite and ussingite predominate. Finely-fibrous aegirine III formed at this stage, filling in the cavities of the rocks in association with natrolite crystals.

Sodalitization, zeolitization, cancrinitization and ussingitization processes have proceeded extensively in the rocks of the differentiated complex. The number of replacing minerals increases from the lower part of the complex to the upper, where nearly all the leucocratic minerals are quite often replaced by natrolite and sodalite in some of the horizons (urtites and foyaites). In all parts of the complex replacement minerals are most abundant at urtite-lujavrite contacts and in the foyaites, zeolitization being characteristic of the urtites and sodalitization of the foyaites. Hydrothermal solutions act on the eudialyte minerals to convert them into catapleite and lovozerite; loparite turns into metaloparite and lomonosovite into murmanite.

CHAPTER FOUR

THE POIKILITIC SYENITE COMPLEX

THE poikilitic syenites make up intrusive bodies up to $1\frac{1}{2}$ km^2 in area and dykes 5 m thick and hundreds of metres long among the eudialytic lujavrites and rocks of the differentiated complex. They are commonest in the south-eastern (Suoluaiv and Malyi Punkaruaiv and along the river Indichiok), north-western, western, south-western (Karnasurt, Alluaiv, Angvundaschorr, Sengischorr, Parguaiv, Strashempakhk and others) and central parts of the massif (Lepkhe-Nel'm and Mannepakhk and the Tyul'bny'unuai, Chinglusuai, Chivruai and other river valleys; see Fig. 5).

The poikilitic syenites are leucocratic coarsely-crystalline rocks of pegmatoid appearance, containing numerous schlieren-like pegmatitic segregations, with gradual transitions to the parent rock. The main minerals are potassium feldspar with poikilitic intergrowths of nepheline, sodalite, hydrosodalite and aegirine. The interstices between the large segregations of microcline (up to $15 \times 10 \times 3$ cm) and aegirine (up to $10 \times 2 \times 0.5$ cm) are filled with fine-grained sodalite, nepheline and other minerals.

The rocks vary in colour from light grey to dark grey, almost black; on a fresh fracture one can often see a pinkish tint, owing to the presence of hackmanite.

Depending on the composition of the poikilitic inclusions in the potassium feldspar, three varieties of poikilitic syenite can be distinguished: nepheline, sodalitic (hackmanitic) and hydrosodalitic. The sodalitic varieties tend to concentrate in the upper parts of the massif and are situated in the eudialytic lujavrite complex or at the top of the differentiated complex (Alluaiv, Angvundaschorr, Sengischorr, Karnasurt and the Chinglusuai and other river valleys). Varieties with nepheline and hydrosodalite are usually situated at lower levels, chiefly in the lower parts of the differentiated complex, and are developed in the eastern and south-eastern parts of the massif (Ninchurt, Malyi Punkaruaiv, Lepkhe-Nel'm, Mannepakhk and others).

The proportions of the principal rock-forming minerals fluctuate greatly (feldspar, 15-48 per cent; sodalite, 0-70 per cent; nepheline, 2-75 per cent; hydrosodalite, 0-70 per cent; aegirine, 4-15 per cent). In some outcrops sectors of irregular shape occur, enriched in feldspar, nepheline or aegirine, with the result that a number of investigators have identified foyaites, urtites and tawites in this complex (Eliseev, 1953).

Apart from the main rock-forming minerals the poikilitic syenites contain

(Table 23): lomonosovite, murmanite, chinglusuite, nordite, rinkolite, lamprophyllite, eudialyte, mesodialyte, eucolite, lovozerite, loparite, neptunite, villiaumite, ramsayite, apatite, sphene, hornblende, manganilmenite, albite, ussingite, cancrinite, natrolite, galena, sphalerite, molybdenite, fluorite and others.

Comparison of the different varieties of poikilitic syenites in terms of mineral composition shows that there are gradual transitions from one to another, through rocks of intermediate composition such as nepheline-sodalite and nepheline-hydrosodalite varieties. Microcline, which is characteristic of poikilitic sodalite-syenites, is gradually replaced by orthoclase in the hydrosodalitic varieties.

The sodalitic varieties are the most highly mineralized, containing not only more rare-metal minerals, but also such minerals as nordite, chinglusuite, villiaumite, lomonosovite and rinkolite, which do not occur in the other varieties of poikilitic syenite. A calcic association of rare-metal minerals is more characteristic of the poikilitic hydrosodalite-syenites than of the other varieties. Apatite, sphene, manganilmenite and eucolite are invariably present in them.

The content of rare-metal minerals diminishes from the sodalitic to the nepheline and hydrosodalitic varieties.

There has been extensive sodalitization and hydrosodalitization of the nepheline and, to a smaller extent, of the potassium feldspars in these rocks. Replacement of sodalite and potassium feldspars by ussingite and the development of natrolite from them has occasionally been noticed.

A characteristic feature of the chemical composition is a marked predominance of sodium over potassium (Table 24), corresponding with a minute amount of potassium feldspar and a very large sodalite (hackmanite) content in the sodalitic varieties and nepheline and hydrosodalite content in the nepheline and hydrosodalitic syenites.

In addition, the rocks of the poikilitic syenite complex contain more volatile constituents—water, chlorine, fluorine and sulphur—than other Lovozero rocks. Compared with the nepheline and hydrosodalitic varieties, the sodalite-syenites and tawites are richer in chlorine, sulphur and fluorine (carried in the sodalite and villiaumite) but poorer in water, a phenomenon connected with the less extensive development of hydrosodalite and natrolite in them. Apart from the elements listed in Table 24 the poikilitic sodalite-syenites of Karnasurt were found by chemical assay to contain 0·001 per cent of beryllium (analyst S. N. Fedorchuk).

TABLE 23 Quantitative mineralogical composition

Variety of syenite	Nepheline	Microcline	Orthoclase	Albite	Aegirine	Hornblende	Sodalite	Hydro-sodalite	Natrolite	Ussingite
Sodalite	2·1-3·4	10-48	—	0·8-3·9	0·4-4·5	0·7-1·8	45-71·6	—	0-6·7	0-10·3
Nepheline	40-75	15-35	0-8·5	2·3-5·5	3·5-15·7	0·3-2	0-1·5	0-2·5	0·5-10·3	—
Hydro-sodalite	5·5-10	—	20-45	0-0·5	4·5-8·5	0·5-1·5	0·8-1	40·5-70	3·8-15·4	—

Gallium (0·004-0·03 per cent), strontium, vanadium, copper, lanthanum and nickel have been detected spectrographically.

*   *   *   *

The rocks of this complex are distinguished from those of the other complexes by the following characters:

(1) the large size of the microcline segregations (the crystals are sometimes as large as $15 \times 10 \times 3$ cm, against a maximum size of $2 \times 1·5 \times 0·3$ cm in the foyaites —the coarsest-grained rocks of the other complexes);

(2) the poikilitic texture, due to the presence of idiomorphic inclusions of nepheline and early sodalite in the potassium feldspars;

(3) the absence of stratiform differentiation;

(4) an abundance of small schlieren-like pegmatitic segregations and pegmatoid facies in the upper parts of the intrusions, particularly in the vicinity of contacts with the country rocks;

(5) the great variety of rare-metal minerals; the sodalite-syenites, for example, contain large amounts of all the rare-metal minerals occurring in the other complexes and certain minerals that have not been detected elsewhere, whereas the rocks of the other complexes are characterized by an abundance of one, two or three rare-metal minerals and an insignificant development or total absence of others;

(6) an abundance of volatile components (water, chlorine, fluorine and sulphur), which has led to the formation, along with nepheline, aegirine and potassium feldspars, of such major rock-forming minerals as hackmanite, hydrosodalite, ussingite and natrolite.

All the characteristics noted above, taken in conjunction with the late formation of the poikilitic syenites, indicate that these rocks represent essentially a pegmatoid phase in the history of the massif and were formed from a magma enriched in volatile compounds and rare elements.

The order of crystallization in these rocks, as revealed by the mutual relations of the minerals, is shown in Fig. 23.

The principal leucocratic minerals—nepheline, early sodalite and potassium feldspars, together with aegirine I, loparite, apatite and sphene—crystallized during

of the poikilitic syenites (per cent)

Murmanite-lomono-sovite	Loparite	Eudialyte	Lampro-phyllite	Ramsayite	Nordite	Ching-lusuite	Sphene	Apatite	Mangan-ilmenite	Sulphides	Villiaumite
0-3	0·1-2	0·7-8·3	0·1-1·3	0·2-0·3	0-0·2	0-1·5	—	—	—	0·05-0·2	0-2
0-1·5	0·3-5	0·5-3·5	0-0·9	0-1	—	—	0-0·2	0-0·3	0-0·4	—	—
0-0·3	0-0·5	0·1-2·5	0-0·3	0-0·5	—	—	0·5-2	0·2-0·7	0-1·5	—	—

the first stage. The first was aegirine I, small crystals of which are found as poikilitic inclusions in early sodalite and nepheline and also in microcline. After aegirine I early sodalite and nepheline crystallized, so that they form poikilitic inclusions in the potassium feldspars and other minerals. A certain amount of early sodalite may have formed before the nepheline, for idiomorphic crystals of sodalite are sometimes found poikilitically enclosed in nepheline. The main part of the early sodalite, forming poikilitic inclusions in microcline, seems to have crystallized at the same time as the nepheline of the poikilitic inclusions. Nepheline separated out side by side with early sodalite before microcline. It occurs either as poikilitic inclusions in microcline crystals or as nepheline grains in between these crystals, the microcline accommodating itself to the shapes of the nepheline segregations. Apatite, loparite and sphene crystallized side by side with the microcline. Crystals of these minerals are found within segregations of microcline and aegirine II or at the boundaries between segregations of these minerals, which have adopted shapes conforming to the loparite, apatite and sphene crystals.

TABLE 24 Chemical compositions of rocks

Constituent	Poikilitic sodalite-syenites		Poikilitic nepheline-syenites		
	Karnasurt	Chinglusuai valley	Ninchurt		Ankisuai
			Analysis 1	Analysis 2	
SiO_2	46·58	47·57	50·54	49·20	48·04
TiO_2	0·67	0·44	1·51	0·27	0·50
ZrO_2	not determined	0·37	0·16	—	0·49
$(Nb, Ta)_2O_3$	,, ,,	0·41	—	—	—
RE_2O_3	,, ,,	—	—	—	—
Al_2O_3	24·95	21·90	21·18	22·29	19·83
Fe_2O_3	4·16	5·18	3·72	2·88	5·19
FeO	1·02	0·85	0·72	1·73	0·86
MnO	0·17	0·38	0·10	0·24	0·18
MgO	0·01	0·34	1·03	0·65	0·62
CaO	0·01	0·66	1·88	2·16	5·08
BaO	not determined	—	0·03	—	trace
SrO	,, ,,	—	—	—	—
Na_2O	12·49	12·78	12·09	12·36	7·44
K_2O	5·08	5·58	4·22	4·42	4·08
V_2O_5	not determined	—	nil	—	—
P_2O_5	,, ,,	0·71	0·36	0·48	0·62
S	0·53	0·51	0·56	—	nil
F	0·11	0·25	—	—	—
Cl	5·56	2·69	—	0·09	0·05
H_2O^+	0·18	0·94	0·60	0·65	0·85
H_2O^-	0·73	0·11	1·21	2·44	6·11
Total	102·25	101·67	99·91	99·86	99·94
Analyst	Khalesova	Gerasimovskii's data			
Reference	—		Minerals of the Khibiny and		

In addition to early loparite, late loparite is also found, filling up the interstices between the principal rock-forming minerals and also between most of the accessory minerals.

During the second stage aegirine II, arfvedsonite and the high-temperature rare-metal minerals lamprophyllite, ramsayite, lomonosovite, eudialyte, chinglusuite and others crystallized. The aegirine II crystals have a poikilitic texture with nepheline and microcline inclusions. Arfvedsonite developed from aegirine. Lamprophyllite began to separate at the end of the period of aegirine II formation, as is shown by the presence of idiomorphic lamprophyllite crystals included in the peripheral parts of the aegirine crystals. Lomonosovite formed after lamprophyllite. Segregations of this mineral contain inclusions of idiomorphic lamprophyllite crystals or are moulded on them. Eudialyte and eucolite form xenomorphic grains filling up the interstices between the minerals already described. Chinglusuite and rinkolite seem to have formed after eudialyte but before replacement sodalite. Villiaumite separated after eudialyte but before pectolite; its grains fill up the interstices between segregations of eudialyte or are included in pectolite.

of the poikilitic syenite complex (per cent)

Poikilitic hydrosodalite-syenites		Tawites	
Ninchurt		Tavaiok valley	
Analysis 1	Analysis 2	Analysis 1	Analysis 2
47·16	49·76	44·58	47·29
0·72	0·66	1·51	not determined
—	—	not determined	—
—	—	—	—
—	—	—	—
22·73	19·94	21·74	15·46
2·19	4·26	6·80	12·00
1·73	1·12	1·20	2·35
0·15	0·14	0·13	trace
1·43	0·82	0·31	1·32
2·68	1·68	0·81	1·61
—	nil	not determined	—
—	—	—	—
12·36	11·49	16·28	14·74
3·80	4·77	1·34	1·23
—	—	—	—
—	0·15	—	—
0·43	1·70	0·32	trace
—	—	—	—
0·08	trace	2·56	not determined
} 4·52	3·77	2·62	1·85
99·98	100·26	100·20	97·85
Moleva		Blanket	
Lovozero tundras (1937)		W. Ramsay (1897-1899)	

During the third stage albite separated, along with minerals containing volatile substances: late sodalite, pectolite and cancrinite. The late sodalite formed after the villiaumite, pectolite and some of the neptunite, grains of which are included

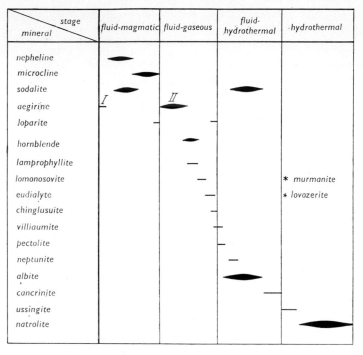

Fig. 23. Order of crystallization of mineral in poikilitic sodalite-syenites

in it. This sodalite replaces mainly nepheline and more rarely microcline and albite. Sodalitization is most apparent in the poikilitic sodalite-syenites.

Ussingitization and natrolitization occur during the fourth stage, the ussingite developing after sodalite and microcline, forming irregular accumulations and filling up cracks in the microcline. Natrolite was the last of the poikilitic syenite minerals to appear, replacing nepheline, microcline and late sodalite. Under the influence of natrolite-forming solutions there is also an alteration of lomonosovite into murmanite, of eudialyte into lovozerite, and a development of neptunite from lomonosovite, eudialyte and lamprophyllite.

CHAPTER FIVE

DISTRIBUTION PATTERN OF THE LOVOZERO MINERALS

THE geological facts and chemical-mineralogical analyses given in the preceding chapters reveal a number of clear patterns in the distribution both of the Lovozero rocks themselves and of the principal rock-forming and rare-metal minerals composing them.

The rocks are made up 90-95 per cent of nepheline, microcline and aegirine. the varying proportions of these minerals produce a very wide variety of rocks, while their spatial distribution gives the massif its layered structure and is responsible for the distribution of rare-metal minerals within it.

DISTRIBUTION OF PRINCIPAL ROCK-FORMING MINERALS

The relative proportions of the principal rock-forming minerals vary greatly, not only from one type of rock to another, but also within rocks of the same type as regards strike and thickness of horizon, reflecting different degrees of differentiation (Table 25).

In all the complexes described the marked differentiation constitutes a typical feature, expressed in the alternation of rocks of different mineralogical composition. The principal rock-forming minerals tend to separate in exactly the same way both in the differentiated and in the eudialytic lujavrite complexes, imparting a stratification to the massif, whereas in the poikilitic syenites the differentiation is of a local character. In the eudialytic lujavrites differentiation is less clearly apparent than in the differentiated complex.

Three classes of three-component rock groups, differing in the degree of layering, can provisionally be distinguished in these complexes: (1) a well-layered group, (2) a partially-layered group and (3) a poorly-layered group. The well-

TABLE 25 Quantitative ratios of main minerals in various rock-types (per cent)

Rock	Feldspars	Nepheline	Aegirine + arfvedsonite
Foyaites	51-85	10-45	5-15
Lujavrites	28-60	18-45	12-45
Poikilitic syenites	10-48	45-75	1-18
Urtites	4-20	66-95	3-23

layered foyaite-urtite-lujavrite assemblages are characterized by a very high degree of differentiation. An almost monomineralic urtitic horizon has developed in them, along with horizons of typical foyaites and lujavrites. As an example, we may take the assemblages in the upper part of the differentiated complex. The partially-layered groups contain clearly-marked foyaites and lujavrite horizons, sometimes with a poorly-developed urtitic horizon between them, or an enrichment of the lower wall of the foyaite horizon in nepheline. Such groups have developed widely in the middle and lower parts of the differentiated complex but are present also in the upper part. In the poorly-layered groups differentiation has not advanced to the stage of forming urtitic horizons, while foyaitic horizons are also either lacking or only little developed. Leucocratic lujavrites, with gradual transitions to foyaites in certain parts of the massif, are usually present in such groups instead of foyaites. Layered groups of this kind are typical of the middle part of the differentiated complex and also of the eudialytic lujavrite complex.

The perfection of layering in the various three-component groups may vary along the strike or dip of the rock horizons.

Within each group there are gradual transitions from the foyaites to the aegirine-lujavrites of the overlying group and to the underlying urtites. The gradual transition from urtites to the underlying aegirine-lujavrites occupies a very small interval, through a thin (up to $\frac{1}{2}$ m) interlayer of rock, intermediate in mineralogical and petrographical composition, between urtite and lujavrite.

The rock horizons, and therefore also the groups of layers, vary in thickness from one part of the massif to another, the urtite horizons from 0·5 to 20 m, the foyaite horizons from 1 to 75 m, and the lujavrite horizons from 3 to 100 m. In each group an increase in the thickness of one rock horizon is matched by a corresponding increase in the thickness of the others. It has been established that there is a direct relationship between the thickness of the individual horizons and the perfection of layering of the stratal group; the thicker and the more monomineralic the urtite horizon the more distinct, as a rule, is the differentiation within the group.

The separation of the main rock-forming minerals in space is most evident in the well-layered groups of the differentiated complex. Let us take as an example the three-component group of the Karnasurt profile shown in Fig. 24, which contains urtites and aegirine-lujavrites in the third horizon, and overlying foyaites. In this group the lowest nepheline content, *plus* natrolite derived from it (10-15 per cent), is observed in the uppermost part of the foyaite horizon. The proportion gradually increases towards the base of this horizon (50-60 per cent), and reaches a maximum (up to 80-95 per cent) in the lower part of the almost monomineralic urtitic horizon. In the transition from the urtites to the underlying aegirine-lujavrite horizon the nepheline content falls comparatively rapidly to 30-50 per cent, and thereafter gradually diminishes from the melanocratic to the underlying leucocratic aegirine-lujavrites and beyond to the base of the foyaitic horizon in the next stratal group, where it reaches a new minimum.

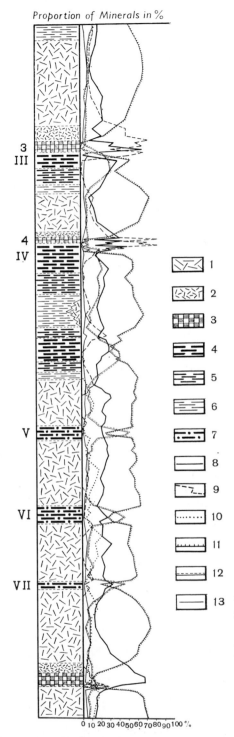

Proportion of Minerals in %

The reverse pattern governs microcline distribution in this group: the maximum microcline content coincides with the minimum nepheline content. In the upper part of the foyaitic horizon, for example, the microcline content reaches its highest figure in the whole of the three-component group (up to 70-80 per cent). Towards and within the urtitic horizon below the proportion of microcline gradually diminishes to 5 per cent or less at its base. It increases fairly rapidly to 15-20 per cent from the urtite to the underlying aegirine-lujavrite. In the lujavritic horizon there is a smoother increase in the proportion of microcline towards the leucocratic lujavrites at the base of the horizon (to 55-60 per cent) and beyond towards the upper or central part of the foyaitic horizon in the next group, and so on.

The lowest proportion of aegirine occurs towards the central part of the foyaitic horizon, below which it remains roughly constant at 3-8 per cent all the way to the base of the urtitic horizon, where the aegirine content increases slightly to 10-20 per cent. In the underlying melanocratic aegirine-lujavrites the highest proportion of aegirine is found in the upper part of the horizon (30-50 per cent),

FIG. 24. Distribution of minerals in rocks of the upper part of the differentiated complex, Karnasurt (after E. M. Es'kova)

1. foyaite; 2. juvite; 3. urtite; 4. melanocratic aegirine-lujavrite; 5. mesocratic aegirine-lujavrite; 6. leucocratic aegirine-lujavrite; 7. hornblende-lujavrite. Mineral distribution curves: 8. nepheline; 9. natrolite; 10. sodalite; 11. microcline and albite; 12. aegirine and hornblende; 13. rare-metal minerals. The urtitic horizons are numbered in arabic figures, the lujavrite horizons in roman figures

diminishing gradually to 10-15 per cent towards the base. There is a gradual reduction in the amount of aegirine in the transition from the leucocratic lujavrites to the underlying foyaites, and towards the centre of the foyaitic horizon, where it again reaches a minimum. The distribution pattern of aegirine is thus intermediate between that of microcline and that of nepheline: the smallest amounts are found in rocks with a maximum microcline or nepheline content and the largest amounts in rocks with a medium tenor of these minerals.

The picture recurs in the other three-component groups, indicating a strict rhythm in the distribution of the main rock-forming minerals throughout the massif.

In the poorly-layered groups of the differentiated complex the process of spatial separation of nepheline, microcline and aegirine stopped in the early stages. In these groups the urtitic horizons are thin and, by comparison with the monomineralic urtites of the fully-differentiated groups, contain large proportions of microcline (up to 14 per cent) and aegirine (up to 20 per cent). The foyaites are greatly enriched in nepheline (up to 45 per cent) and aegirine (up to 15 per cent), whereas in the aegirine-lujavrite horizons there is in many cases no regular succession of the melanocratic, mesocratic and leucocratic varieties from top to bottom. In groups where no urtitic horizon has developed, nepheline accumulates in the lower parts of the foyaitic horizons or is distributed throughout their thickness. In the eudialytic lujavrite complex, made up of alternating horizons of leucocratic, mesocratic and melanocratic eudialytic lujavrites with occasional intercalations of feldspar-rich rocks similar to foyaites, essentially the same stratal groups are represented, but are poorly-layered. The earliest stage in the spatial separation of the principal rock-forming minerals is expressed as a certain degree of segregation of the leucocratic minerals (microcline and nepheline) from aegirine. In the porphyritic varieties of the eudialytic lujavrite complex the layering process has sometimes developed to the stage of forming foyaitic varieties and juvites (Alluaiv, Sengischorr and Angvundaschorr) or, more rarely, poorly-developed urtites (Karnasurt).

The principal rock-forming minerals are also separated in time of crystallization. This is particularly apparent in the well-layered three-component groups. In the aluminium-rich and sodium-rich urtites, for example, nepheline appears earlier than microcline. In the potassium-rich and silicon-rich foyaites it separated after microcline. In the aegirine-lujavrites, either nepheline and microcline are of almost contemporaneous precipitation or the nepheline has crystallized somewhat earlier than the microcline. In nearly all the rocks aegirine separated later than nepheline and microcline.

The time difference between precipitation of one principal rock-forming mineral and another gradually disappears as the layering in the three-component groups becomes less perfect. In the poorly-layered three-component groups nepheline usually appears somewhat earlier than microcline.

DISTRIBUTION OF RARE-METAL MINERALS

The typical rare-metal minerals of the Lovozero rocks are those of the eudialyte and lomonosovite groups, loparite, rare-earth apatite and, to a smaller extent, lamprophyllite, lovozerite and ramsayite, the proportions of which vary greatly from one type of rock to another as do the chemical composition and physical properties of each rare-metal mineral.

Some of the rare-metal minerals are accessory (0·01-0·5 per cent) in rocks of one kind, minor (up to 3-5 per cent) in others, and constitute the principal rock-forming minerals in yet a third type of rock (eudialyte). In the last case they account for 5-10 per cent, or sometimes several tens per cent of the total. Apatite, for example, is accessory in the foyaites, aegirine-lujavrites, porphyritic lujavrites and poikilitic sodalite-syenites, but is slightly more plentiful in the urtites and ijolite-urtites. It occurs in proportions of 3-25 per cent in individual small parts of the urtitic horizons but sometimes forms almost monomineralic thin (1-3 cm) intercalations in their lower parts.

Minerals of the eudialyte group are particularly characteristic of the rocks in the eudialytic lujavrite complex, where they are the chief rock-forming minerals (up to 25 per cent). In the eudialytites the amount of eudialyte and mesodialyte increases to 60-80 per cent, but in the foyaites, aegirine-lujavrites, hornblende-lujavrites and poikilitic syenites these minerals are minor, while in the urtites and ijolite-urtites they are accessory.

The chemical composition and optical properties of any particular mineral species change with the chemical and mineralogical composition of the rock and its position in the massif. This is particularly obvious in the case of minerals that include elements exhibiting diadochy as in minerals of the eudialyte group, apatite and loparite.

The compositions of the eudialyte minerals depend mainly on the calcium-to-sodium ratio in the rock. Eudialyte is most characteristic of rocks poor in calcium (the foyaites and poikilitic sodalite-syenites), mesodialyte of rocks richer in calcium (urtites, ijolitic urtites and eudialytic lujavrites).

The most important variations in the composition of apatite involve its rare-earth content, which varies with the rare-earth content in the rock. The highest proportion of rare earths is found in apatites occurring at the bases of urtitic horizons in the differentiated complex, where the rare-element and, in particular, the rare-earth content is highest. In the apatite of the eudialytic lujavrites the content of rare-earths is appreciably smaller although the average amount in the rock is much the same as in the urtites. This may be because the eudialytic lujavrites contain many minerals of the eudialyte group, which, crystallizing before the apatite, capture crystallochemically the greater part of the rare earths.

Apatite is not characteristic of the foyaites in the differentiated complex, which contain much less calcium than the urtites and the aegirine-lujavrites. Rare earths are present in negligible amounts, and then only in minerals of the eudialyte group. Apatite is widely distributed only in the contaminated foyaites that have assimilated Devonian augite-porphyrites and are richer in calcium.

The composition of the rare-metal minerals depends also on the variation in chemical and mineralogical composition of a particular rock. The composition of the loparite in the urtitic horizons of the differentiated complex, for example, follows a regular pattern of change in the vertical direction, depending on the ratios of calcium, strontium, rare-earths, niobium and other elements in the horizons.

Each rock complex has its own characteristic association of rare-metal minerals and rare elements.

Mesodialyte, eudialyte, lovozerite, lamprophyllite, murmanite, loparite, ramsayite, apatite, sphene and other minerals all enter into the constitution of the eudialytic lujavrites, those of the eudialyte group taking first place, because of the high zirconium content in the rocks (five times higher than the average for the massif as a whole). Mesodialyte, the commonest of the eudialyte minerals in the eudialytic lujavrites, is found in large quantities in the melanocratic eudialytic lujavrites of the upper horizons in the complex. In the leucocratic varieties at the bottom of the complex eudialyte appears along with mesodialyte. This distribution of the eudialyte minerals is apparently due to an increase in the calcium content at the top of the intrusion through the influence of the roof.

The proportion of eudialyte minerals in the eudialytic lujavrites varies within wide limits (from 3·8 to 25·1 per cent), and is highest in the melanocratic varieties (10·8 to 25·1 per cent). The amount of eudialyte and mesodialyte gradually decreases to 7·3 to 12·5 per cent with transition to the mesocratic eudialytic lujavrites. Lastly, the amounts of these minerals in the leucocratic varieties vary from 3·8 to 8·2 per cent. The proportion of minerals belonging to this group thus tends to fall as the eudialytic lujavrites become increasingly leucocratic.

In the eudialytic lujavrites a maximum content of minerals of the eudialyte group usually corresponds to a minimum amount of niobium, titanium and rare-earth minerals (loparite, murmanite, lamprophyllite), the reason being that these elements may enter the crystal lattice of the eudialyte minerals.

Loparite is present in minute amounts in the rocks we are describing, primarily in the leucocratic varieties (0–0·2 per cent). The murmanite content usually rises, from the melanocratic varieties (0·08 per cent) to the leucocratic (0·2–0·3 per cent). Sometimes foyaitic portions, where the murmanite content increases to 2–3 per cent, can be seen in the eudialytic lujavrites near their contact with rocks of the differentiated complex. The lamprophyllite content reaches a maximum in the leucocratic eudialytic lujavrites (up to 2·3 per cent) and gradually falls off, to 0·8–1 per cent, in their mesocratic and melanocratic varieties.

In the porphyritic rocks of the complex the relative abundances of the rare-metal minerals are unequal in the differentiated and the undifferentiated parts. In the latter, consisting primarily of porphyritic lujavrites, the predominant rare-metal minerals are eudialyte and mesodialyte, or lovozerite developed after them; lamprophyllite and murmanite are sometimes present in large quantities. In the differentiated parts, loparite and murmanite can be counted as the most important rare-metal minerals, the highest concentration of these occurring in the leucocratic varieties, juvites and foyaites, which contain the smallest amounts of eudialyte minerals.

As in the eudialytic lujavrites, so too in the porphyritic rocks, the content of eudialyte minerals rises from the leucocratic (0·6-2·5 per cent) to the melanocratic (10-12 per cent) varieties.

Loparite is more widespread in the porphyritic varieties than in the eudialytic lujavrites and is usually lacking or of rare occurrence and negligible in amount in the unlayered sectors. In the layered parts of the porphyritic rocks the largest amounts of loparite occur in the juvites. In the porphyritic lujavrites the loparite content is high near their contacts with the juvites, but gradually diminishes away from this. As in the differentiated complex, the largest amounts of loparite occur in the most highly differentiated parts.

Minerals of the lomonosovite-murmanite group are characteristic of the feldspathic rock-types, the porphyritic foyaites (up to 2·2 per cent). In the porphyritic juvites their amount does not exceed 0·1 per cent. These minerals are practically absent in the porphyritic lujavrites but the occasional presence of zones rich in murmanite has led some investigators to distinguish murmanitic varieties of these rocks. Minerals of the lomonosovite-murmanite group are thus associated, in the differentiated parts of the eudialytic lujavrite complex, with rocks rich in potassium feldspar.

Lamprophyllite is present in proportions of 0·1 to 0·8 per cent, or more, in the layered parts of the porphyritic lujavrites. In the differentiated parts its concentration rises to 2·2 per cent in the porphyritic foyaites, but it is hardly present at all in the porphyritic lujavrites (0·05 per cent).

The paragenetic associations of rare-metal minerals in the eudialytic lujavrites and in the porphyritic rocks are similar. The difference is that in the porphyritic rocks, loparite and murmanite are present in the layered regions along with eudialyte. The niobium, rare-earth and titanium minerals are spatially most widely separated from the zirconium minerals in the well-differentiated parts. The separation of these groups of minerals gradually disappears as the perfection of layering diminishes. In the differentiated complex niobium, rare-earth and titanium minerals are plentiful. Zirconium minerals of the eudialyte group are less abundant here than in the eudialytic lujavrite complex. The rare-metal minerals are not uniformly distributed in the various rocks of the complex, their amount and specific or varietal identity being determined by the nature of the rock-forming minerals, and their distribution varying from the well-layered to the poorly-layered parts of the differentiated complex. In the former, it follows a well-defined pattern, which recurs in each three-component stratal group.

The foyaites of the three-component groups have a characteristic sodium association of rare-metal minerals: minerals of the lomonosovite-murmanite group, lamprophyllite and eudialyte. These occur in the uppermost or central parts of the foyaite horizons, that is, in the parts enriched in microcline. The amount of rare-metal minerals gradually decreases from top to bottom of the layer (in the direction of the urtites). Many of the minerals also display compositional variation in the same direction and a variable degree of replacement by other minerals. As the lomonosovite and murmanite content decreases, for example, minute amounts of loparite and apatite appear, increasing slightly towards the bases of the foyaite horizons. The calcium content in the eudialyte also increases in this direction, its optical properties change and it is progressively replaced by mesodialyte.

As the foyaites give way to urtites the quantity of rare-metal minerals sharply declines and in the central parts of the urtitic horizons these minerals are often lacking. Towards the bases of the urtitic horizons the rare-metal content again increases (Fig. 25), mainly in the form of calcium minerals—loparite and apatite; it is highest in the lower part of each urtitic horizon, where the nepheline content is highest. Loparite and apatite become abundant in a zone 0·1–0·5 m thick near the contact. It is noteworthy that apatite is rarely present in the urtites of the upper horizons of the complex, where loparite is the predominant rare-metal mineral. Both minerals occur in the urtites below horizon IV, the apatite tenor increasing in lower horizons; but both minerals occur in more or less constant amount along the strike of any particular urtite horizon. The thicker and more nearly monomineralic the urtitic horizon the more concentrated are the loparite and apatite at its base; a thin interlayer of apatite, for example, can be observed at the base of one of the thickest ijolitic-urtite horizons.

In the urtitic horizons of the middle, poorly-layered part of the complex, where there is much potassium feldspar, the loparite and apatite are not completely segregated at the lower surfaces of layers; the degree of layering evidently influences the distribution of these minerals. They occur throughout the thickness of each layer, but are concentrated most heavily in the lower parts.

Other rare-metal minerals (mesodialyte, murmanite, lomonosovite and lamprophyllite) occur in the urtites in minute amounts in small pockets. In the lower surfaces of the urtitic horizons one sometimes finds pegmatoid areas enriched with these minerals.

In the upper parts of the aegirine-lujavrite horizons the same rare-metal minerals are present as in the urtites, but in appreciably smaller quantities. Loparite and apatite are concentrated mainly in a 0·3–0·5 m zone in the immediate vicinity of the urtite contact; the greater the abundance of rare-metal minerals in the base of the urtitic horizon, the more plentiful they are in the upper parts of the underlying aegirine-lujavrite horizon. This is evidence of a genetic interrelationship between the urtites and the lujavrites, indicating that they formed from a single magma. Towards the central parts of the aegirine-lujavrite horizons the loparite and apatite content gradually diminishes and eudialyte, lomonosovite, murmanite and lamprophyllite appear, becoming slightly more plentiful with proximity to the underlying foyaites.

In the aegirine-lujavrite horizons, then, the tenor of loparite and apatite —minerals characteristic of urtites—gradually diminishes from the upper to the lower surfaces as the horizons become less melanocratic, while the tenor of murmanite, lomonosovite, lamprophyllite and eudialyte—minerals characteristic of the foyaites—rises.

Each of the well-layered three-component groups thus contains two zones rich in rare-metal minerals: (1) the lower parts of the urtitic horizons and the upper parts of the aegirine-lujavrite horizons; and (2) the roofs and central parts of foyaite horizons. Each of these zones has its own special association of rare-metal minerals. The first is enriched in the calcium-bearing non-silicate minerals of niobium, rare earths and titanium (loparite, apatite), while the rare-metal minerals of the foyaites are sodium silicates of niobium, titanium and zirconium (murmanite, lomonosovite, lamprophyllite, eudialyte).

The regularities described above, relating to the distribution of the rare-metal minerals, are applicable also to the poorly-differentiated stratal groups, but they are here less well expressed. In the urtites of these groups the most characteristic rare-metal minerals remain loparite and apatite, confined mainly to the floors of the horizons. But their content here is considerably lower than in the floors of the urtite horizons of the well-layered groups. Part of these minerals is scattered throughout the thickness of the urtitic horizons and even in the overlying foyaites. The rare-metal minerals characteristic of foyaites (lomonosovite, murmanite, lamprophyllite and eudialyte) extend, as it were, into the urtitic horizons below, where there is a mixture of the characteristically urtitic and foyaitic rare-metal minerals.

In the poorly-stratified groups of the middle part of the differentiated complex the pattern of rare-metal distribution is less well-defined. Here all the rare-metal minerals characteristic of the complex occur in the aegirine-lujavrites, and in larger amounts than in the lujavrites of the well-layered groups. The tenor of murmanite, lomonosovite and other minerals characteristic of foyaites rises as the rocks become more leucocratic, while the loparite and apatite content increases as they become more melanocratic. The trend is thus the same as elsewhere.

A definite zonal pattern of alternating concentration and paucity of rare-metal minerals within the three-component groups is thus a typical feature of the differentiated complex, especially in its well-layered parts (see Fig. 25).

In the poikilitic syenite complex, the niobium, rare-earth and titanium minerals characteristic of the differentiated complex have developed in roughly the same degree as the zirconium minerals. In addition to loparite, the lomonosovite-murmanite minerals, rare-earth apatite, eudialyte minerals, ramsayite, lamprophyllite and minerals characteristic of rocks belonging to other complexes, these rocks contain chinglusuite, nordite and steenstrupine, which are peculiar to this complex. The rare-metal minerals are most plentiful in the sodalitic (hackmanitic) poikilitic syenites.

In the poikilitic syenites we find a pocket-like distribution both of the principal rock-forming and of the rare-metal minerals, the latter concentrated mainly in the pegmatoid sectors.

Among the rare-metal minerals of the poikilitic syenite complex two associations, sodic and calcic, can be more or less clearly distinguished. The sodic association is characteristic of the sodalitic varieties and is rarely found in the nepheline varieties. It includes murmanite, lomonosovite, lamprophyllite, loparite, eudialyte, ramsayite, nordite, steenstrupine, rinkolite, chinglusuite and other minerals. These particular poikilitic syenites contain, in addition to titanium, niobium, rare-earth and zirconium minerals, high concentrations of gallium (0·015-0·03 per cent), lithium (up to 0·08 per cent) and beryllium (0·001 per cent), which do not form independent minerals. In the pegmatites genetically associated with these rocks we find minerals of lithium (polylithionite, tainiolite), beryllium (epididymite, eudidymite, leucophane) and high concentrations of gallium (0·02-0·043 per cent) in hackmanite and natrolite.

The calcic association of rare-metal minerals is characteristic of the poikilitic syenites with hydrosodalite and to a lesser extent of the poikilitic nepheline-syenites (Lepkhe-Nel'm, Ninchurt and Mannepakhk, the Suoluaiv valley and elsewhere). In these rocks, along with sodium rare-metal minerals, which occur in negligible amounts, sphene, apatite, mesodialyte, eucolite, manganilmenite and other minerals are widely developed. The formation of the minerals of the calcic association may be connected with assimilation of the Devonian augite-porphyrite roof-rocks by the intrusions of poikilitic syenite, for it is noteworthy that this association is found in all the complexes where there is evidence of such assimilation. The rare elements in this case form minerals rich in calcium, silicon, iron, manganese and magnesium, but poor in alkalis. Instead of eudialyte, zircon forms and instead of loparite, lomonosovite and murmanite, we find manganil-menite sphene and apatite.

The spatial distribution of the rare-metal minerals in the Lovozero rocks, and to an appreciable extent their composition, thus depends on the distribution of the main rock-forming minerals (nepheline, microcline and aegirine) and the extent to which they are separated. The greater the differentiation of the rocks, or in other words, the more the rock-forming minerals are separated in space and time of formation, the more distinctly are the paragenetic associations of rare-metal minerals in them confined to particular types of rock.

PART TWO

PEGMATITES

INTRODUCTION

MUCH less attention has been paid to the pegmatites of alkali rocks than to granitic pegmatites, both because they occur less frequently and because their practical importance is less. It is only recently that alkali pegmatites have become the subject of more detailed research, in connexion with the industrial use of niobium and zirconium. Their study has an extremely important bearing on the solution of a number of problems in petrography, mineralogy and geochemistry. They are even more closely connected with parent intrusions than are granitic pegmatites, rarely extend beyond these intrusions and in a number of cases form quite gradual transitions with them, thus helping us to clarify the conditions under which they were formed.

It is particularly important to study the pegmatites of the Lovozero massif since the ideally differentiated intrusion of the Lovozero pegmatites makes them a suitable example from which to clarify the factors involved in the formation of pegmatites and to establish the relative parts played in their formation by emanations and crystallization from melts.

The Lovozero massif is rich in pegmatitic formations, of which there are more than a thousand. A distinction is drawn between pure and hybrid pegmatites.

Pegmatites can be divided into three groups by form and by their relationship to the country rocks: (1) facies, (2) phase and (3) facies-phase (transitional between groups (1) and (2)).

The group of facies pegmatites comprises irregular bodies varying from a few tens of centimetres to 20-30 m in cross section, bedded in and gradually merging with the parent rocks. Such pegmatites have developed in the main in non-trachytoid rocks—foyaites, poikilitic syenites and eudialytic lujavrites. This group also includes pegmatite horizons that are subordinated to the general stratification of the massif and can be traced intermittently throughout its area. These horizons are encountered only in the differentiated complex. Intrusive contacts and apophyses in the country rocks are associated in some districts with the thickest pegmatitic horizons, which are in essence facies-phase bodies.

Phase pegmatites are represented by veins or stocks injected into fissures or zones of weakness in the parent rocks. Vein-forming pegmatitic bodies are found mainly in the lujavrites and foyaites of the differentiated complex. They vary in thickness from a few centimetres to 4 m, and they can be traced along the strike for between 30-60 m and several hundred metres. Large pegmatitic stocks (15-60 m in diameter) are found only in or immediately adjacent to poikilitic syenites. When such pegmatitic bodies are emplaced directly in the parent rocks it is not always possible to decide whether they are phase or facies-phase pegmatites. The possibility is not excluded that such bodies may be connected by their roots with the pegmatite hearth.

There are considerable qualitative and quantitative differences between the mineralogical composition of the pegmatites and that of the parent rocks. This is reflected in the much lower nepheline content of the pegmatites (Gerasimovskii, 1939_1) and in their richness in rare-metal minerals and in replacement minerals.

More than 130 minerals are known at present in the pegmatites of the massif. The major minerals include orthoclase, aegirine, nepheline, hackmanite (less frequently sodalite), eudialyte, ramsayite, lamprophyllite, albite, ussingite, natrolite and analcite. Only the orthoclase, eudialyte and aegirine are major minerals in all the pure pegmatites and the rôle of the others may vary. In addition to the major minerals, some pegmatites contain considerable quantities of chinglusuite, lomonosovite, murmanite, polylithionite, tainiolite, nenadkevichite, beliankinite, arfvedsonite, aenigmatite, steenstrupine, hydrocerite, neptunite, epididymite, ilmenite, apatite and other minerals.

The pegmatites of each rock complex have their own particular rare-metal minerals that reflect in varying degrees the chemical composition of the parent rocks, show characteristic forms of spatial connexion with the parent rocks and exhibit varying degrees of differentiation.

For example, predominance of the zirconium minerals (the eudialyte and eucolite groups) over titanium and niobium minerals (ramsayite, murmanite and lamprophyllite) is a feature of the pegmatites of the eudialytic lujavrites, which are usually facies confined to the lower part of the eudialytic lujavrite series.

In the pegmatites of the differentiated complex, titanium and niobium minerals join zirconium minerals as major minerals, as in the parent rocks. The pegmatites of this complex are represented by facies pegmatite horizons and by veins intersecting one or more rock horizons.

The chemical and mineralogical composition and structure of the poikilitic syenite complex pegmatites is more complex. In addition to zirconium, titanium and niobium minerals they include considerable amounts of rare-earth minerals and thorium, lithium and beryllium minerals and a whole series of others that are not found (or are present in very small quantities) in the pegmatites of the other complexes. The most developed pegmatite bodies of the poikilitic syenite complex are large, rounded, almost spheroidal masses with a distinct zonal structure involving monomineralic zones of potassium feldspar, hackmanite and natrolite, and zones of replacement.

Hybrid pegmatites are represented by thin veins emplaced in xenoliths of Devonian rocks or in Archaean gneissose granite near a contact with the alkali rocks. They differ from pure pegmatites in the paragenesis of the minerals, which are typified by a higher calcium, magnesium and iron content.

In the central sector of the massif (the Seidozero district) and in certain other districts where xenoliths of Devonian rocks abound, the pure pegmatites of the differentiated complex and of the poikilitic syenite complex contain, in addition to their own characteristic minerals, minerals that are typical of the hybrid pegmatites. These pegmatite bodies would seem to be transitional. Their mineralization is mixed and they contain zircon, sphene, ilmenite, apatite and biotite in addition to eudialyte, ramsayite, murmanite, lamprophyllite and other minerals. This is clearly connected with assimilation of xenoliths of Devonian rocks rich in calcium, magnesium and iron by the alkali magma of which the pegmatites are differentiates.

CHAPTER ONE

PEGMATITES OF THE EUDIALYTIC LUJAVRITE COMPLEX

A GREAT many pegmatite bodies are associated with the rocks of the eudialytic lujavrite complex, especially in its upper and lower parts. In the upper part they are typically small pockets, schlieren-like, lenticular and vein pegmatitic facies, of which there are many thousands. In area these bodies vary between 10×10 cm and several square metres. Their contacts with the parent rocks are distinct, owing to the sharp change in texture and, partly, in mineralogical composition, though it is clearly apparent in the field that they were formed where they occur. The mineralogical composition of the pegmatites in the complex is close to that of the eudialytic lujavrites, from which they differ in having a higher content of rare-metal minerals and a coarsely crystalline texture. The large pegmatitic bodies are concentrated in the lower part of the complex near the contact with the rocks of the differentiated complex. They form a distinctive belt more than 30 m thick that can be traced in the northern and western sectors of the massif (see Fig. 5).

We have studied some thirty large pegmatitic bodies, genetically associated with eudialytic lujavrite (on the northern slope of Kedykvyrpakhk, in the upper reaches of the Tyul'bn'yunuai, in the Sengis"yavr cirque, on the watershed between the upper reaches of the Chivruai and Kitkuai and in the upper reaches of the Kitkuai valley).

From their form and their relationship to the country rocks in the lower part of the complex these are facies and phase pegmatites. The facies (schlieren-like) pegmatites are normally irregular in form and their transitions to the country rocks are gradual; their dimensions vary from a few metres to a maximum of 40 m. Sheets of phase pegmatite between 0·3 and 3 m thick, normally showing sharp contacts with the enclosing eudialytic lujavrites, can sometimes be traced for several hundred metres.

The pegmatites of this complex are normally grouped in several isolated exposures (sometimes as many as ten) that are either separate pegmatitic bodies or separate outcrops of the same irregular pegmatitic body. These groups are normally quite close together and their chemical and mineralogical composition and structure are similar.

The majority of the pegmatitic bodies are associated with the lower part of the eudialytic lujavrite complex. The enclosing eudialytic lujavrites are more leucocratic and their distinctive features include variability of mineralogical composition, fine-grained texture and the abundance of small pegmatitic facies alongside large pegmatitic bodies.

The largest pegmatites, and those that are most interesting because of their mineralogical composition, are to be found on Kedykvyrpakhk, in the valley of the Tyul'bn'yunuai and in the cirque of lake Sengis''yavr. They will be described in this chapter.

1. THE PEGMATITES OF KEDYKVYRPAKHK

There are nine irregular outcrops of pegmatites varying in dimensions between 1.8×3 and 7×15 m approximately 400 m above the level of lake Il'mo on the northern slope of Kedykvyrpakhk. They are usually elongated in a north-easterly or north-westerly direction. There are also two oval areas of large disrupted pegmatite blocks (18×12 and 20×10 m) that extend down the slope.

Since the mountain slope in the area of the pegmatite outcrops is covered with coarse scree, it is impossible to establish whether these outcrops are separate formations or parts of one large irregular pegmatitic body, but the latter explanation can be assumed to be correct in view of the close spacing of the outcrops and the similarity of their mineralogical composition and structure.

The pegmatites are emplaced in the fine-grained leucocratic eudialytic lujavrites of the lower part of the complex, approximately 30 m above the porphyritic lujavrites. At the contact with the pegmatites the eudialytic lujavrites are enriched in aegirine, eudialyte, murmanite and lamprophyllite and are replaced to a considerable extent by natrolite. Although the contact between the pegmatites and the country rocks is distinct, it is uneven and meandering, with many apophyses of pegmatite and small schlieren-like pegmatitic masses in the rock adjacent to the contact. Some crystals of feldspar have one edge in the country rock and the other in the pegmatite. In all probability these pegmatites are facies formations that crystallized where the pegmatitic melt was segregated. This is shown by their irregular contours and gradual transitions and by the similarity between their chemical and mineralogical composition and that of the country rocks.

Zonal structure is poorly defined in the pegmatites; the following zones can be distinguished from the periphery to the centre: (1) outer equigranular zone, (2) block zone, (3) replacement zone.

1. The outer zone is typical of most pegmatitic bodies. It is fine-grained in texture and consists of aegirine I, microcline, nepheline and eudialyte, with a predominance of leucocratic minerals. Its thickness is approximately 20-30 cm. Grain size varies from 0.3 to 3 cm in cross-section. The transition between this zone and the second, or block zone, is gradual.

2. The block zone normally comprises the major bulk of pegmatitic bodies. The texture is inequigranular and porphyritic. Large segregations (blocks) of microcline (Fig. 26) and nepheline occur haphazard in the fine-grained ground-mass, which consists of 50 per cent aegirine II in addition to microcline, nepheline,

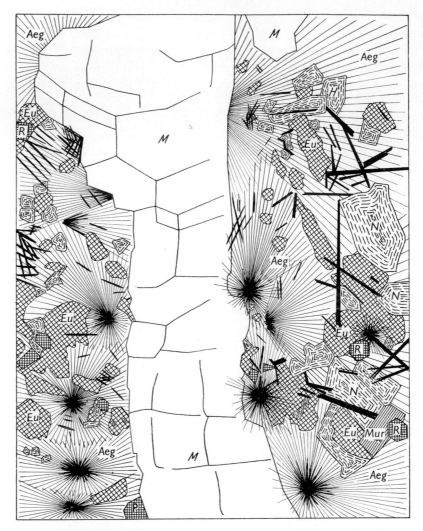

FIG. 26. Microcline block (M) in fine-grained pegmatite mass

N—nepheline; Eu—eudialyte; Mur—murmanite; R—ramsayite; Aeg—aegirine II (arfvedsonite—black). ¼ natural
size

eudialyte and ramsayite. Small quantities of murmanite, lamprophyllite and arfvedsonite are found. Grain size in the groundmass varies between a few millimetres
and 3-5 cm in cross-section.

3. The replacement zone is found only in the central sector of the extreme
north-east of the largest area of disrupted pegmatite. The composition is 80 per
cent cryptocrystalline and macrocrystalline natrolite with lesser amounts of hackmanite, schizolite, manganese-chlorite, the hydrous silicophosphates of rare earths,
staffelite [francolite] and neptunite, in addition to microcline, aegirine II, arfvedsonite and others. The thickness of this zone varies between 1 and 3 m.

The pegmatites of the area described are composed in the main of microcline, nepheline, aegirine, arfvedsonite, eudialyte and ramsayite. Lamprophyllite, murmanite, sodalite, aenigmatite, natrolite, schizolite and staffelite [francolite] also occur. The minerals are unevenly distributed. Thus, the microcline content varies in different sectors from 20-30 to 70-80 per cent, that of late fibrous aegirine from 10-15 to 50-60 per cent, that of eudialyte from 10 to 60 per cent, of ramsayite from 1-3 to 20-30 per cent and of natrolite from 5 to 80 per cent and so on.

The *microcline* forms segregations from fractions of a centimetre to 5 cm in length and up to 1·5 cm thick in the outer zones and in the fine-grained groundmass of the block zones' and large blocks, and up to 1 m in length and 40×20 cm in cross-section in the block zones. The colour is a light creamy grey and there are idiomorphic inclusions of arfvedsonite, aegirine I, nepheline and ramsayite. The microcline is idiomorphic with respect to eudialyte, lamprophyllite and aegirine II. It is replaced by natrolite along cleavage cracks and is albitized at the contact with the country rocks.

The *nepheline* forms inclusions of from 3 mm to 5 cm in cross-section in the fine-grained groundmass of the pegmatites and large inclusions up to 20 cm in cross-section in the block zones. The colour is greenish-grey and it contains inclusions of idiomorphic arfvedsonite and aegirine I crystals. It is distinctly idiomorphic in relation to microcline and eudialyte. In the replacement zone large inclusions of nepheline are entirely replaced by hackmanite and natrolite, and less frequently by cancrinite.

Arfvedsonite is present in both the outer and the block zones. It usually occurs as black crystals randomly orientated or forming radiate-fibrous growths ('suns') in the fine-grained groundmass of the block zones. The dimensions of the crystals vary from a few millimetres in length in the outer zones to $10 \times 0·8 \times 0·3$ cm in the block zones.

The arfvedsonite separated first and is almost invariably in well-formed crystals. Arfvedsonite inclusions are found in microcline, nepheline, aegirine II, eudialyte, ramsayite and other minerals.

Three generations of *aegirine* are found. Aegirine II is the most abundant and aegirine I and aegirine III account for approximately 3-5 per cent of the total aegirine content.

Aegirine I forms small elongated microcrystals, a few hundredths of a millimetre in length, in nepheline and microcline. It accounts for 5-7 per cent of some crystals of these minerals. Crystals of aegirine I in microcline are orientated in the majority of cases parallel to the face (001). No specific orientation of aegirine I is observed in nepheline.

Aegirine II is represented by a green and greyish-green densely fibrous mass consisting of many small close-packed acicular crystals. The segregations are irregular in shape and usually occur as radial forms varying in size from a few millimetres to $25 \times 25 \times 15$ cm. Aegirine II fills the spaces between crystals of microcline (see Fig. 26), nepheline, arfvedsonite and other minerals.

Aegirine III is encountered as small light-greenish crystals, 1-2 mm long, on the walls of miarolitic and solution cavities.

Eudialyte accounts in places for up to 30 per cent of the pegmatite mass. It forms crystals (of from 1 mm to 4 cm in cross-section) or irregular segregations of up to 3 × 10 cm in area. The colour is brown and reddish-brown. Microcrystalline eudialyte is usually confined to the area round contacts, where it forms mono-mineralic accumulations. This eudialyte is normally included in a block mass of aegirine II. The larger crystals or irregular eudialyte segregations are found

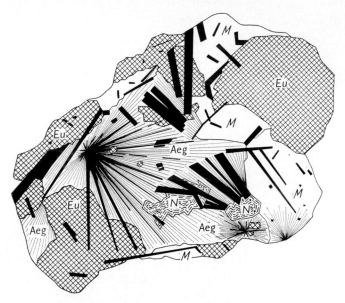

FIG. 27. Interrelationship of eudialyte (Eu), nepheline (N), microcline (M), aegirine II (Aeg) and arfvedsonite (black). Natural size

together with ramsayite, microcline, arfvedsonite and other minerals in block zones. This eudialyte contains inclusions of arfvedsonite (Fig. 27), aegirine I and ramsayite. In some cases the eudialyte is idiomorphic with respect to microcline, though the main mass is confined to the interstices between the microcline crystals. Under surface conditions the eudialyte is sometimes replaced by zirfesite and other secondary minerals.

Ramsayite is an abundant mineral in pegmatite block zones. It is encountered as crystals or irregular brown segregations with a cross-section of between 0·5 and 5 cm. It is sometimes weathered at the surface and some crystals contain solution cavities. Ramsayite is a late mineral normally idiomorphic with respect to aegirine II and less frequently to microcline, or forming irregular inclusions in eudialyte. In most cases its relationship to eudialyte and microcline cannot be established owing to the indistinct nature of the contacts. Ramsayite frequently contains regular crystals of arfvedsonite. The interstices between ramsayite segregations are filled with aegirine II.

Lamprophyllite is present in quantity. It forms tabular crystals that may reach dimensions of $7 \times 1 \times 0.7$ cm, though usually smaller, or golden-brown radiate-fibrous rosettes, 2-3 cm in diameter, included in aegirine II and less frequently in the microcline, murmanite and eudialyte of block zones. The interstices between lamprophyllite crystals are normally occupied by aegirine II or natrolite. It contains as inclusions idiomorphic arfvedsonite crystals. In the replacement zone 'rutile-leucoxene' develops as a yellow ochreous mass on lamprophyllite.

Murmanite is present in small quantities. It forms tabular segregations varying between $2 \times 1 \times 0.2$ and $20 \times 15 \times 0.5$ cm in the outer and block pegmatite zones. The colour is dark brown, violet to rose and less frequently yellow. The violet to rose murmanite is encountered only round contacts, where it forms irregular tabular segregations of up to $3 \times 2 \times 0.1$ cm. The dark-brown murmanite is uniformly distributed in all pegmatite outcrops and is most plentiful in the extreme north-eastern disrupted block zone. Its segregations are usually greatly disintegrated. The yellow variety is encountered as tabular segregations of up to $2 \times 2 \times 0.2$ cm. Murmanite is usually included in aegirine II and contains inclusions of microcline, nepheline and arfvedsonite, and less frequently of eudialyte and lamprophyllite. Manganese beliankinite sometimes develops on it in the replacement zone.

Natrolite occurs in both the macrocrystalline and cryptocrystalline varieties, the latter being more plentiful. Macrocrystalline natrolite is encountered as irregular relicts, 1-5 cm in cross-section, in cryptocrystalline natrolite. A compact cream-coloured aggregate of cryptocrystalline natrolite makes up the greater part of the central zone, which also contains other minerals. Both varieties were formed by replacement of nepheline, microcline and sodalite (hackmanite), as can be seen from the existence of relicts of these minerals in natrolite.

Small amounts of *hackmanite* are found in the central zone as irregular relicts of up to $4 \times 4 \times 3$ cm in cryptocrystalline natrolite. It is also sometimes encountered in the outer zones as idiomorphic segregations of up to $5 \times 4 \times 1$ cm in aegirine II, replaced peripherally by natrolite.

Aenigmatite is rarely found. It forms rounded or sub-triangular black segregations of up to 4×1.5 cm in the aegirine II of the block zones. 'Coronites' (radiate-fibrous margins of fine-acicular aegirine with lamprophyllite) are often present round aenigmatite segregations. This mineral is hardly ever encountered in a pure form. It has normally been completely converted to a greenish-brown ochreous mass of chloritoid.

Schizolite is present in the central zone in minute amounts. It forms elongated black crystals of up to $10 \times 0.7 \times 0.3$ cm. The mineral is extremely brittle, can be crumbled with a knife and is greatly altered and converted into a black ochreous mass of manganese hydroxides. It is normally included in sodalite and cryptocrystalline natrolite or in aegirine II.

Neptunite occurs as weathering crusts on the surfaces of aegirine concretions and also as irregular segregations of up to 0.7×0.4 cm. The colour is dark-red to black.   Neptunite occupies the interstices between crystals of arfvedsonite, ramsayite and aegirine II in block zones and is less frequently included in the natrolite of the replacement zone.

Manganchlorite takes the form of stellate segregations 1-1·5 cm in diameter, consisting of very fine brownish flakes. It is brittle and can easily be crumbled with a knife. In some places it forms fine scaly incrustations of up to 5 × 2 cm area. Manganchlorite is closely associated with the natrolite of the central zone.

Staffelite [francolite] is present in small quantities in the cavities of crypto-crystalline natrolite as white spherulites with a pearly lustre up to 2 mm in diameter. The spherulites consist of concentric zones with a brownish centre and colourless opaque periphery. The staffelite crystals of which the spherulites are formed have a hexagonal cross-section.

2. The Pegmatite Body of the Upper Reaches of the Tyul'bn'yunuai Valley

The pegmatite body lies on the left slope of the Tyul'bn'yunuai valley, in its central part, approximately 60 m above the river bed. The body is irregular, pinches and swells, and has many apophyses (Fig. 28), and strikes practically east and west. The total length is approximately 50 m. The exposed part is 1·5-3 m wide and up to 5 m wide in swells. The thickness is fairly well maintained in the western part of the body (approximately 25 m along the strike), while in the eastern sector there are two large swells with many irregular sinuous and branching apophyses, which often merge to give the impression that the pegmatite is thicker than it is.

The pegmatite body is emplaced in fine-grained mesocratic eudialytic lujavrites of the lower part of the complex. The contact between the pegmatite body and the country rocks, is distinct and the contact line meanders. The country rocks are enriched with eudialyte at the contact, and less frequently with pink murmanite, lamprophyllite, aegirine I and albite. Irregular areas of rock, similar in composition and texture to the enclosing eudialytic lujavrites, can be seen in the pegmatite body near the contact.

The facies nature of the pegmatite is shown by the gradual transitions between it and the country rock, the existence of small schlieren-like pegmatite formations in the rock in the contact zone, the absence of contact alteration of the country rocks, the lack of orientation of individual minerals in relation to the contact, the absence of xenoliths of country rock in the pegmatite body and the spatial disposition of the body, which is not related to any system of faults. It should be noted that signs of the pegmatitic process can be seen at a considerable distance (tens of metres) from the pegmatitic body in the country rocks (as in all other cases in the lower part of the eudialytic lujavrite complex). Small pegmatoid patches composed mainly of one or two of the main rock-forming minerals appear. These differ from the parent rocks in that their texture is coarser-grained. Nearer the pegmatitic body these patches become increasingly large, the quantitative mineralogical composition of the rocks becomes increasingly variable and there is an increase in the size and number of the schlieren-like pegmatitic aggregations.

Except in the western sector there is no observable pattern to the distribution of the minerals of which the pegmatitic body is composed. The contact zones are normally close-grained in texture and composed chiefly of microcline. The remainder of the pegmatitic body is composed of large segregations of microcline, the interstices between which are filled with aegirine II and other minerals.

An upper leucocratic and a lower melanocratic zone can be distinguished in the western sector of the body. The 20-60 cm thick leucocratic zone has approximately the following mineralogical composition (per cent): microcline, 60-70;

Fig. 28. The shape of the pegmatitic body in the upper reaches of the Tyul'bn'yunuai

aegirine II, 5-10; eudialyte, 5; arfvedsonite, 5; nepheline, 5-10; hackmanite and ussingite, 5-7. There are small quantities of aegirine I, murmanite and lamprophyllite (up to 3 per cent). This zone gives way gradually to the lower melanocratic zone by an increase in the amount of aegirine II and a decrease in the microcline content. The aegirine II content of the melanocratic zone reaches 40-50 per cent, that of arfvedsonite 20 per cent, and hackmanite 15-20 per cent; the amount of microcline falls to 10-15 per cent. The main mass of rare-metal minerals and replacement zone minerals is confined to this zone.

The pegmatitic body is weathered near the surface; it is found to contain a considerable number of leaching cavities, which are normally confined to the interstices between microcline crystals. These cavities, irregular in shape, clearly result from the destruction of eudialyte and other rare-metal minerals.

The average mineralogical composition of the pegmatitic body is approximately as follows (per cent): microcline, 50; aegirine II, 25; arfvedsonite, 5-8;

nepheline, 5; ramsayite, 5; eudialyte, 3; lamprophyllite, 2; hackmanite and ussingite, 5-8; and murmanite, 1. In addition there are very small quantities of albite, neptunite, schizolite, loparite and natrolite.

Microcline forms the main mass of the pegmatitic body. It builds fairly regular light-grey crystals of from $3 \times 2 \times 1$ cm at the contacts to $50 \times 15 \times 10$ cm in the leucocratic zone of the pegmatite, where it often forms monomineralic parts. In the melanocratic zone the microcline is found as small crystals with a long axis a few centimetres long.

Microcline is one of the earliest minerals to have separated. The only idio-morphic inclusions that it contains are arfvedsonite and aegirine I. The inter-

FIG. 29. Arfvedsonite inclusions (Arf) in aegirine II. ×46.
Without analyser

stices between its crystals are normally filled with aegirine II, ramsayite, lampro-phyllite, eudialyte and murmanite. Microcline is replaced by ussingite and natrolite and less frequently by albite and hackmanite along cleavage planes and crush-zones.

Nepheline, of a dark-grey colour, forms irregular segregations with a cross-section of up to 3 cm in the melanocratic zone or small grains in the marginal part of the pegmatitic body. In the melanocratic zone it is usually entirely replaced by hackmanite and natrolite. Nepheline is commonly found in aegirine II in the interstices between microcline crystals and contains inclusions of aegirine I and very rarely of loparite.

Arfvedsonite occurs as elongated black crystals that may reach $20 \times 1 \times 1$ cm but are more frequently $5 \times 0.5 \times 0.5$ cm, included in aegirine II (Fig. 29) or forming bundles or radiate-fibrous aggregates ('suns'). It is one of the earliest minerals to have separated, and is found as inclusions in microcline, eudialyte, murmanite and other minerals.

Aegirine has two generations in this pegmatitic body. Aegirine I forms small crystals (hundredths of a millimetre) included in nepheline and microcline. Aegirine II and microcline form the groundmass of the pegmatitic body. It is present in greatest quantity in the melanocratic zone of the western part. It occurs as a dense green mass that often forms radiate-fibrous circular bundles of up to 25 cm in diameter. Aegirine II is one of the latest minerals to have separated. It fills the interstices between microcline, arfvedsonite, lamprophyllite, ramsayite and other minerals or fills cracks in them.

Eudialyte is commonly present in the aegirine, and less frequently in the feldspathic parts of the pegmatite body as reddish-pink isometric segregations with

Fig. 30. Lamprophyllite (Lp) in aegirine II.
×46. Without analyser

a cross-section of between 0.5×0.3 and 5×4 cm. Its main mass is concentrated in the interstices between microcline aggregates, but it sometimes presents idiomorphic outlines towards microcline. Inclusions of idiomorphic aegirine I and arfvedsonite crystals are found in eudialyte; it is xenomorphic to lamprophyllite. The interstices between its segregations are filled with aegirine II. Eudialyte is leached near the surface and is often converted to a friable dark-brown mass. Lovozerite sometimes forms on it.

Ramsayite is confined to the aegirine-bearing parts of the pegmatitic body, where it forms dark-brown isometric crystals with a cross-section of up to 3×3 cm. Aegirine is one of the minerals that separated early; it is idiomorphic to lamprophyllite and xenomorphic to arfvedsonite and eudialyte. Its segregations are commonly peripherally replaced by vinogradovite.

Lamprophyllite is also confined to the aegirine-bearing parts of the pegmatitic body. It forms tabular golden-brown crystals (sometimes reaching $7 \times 4 \times 1$ cm, but more commonly $3 \times 0.5 \times 0.2$ cm) in aegirine II (Fig. 30) or radiate-fibrous aggregates with interstices filled with aegirine II. Lamprophyllite is xenomorphic to microcline and arfvedsonite but idiomorphic to eudialyte and ramsayite.

Murmanite is present in minute amounts in the aegirine-bearing zones of the pegmatitic body as tabular light-brown and violet-pink crystals. The yellow variety is found very occasionally in the feldspathic zones. The dimensions of the crystals vary from $5 \times 3 \times 0.4$ to $15 \times 15 \times 3$ cm. Murmanite is commonly included

FIG. 31. Replacement of microcline (M) by ussingite (U). $\times 46$. Crossed nicols

in aegirine II in the interstices between microcline crystals, and contains inclusions of idiomorphic arfvedsonite crystals. It is much leached near the surface and is sometimes entirely destroyed.

Hackmanite occurs mainly in the aegirine-bearing parts of the pegmatites, typically as irregular segregations varying from a few millimetres to 8 cm in diameter. The colour is grey, and the raspberry-red of a fresh fracture soon disappears when exposed to the air. Hackmanite is commonly included in aegirine II or as irregular relicts in ussingite. Microscopic relicts of nepheline are sometimes found in hackmanite. It was probably formed by replacement of nepheline. There are also signs that it has replaced microcline.

Small quantities of *natrolite* occur as a dense white aggregate that normally develops on hackmanite, microcline and nepheline or fills the interstices between them. It is often mixed with ussingite and sometimes fills fissures in ramsayite, eudialyte and aegirine II.

Ussingite, which is quite widely distributed, is found in the main in the feldspathic part of the pegmatitic body. It forms 1-3 mm veinlets that cross microcline segregations in different directions and often form a network. It occurs less frequently as irregular pink segregations several centimetres across formed during the replacement of microcline (Fig. 31) and hackmanite, with only small relicts of the latter remaining.

There are very small amounts of *albite* in the leucocratic zone, where it occurs as fine veinlets (up to 3 mm) in microcline; these are visible only under the microscope. Less frequently it fills the interstices between microcline, nepheline and aegirine II crystals and replaces microcline.

Schizolite occurs rarely, as clearly-defined regular black crystals (with a cross-section of up to 2×1.5 cm) included in hackmanite. It is commonly much altered and converted to a friable brownish-black mass.

Small amounts of *neptunite* are found as red radiate-fibrous or granular segregations of up to 2 cm in diameter in cavities filled with aegirine II. Neptunite is red, but on weathered surfaces it is brown.

Loparite is detected only in thin sections as isolated black crystals, measured in hundredths of a millimetre, included in nepheline.

It is evident from the description here given that there is some differentiation in the pegmatitic body, revealed in the formation of essentially feldspathic and essentially aegirine-bearing zones in the western part of the body. Differentiation has not, however, been sufficiently complete to lead to the formation of distinct zoning throughout the pegmatitic body.

Replacement processes (albitization, natrolitization and ussingitization) are quite pronounced in this pegmatitic body.

3. The Pegmatites of the Sengis''yavr Cirque Emplaced in Eudialytic Lujavrites

These pegmatites were discovered by Tikhonenkov and are here described, in the main, from his data. There are ten small and four large pegmatite outcrops on the northern slope of the cirque, approximately 10 m below the upper rocky outcrops, opposite an alluvial fan that descends into the lake as a wide peninsula. They are all intercalated in trachytoid leucocratic eudialytic lujavrites that form a 20 m thick horizon traceable for 2 km. This horizon lies above the porphyritic lujavrites and is the lower leucocratic part of the complex.

The small pegmatitic formations are randomly distributed throughout the horizon. These bodies, which do not exceed one and a half metres across, pass by gradual transitions into the enclosing parent rock, to which they are similar in mineralogical composition. One distinctive feature is the almost total absence of aegirine II. The large pegmatite outcrops, which are clearly parts of a single layered body, differ markedly from the small outcrops both in form and relationship with the country rocks and in mineralogical composition. The abundance of aegirine II in them is a distinctive feature.

LAM G

The large layered pegmatitic body, which is approximately conformable with the trachytoid structure of the leucocratic eudialytic lujavrites, can be traced for more than 200 metres from the western slope of the cirque to the eastern slope as four outcrops linked by areas of coarse rubble. The thickness of the outcrop varies from 1 to 3 m and the lower contact is buried under scree. The contact between the upper surface and the country rock is distinct but uneven. In a number of cases apophyses up to 0·5 m thick and 30 m long run from this body into the country rocks. These apophyses may be conformable with the trachytoid

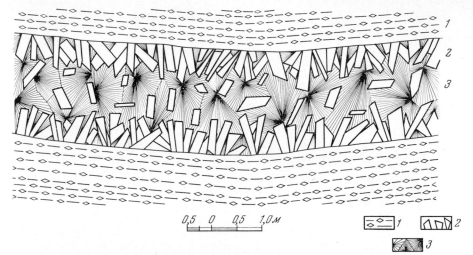

FIG. 32. Diagrammatic sketch of pegmatite (after Tikhonenkov)

1. leucocratic eudialytic lujavrite; 2. leucocratic microcline zone; 3. melanocratic aegirine zone

structure of the eudialytic lujavrites or cross it at various angles. The contacts between the apophyses and the country rocks are sharp and intrusive.

Two zones can be distinguished between the contacts and the centre of the pegmatitic body: an outer leucocratic zone and a central melanocratic zone (Fig. 32).

The leucocratic zone, which is composed in the main of microcline, nepheline and arfvedsonite, has a pegmatoid texture. There is an increase in the content of well-formed eudialyte crystals and less frequently of ramsayite crystals in the contact facies of the pegmatite, especially on the lower wall. Large arfvedsonite crystals that are similarly orientated to the microcline crystals, more or less perpendicular to the contact, are often found among the leucocratic minerals in the hanging wall.

The melanocratic zone has a block structure: large segregations of microcline, nepheline, eudialyte, hornblende and ramsayite are distributed in a radiate-fibrous mass of aegirine II. When this zone is poorly developed, as it sometimes is, aegirine II forms separate areas with a cross-section of up to 30 cm from which inclusions of early minerals are almost invariably lacking. The transition between the leucocratic and melanocratic zones is gradual, and is revealed by an increase in the amount of aegirine II and a decrease in the content of leucocratic minerals.

The pegmatitic body is composed mainly of microcline and albite (30-50 per cent), aegirine II (15-20 per cent), and natrolite (up to 10 per cent), arfvedsonite (10-15 per cent), eudialyte (5-10 per cent), ramsayite (5-10 per cent), and murmanite (5-10 per cent). Small amounts of lamprophyllite, neptunite, hackmanite and other minerals are found.

Microcline is confined to the contact zone. Its crystals, which are greyish-white with a yellow tinge and less frequently greyish-green, may be as large as $70 \times 30 \times 10$ cm. The central parts of large crystals do not normally contain inclusions, although the peripheral zones may be seen to contain inclusions of idiomorphic ramsayite, eudialyte, arfvedsonite and lamprophyllite crystals. Microcline is sometimes replaced by natrolite and less frequently by albite.

Nepheline is found mainly in the contact zone as crystals with a cross-section of up to 10-20 cm. Fresh nepheline is greenish-grey with a greasy lustre. Inclusions of idiomorphic crystals of aegirine I, arfvedsonite and ramsayite are sometimes to be seen in its peripheral parts.

In most cases nepheline is replaced by hackmanite, natrolite or a fine-grained mixture of natrolite and hydrargillite. Complete pseudomorphs of natrolite after nepheline included in microcline are found. Very occasionally one finds more or less fresh crystals of nepheline that are only peripherally replaced by natrolite.

Eudialyte is fairly evenly distributed in the body of the pegmatite, but its content increases towards the lower wall. The dimensions of its crystals decrease in the same direction from 5 cm in cross-section in the central sector of the pegmatite to 2 cm at the lower wall. Eudialyte, which is brownish-red, is an early pegmatite mineral. It is usually found in the interstices between microcline crystals, and is more idiomorphic than ramsayite. It stands in a dual relationship to arfvedsonite: it is xenomorphic to arfvedsonite in most cases, but eudialyte inclusions are sometimes found in the peripheral sectors of arfvedsonite crystals.

Eudialyte and ramsayite are corroded by aegirine II, which penetrates along cracks in them (Fig. 33). In the outer zones eudialyte is usually fairly fresh, whereas in the central part it has normally been altered by late solutions and it becomes pink along fissures. In these places the eudialyte is extremely pleochroic.

As a result of supergene alteration eudialyte becomes opaque and brown (to black) and is replaced by zirfesite and manganese hydroxides.

Ramsayite always accompanies eudialyte in the pegmatitic body, forming brownish crystals of up to $5 \times 3 \cdot 5 \times 2$ cm. It is the most stable pegmatite mineral under surface conditions. It crystallized later than arfvedsonite and eudialyte, the crystals of which occur as idiomorphic inclusions in it. At the same time ramsayite crystals are found as inclusions in the peripheral zones of microcline and nepheline.

Arfvedsonite is most often found at the hanging wall of the pegmatite body, where it forms black elongate-prismatic crystals of up to $30 \times 1 \times 1$ cm. It is a comparatively early mineral, crystals of it being included in the peripheral sectors of microcline and nepheline and also in ramsayite and murmanite, but they often contain inclusions of idiomorphic nepheline and microcline crystals.

Lamprophyllite is found mainly in the outer zone among leucocratic minerals. Some of its elongate-tabular golden-yellow crystals reach a length of 8 cm. Lamprophyllite is an early mineral. Its idiomorphic crystals are found as inclusions in the peripheral parts of microcline and nepheline, and also in ramsayite and eudialyte.

Murmanite is confined to the central part of the pegmatite body, where its tabular crystals may be as large as 10×10 cm. It is commonly included in aegirine

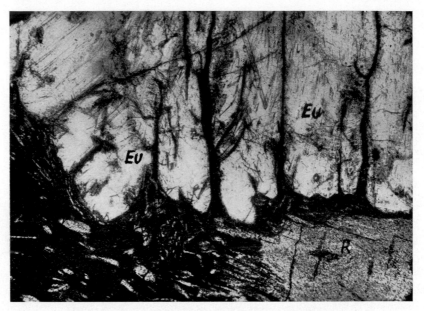

FIG. 33. Interrelationship of aegirine II (black) with eudialyte (Eu) and ramsayite (R). ×46. Without analyser

II, in which its crystals are curved, crushed, greatly altered and converted into an ochreous mass.

There are two generations of *aegirine* in this pegmatitic body. Aegirine I is seen only in thin sections as small acicular crystals (up to 1-2 mm) included in nepheline and microcline. The main mass of the aegirine consists of radiate-fibrous bundles of green aegirine II filling the interstices between large nepheline and microcline crystals.

Natrolite occurs in small quantities mainly in the central zone as whitish aggregations of irregular shape filling the interstices between other minerals.

There are very small amounts of *neptunite*. It forms incrustations and less frequently crystals (up to 0·3 cm long) in leaching cavities. The colour is dark-cherry and the streak bright orange.

In addition to the minerals described above, the pegmatitic body contains small amounts of albite, developed mainly on microcline, and hackmanite replacing nepheline. These minerals are confined mainly to the central zone.

There are many leaching cavities ('elatolites') in this pegmatite body. They form parallel series extending from a central column and forming structures reminiscent of the arrangement of fir-tree branches. The leached mineral was clearly the earliest, since the cavities are confined to microcline. How the 'elatolites' were formed remains unresolved.

The majority of the pegmatites of the Sengis"yavr cirque are genetically connected with the leucocratic eudialytic lujavrites and are of the facies type. The largest layered body is probably facies-phase. The facies nature of this pegmatite is shown by its layered form and conformability with the trachytoid texture of the country rocks, as well as by the absence of contact alteration in the country rocks and uneven diffuse contacts. One can therefore assume that this pegmatite body was formed where the pegmatitic melt was segregated during the process of crystallization differentiation. The existence of apophyses with intrusive contacts indicates that parts of the pegmatitic melt was displaced into fissures in the country rocks during the crystallization of the main pegmatitic body.

4. The Pegmatites of the Sengis"yavr Cirque Emplaced in Porphyritic Lujavrites

A pegmatitic vein consisting of three outcrops and areas of coarse rubble can be traced for more than 100 m along the strike to the north of the Lake Sengis"yavr cirque. Its apparent thickness is up to 1 m. The vein was discovered and studied by Tikhonenkov and is here described from his data.

It is emplaced in porphyritic lujavrites, which reach a thickness of 10 m and more in this part of the massif. Large arfvedsonite crystals appear in the country rocks at the contact with the pegmatite and the murmanite content increases; the amount of eudialyte increases towards the contact and the rock becomes greyish-red in colour. The amount of aegirine is greatly reduced. The nepheline and microcline in the groundmass are almost entirely replaced by natrolite, and the coloured minerals are therefore contained in a mass of fine-grained natrolite.

There is a distinct welded contact between the pegmatite of the hanging wall and the country rock. The lower wall is buried beneath rubble consisting of pegmatite and country rock. The line of contact is uneven, with many tongues and branches from the pegmatitic vein into the country rocks. The pegmatite typically contains a large number of porphyritic lujavrite xenoliths of varying shapes and dimensions, the largest of which does not exceed $1.5 \times 1 \times 0.5$ m. The xenoliths have usually been much reworked by the pegmatitic melt and enriched in eudialyte or arfvedsonite. All these features indicate that this body has been injected.

There is no clear pattern to the distribution of the minerals of which the body is composed. One can only note the existence of fine-grained melanocratic and

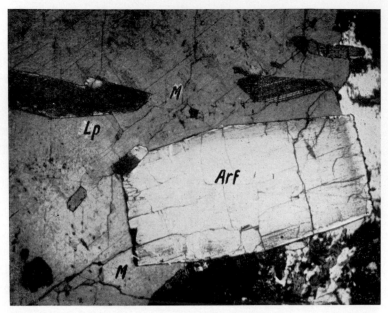

FIG. 34. Arfvedsonite (Arf) and lamprophyllite (Lp) in microcline
(M). × 20. Crossed nicols

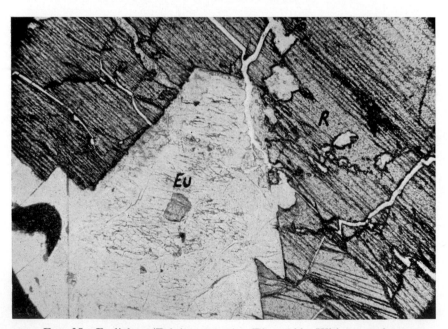

FIG. 35. Eudialyte (Eu) in ramsayite (R).   × 46. Without analyser

FIG. 36.   Arfvedsonite (A) in fissures of aegirine I crystals (Aeg).   × 46.
Without analyser

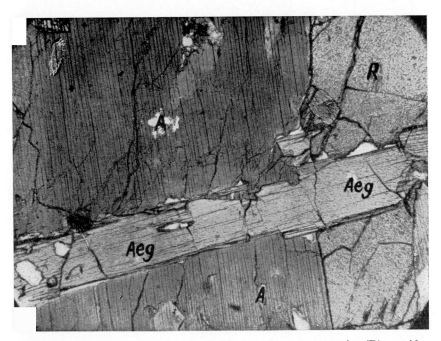

FIG. 37.   Aegirine I (Aeg) in arfvedsonite (A) and ramsayite (R).   × 46.
Without analyser

coarse-grained comparatively leucocratic parts, distributed at random throughout the pegmatite. The general appearance of the pegmatite is melanocratic. The aegirine II content is typically relatively small. The texture is usually inequi-granular and less frequently block structure is found, in parts containing aegirine II.

The content of minerals in the various parts of the pegmatite body is as follows: microcline, 30-80 per cent; ramsayite, 20-60 per cent; arfvedsonite, up to 60 per cent; eudialyte, up to 20 per cent; aegirine, 10-20 per cent; nepheline, up to 10 per cent; murmanite, 10 per cent; lamprophyllite, up to 5-10 per cent. There are small quantities of natrolite, loparite and neptunite.

Microcline forms tabular greenish-yellow crystals of up to $20 \times 10 \times 5$ cm occurring quite frequently in bundles of crystals. The structure is typically isoperthitic. The microcline contains inclusions of idiomorphic aegirine I crystals. The boundaries of large crystals are always xenomorphic to eudialyte, lampro-phyllite and arfvedsonite (Fig. 34). No inclusions of these minerals are found in the central parts of crystals. Microcline is usually replaced to some extent by natrolite or an aggregate of clay minerals, in which case the clouded parts are elongated and orientated parallel to the cleavage.

Nepheline occurs as columnar hexagonal crystals that are often completely converted to spreustein. They do not normally exceed 3×3 cm in cross-section but may on occasion reach 5×5 cm. Nepheline is an early mineral and the only inclusions that it contains are aegirine I crystals. Other minerals are moulded on it. Nepheline is usually greatly natrolitized.

Eudialyte occurs widely. It forms orange-brown crystals with a cross-section of up to 2×2 cm and is xenomorphic in the main to nepheline and microcline, which indicates its later crystallization, but is idiomorphic in the peripheral parts of microcline crystals. Eudialyte is more idiomorphic than ramsayite (Fig. 35). It frequently contains idiomorphic arfvedsonite crystals. The fact that eudialyte crystals are often leached leads to the occurrence of cavities with the crystallo-graphic outlines typical of this mineral in the pegmatite mass.

Arfvedsonite is the main dark mineral of the vein. It occurs as regular elongate-prismatic black crystals with a length that does not exceed 9 cm for a cross-section of 0.5×0.5 cm. The structure of its crystals is usually zonal, their cores being lighter and with irregular etched boundaries.

Arfvedsonite is a mineral of comparatively early crystallization, and idio-morphic crystals of it are often included in eudialyte and ramsayite. It is later than aegirine I, filling the interstices between aegirine I crystals and healing fractures in them (Fig. 36). Lamprophyllite crystallized at approximately the same time as arfvedsonite, and bears a dual relation to it. Idiomorphic lampro-phyllite crystals are sometimes found as inclusions in arfvedsonite, in which case the arfvedsonite heals their fissures. In other cases lamprophyllite grows round well-shaped arfvedsonite crystals. Aegirine II corrodes these crystals.

Ramsayite forms dark-brown crystals, with a cross-section of up to 3×3 cm, and irregular segregations in the interstices between eudialyte, nepheline, micro-cline, lamprophyllite and arfvedsonite crystals. It is xenomorphic to lamprophyllite. Aegirine I forms regular crystals in it. Ramsayite is earlier than the other minerals.

Aegirine, unlike the other pegmatites of this complex, is represented mainly by the first generation, which forms black elongate-prismatic crystals and radiate-fibrous bundles of up to 10 cm in diameter. The crystal cross-sections do not exceed 0.8×0.5 cm. The crystals are often zoned.

Aegirine I is the earliest mineral of the pegmatite. Idiomorphic crystals of it are included in nepheline, microcline, lamprophyllite, ramsayite, eudialyte and arfvedsonite (Fig. 37).

Aegirine II is rarely found, and then mainly in the leucocratic sectors of the pegmatite as radiate-fibrous bundles of crystals in the interstices between early minerals.

Murmanite forms large tabular crystals of up to $10 \times 8 \times 0.5$ cm that are often curved and shattered. The mineral is almost completely altered. It is usually associated with aegirine II.

Lamprophyllite occurs as radiate-fibrous segregations of up to 1 cm in diameter, or as elongated crystals up to 3 cm long. It is normally found in the melanocratic parts of the vein, where it is intimately associated with ramsayite, aegirine I, arfvedsonite and eudialyte. Lamprophyllite is late in relation to aegirine I and idiomorphic in relation to microcline and eudialyte. We have already mentioned that it stands in a dual relationship to arfvedsonite.

Loparite is found in the melanocratic parts of the vein as regular black crystals with a cross-section of up to 1.5 mm. It is found included in ramsayite, arfvedsonite and aegirine I, and thus crystallized earlier than these minerals.

Neptunite is extensively developed in this pegmatite body. It forms dark-red crystals of up to $3 \times 2 \times 1$ mm that are normally zonal. It was one of the latest minerals of the pegmatite to separate. Together with natrolite it fills the interstices between all the minerals mentioned.

Natrolite occurs only in the leucocratic parts of the vein, where it forms irregular segregations filling the interstices between all the other minerals. The replacement of nepheline and microcline by natrolite is extensively shown.

In addition to the minerals mentioned above, a yellowish-brown radiate-fibrous mineral intimately associated with altered murmanite has been encountered in this pegmatitic body. Its segregations do not exceed 1 mm in cross-section and it has remained unstudied for lack of material.

With the exception of arfvedsonite, ramsayite and aegirine I, the minerals of which the pegmatite vein is composed are greatly altered and often crushed and leached; the surface of the vein at the outcrops is therefore irregular and porous. The presence of 'elatolites' (leaching cavities, reminiscent in shape of the arrangement of fir tree branches) is typical.

Typical Features of the Pegmatites of the
Eudialytic Lujavrite Complex

Study of the pegmatites shows that their chemical and mineralogical composition reflects the composition of the parent rocks to a varying degree. Minerals of the eudialyte-eucolite group predominate among the rare-metal minerals in both. On the other hand, the pegmatites contain considerable quantities of ramsayite, lamprophyllite, murmanite and neptunite, which are typical of the rocks and pegmatites of the differentiated complex, in addition to zirconium minerals. These minerals are accessories and less frequently minor minerals in the rocks, but usually principal minerals in the pegmatites.

In most of the small pegmatitic bodies the texture is typically equigranular and the size of the mineral constituents increases gradually from the periphery to the centre, though there is no clear regularity in the distribution of the main minerals. In the larger pegmatitic bodies there is some differentiation, leading to the appearance of block zones in the central parts (see the description of the Kedykvyrpakhk pegmatites). In even larger pegmatitic bodies there is a poorly-defined zoning, either throughout their extent or in limited parts (see the description of the Sengis"yavr cirque pegmatites). The peripheral zones of these bodies are usually composed in the main of microcline with lesser amounts of eudialyte, nepheline, ramsayite, aegirine I, arfvedsonite and other minerals, while the central zones consist mainly of aegirine II. In the largest swells of some pegmatitic bodies (Kedykvyrpakhk) there is one further central zone, consisting mainly of natrolite (80-90 per cent) with a lesser amount of hackmanite and schizolite.

Replacement processes (natrolitization, albitization, sodalitization and ussingitization) are quite marked in the pegmatites of the complex. The earliest processes are sodalitization of nepheline and albitization of microcline, which are developed to some degree in all the pegmatites of the complex except those bedded in porphyritic lujavrites. The processes of natrolitization and ussingitization occurred later, at approximately the same stage, but are exhibited in different pegmatitic bodies. Natrolitization is best developed in the pegmatites of Kedykvyrpakhk, where the natrolite forms the groundmass of the central zone of the largest pegmatite outcrop, enclosing relicts of hackmanite and feldspar. Ussingitization is found in only one pegmatite of the Tyul'bn'yunuai valley, where ussingite replaces microcline along fissures. Natrolite in this pegmatite is present in minute quantities.

*   *   *   *

One can provisionally distinguish four main stages in the formation of the pegmatites of the eudialytic lujavrite complex: (1) fluid-magmatic, (2) fluid-gaseous, (3) fluid-hydrothermal and (4) hydrothermal (Fig. 38).

Nepheline, aegirine I, loparite, the main mass of the microcline and in a number of cases arfvedsonite, lamprophyllite and ramsayite crystallized in the first stage. The first to separate were aegirine I and loparite, usually contained in nepheline, which clearly crystallized with, or slightly later than, arfvedsonite. All these minerals have good crystallographic form, not distorted by the development of other minerals, and they are idiomorphic to microcline. The main mass of the microcline was formed after nepheline and the rare-metal minerals (ramsayite, lamprophyllite, etc.) began to separate when its crystallization was complete.

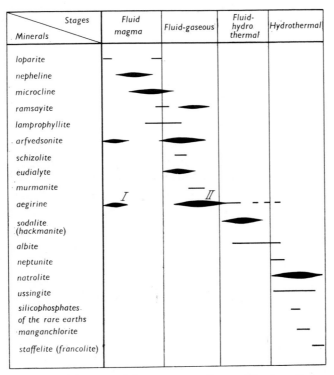

FIG. 38. Diagram of the sequence of crystallization of the minerals in the eudialytic and porphyritic lujavrite complex

Small undifferentiated pegmatitic bodies were formed in the main in the first stage.

The second stage saw the crystallization of the high-temperature rare-metal minerals eudialyte, ramsayite, lamprophyllite and murmanite, as well as arfvedsonite and aegirine II. The crystallization periods of the rare-metal minerals and arfvedsonite overlap, as a result of which their interrelationships are sometimes found to be quite complex and one cannot decide on their relative times of crystallization with any certainty. Nevertheless, the general sequence of crystallization is quite clearly evident. Such minerals as eudialyte, ramsayite, arfvedsonite and lamprophyllite sometimes form idiomorphic inclusions in the peripheral parts of microcline and nepheline crystals, while the central parts of these minerals do not contain inclusions of coloured minerals.

The main mass of the coloured minerals is concentrated in the interstices between microcline and nepheline segregations. This enables us to deduce that arfvedsonite, eudialyte, ramsayite and lamprophyllite began to separate at the end of the period in which microcline crystallized. They were followed by the crystallization of murmanite, which is found only in aegirine II and which is xenomorphic to the minerals that separated earlier. Crushing often occurred in the pegmatites in the second stage, which ended with the crystallization of aegirine II, and previously crystallized minerals were displaced. One finds cases, for example, in which arfvedsonite crystals have been crushed and the fragments have been displaced relative to each other along an aegirine vein. The crushing of murmanite and eudialyte, with aegirine II filling the fissures, can also be observed. Crystallization of the pegmatites of the eudialytic lujavrite complex was completed in the main in the second stage. In the third stage nepheline is replaced by sodalite (hackmanite) and microcline by albite. In the fourth stage natrolite and ussingite crystallized in the central parts of the largest pegmatite bodies. In the other pegmatites the replacement of microcline, nepheline and hackmanite by natrolite and ussingite takes place at this stage.

The fact that the large pegmatitic bodies are confined to the lower horizons of the complex and are similar in mineralogical composition indicates that we are concerned with a specific pegmatitic belt. This is also indicated by the abundance of small facies pegmatitic formations and the extremely variable quantitative mineralogical composition of the eudialytic lujavrites in this horizon. In all probability rare elements and volatile compounds accumulated in this horizon during the crystallization of the rocks of the complex, under the influence of pressure from above and emanations from below. This facilitated the development and appearance of pegmatitic hearths at approximately the same level.

CHAPTER TWO

PEGMATITES OF THE DIFFERENTIATED COMPLEX

THE differentiated complex is very rich in pegmatitic formations. More than 30 large pegmatitic bodies belonging to this complex have now been studied, in addition to small veins and schlieren-like pegmatites, of which there are many hundreds.

The pegmatites of the differentiated complex include facies, facies-phase and phase varieties. The former are pegmatitic horizons associated with the lower surfaces of urtite and ijolitic urtite horizons.

They can be traced intermittently for many kilometres and are between 20 cm and 2·5 m thick. The pegmatitic horizons usually have distinct contacts against the country rocks. The content of eudialyte, and more rarely of lamprophyllite, ramsayite and murmanite in the country rocks increases near pegmatitic horizons and there are sometimes apophyses from the pegmatitic horizons into the country rocks, in which case they are really facies-phase rather than facies formations.

In the exposed part of the differentiated complex there are six discontinuous pegmatitic horizons associated with the lower surfaces of: (1) urtites of horizon III, (2) urtites of horizon IV, (3) urtites in genetic association with malignites, (4) ijolitic urtites, (5) urtites of horizon V, and (6) porphyritic lujavrites. The third and fourth pegmatitic horizons are the thickest, and the latter consists of a series of pegmatitic stratified bodies. Boreholes reveal that pegmatitic horizons are also a typical feature of deeper parts of the intrusion, where they are associated with the lower surfaces of urtites.

The facies pegmatites also include irregular schlieren-like pegmatites of small dimensions (up to 25-30 m²) that merge gradually with the parent rocks.

Phase pegmatites are represented by steeply dipping cross-cutting and sheet veins, and less frequently by irregular bodies that form sharp contacts with the country rocks, sometimes contain xenoliths, and may have a clearly defined symmetrically zonal structure. Vein pegmatites do not normally exceed 100 m in length and the maximum thickness is 4 m.

We shall now describe the largest pegmatitic bodies of the differentiated complex.

5. The Pegmatitic Horizon beneath the Ijolitic Urtites

This is the largest pegmatitic horizon (see Fig. 16), and its study has particular bearing on the genesis of pegmatites. The first brief description was given by V. I. Gerasimovskii (1939₁) and it has since been studied in detail by members of the Kola expedition of the USSR Academy of Sciences, including I. P. Tikhonenkov, whose data have been drawn on in this work.

This horizon consists of a series of sub-parallel layered pegmatites (up to six), in the main bedded one above another conformably with the containing aegirine-lujavrites. They can be traced along the northern, western and south-western slopes of the massif, with some interruptions, for many kilometres. The horizon is well exposed on Karnasurt, Alluaiv, Sengischorr, Angvundaschorr and Kuftn'yun. The largest upper pegmatitic body maintains an average thickness of 1·5-2·5 m fairly consistently throughout its extent, and it is only to the east of the Second

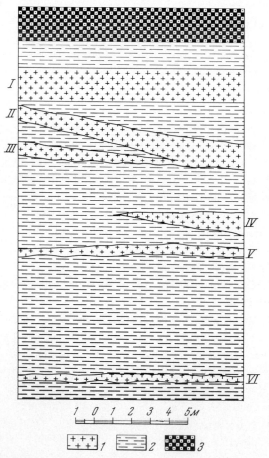

Fig. 39. Diagram of outcrops of the pegmatitic horizon at the First Eastern stream on Karnasurt (compiled by Kuz'menko)

1. pegmatites; 2. aegirine-lujavrite; 3. ijolitic urtite; I-VI numbers of the pegmatitic bodies

Eastern stream on Karnasurt that its thickness diminishes to 20 cm. The underlying pegmatitic bodies are less thick and less well maintained along the strike: in some parts of the massif they peter out.

Below the main pegmatitic body in the First Eastern stream on Karnasurt a second body (Fig. 39) is revealed, separated from the first by a horizon of leucocratic lujavrites up to 1·5 m thick, in which the content of dark-coloured constituents is seen to increase from the top downwards. This pegmatitic body, which is 0·6-1·2 m thick, is unconformably interlayered with the country rocks and merges with the main body of the pegmatitic horizon on the north-eastern slope of the stream, and with the underlying third pegmatitic body on the south-western slopes. Highly natrolitized leucocratic lujavrites, differing from the lujavrites of the roof in the almost total absence of eudialyte, are bedded in the floor of the second pegmatitic body.

The third pegmatitic body, which is 60-70 cm thick, is separated from the second by a 1-2 m stratal group of leucocratic lujavrites. It is conformably bedded with the country rocks and is in general parallel to the main body of the pegmatitic horizon. It should be noted that the melanocratic nature of the lujavrites that enclose the pegmatitic bodies increases from the top downwards and that they are almost mesocratic in the roof of the third pegmatitic body.

The fourth pegmatitic body is lenticular in form and can be traced for 15 m with a maximum thickness of 1 m. It is bedded in melanocratic lujavrites and is separated from the third pegmatitic body by a group of mesocratic lujavrites more than 3 m thick. The lujavrites at the upper contact of the pegmatite are greatly enriched in aegirine and eudialyte. At the lower contact the lujavrites are enriched in loparite and there are large crystals of microcline orientated perpendicular to the trachytoid texture and extending into the pegmatite.

The fifth pegmatitic body (15-40 cm thick) is separated from the fourth by a group of melanocratic lujavrites 70-80 cm thick. The melanocratic lujavrites are greatly enriched in eudialyte at the contacts. The pegmatitic body, which is stratified, is conformably bedded with the country rocks. In its western part it contains small xenoliths of the enclosing lujavrites, the trachytoid texture of which is conformable with that of the enclosing melanocratic lujavrites. Thin apophyses conformable with the stratification of the country rocks extend from the pegmatitic body.

The sixth pegmatitic body is separated from the fifth by a group of melanocratic lujavrites 6 m thick. It is a thin (15-20 cm) stratified body that is conformably bedded with the enclosing lujavrites.

The pegmatitic horizon is separated from the overlying thick horizon of ijolitic urtites by a thin zone consisting mainly of leucocratic lujavrites with subordinate foyaites, juvites or urtites. There is considerable variation in the thickness of this zone, but it does not normally exceed 1·5 m. At their upper surfaces the pegmatites normally form contacts with leucocratic or mesocratic lujavrites, but these rocks peter out at some points and the pegmatitic body is then in contact with the overlying juvites, urtites and foyaites or directly with the ijolitic urtites.

The main pegmatitic body makes sharp straight contacts with the leucocratic
lujavrites and the trachytoid structure of the rocks is normally parallel to the contact planes. When the pegmatite makes a contact with rocks of non-layered structure (foyaites, urtites and juvites), the contact surface is irregular and hummocky.

This pegmatitic horizon was probably formed by the separation of the pegmatitic melt *in situ* and is a specific facies of rocks of the differentiated complex.
This is indicated by its great extent, the strict constancy of its [stratigraphic]
position in the differentiated complex and its conformable bedding with other
rocks. At any point on the massif where the contact of the ijolitic urtites and the
lujavrites is laid bare the pegmatitic horizon is always present, and some of its
outcrops are 3-5 km long. The facies nature of the pegmatitic horizon is also
shown by the gradual increase in the content of rare-metal minerals (eudialyte,
ramsayite and lamprophyllite) in the country rocks near the pegmatitic horizon
and the absence of exogenous contact effects such as occur near veins. On the
other hand the presence of xenoliths of the country rocks in the marginal parts of
some pegmatitic bodies (Karnasurt) and the existence of small pegmatite apophyses

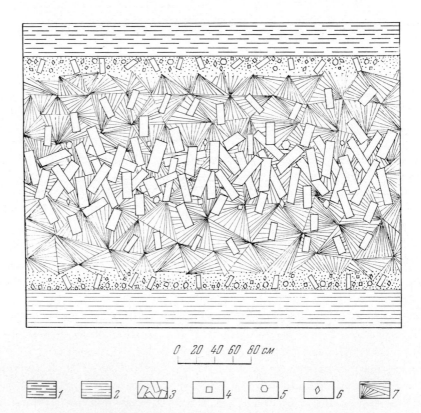

FIG. 40. Symmetrically zonal structure of the main body of
the pegmatitic horizon (after Tikhonenkov)

1. mesocratic lujavrite; 2. leucocratic lujavrite; 3. microcline;
4. nepheline; 5. eudialyte; 6. ramsayite; 7. fine-grained groundmass of aegirine II and other minerals

FIG. 41. Contact of leucocratic zone of pegmatite with the lujavrite of the roof. Alluaiv stream. Natural size

from the main pegmatitic body in the country rocks indicates that part of the pegmatitic melt was injected along planes of parting and tectonic fissures into country rocks that had already crystallized.

The zoning of all the bodies in this pegmatitic horizon is symmetrical. The general features of the zoning are revealed by the fact that late leucocratic and rare-metal minerals (nepheline, microcline, lamprophyllite, eudialyte, ramsayite and arfvedsonite) are confined to the border zones of the pegmatites, while late minerals (aegirine II, natrolite and albite) are confined to the central cores.

The zones differ both in the proportions of the main minerals and in structure. The typomorphic rare-metal minerals are present in each zone. There are considerable variations in the thickness of the zones and in the proportions of the main minerals in them, along the strike of the horizon, but the general character of the zoning is preserved. It is most clearly defined in the main pegmatitic body, in which the following three zones can be distinguished between the contacts and the centre: an outer, an intermediate and a central zone.

The outer (leucocratic) zone (Fig. 40) lies along the contacts between the pegmatite and the country rocks and is made up in the main of microcline, arfvedsonite and nepheline, the interstices being filled with smaller inclusions of the same minerals as well as with aegirine I, eudialyte and ramsayite. The texture of the zone is pegmatoid and the microcline crystals are orientated perpendicularly to the contact (Fig. 41), while the thickness varies from 5 to 30 cm. In some outcrops (the river Shomiok) there is in this zone a 1-5 cm fringe in the immediate vicinity of the contacts with the foyaites, consisting mainly of nepheline and the rare-metal minerals eudialyte, ramsayite and lamprophyllite. Loparite is a typical associate of this fringe and is more plentiful in the upper contact than on the lower walls. Unlike the greater part of the leucocratic zone, the texture of the fringe is fine-grained. As it gives way gradually to the coarse-grained leucocratic zone the nepheline content declines and the size of the crystals increases.

The main mass of the pegmatitic body is made up of the intermediate melanocratic zone, the total thickness of which is 60-70 cm. Its transition to the outer zone is gradual. The melanocratic zone is composed mainly of fine-grained rock, consisting of nepheline, microcline, eudialyte and ramsayite, with the interstices filled with aegirine II. The dimensions of the individual grains in the rock do not normally exceed 0·3 cm and the cross-section rarely reaches 0·5-1 cm. The porphyritic texture of the zone is due to the inclusion of rare large crystals of nepheline, microcline, ramsayite and murmanite in this mass. The size of the phenocrysts varies between 3 cm in cross-section (for eudialyte) to $50 \times 30 \times 10$ cm (for microcline), and they are very few in number near the outer zones. The number and dimensions of the phenocrysts increases from the periphery to the centre, and they account for 30-40 per cent of the total rock mass near the central zone.

In mineralogical composition the melanocratic zone differs from the leucocratic zone in having a higher aegirine content (up to 40 per cent). The typomorphic rare-metal minerals are murmanite and ramsayite. There are cavities, the walls of which are covered with acicular crystals of aegirine III and with prismatic crystals of natrolite and sometimes of neptunite and analcite.

The central (macrocrystalline) zone is not found everywhere. Its thickness varies along the strike of the horizon from a few centimetres to 25-30 cm. In this zone large discrete crystals of microcline, nepheline, eudialyte and ramsayite are included in a fine-grained mass consisting of aegirine II, microcline, nepheline and other minerals. The central zone differs from the melanocratic zone in that the large crystals of these minerals predominate over the fine-grained ground-mass. In some parts the interstices between the large crystals are filled with compact fine-fibrous aegirine II, sometimes mixed with fine-grained natrolite and albite.

The axial part of the zone contains lenticular patches composed of fine-grained natrolite (up to 60 per cent) and fibrous aegirine III (Fig. 42) containing irregular segregations of eudialyte. It is clear from sections that aegirine fills the interstices between natrolite crystals and that its crystals are frequently orientated perpendicular to the elongation of the natrolite crystals. The central zone also contains small areas composed of practically pure albite in the form of small laths up to 0·1 mm long (Fig. 43), mainly orientated parallel to the contacts.

Miarolitic cavities up to 5×5 cm in section are common in the radiate-fibrous aegirine II of the central zone. The surface of the cavities is covered with fine acicular crystals of aegirine III and prismatic crystals of natrolite up to $0.5 \times 0.3 \times 0.2$ cm in dimensions. There are also regularly bounded segregations of analcite with a cross-section of up to 0·5 cm.

Neptunite, analcite, psilomelane, apatite, elpidite, epididymite, quartz and chalcedony, not found in the other zones, occur in this zone in intimate association with albite, natrolite and aegirine III.

The pegmatitic bodies underlying the main body described are similar in mineralogical composition and structure. The thickness of the intermediate melanocratic zones decreases from the upper body to the lower, and there is a relative increase in the thickness of the central macrocrystalline leucocratic zone, i.e. the quantity of aegirine in the pegmatites decreases as its proportion in the enclosing lujavrites increases. The fifth pegmatitic body is macrocrystalline in texture and leucocratic in composition. There is also an increase in the content of ramsayite, which is located in the central zones.

These pegmatites are approximately four-fifths nepheline, microcline, arfved-sonite, aegirine, eudialyte, ramsayite and murmanite and the proportions of these minerals are approximately the same in all the outcrops of the pegmatitic horizons. The secondary minerals, which are encountered sporadically, include albite, natrolite, lamprophyllite, aenigmatite, loparite, elpidite, ilmenite, neptunite, sodalite, eudidymite, psilomelane and analcite.

The pegmatites are poorer than the country rocks in nepheline, and to some extent in microcline, and richer in aegirine, arfvedsonite, eudialyte, ramsayite, murmanite and lamprophyllite, and this accounts for their melanocratic character. The pegmatites also contain such rare minerals as epididymite, eudidymite,

Fig. 42. Densely fibrous aggregate of natrolite (light) and aegirine III (dark). × 10. Without analyser

Fig. 43. Albite in the central zone of the pegmatitic body. × 46. Crossed nicols

FIG. 44. Relationship of aegirine III (black) and microcline (light). ×46. Without analyser

FIG. 45. Aegirine I crystal (Aeg) included in a large segregation of eudialyte (black) and growing round a small crystal of early eudialyte (Eu); M—microcline; A—arfvedsonite. ×46. Crossed nicols

elpidite, psilomelane, analcite, quartz, nontronite, chalcedony, thomsonite, hydrargillite and others that are absent from the rocks.

Microcline accounts for 30-50 per cent of the total mass of the pegmatites. In the outer zone it forms large prismatic crystals or irregular segregations up to $20 \times 10 \times 6$ cm of a creamy-grey colour. There is less microcline at the upper contacts than at the lower and the axial length of its crystals does not exceed 5-6 cm. In the central zone and among the phenocrysts of the intermediate zones its crystals reach $30 \times 15 \times 8$ cm, while in the fine-grained mass of the melanocratic zone it forms small laths that are xenomorphic towards nepheline.

Microcline is one of the earliest minerals. It contains idiomorphic crystals of aegirine I, nepheline and eudialyte, but the main mass of the eudialyte is xenomorphic to microcline. Probably the microcline crystallized later than the aegirine I and nepheline, but earlier than the main mass of the eudialyte, ramsayite, and arfvedsonite, which began to separate at the end of the period of microcline crystallization and occur as well-formed crystals in its marginal parts. Microcline is earlier than aegirine II. Aegirine II corrodes microcline, forming veinlets in it and penetrating along cleavage cracks (Fig. 44).

Unlike the other pegmatites of the massif, the microcline of the pegmatitic horizon is replaced by polysynthetically twinned albite, which is typical only of the rocks of the massif. The albitization of microcline is, however, poorly developed, the microcline being more frequently replaced by natrolite.

Nepheline, accounting for 15-20 per cent of the leucocratic zone of the pegmatitic bodies, forms regular greenish-grey crystals with a cross-section of from 0.2×0.2 to 2×2 cm. The nepheline crystals at the upper contacts are usually large, while at the lower contacts they are always small. Nepheline phenocrysts in the intermediate zone consist of prismatic rose-grey or dark-grey crystals up to 7×3 cm in area. In the fine-grained mass nepheline occurs as small oval grains and rarely as square-section grains with a cross-section of up to 0.5 cm.

Nepheline is a mineral of early separation. It is idiomorphic towards all the minerals except aegirine I. Nepheline inclusions usually surrounded by natrolite are of frequent occurrence in microcline. Idiomorphic grains of nepheline are also found in large zonal segregations of eudialyte, where they are usually greatly spreusteinized and sodalitized.

The nepheline has undergone sodalitization, spreusteinization and natrolitization in all zones. It is little altered in the fine-grained margins near contacts.

There are three generations of *aegirine* in the pegmatitic horizon. Aegirine I forms small prismatic inclusions, measured in tenths and hundredths of a millimetre and rarely attaining 2 mm in length in the nepheline and microcline of the outer leucocratic zone. It is green in thin sections and colourless in small crystals. Aegirine I was the earliest mineral to separate. Idiomorphic crystals of it are found as inclusions in all the other minerals, but the largest crystals are sometimes xenomorphic towards small inclusions of eudialyte (Fig. 45).

Aegirine II is found in all the zones, but does not exceed 5 per cent in the outer zone, increasing to 40-50 per cent in the intermediate zones. In the central zone the aegirine II content is once again reduced. It forms radiate-fibrous aggregates up to 5 cm in diameter in the central zone and often constitutes large monomineralic areas in the intermediate zones, near the central zones. In such areas aegirine II forms a randomly fibrous aggregate cemented by black manganese hydroxides or by fine-grained natrolite, which occupies the fissures. The aegirine II fibres vary in length from fractions of a millimetre to 7 mm.

Aegirine II separated later than microcline, eudialyte, ramsayite and murman-

FIG. 46. Arfvedsonite (A) in natrolite. × 46. Crossed nicols

ite, which it apparently cements and partly corrodes, this corrosion affecting the microcline crystals most strongly, invading fissures and penetrating along cleavage planes.

Aegirine III forms druses of fine-acicular crystals in leaching cavities in the central zones of the pegmatitic bodies in association with natrolite and neptunite. Its colouring varies from practically colourless to dark-green, and the crystals vary in length from hundredths of a millimetre to 2 cm.

Arfvedsonite is found in all the zones of the pegmatitic bodies. It does not exceed 10 per cent in the outer zone, increases to 20 per cent in the intermediate zone and again declines to 3-5 per cent in the central zone. It is the main dark-coloured mineral in the outer zone, where it is present as large black elongate-prismatic crystals reaching sizes of $10 \times 1 \times 1$ cm. It occurs in the intermediate zone either as regular elongate-prismatic crystals of up to $3 \times 0.3 \times 0.3$ cm, or as very fine acicular crystals associated with aegirine II and murmanite in filling the interstices between clusters of early minerals. In the central zone arfvedsonite also forms elongate-prismatic crystals of between $1 \times 0.1 \times 0.1$ and $10 \times 1 \times 1$ cm included in a fine-grained aggregate of aegirine II and natrolite.

Large arfvedsonite crystals are usually idiomorphic towards microcline and to the main mass of eudialyte, and at the same time contain inclusions of small eudialyte and aegirine I crystals. Small segregations of nepheline, microcline and lamprophyllite crystals occur less frequently as inclusions in arfvedsonite. Acicular crystals of arfvedsonite are late by comparison with nepheline, microcline, eudialyte and ramsayite and also by comparison with large crystals of arfvedsonite. It is probable that two varieties of arfvedsonite should be distinguished in the pegmatitic horizon on the basis of time of crystallization: early arfvedsonite, which crystallized simultaneously with microcline, and late arfvedsonite, formed after the microcline and approximately at the same time as aegirine II and murmanite.

In the central zones, where all the leucocratic minerals are entirely replaced by fine-grained natrolite, arfvedsonite is normally included in the natrolite and can be seen to have been corroded by it (Fig. 46).

Eudialyte occurs in all the zones of the pegmatitic bodies. It forms crystals varying in size from fractions of a millimetre in the fine-grained mass of the intermediate zones to 1·5 cm in cross-section in the central and outer zones. The small clusters are usually regular hexagonal crystals, whereas the large aggregates are of irregular form and zonal structure, with reddish-brown cores and pink borders. The pink colour develops in eudialyte both at the borders and along fissures penetrating the interior regions, so that the colour of the grain is entirely converted to pink in some cases.

Two generations of eudialyte—early and late—are distinguished. The first eudialyte generation includes small well-formed crystals in microcline, ramsayite, late eudialyte and other earlier minerals. Large segregations of second-generation eudialyte are always xenomorphic towards aegirine I, microcline, nepheline and arfvedsonite. Late eudialyte is earlier than aegirine II, which corrodes it and fills cracks in it.

In the course of supergene alteration eudialyte is replaced by zirfesite and manganese hydroxides. Its large aggregations in the central zones of the pegmatites are usually greatly altered and leached.

Ramsayite is found in large quantities in the intermediate and central zones. It is not so plentiful in the outer zone, where it is localized as crystals of no more than 3-4 mm in length in the roofs of the pegmatitic bodies.

Its phenocrysts in the intermediate and central zones are thick tabular crystals of up to $4 \times 3 \times 2$ cm. In the pegmatitic bodies bedded below the main body (First Eastern stream, Karnasurt) the ramsayite content increases and reaches 30 per cent in the third and fifth pegmatitic bodies, for example. Here the ramsayite is confined to the central zones, where it forms large irregular aggregations of up to $13 \times 10 \times 7$ cm. The colour is dark brown with a vitreous lustre on cleavage planes.

The main mass of ramsayite is later than microcline; it contains crystals of microcline and replaces it (Fig. 47). On the other hand inclusions of ramsayite are sometimes found along the margins of microcline crystals. It is normally idiomorphic towards late eudialyte (Fig. 48). Ramsayite is sometimes replaced by

FIG. 47. Relationship of ramsayite (R), microcline (M) and eudialyte (black). × 46. Crossed nicols

FIG. 48. Idiomorphism of ramsayite (R) to eudialyte (E); N—fine-grained groundmass of natrolite; A—arfvedsonite; M—microcline. × 20. Crossed nicols

murmanite, as can be seen from the presence of ramsayite relicts in murmanite. Ramsayite is also replaced by neptunite and vinogradovite, which form along fissures in the peripheral parts of its crystals. Ramsayite is usually highly-fissured and may in places be entirely converted to a friable aggregate.

Lamprophyllite is found in small quantities, primarily in the leucocratic zones (outer and central). In the outer zone it forms small 'suns' (up to 1 cm in diameter) in the fine-grained margins. In the central zones it occurs as elongated

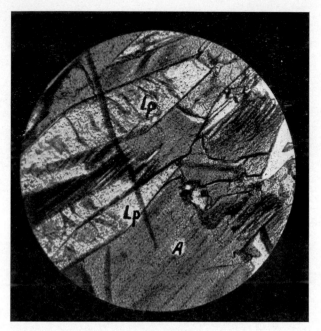

FIG. 49. Lamprophyllite inclusions (Lp) in arfvedsonite (A). ×10. Crossed nicols

tabular crystals up to 1·5 cm in length or radiate-fibrous golden-brown aggregates up to 3 cm in diameter.

Lamprophyllite is one of the earliest minerals. It occurs as idiomorphic inclusions in nepheline, microcline, arfvedsonite (Fig. 49) and in large segregations of late eudialyte. Large segregations of lamprophyllite are usually greatly altered and replaced by anatase.

Murmanite is one of the main minerals in the intermediate zone, where its content reaches 10 per cent. It forms brownish-pink tabular crystals of up to 1·5 × 1·5 × 0·2 cm in the fine-grained groundmass and up to 8 × 5 × 1 cm amongst the phenocrysts. Murmanite is normally intimately associated with aegirine II, greatly altered and corroded by late aegirine, in which remnants of it can be found.

Murmanite is a late mineral of the pegmatitic horizon. It normally grows over arfvedsonite and eudialyte crystals or contains them as regular inclusions. We have already mentioned that ramsayite is sometimes replaced by murmanite.

FIG. 50. Elpidite (light, radiate-fibrous) in the central zone of pegmatite. × 10. Crossed nicols

FIG. 51. Quartz (Qu) in fine-grained albite. × 90. Crossed nicols

Murmanite is normally greatly altered and in places may be totally converted to a brown friable mass.

Neptunite forms irregular segregations and crystals with a cross-section of up to 1 cm that are partly zonal, varying in colour from dark-red to black. Neptunite is found only in the central zone among late aegirine, albite and natrolite, where it often forms columnar microcrystals (from microscopic dimensions up to 1·5 mm long) in leaching cavities in microcline and aegirine II, heals fissures in microcline and also develops during the replacement of ramsayite. Neptunite is one of the latest minerals, as is shown by its close association with aegirine III and replacement minerals.

Aenigmatite is found in the melanocratic zones of the pegmatitic bodies to the east of the Second Eastern stream on Karnasurt. It forms irregular black segregations in the interstices between crystals of microcline and high-temperature rare-metal minerals.

Natrolite is of common occurrence in the intermediate and central zones. In the intermediate zones it forms from nepheline. The natrolitization of nepheline is highly developed. In this case natrolite forms aggregates similar to chalcedony or small druses of idiomorphic crystals up to 0·5 cm in length on the walls of cavities developed by leaching of the nepheline. In the central zones natrolite occurs as white radiate-fibrous segregations or matrix that replaces early leucocratic minerals. It sometimes cements fragments of broken arfvedsonite crystals or forms pseudomorphs after nepheline; the central parts of natrolite pseudomorphs are bluish and the margins are dark. Natrolite also forms lenticular segregations in combination with aegirine III and albite in the axial sectors of the central zones.

Albite is quite plentiful in the pegmatitic horizon described. This horizon differs from the other pegmatites of the massif in that replacement albite is present in addition to the late albite that is typical of pegmatites showing complex replacements. This albite consists of irregular segregations containing polysynthetic twins, normally orientated in one plane, and developing on microcline, which it replaces from the periphery and along cleavage fissures. Late albite forms a fine-grained mass of elongated lath-like pink crystals, sometimes mixed with aegirine III and natrolite in the axial parts of the central zones, where replacement processes are greatly developed.

Elpidite has been discovered in the central zone of the pegmatitic body on Alluaiv as radial clusters of whitish crystals (Fig. 50) with an area of 8×8 cm. The individual crystals do not exceed $1·3 \times 0·2 \times 0·2$ cm. Elpidite is intimately associated with light pink and, less frequently, with dark pink albite, late aegirine, greatly altered murmanite and eudialyte. It may owe its origin to the decomposition of eudialyte in the replacement stage.

Eudidymite occurs among dark pink albite in the central zone of one of the pegmatitic bodies on Alluaiv. It forms clusters of small whitish crystals of up to 5×5 cm. It is normally associated with albite, nontronite, murmanite, elpidite and aegirine III. It is apparently earlier than albite, since its segregations are always included in albite and are cemented by it.

Apatite occurs only in conjunction with quartz, elpidite and eudidymite in thin sections of the pink albite of the central zones. It forms fine-grained clusters of up to $0.1 \times 0.1 \times 0.3$ mm. The textural relations of apatite indicate that it is one of the late-crystallizing minerals of the pegmatites.

There is a small amount of *manganostaffelite* [manganese-bearing francolite] in the central part of the pegmatitic bodies of the First Eastern stream of Karnasurt. It forms radiate-fibrous rosettes of fine prismatic crystals up to 0.5 cm in length and 1 mm in cross-section and dark red in colour. It is normally confined to zeolitized parts and largely to leaching cavities.

Analcite is present in small amounts in the central zone of the pegmatitic body on Alluaiv, where it forms regularly-bounded white segregations of radiate-fibrous structure with a cross-section of up to 0.5 cm. It normally occurs with natrolite in leaching cavities.

Psilomelane occurs extremely rarely in the central zones in association with replacement minerals. It forms black concretions up to 2 cm in cross-section. Microcrystals of neptunite are often found inside these concretions.

Quartz is found only in thin sections as irregular elongated or rounded grains intimately associated with late light-pink albite (Fig. 51). Its textural relations make it one of the latest pegmatite minerals crystallizing later than albite.

Chalcedony forms clusters of small spherulites (up to 1 mm in diameter) and irregular segregations (up to 5×5 cm in area), greyish-green in colour, in the central zones of the pegmatitic bodies. Under the microscope the structure of the chalcedony is found to be radiate-fibrous with a thin external crust of quartzine.

Nontronite forms as crusts, powdery coatings and irregular aggregations with a cross-section of up to 1 cm produced by the decomposition of aegirine and arfvedsonite; in albitic sectors it forms pseudomorphs after arfvedsonite. Its lustre is extremely greasy and the colour pistachio-green.

In addition to the minerals described above, considerable amounts of loparite, ilmenite, sodalite, thomsonite, hydrargillite and other minerals also occur in the pegmatitic horizon.

6. The Pegmatitic Body of the Tyul'bn'yunuai Valley
('Bear's Den')

This pegmatitic body lies on the left flank of the Tyul'bn'yunuai Valley approximately 1 km from the river mouth and 70 m above the watercourse. It lies in the upper foyaite horizon of the differentiated complex beneath the porphyritic lujavrites and can be clearly seen from a distance owing to the presence of a large cave. The pegmatitic body has been described in detail by Yu. S. Slepnev whose findings have been taken into consideration in this book.

The pegmatitic body extends north-south (26 m long, concealed thickness 3-10 m), the strike being almost meridional (azimuth 5°). Three apophyses up to 11 m long and from 0.25 to 0.6 m thick extend from it to the north, south-west and south-east (Fig. 52). On the west side the contact of the pegmatite with the country rocks can be traced throughout its extent. On the east it is buried under drift and can be traced only in the southern sector where the pegmatitic body is 10 m thick.

Genetically this pegmatitic body is probably of the facies-phase type. The main mass of the pegmatite was apparently crystallized where the pegmatitic melt accumulated, as can be seen from the irregular contours of the body and its

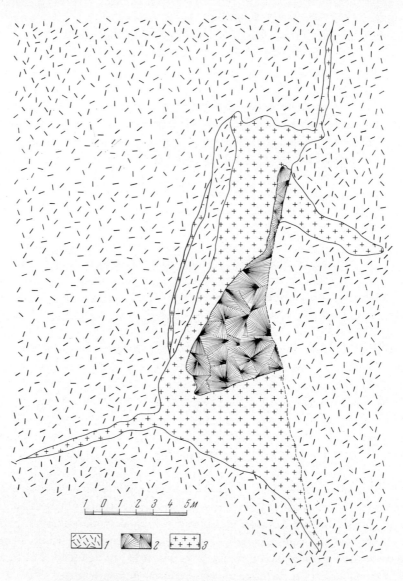

FIG. 52. Diagram of the 'Bear's Den' ('Medvezh'ya berloga') pegmatitic body (after Slepnev)

1. foyaite; 2. small block microcline-aegirine zone; 3. fine-grained zone

gradual transitions into the country rock. The gradual dying-out of pegmatitic conditions of crystallization from the centre to the periphery is clearly revealed by the decline in the amount of eudialyte, ramsayite and other rare-metal minerals and also by the size of the mineral grains. The existence of pegmatite apophyses in the country rocks shows that tectonic movements during the formation of the pegmatitic body led to the development of fissures in the country rock that were filled by the pegmatitic melt.

The composition of the foyaites near the contact is variable owing to fluctuations in the aegirine and eudialyte ratios. At the contact the foyaites are normally greatly enriched with these minerals. They also contain a great many small schlieren-like pegmatitic segregations made up of feldspar, eudialyte and aegirine and differing from the country rocks, into which they pass by gradual transitions, in having a coarser-grained texture. Small schlieren-like pegmatitic bodies are also found at a distance from the main body, as if framing it. It follows that the pegmatitic process developed in the country rock and reached its maximum where the pegmatitic body is emplaced.

Zonal structure is a typical feature of the pegmatitic body. The outer inequigranular zone accounts for approximately two-thirds of the total area. It consists of eudialyte, microcline, nepheline, aegirine, arfvedsonite and ramsayite. The fine-grained groundmass of these minerals contains areas of medium- and coarse-grained texture in which eudialyte crystals reach 3-5 cm in cross-section and microcline crystals are as much as 5-8 cm long. Coarseness of grain is also typical of the small schlieren-like formations and apophyses. The mineralogical composition of the zone is not constant. In the neighbourhood of the contact the pegmatite contains less eudialyte, for example, than in the central parts. The eudialyte content increases to 70 per cent 1-2 m inside the contact and reaches 80-90 per cent near the central zone.

The central macrocrystalline (block) zone is revealed in the eastern part of the pegmatitic body and can be traced for 15·5 m. Its contact with the outer zone is distinct. The eastern boundary is buried under foyaite scree throughout almost all its extent. The exposed part of the block zone is irregular in shape and varies in thickness from 1 m in the northern part (see Fig. 52) to 7 m in the southern.

The mineralogy of the block zone is more complex than that of the outer zone. It consists in the main of aegirine II, microcline, beliankinite, arfvedsonite, eudialyte, natrolite and ramsayite. There are small amounts of neptunite, albite, schizolite and yellow murmanite. The block structure is due to the arrangement of large microcline crystals in a fine-fibrous mass of aegirine II (Fig. 53). Almost all the remaining minerals, except albite and natrolite, are included in the aegirine II.

The mineralogical composition of the zone is typically variable. One can distinguish regions enriched in microcline, aegirine II, eudialyte and belyankinite. Thus, the north-eastern part is largely composed of microcline (as much as 80 per cent). In addition to the microcline there is aegirine II (15 per cent), eudialyte (5 per cent) and ramsayite (1-2 per cent). Further to the south-west the amount of microcline decreases (to 20 per cent) and there is an increase in the content of aegirine II (to 60-70 per cent) and eudialyte (to 8-10 per cent) while belyankinite (1-2 per cent) appears. In the central area the belyankinite content increases to 8-10 per cent.

The main minerals of the pegmatitic body are microcline, aegirine II and eudialyte. The accessory minerals include belyankinite, ramsayite, murmanite, arfvedsonite and lamprophyllite.

Microcline is present in the outer and central zones. In the outer zone, where its average content is 5-10 per cent, it occurs as small crystals up to 1 cm long. In

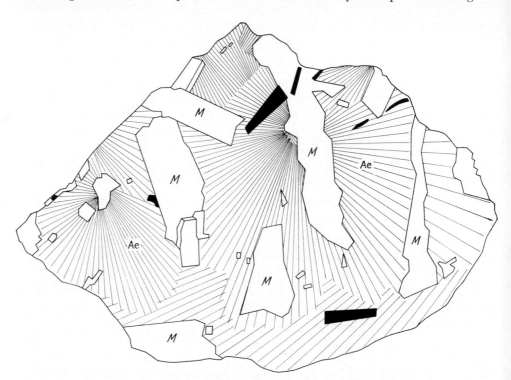

Fig. 53. Microcline blocks (M) in aegirine II (Ae); black—aegirine I. $\frac{1}{5}$ natural size

the block zone the amount of microcline reaches 70-80 per cent in the peripheral part and 20-30 per cent in the central part. It here forms large light-grey crystals measuring up to $50 \times 30 \times 15$ cm containing idiomorphic crystalline inclusions of aegirine I. It is sometimes xenomorphic with respect to eudialyte and less frequently to belyankinite. The interstices between its crystals are filled with aegirine II in the central zone and with small eudialyte segregations in the outer zone. Microcline is replaced by albite and natrolite in the pneumatolytic-hydrothermal and hydrothermal stages.

Nepheline is rare. It forms greenish-grey aggregates of up to 4 cm in cross-section. In the central zone it is associated with microcline and aegirine II, to which it is idiomorphic. In the outer zone it is included in eudialyte and ramsayite. Nepheline is replaced by natrolite from the periphery.

There are two generations of *aegirine*. Aegirine I forms regular prismatic black crystals fractions of a millimetre to 5 cm long. In some parts of the outer zone, at the contact with the foyaites, the aegirine I content is as much as 53-80 per cent. Aegirine I crystallized very early. Small crystals are often present as inclusions in nepheline and microcline. Large crystals are also idiomorphic to nepheline, eudialyte and microcline.

Aegirine II accounts for the main mass of the central zone (50-60 per cent) where it forms felted radiate-fibrous clusters as much as 30 cm in diameter, green

FIG. 54. Altered belyankinite (B) in aegirine II (Ae)

to dark-green in colour. It normally fills the interstices between nepheline, microcline, beliankinite and eudialyte crystals.

Eudialyte is found in both zones of the pegmatitic body. Its content reaches 50-70 per cent in places in the outer zone, whereas in the central zone it does not exceed 10 per cent. In the outer zone eudialyte forms compact granular aggregates (a few centimetres across) or small hexagonal crystals (up to 1 cm). The latter are normally confined to the interstices between microcline and nepheline. In the central zone the cross-section of eudialyte crystals may be as much as 5 cm.

The eudialyte is light-brown, more rarely brown and reddish-brown in the peripheral sectors. It is normally xenomorphic to microcline, but well-formed eudialyte crystals occur as inclusions in the marginal parts of microcline. Eudialyte is always idiomorphic to aegirine II, ramsayite and arfvedsonite.

Zirfesite and catapleite form pseudomorphs after eudialyte.

Belyankinite is a typical mineral of the central zone, where it may reach 10 per cent in some parts. It forms tabular segregations of up to $10 \times 8 \times 1$ cm and more, rarely as much as $25 \times 15 \times 1.5$ cm. The creamy-white colour is reminiscent of ivory. It is highly contaminated with black and brown films and is sometimes greatly fissured, altered and shattered (Fig. 54).

Belyankinite occurs typically in intimate association with aegirine II, than which it is earlier. The belyankinite crystals are sometimes partly included in microcline. The frequent occurrence of murmanite relics in belyankinite indicates that it was formed as a replacement of murmanite.

Arfvedsonite occurs in both zones and is more plentiful in fine-grained areas. In the outer zones it occurs as isolated small crystals or groups of crystals of up to $5 \times 0.5 \times 0.3$ cm. In the central zone it forms radiate-fibrous bundles, 2-3 cm in diameter. It is usually xenomorphic to eudialyte. The interstices between its crystals are filled with aegirine II.

Ramsayite occurs mainly in the marginal zone at the contacts with the central zone and less frequently in the central zone. It forms irregular dark-brown segregations up to $3 \times 2 \times 1.5$ cm. In the fine-grained zone it is sometimes idiomorphic to eudialyte, but is more commonly confined to the interstices between microcline and eudialyte crystals. Its crystals are found as inclusions in marginal parts of microcline crystals in the central zone.

Lamprophyllite has been discovered in one fine-grained pegmatite apophysis. It occurs as small crystals (up to 3×0.5 mm in cross-section) in the interstices between nepheline and microcline. It is idiomorphic to aegirine II.

Yellow *murmanite* is found in the fine-grained zone at the contact with the foyaites. Its crystals (up to $1 \times 0.8 \times 0.3$ cm and frequently smaller) are intimately associated with aegirine II.

Schizolite is found in the central zone, where it forms elongated or equant black segregations of up to 3×0.3 cm in aegirine II.

Albite is represented by fine-grained lath-like aggregates filling the interstices between microcline and nepheline crystals and replacing microcline. Albite is replaced in its turn by fine-grained natrolite.

Neptunite is found in small amounts in the central zones. It forms irregular segregations, 1-2 mm long, infilling small cavities in microcline. The colour is dark red. The mineral is leached near the surface.

Natrolite is found in both zones as prismatic crystals (1-2 mm across) in leaching cavities in aegirine II, microcline and beliankinite. It is sometimes formed during the replacement of nepheline and microcline.

7. The Pegmatitic Vein of the Southern Slope of Kuftn'yun

The pegmatitic vein on the southern slope of Kuftn'yun has been studied by E. I. Semenov and is here described from his data.

The vein has been traced along the strike for approximately 200 m. Its thickness varies from 1-4 m. It is thickest (4 m) in the centre of the vein where there is

a 70 m bulge. The vein is almost vertically disposed in foyaites and is of north-
easterly strike, the dip being 80-90° in the direction 315°.

The containing foyaites have a slightly trachytoid structure and are murmanite-
enriched in some places. From their stratigraphic setting they belong to the upper
group of the differentiated complex and are the country rocks for the malignite
horizon. The trachytoid structure and jointing in the foyaites dips uniformly to
the north at an angle of 7-10°.

The contact between the pegmatitic vein and the foyaites is sharp. There is
considerable development of natrolite, nontronite, montmorillonite and limonite,

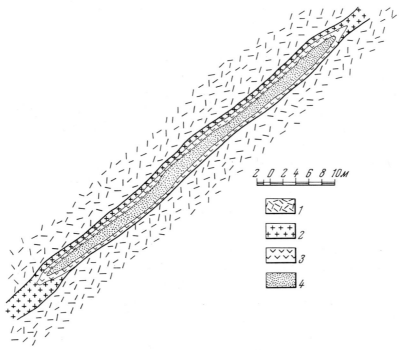

FIG. 55. Sketch of the albitic pegmatite bulge on the southern slope of
Kuftn'yun (after Semenov)

1. foyaite; 2. outer melanocratic zone; 3. intermediate aegirine-feldspathic zone;
4. central albitic zone

in the foyaites at the contact with the pegmatite. The foyaites near the contact
also contain veinlets of macrocrystalline eudialyte up to 20 cm long, separated
from the main pegmatitic body by a 5-10 cm foyaite layer and orientated parallel
to the contact. The structure of the pegmatitic vein in its central, thickest sector
is zonal, three zones being distinguished between the periphery and the centre:
(1) outer melanocratic zone, (2) intermediate aegirine-feldspar zone and (3) central
albitic zone (Fig. 55).

The outer zone can be traced only in the north western (hanging) wall of the
bulge, where it is no more than 10-20 cm thick. This zone is fine-grained in
texture and consists mainly of aegirine I, arfvedsonite, nepheline and microcline
with a small quantity of eudialyte and ramsayite.

The aegirine-feldspathic zone, which is up to 1 m thick, is composed in the main of microcline (up to 50 per cent) eudialyte (up to 20 per cent) arfvedsonite (up to 10 per cent) and aegirine II (up to 20 per cent). There are also considerable amounts of ramsayite and nepheline. The texture of the zone is massive and macrocrystalline. The amount of aegirine II increases towards the centre and an additional zone up to 15 cm thick consisting of practically monomineralic aegirine II can sometimes be traced between the aegirine-feldspathic and albitic zones.

The 0·6-1 m thick albitic zone is composed mainly (80 per cent) of drusy albite with a subordinate amount of analcite and montmorillonite. The main mass of the low-temperature rare-metal minerals from the epididymite and elpidite group is confined to this zone.

Outside the bulge the zoning of the vein is not clearly defined. In these regions it is composed mainly of fine-grained melanocratic rock consisting of aegirine I, arfvedsonite, nepheline and microcline, similar to the rock of the outer zone of the bulge. Microcline enrichment makes the composition of the 15-20 cm contact zone more leucocratic. The microcline crystals in these leucocratic zones are larger and are usually arranged at an angle of 60-90° to the contact. Small quantities of ramsayite and eudialyte grains with a cross-section of up to 1 cm occur in these zones. A porphyritic texture is conferred upon the leucocratic zones by the presence of fine-grained melanocratic rock that accounts for the main mass of these parts of the pegmatitic body in the interstices between the microcline crystals and other minerals. Considerable enrichment with the accessory ferruginous minerals nontronite and limonite is typical of fine-grained melanocratic zones.

The main minerals of the pegmatitic vein are microcline, nepheline, albite, aegirine, arfvedsonite and eudialyte. Other minerals that are found include ramsayite, murmanite, loparite, elpidite, staffelite [francolite], manganostaffelite, hydrargillite, hydrogoethite, cryptomelane, pyrolusite, minerals of the epididymite group, natrolite, chabazite, analcite, montmorillonite, kaolinite, nontronite and chalcedony.

Microcline is a main mineral of the outer and intermediate zones. It forms greyish-white prismatic crystals of up to $20 \times 8 \times 3$ cm. It is an early-crystallized mineral containing inclusions of aegirine I, arfvedsonite and nepheline only, but is sometimes xenomorphic to eudialyte and ramsayite.

Nepheline occurs in the melanocratic and aegirine-feldspathic zones as grains of up to 0·5 cm in cross-section idiomorphic to microcline and containing inclusions of aegirine I. It is normally greatly altered and replaced by secondary minerals. Chalcedonic natrolite and spreustein pseudomorph it in the aegirine-feldspathic zone and pink montmorillonite and kaolinite in the melanocratic zone.

Aegirine is represented by two generations. Aegirine I, the main mineral of the melanocratic zone, forms black acicular or prismatic crystals up to 2 cm in length. Crystals 30 cm long occur occasionally. Aegirine I is the earliest mineral to separate, and idiomorphic crystals of it occur as inclusions in nepheline, microcline and eudialyte.

Aegirine II is primarily concentrated in the aegirine-feldspathic zone, especially at its contacts with the albitic zone. It forms large dark-green spherulites (up to 15 cm in diameter) and fine-acicular dense aggregates, that are sometimes bluish, in the interstices between microcline and the high-temperature rare-metal minerals eudialyte, ramsayite and murmanite. The needles of aegirine II are often cemented with a black opaque mass of manganese hydroxides.

Arfvedsonite is quite widely distributed in the melanocratic and aegirine-feldspathic zones, where it forms black prismatic crystals of up to $5 \times 1 \times 1$ cm. It is one of the earliest minerals to separate, idiomorphic crystals being found as inclusions in microcline and nepheline.

Large amounts of *eudialyte* are found in all the zones of the pegmatitic vein. It forms reddish-brown equant segregations with a cross-section of from 0·5 cm in the marginal zones to 10 cm in the central zone. It is located in the interstices between microcline crystals but is sometimes idiomorphic to microcline. Large eudialyte segregations in the central part of the vein are usually entirely replaced by a yellowish-brown aggregate consisting of fine-acicular catapleite crystals, green nontronite grains and acicular elpidite crystals.

Ramsayite forms irregular brown segregations with a cross-section of up to 1·5 cm in the aegirine-feldspathic zone. It is located in the interstices between microcline crystals and is included in aegirine II. Sometimes there is a white leucoxene margin up to 2 mm thick round ramsayite segregations.

Murmanite occurs in the aegirine-feldspathic and albitic zones, where it forms tabular segregations of up to $5 \times 3 \times 1$ cm. It is greatly altered in the central zone, where it is converted to a soft white mass.

Albite is the main mineral of the central zones. Fine-grained albite forms pink and brownish-pink hollow segregations of up to $40 \times 30 \times 39$ cm enclosing druses lined with albite crystals. Elpidite, cryptomelane, analcite, chabazite and other minerals are found in association with albite.

Analcite is fairly widely distributed in the central zone, where it occurs as white granular aggregates of up to $7 \times 5 \times 5$ cm, and less frequently as poorly-defined crystals. It is converted to a white powdery mineral near the surface.

Chabazite forms white crusts up to 0·4 cm thick on catapleite pseudomorphs after eudialyte. The form of chabazite crystals of up to 3 mm in cross-section is typically rhombohedral.

Natrolite occurs in small quantities in all the zones. In the melanocratic and aegirine-feldspathic zones it forms pseudomorphs after nepheline. In the central zone it is found as a fine-grained aggregate mixed with analcite and other zeolites.

Labuntsovite occurs extremely rarely in the central zone as small pink prismatic crystals up to $1 \times 0.3 \times 0.2$ cm in miarolitic cavities in intimate association with albite, natrolite and altered murmanite.

Elpidite occurs rarely in the central zone in the cavities of albitic segregations. It forms prismatic crystals up to 0·5 cm long and coarse-acicular spherulites up to 3 cm in diameter and white to light-brown in colour. It also occurs among the alteration products of eudialyte.

Manganostaffelite has been found as lilac-coloured tabular inclusions and spherulites in brownish-pink albite in the central zone. It is sometimes altered near the surface. In addition to manganostaffelite greyish-white cryptocrystalline segregations of strontium-staffelite with a cross-section of up to 1 cm are found in the pegmatitic vein.

Hydrogoethite forms reddish-brown dense concretions and encrustations of up to $8 \times 4 \times 2$ cm in the central zone (near the aegirine-feldspathic zone). Surficially the concretions are covered with an orange crust and sometimes with a black film (goethite?). Hydrogoethite may possibly be formed in the alteration of aegirine. The colloform encrusting structure of the hydrogoethite is apparent in thin sections.

Cryptomelane occurs in the central zone as large greyish-black segregations (up to $5 \times 3 \times 1$ cm) with a submetallic lustre. It is intimately associated with albite and hydrogoethite. It may possibly have been formed in the alteration of schizolite, since cavities formed by the leaching of a prismatic mineral of a form similar to schizolite have been found in albite. Black films of pyrolusite sometimes found on the surface of cryptomelane segregations were probably formed during its oxidation and dehydration.

The minerals of the epididymite group occur in the albitic zone as irregular whitish segregations with a cross-section of up to 15×10 cm. Fine leaves are colourless and reveal a clearly-defined micaceous cleavage. Pseudo-hexagonal crystals of these minerals (up to $3 \times 3 \times 1$ cm) are sometimes found.

In addition to the minerals here described, this pegmatitic vein contains trace amounts of loparite, hydrargillite, neptunite, montmorillonite, kaolinite, nontronite and other minerals.

Differentiation is clearly revealed in the vein by the spatial separation of the minerals; the high-temperature minerals (nepheline, microcline, aegirine, arfvedsonite, ramsayite and eudialyte) are located in its outer zone and the low-temperature minerals (albite, analcite, epididymite and elpidite) in the central zone.

8. The Pegmatitic Vein on the Northern Slope of Kitkn'yun

This pegmatitic vein lies in the valley of the uppermost left tributary of the Kitkuai, 0·5 km from its mouth. The vein has been studied in detail by E. B. Khalezova and E. I. Semenov and is here described from their findings.

Mesocratic aegirine-lujavrites containing a conformably-bedded pegmatitic sheet vein (up to 2·5 m thick) composed of microcline, nepheline and aegirine, are exposed on the steep left flank of the valley. The solid outcrop of the vein is continuously exposed for 20 m. Isolated large outcrops of pegmatite interspersed with disintegrated blocks occur for 100 m downstream below the main exposure. The erosion has apparently exposed the dip slope of the vein and it is revealed over a large area. A series of stringers up to 20 cm thick run from the pegmatitic vein into the country rocks.

There are several lujavrite xenoliths of lenticular form (up to $1·5 \times 0·2$ m) in the hanging wall of the vein. The direction of the trachytoid structure in these xenoliths coincides with that of the original lujavrites. There is a sharp boundary between the pegmatite and the lujavrite. Zones of arfvedsonite enrichment and eudialytic veinlets occur in the lujavrites adjacent to the hanging wall of the pegmatitic vein and run parallel to the contact. The underlying lujavrites are aegirine-enriched.

The scree contains large pegmatite blocks in which the pegmatite is intersected by lamprophyre veins up to 15 cm thick.

The sharp contacts between the vein and the enclosing lujavrites, and the existence of lujavrite xenoliths in it and of pegmatite apophyses in the country rocks indicate that this is an injected vein.

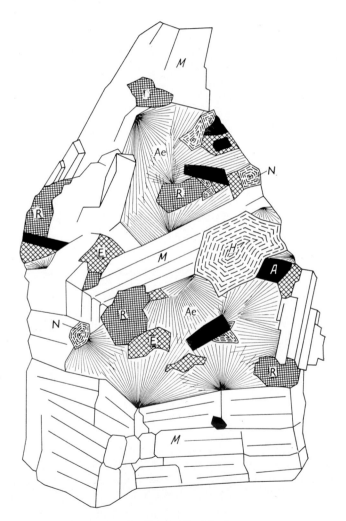

FIG. 56. Pegmatite block zone

M—microcline; N—nepheline; R—ramsayite; E—eudialyte; A—arfvedsonite; Ae—aegirine II. $\frac{1}{3}$ natural size

Three zones can be distinguished in the vein between the margins and the centre: (1) a fine-grained microcline-eudialytic contact zone, (2) an intermediate (block) microcline-nepheline-aegirine zone and (3) a central albitic zone. Transitions between the zones are gradual.

The 10-15 cm contact zone is composed of microcline with eudialyte in the interstices between its crystals. The intermediate zone is largely composed of large crystals of microcline (up to 55 per cent) and nepheline (10 per cent). The interstices between them are filled with a finer-grained melanocratic mass consisting of eudialyte, ramsayite and lamprophyllite, apparently cemented by acicular green aegirine II (Fig. 56). In addition, the melanocratic mass contains large black prismatic crystals of arfvedsonite and aenigmatite. The central zone is developed only in certain parts of the pegmatitic vein. It is represented by small lenses of up to 20×10 cm, four-fifths composed of pink fine-grained albite.

The main minerals of the vein are microcline (55 per cent), nepheline (10 per cent), aegirine I (5 per cent), aegirine II (15 per cent), eudialyte (7 per cent), ramsayite (3 per cent) and lamprophyllite (2 per cent). There are also small quantities of arfvedsonite, aenigmatite, murmanite, neptunite, schizolite, ilmenite, manganchlorite, epididymite, natrolite, montmorillonite, albite, sodalite, analcite, hydrargillite, boehmite, psilomelane and other minerals.

Microcline forms large white and grey prismatic crystals of up to $5 \times 2 \times 2$ cm in the contact zone and up to $40 \times 15 \times 10$ cm in the intermediate zone, gradually decreasing in size from the centre to the periphery. The microcline crystals are orientated at an angle of 45-90° to the contact. Microcline is a mineral that separated early. It contains inclusions of aegirine I and nepheline, and grains of eudialyte that were evidently captured in the late stages of crystallization are present in the marginal parts of the crystals. Along cleavage cracks microcline is extensively replaced by albite, which forms veinlets up to 5 mm thick in it. Elatolitic cavities are sometimes found in microcline.

Nepheline is represented by large hexagonal prismatic crystals (up to $30 \times 10 \times 10$ cm) in the intermediate zone and by small crystals (up to $3 \times 2 \times 2$ cm) in the contact zone. The colour is greenish-grey. This is one of the earliest minerals in the vein. Its crystals are normally included in microcline and aegirine II and it is very occasionally adapted to the forms of microcline segregations. Inclusions of black prismatic crystals of aegirine I are found in nepheline.

In the central part of the vein, near the albitic zone, the nepheline is greatly altered and is often totally replaced by secondary minerals. The cores of crystals are usually replaced by spreustein; there is a white or grey fringe (up to 1 cm thick) of chalcedonic natrolite round the margins. This is also sometimes found in the central parts of pseudomorphs. Colourless tabular crystals of hydrargillite and white montmorillonite segregations that are also alteration products of nepheline are found in the leaching cavities of spreusteinized nepheline crystals.

Aegirine is represented by two generations. Aegirine I is found mainly in the contact zone as black prismatic crystals of up to $0.5 \times 0.5 \times 5$ cm. Nearer the central part of the vein it forms radiate-fibrous aggregates 5-7 cm in diameter.

Aegirine I was the earliest mineral to be precipitated. Its crystals occur as idio-morphic inclusions in nepheline, microcline and other minerals. The interstices between large prismatic crystals of aegirine I are filled with eudialyte and ram-sayite. Aegirine II occurs only in the intermediate zone, as a fine-acicular aggregate filling the interstices between other minerals. Radiate-fibrous segrega-tions of aegirine II up to 7 cm in diameter are sometimes formed round small crystals.

Arfvedsonite occurs only near the central zone, where it forms large black prismatic crystals of up to $1 \times 1 \times 7$ cm. Large curved and shattered crystals of arfvedsonite, the fissures of which have been healed by albite, are found in the rose albite of the central zone.

Eudialyte is found in all zones of the pegmatitic vein. It forms reddish-brown segregations with a cross-section of up to 4 cm. The crystallographic habit of the grains in the central sector of the vein is poorly defined; in the contact zone it fills the interstices between aegirine I, nepheline and microcline. Idiomorphic crystals of nepheline occur as inclusions in eudialyte. One sometimes finds grains of eudialyte with their margins embedded in microcline. Eudialyte is idiomorphic to ramsayite. Its grains are sometimes the centres round which radiate-fibrous segregations of aegirine II form. Eudialyte is commonly replaced by zirfesite and catapleite.

Catapleite is found as irregular segregations forming a fine scaly grey-brown and light-brown aggregate.

Ramsayite forms brown tabular crystals of up to $4 \times 3 \times 2$ cm included in aegirine II in the intermediate zone. It is xenomorphic to eudialyte. Near the central zone its replacement by leucoxene can be observed.

Lamprophyllite is found in the intermediate zone, where it forms golden-brown fine platy crystals of up to $2 \times 0 \cdot 2 \times 0 \cdot 2$ cm and radiate-fibrous aggregations ('suns') up to 2 cm in diameter. It is one of the earliest minerals in the vein. Its crystals are often included in ramsayite, eudialyte and the peripheral parts of microcline and nepheline crystals. During the alteration of lamprophyllite it is converted into a fine scaly yellow aggregate of leucoxene.

Aenigmatite forms black prismatic crystals (up to $8 \times 2 \times 2$ cm) in the inter-mediate zone. A margin of fine-acicular aegirine and lamprophyllite ('coronite') up to 2 mm thick can sometimes be seen round its crystals. The fact that idio-morphic crystals of eudialyte occur as inclusions in aenigmatite indicates that the aenigmatite separated later than the eudialyte.

Murmanite is found occasionally in the intermediate zone as white and brown tabular segregations of up to $4 \times 3 \times 1$ cm entirely altered and replaced by leucoxene. It separated later than eudialyte, which occurs as inclusions in it.

Neptunite is fairly widely distributed in this vein. It forms irregular orange-red segregations with a cross-section of up to $0 \cdot 5$ cm in leaching cavities and isolated crystals in pink albite. Neptunite is often associated with ramsayite and murmanite, of which it is possibly an alteration product.

Schizolite occurs in pink albite as prismatic crystals of up to $5 \times 1 \times 1$ cm. It is greatly altered and often entirely converted to black manganese oxides, which are sometimes leached.

Ilmenite is occasionally found in association with eudialyte and microcline in the contact zone. It forms tabular crystals of up to $3 \times 3 \times 0.2$ cm that are idiomorphic to eudialyte and microcline or included in these minerals. Ilmenite is sometimes replaced by fibrous astrophyllite.

Epididymite is found as a white fine-grained mass, forming irregular segregations of up to $2 \times 1 \times 1$ cm in cavities in the pink albite of the central zone.

Natrolite is of very limited distribution in this vein. It is the principal component of the spreustein that forms pseudomorphs after nepheline. Greyish chalcedonic natrolite is developed along the edges of the crystals in the pseudomorphs and brownish fine scaly natrolite in the centre.

Albite accounts for four-fifths of the central albitic zone, where it forms large pink monomineralic segregations (up to $20 \times 10 \times 10$ cm) intimately associated with schizolite, analcite and neptunite.

Sodalite is observed only in thin sections as irregular or elongated segregations up to 1 cm long in a fine-acicular mass of aegirine II.

Analcite is present in pink albite as rounded light-yellow grains of up to $3 \times 2 \times 2$ cm.

Hydrargillite is found as colourless tabular crystals (up to $2 \times 2 \times 0.3$ cm) in the central part of spreusteinized nepheline crystals.

Psilomelane forms black encrusting segregations (up to $1 \times 0.5 \times 0.5$ cm) in the cracks in microcline crystals, in intimate association with albite.

9. THE EUCOLITE-RAMSAYITE PEGMATITIC VEIN OF FLORA

This vein was discovered and studied in 1948 by L. S. Borodin and is here described from his findings. It is situated on the northern slope of the mountain, where it forms four outcrops at the contact between the foyaites and the underlying lujavrites. The identical structure and mineralogical composition of all four outcrops leads us to assume that they are parts of one irregular pegmatitic body. The largest outcrop, which is bedded in trachytoid foyaites, is up to 10 m thick and extends east-west for 50 m. Small outcrops of lenticular habit in profile up to 12 m long and 5 m wide occur in the overlying lujavrites. There is a foyaitic xenolith of up to 10×2 m dimensions and with sharp contacts in the largest outcrop. The contact between the pegmatites and the foyaites is distinct; the foyaites are finer-grained in a 50-60 cm thick zone at the southern contact, where they have lost their trachytoid structure and are highly albitized and enriched with eudialyte and ramsayite.

The phase nature of the body is indicated by its sharp contact with the country rocks and by the presence of foyaitic xenoliths and alterations round the veins.

The porphyritic texture of this pegmatitic body is due to the presence of macrocrystalline areas, eucolite schlieren and large nepheline phenocrysts. The distribution of the minerals is very uneven in the finer-grained groundmass that consists of aegirine, nepheline, microcline, ramsayite and eudialyte. In some regions the eudialyte or nepheline content is 80-90 per cent, whereas in others it is considerably less. In addition to these minerals the groundmass contains small amounts of murmanite and arfvedsonite. Where the groundmass is eudialyte-enriched it becomes reddish in colour.

The albitized areas at the southern contact seem to form an albitization zone

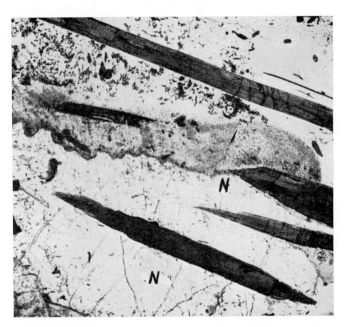

Fig. 57. Arfvedsonite inclusions (dark, columnar) in nepheline (N). × 10. Without analyser

approximately 1 m thick. These areas are composed chiefly of fine albite laths with a lesser amount of aegirine III filling the interstices between them.

The eucolite schlieren are four-fifths eucolite with isolated segregations of microcline (up to 10 per cent) and arfvedsonite (up to 10 per cent) between the large crystals of eucolite. Small quantities of lamprophyllite, nepheline and murmanite are also found in the schlieren.

The macrocrystalline regions of the pegmatitic body are composed mainly of microcline, aegirine, eudialyte and arfvedsonite. A little nepheline and murmanite is found. They differ from the eucolite schlieren in having a higher content of microcline (30-40 per cent) and arfvedsonite (15-20 per cent) and also in the presence of aegirine II.

The main minerals of the pegmatitic body are nepheline, aegirine, microcline, albite, eudialyte and ramsayite. There are small quantities of arfvedsonite, loparite, lamprophyllite and murmanite.

Nepheline occurs as large porphyritic segregations, isolated idiomorphic crystals in the macrocrystalline areas and small grains in conjunction with other minerals in the groundmass of the vein. Nepheline is usually idiomorphic to microcline, eudialyte and ramsayite, and contains inclusions of fine-acicular aegirine I and arfvedsonite. Sometimes there is a natrolite fringe round nepheline grains. It has often been entirely replaced by a brown opaque aggregate of spreustein, especially in the finer-grained groundmass.

Microcline forms grey tabular crystals up to 9 cm in length, and small segregations in the groundmass. The typical structure is isoperthitic twinning. Idiomorphic inclusions of lamprophyllite and arfvedsonite are found in microcline.

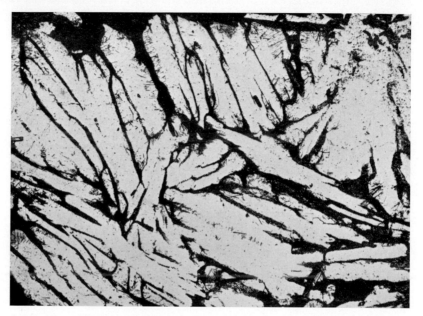

FIG. 58. Filling of interstices between albite laths (light) by aegirine III (dark). ×46. Without analyser

Eudialyte and murmanite adapt themselves to the form of the microcline crystals. The interstices between microcline crystals are filled by aegirine II with eudialyte and murmanite.

The eudialyte-eucolite group of minerals is represented by eudialyte and eucolite. Eudialyte occurs as isolated equant grains or as dense segregations in macrocrystalline areas and in the finer-grained groundmass of the vein. There are various shades of pink. The mean cross-section of the grains is 0·5-1 cm. Eudialyte is often found to have zonal structure in microsections.

Eucolite forms schlieren-like aggregations in the fine-grained pegmatite mass and, unlike eudialyte, is not found in the coarse-grained areas nor as one of the minerals constituting the principal part of the fine-grained pegmatite mass. Eucolite is brownish-red.

Eucolite and eudialyte stand in contrasting relationships to the other minerals. Eucolite is an early mineral in schlieren aggregations. The other minerals in these aggregations, including microcline, lamprophyllite and arfvedsonite, adapt themselves to its grain form. Eudialyte is a late mineral that usually fills the interstices between other minerals together with aegirine II.

Arfvedsonite is found in coarse-grained parts and also in the groundmass as elongate-prismatic crystals with a long axis of up to 3-4 cm, or as irregular black segregations. Its textural relationships show it to be an early mineral. Arfvedsonite inclusions are found in nepheline (Fig. 57), microcline, eudialyte and other minerals. It is xenomorphic to eucolite.

There are three generations of *aegirine* in this pegmatitic body. Aegirine I forms acicular microcrystals included in nepheline and other minerals. Aegirine II is one of the main minerals in the groundmass and in the macrocrystalline parts of the pegmatitic body. It is represented by dark-green fine-acicular crystals that often form a dense felt-like mass filling the interstices between other minerals. Aegirine III is typical only of albitized regions, where it occurs as a fine-acicular aggregate filling the interstices between albite laths (Fig. 58).

Loparite is intimately associated with eudialyte in the fine-grained groundmass and forms small regular black crystals, with a cross-section of up to 1-1·5 mm, that are sometimes penetration twins of a cube and octahedron. It is usually included in eudialyte. The fissures in loparite are sometimes filled with natrolite and less frequently with aegirine II.

Lamprophyllite occurs only in eucolite schlieren as inclusions in microcline or as irregular segregations filling the interstices between eucolite crystals.

Murmanite is represented by small cream-coloured tabular segregations up to 1 cm long in both macrocrystalline parts and the finer-grained mass. It is usually considerably altered and frequently contains inclusions of idiomorphic eudialyte, ramsayite and aegirine II crystals.

Ramsayite occurs in the fine-grained groundmass, where its content may be as much as 20-30 per cent. It forms short-prismatic brown crystals with a cross-section of up to 1 cm. Despite its idiomorphic crystallographic forms, ramsayite is not a very early mineral. It often contains nepheline inclusions and is, in its turn, sometimes included in eudialyte and murmanite.

Albite forms dense microcrystalline segregations consisting of randomly oriented lath-like crystals in the albitization zone, where it fills the interstices between grains of other minerals. The composition of the albite is An_6.

10. The Nepheline-Eudialytic Pegmatitic Vein of Flora

This vein is on the northern slope of Flora, approximately 600 m to the south of the vein described above. It was discovered and studied by E. B. Khalezova and L. S. Borodin and is here described from their findings. This vein is of great scientific interest, since it cuts across widely differing rocks: mesocratic aegirine-lujavrites, urtites, juvites and foyaites of the upper levels of the differentiated complex. The vein can be traced for 60 m along the strike (Fig. 59). Its northern part is bedded for 20 m in lujavrites and its southern part (40 m) in leucocratic rocks. Its strike is meridional and the dip is almost vertical. The pegmatitic vein is confined to a narrow fissure and its average thickness is approximately 10 cm, though in the northern part this increases to 25 cm.

The pegmatite forms a sharp contact with the lujavrite. Small lujavrite xenoliths are found in the contact zone. In the northern part of the vein the lujavrites are eudialyte-enriched at the contact with the pegmatite. Transitions are gradual at the contact between the pegmatitic body and the urtites, where the urtites have acquired a pegmatoid texture and have been replaced by natrolite to a considerable extent. They also have a higher ramsayite content. The contacts between the pegmatite and the foyaites are distinct but not sharp, since these rocks are highly albitized and murmanite-enriched in the zone round the contact.

The phase nature of the pegmatitic body is revealed by the distinct intrusive contacts with the lujavrites and foyaites and by the contrasting chemical and mineralogical composition. It is highly probable that this vein was formed by the intrusion along a vertical fissure of a liquid pegmatitic melt that had accumulated beneath one of the urtite horizons.

The main minerals are unevenly distributed in the vein. The structure is symmetrically zonal in the northern part of the vein (in the bulge). The contact zone is made up of nepheline (up to 40 per cent), mesodialyte (up to 30 per cent) and arfvedsonite (20-25 per cent). The length of the grains does not exceed 1 cm. Loparite enrichment is typical of the zone. In the central zone nepheline is an auxiliary mineral. Mesodialyte, which is most developed here (up to 60-70 per cent), contains isolated crystals of arfvedsonite, ramsayite and nepheline as inclusions. The interstices between mesodialyte segregations are filled by aegirine II and albite. The nepheline and mesodialyte segregations increase in size in the central zone.

The mineralogical composition and structure of the vein varies along the strike. Its zonal character, for example, is no longer apparent in the thin part

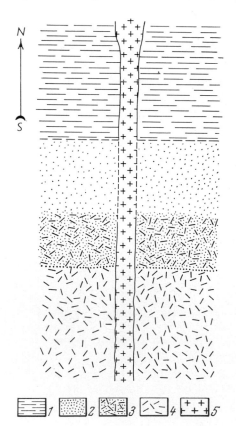

FIG. 59. Sketch of nepheline-eudialytic pegmatitic vein (after Borodin)

1. lujavrite; 2. urtite; 3. juvite; 4. foyaite; 5. pegmatite

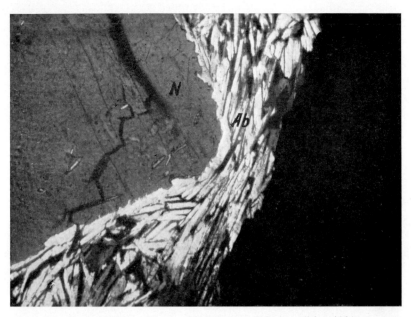

FIG. 60. Partial replacement of nepheline (N) by albite (Ab); meso-dialyte—black. ×10. Crossed nicols

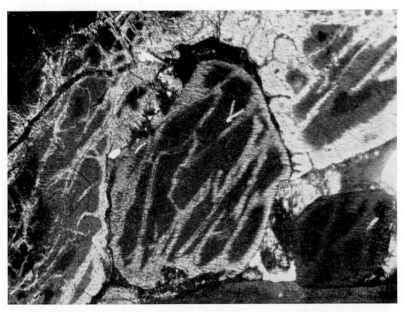

FIG. 61. Replacement of mesodialyte (black) by eudialyte (light). ×20. Crossed nicols

emplaced in lujavrites to the south of the bulge. Here the vein is made up of an equigranular complex of nepheline, mesodialyte and arfvedsonite. Aegirine II, ramsayite and albite are absent. There is an increase in grain size from the contacts to the axial part of the vein and the main mass of the nepheline is located round the contacts.

The structure is not zonal in the central part of the vein emplaced in urtites, where the transitions with the country rocks are gradual. The pegmatitic vein is largely composed of nepheline and mesodialyte, with a lesser amount of ramsayite, which is more or less evenly distributed throughout the vein.

The southern part of the vein emplaced in juvites and foyaites consists mainly of nepheline and mesodialyte with a lesser amount of albite (up to 20 per cent) and murmanite (up to 10 per cent). There is a little ramsayite. There is no discernible pattern in the distribution of the minerals.

Each part of the pegmatitic vein contains its own typomorphic minerals that are typical of the country rocks of the sector. Thus, murmanite and albite are typical of the sector emplaced in foyaites and aegirine and arfvedsonite are typical of the sector emplaced in lujavrites.

The small variation in the chemical and mineralogical composition of the pegmatite along the strike may be due to uptake and some reworking of the country rock by the liquid pegmatitic melt. At the same time it should be stressed that the mineralogical composition of the vein as a whole is not dependent on the differing compositions of the country rocks. The absence of microcline from the vein and the high eudialyte content point to the existence of an independent pegmatite-forming liquid melt.

The main minerals of the pegmatitic vein are nepheline, mesodialyte, arfvedsonite and albite. Smaller amounts of eudialyte, ramsayite, aegirine, loparite and murmanite are also present.

Nepheline occurs chiefly in the contact zone and where the vein is emplaced in urtites, juvites and foyaites; it is also present in considerable quantities in the central zone. It forms dense segregations and, more rarely, isolated grains with a cross-section of up to 1 cm in the contact zone and up to 2 cm in the central zone. Nepheline is idiomorphic to the other minerals. Its only inclusions are acicular microcrystals of aegirine I. The interstices between nepheline grains are usually filled with mesodialyte and arfvedsonite. Natrolite develops after nepheline, and often replaces it entirely. In thin sections nepheline is sometimes found to have been replaced by albite laths (Fig. 60).

Mesodialyte occurs as dense monomineralic segregations and less frequently as equant or hexagonal grains with a cross-section of up to 1-2 cm throughout the vein. The colour is brown. It is often replaced from the periphery by pink eudialyte, which also develops along fissures (Fig. 61). It fills the interstices between nepheline segregations. Mesodialyte inclusions in arfvedsonite and ramsayite indicate that it separated earlier than these minerals.

Arfvedsonite is found as elongate-prismatic crystals, small in the contact zones but reaching lengths of 5-7 cm in the central zone of the northern part.

It crystallized later than nepheline and mesodialyte, since it often contains them as inclusions.

Ramsayite is found in all parts of the vein, but its main mass occurs in the central zone. It forms idiomorphic crystals or equant segregations, dark brown in colour and up to 1-2 cm in cross-section. Thin sections usually reveal that they contain inclusions of arfvedsonite and eudialyte.

Murmanite forms brownish tabular segregations as much as 3 cm long. It is greatly altered and replaced along fissures by leucoxene. It is confined to the part of the pegmatitic body that is emplaced in foyaites. It is later than either nepheline or eudialyte.

Aegirine is represented by two generations. Aegirine I forms microscopic inclusions in nepheline, which sometimes show a preferred orientation. Aegirine II is found in the northern part, in the central zone of the bulge, and is practically absent from the central and southern parts of the vein that are emplaced in urtites and foyaites. It forms acicular microcrystals clustered together in felt-like fibrous-diverse aggregates filling the interstices between other minerals.

Loparite occurs in the nepheline-rich contact facies of the northern part of the vein as idiomorphic crystals or as irregular segregations with a cross-section of up to 1-2 mm. Its later crystallization is shown by the fact that it often contains nepheline and eudialyte inclusions. It is earlier than arfvedsonite, in which it occurs as inclusions.

Randomly orientated laths of *albite* fill the interstices between other minerals, Its composition is An_{2-3}. It occurs mainly in the southern part of the vein and was the last mineral to separate.

Natrolite occurs in small quantities as a fine-grained aggregate replacing nepheline.

11. The Aegirine-Aenigmatite Pegmatitic Vein
of Flora

This pegmatitic body lies on the northern slope of Flora approximately 700 m to the east-south-east of the eucolite-ramsayite pegmatitic body. It is a layered body that is conformably bedded with the layering of the foyaites in the differentiated complex. The strike is north-easterly (15°), and the dip south-easterly at an angle of 9-10°. The length of the outcrop (Fig. 62) is 18 m and its width is approximately 5 m in the southern part decreasing to 2 m in the northern part.

The surface of the pegmatite outcrop is hummocky; the upstanding parts ('hummocks') consist of a dense mass of aegirine II, the microcrystals of which are arranged in radiated aggregates. Foyaite xenoliths are often found in the centre of these aegirine 'hummocks' (Fig. 63).

The roof of the vein has not been examined, since its eastern part is buried beneath foyaite rubble, while in the uncovered western part the upper surfaces and, apparently, the central part of the vein have been removed by erosion. The remaining part of the lower wall is 20-30 cm thick and as much as 40 cm in isolated bulges ('hummocks').

The contact of the pegmatitic vein with the foyaites is sharp and irregular. The foyaites at the contact are greatly enriched in eudialyte and lamprophyllite and the diameter of the eudialyte segregations increases up to 1 cm. The sharp contacts between the vein and the country rocks and the existence of xenoliths in it show that it is a phase-type body.

It is difficult to assess the internal structure of this pegmatitic vein since only its floor has been preserved, and this is really represented only by the outer zone. The main minerals of this zone (aegirine II, microcline and eudialyte) are concentrated at the contact with the foyaites. Large platy crystals or crystal growths of microcline are orientated roughly perpendicular to the contact. To the north-east of the outcrop farther down the slope there is an area of albitic pegmatite rubble up to 15 m long trending 355°. This rubble is clearly the central zone of the pegmatitic body that has been shifted by erosion. The mineralogical composition of this zone differs from that of the outer zone in the absence of microcline and the high content of white fine-grained albite, constituting the main mineral. There is no aenigmatite in this zone. Considerable quantities of aegirine II occur as relict corroded rounded aggregations coated with albite laths, thus giving rise to an ocellar structure in this zone. Inclusions of eudialyte, and less frequently of murmanite, are sometimes noted in aegirine II.

The main minerals of the pegmatitic vein are aegirine II, microcline, albite and eudialyte. There are smaller quantities of aenigmatite, murmanite, manganobeliankinite, nepheline and lamprophyllite.

Microcline accounts for up to 20 per cent of the outer microcline-aegirine zone,

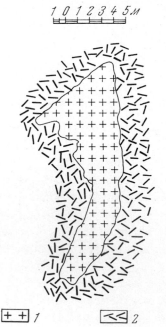

where it consists of isolated creamy-grey tabular crystals of up to $15 \times 5 \times 3$ cm or crystal growths of up to 20×20 cm confined to the vein contacts. The interstices between the microcline crystals are filled with aegirine II, whereas small inclusions of aegirine I and nepheline crystals are observed in the microcline itself. Microcline is xenomorphic to eudialyte and murmanite.

There are three generations of *aegirine*. Aegerine I forms the very fine inclusions in microcline, in which its fine-acicular crystals are randomly distributed.

Aegirine II accounts for approximately 80 per cent of the outer zone and 30 per cent of the central

FIG. 62. Diagram of outcrop of aegirine-aenigmatite pegmatitic vein (after Kuz'menko)

1. pegmatite; 2. foyaite

zone. In the outer zone it is developed as acicular microcrystals that form a greyish-green felt-like mass. Aegirine II crystals are usually assembled in radiate-fibrous bundles with eudialyte or microcline at the centre. In the central zone aegirine II is represented by relict (elongated, rounded or lenticular) segregations in parallel orientation and often coalescing into dense conspicuous bands surrounded by albite laths. Aegirine II is the latest mineral of the outer zone, where

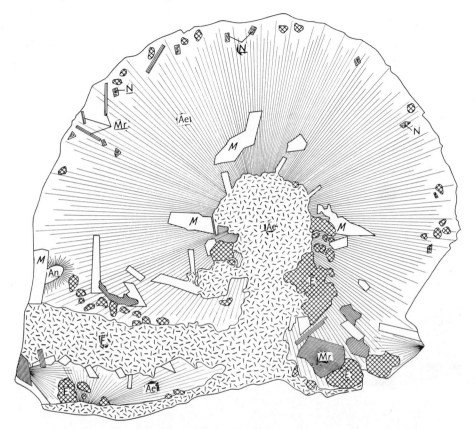

FIG. 63. Foyaite xenolith (F) in pegmatitic vein; M—microcline; E—eudialyte; Mr—Murmanite; N—nepheline; An—aenigmatite; Ae—Aegirine II. ½ natural size

it fills the interstices between all other minerals. It is earlier than albite in the central zone.

Aegirine III is found in small quantities in leaching cavities, where it is closely associated with late zeolites. It forms light-green acicular microcrystals (up to 2 mm in length).

There are large amounts of *eudialyte* in the outer zone. It forms equant aggregations or compact irregular macrocrystalline aggregations of up to 4×5 cm in area included in aegirine II. The cross-section of the individual units does not exceed 2 cm. Eudialyte is idiomorphic to microcline and aenigmatite.

Murmanite is encountered as tabular segregations of up to $10 \times 5 \times 1$ cm. The colour is violet-brown to dark-brown with a bronze chatoyancy on the cleavage planes. It is developed mainly in the outer zones, in the aegirine II mass. Murmanite is found to be idiomorphic to microcline, which adapts itself to the shapes of the murmanite segregations (Fig. 64). Murmanite is usually greatly altered; its replacement by beliankinite is sometimes observed.

Belyankinite is a secondary mineral on murmanite. It forms in the outer zone as creamy-white and black tabular crystals of up to $5 \times 3 \times 0.5$ cm and occasionally larger. In most cases murmanite is converted into the black manganese variety

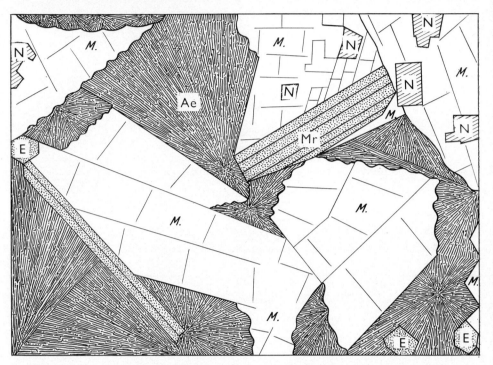

FIG. 64. Relationship of murmanite (Mr), microcline (M), nepheline (N), eudialyte (E) and aegirine II (Ae). Natural size

of belyankinite (mangano-belyankinite) which merges gradually with the brown and dark-brown varieties. It is less often entirely replaced by creamy-white belyankinite. Sometimes one side of a murmanite crystal is found to be replaced by belyankinite and the other side by mangano-belyankinite.

Aenigmatite occurs as irregular segregations and as equant or ovoid black grains up to 15 cm long and 2 cm wide, mainly in the outer zone. It is xenomorphic to eudialyte (Fig. 65).

Lamprophyllite is represented by fine golden-brown bladed crystals up to 0.5 cm long that sometimes form radial aggregates. Fine-acicular lamprophyllite crystals are sometimes found in association with aegirine II as radiate-fibrous fringes round aenigmatite, probably formed during its replacement.

There is only a small amount of *nepheline*. It occurs as small crystals of square cross-section up to 0.5 cm included in the margins of radiate-fibrous concretions of aegirine II or in microcline. Nepheline is often entirely replaced by zeolites or crushed.

Albite accounts for 70 per cent of the central zone. It forms fine-grained whitish aggregates containing relict segregations of aegirine II and other minerals. The brownish-grey variety of albite is found in the outer zone, where albite is

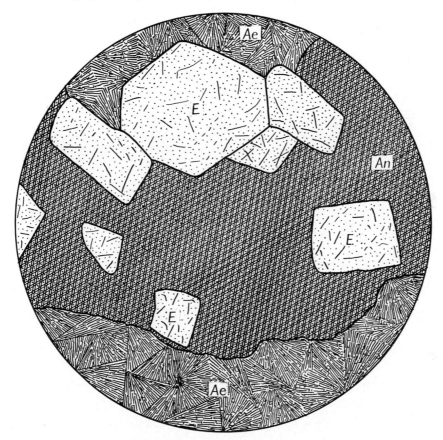

Fig. 65. Relationship of aenigmatite (An) to eudialyte (E) and aegirine II (Ae). Natural size (after Borodin)

formed during the replacement of microcline. It fills the cracks in microcline along the two cleavage directions leaving cells of unreplaced microcline, and giving rise to a distinctive network.

Zeolites are found in small quantities in leaching cavities, where they form crusts of fine white microcrystals intimately associated with aegirine III on the cavity walls.

12. The Lamprophyllitic Pegmatite Vein of Karnasurt

This vein has been studied by E. B. Khalezova, whose findings are here taken into consideration. The vein comes to the surface on the First Eastern stream on

Karnasurt in the zone of transition from the seventh horizon of the hornblende lujavrites to the overlying foyaites, so that the country rocks are hornblende lujavrites on the left slope of the valley and foyaites on the right. It is a layered body that can be traced for 50-60 m along the strike with a thickness of approximately 40 cm. The strike of the vein is 80° and the dip to the south 14-20°. The

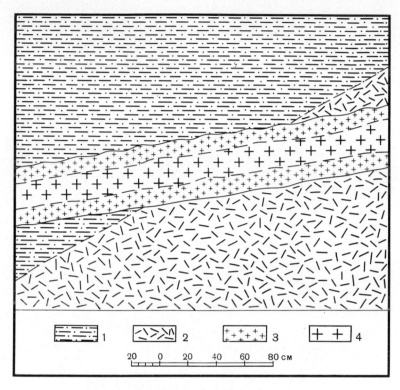

FIG. 66. Sketch of lamprophyllitic vein
1. hornblende-lujavrite; 2. foyaite; 3. outer fine-
grained pegmatite zone; 4. central pegmatite zone

strike of the containing lujavrites is 70°. The pegmatitic body is therefore unconformable with the country rocks (Fig. 66).

Both in the floor and in the roof of the vein the lujavrites are loparite- and eudialyte-enriched. In these parts the pegmatitic vein contains xenoliths of hornblende lujavrite in the form of lenses of up to 3-4 cm thick and 40 cm long. The composition of the xenoliths does not differ from that of the enclosing hornblende-lujavrites, except that it is more natrolitized.

The foyaites at the contact are greatly enriched in eudialyte (15-20 per cent) and sodalite both at the upper and the lower surfaces of the vein. The rare-metal minerals also include loparite, ramsayite and lamprophyllite. The dark-coloured minerals are represented by aegirine and arfvedsonite.

Zonal features are slightly developed in this vein; marginal and central zones can be distinguished.

The fine- and medium-grained peripheral zones consist of microcline, nepheline aegirine I, arfvedsonite and eudialyte, in which leucocratic components predominate. Near the lower contact of the vein this zone is more melanocratic than at the upper contact. The thickness of each marginal zone is approximately 10 cm. The length of the mineral segregations does not exceed 5 cm.

The central macrocrystalline zone is composed of microcline, aegirine II, nepheline and hackmanite, which is at least as plentiful as microcline here, and murmanite. There is less eudialyte, aegirine I and lamprophyllite, and these minerals are found nearest the central zones. There is a small amount of ramsayite.

There is in general, no variation in the mineralogical composition and texture of the vein along the strike, though differentiation is less clearly defined in the western than in the eastern sector. The pegmatite becomes more microcrystalline near a xenolith of hornblende-lujavrite; there is an increase in the content of small acicular aegirine I crystals orientated roughly perpendicular to the contact and also in eudialyte, which here forms small grains. The main minerals of the pegmatitic vein are microcline, nepheline, aegirine I, aegirine II, arfvedsonite, hackmanite, eudialyte, lamprophyllite, ramsayite and murmanite.

Microcline accounts for approximately 40 per cent of the total mass of the vein. In the contacts of the eastern part its greenish-grey crystals, which are orientated roughly perpendicular to the contact-surfaces, may be as large as $1 \times 3 \times 5$ cm. This is not observed in the western part. In the central zone microcline is represented by poorly-formed crystals of up to $15 \times 10 \times 5$ cm. It contains a considerable number of aegirine I inclusions and is replaced by fine-grained natrolite. It is usually xenomorphic to aegirine I, arfvedsonite, lamprophyllite, nepheline and eudialyte.

Nepheline forms dark-grey regular crystals with a cross-section of up to 1.5×2 cm that are idiomorphic to eudialyte and microcline. It contains inclusions of small prismatic aegirine I crystals and is greatly replaced by natrolite.

Hackmanite is represented by a semi-transparent violet-pink variety that soon tarnishes and loses its colour in the light. It is found mainly in the central zone, where it forms a compact mass with microcline and natrolite and partly replaces nepheline. It is normally much replaced by fine-grained and chalcedonic natrolite.

There are two generations of *aegirine*. Aegirine I is included in nepheline and microcline as small prismatic crystals, varying in size from a few hundredths of a millimetre to several millimetres. Aegirine II forms greenish radiate-fibrous aggregates with a diameter up to 7 cm in the interstices between other minerals. Small crystals of microcline (up to 1 cm in length), aegirine I, nepheline and eudialyte are encountered as inclusions in aegirine 'suns'. Aegirine II is concentrated mainly in the central zone but is also found at the margins.

Arfvedsonite is found both at the margins and in the central zone, but the content at the centre is considerably lower. It forms long-columnar prismatic crystals of $0.2 \times 0.3 \times 3$ cm that sometimes reach a length of 6 cm and a cross-section of 0.5 cm. It is normally idiomorphic to eudialyte and microcline but xenomorphic to lamprophyllite.

Eudialyte forms orange-brown crystals with a cross-section of up to $2 \times 1 \cdot 5$ cm and irregular aggregates with a cross-section of up to 3 cm. In the eastern part of the vein it bulks largest in the roof. In the lower part it is found in appreciable quantity only at the contact, where it forms a 1-2 cm thick layer. There is a considerable decline in the quantity of eudialyte towards the centre. In the western part of the vein the eudialyte is fairly uniformly distributed and its content is reduced only in the centre (5-7 cm wide). In the microcline, eudialyte occurs as regular idiomorphic crystals. It is xenomorphic to aegirine I, lamprophyllite, arfvedsonite and nepheline. It is usually considerably replaced by zirfesite.

Lamprophyllite forms golden-brown or golden-yellow radiate-fibrous aggregates ('suns') of fine prismatic crystals up to 2 cm in diameter. It occurs mainly in the eastern part of the vein, where it is confined to the area of transition between the central and outer zones of the lower side. The amount of lamprophyllite in the central zone and in the upper part is insignificant. There is considerably less lamprophyllite in the western than in the eastern sector of the vein; it is fairly uniformly distributed in the marginal zones and is absent from the central zone. It is idiomorphic to microcline, eudialyte and arfvedsonite.

Ramsayite forms irregular brown aggregates with a cross-section of up to 1 cm². It normally contains inclusions of idiomorphic eudialyte crystals.

Murmanite occurs as fine-platy violet-pink crystals up to 7 cm long and 3 cm wide. It contains inclusions of idiomorphic arfvedsonite and microcline crystals and is itself idiomorphic to aegirine II. It is frequently replaced by brown and black decomposition products.

There is a large amount of *natrolite*, especially in the central zone. It occurs as a fine-grained or cryptocrystalline whitish aggregate that replaces microcline, nepheline and sodalite, and also fills fissures in microcline.

Neptunite is found mainly in the central zone in association with aegirine II. It normally occurs with zeolites as irregular microscopic orange aggregates that rarely attain a cross-section of 2 mm in cavities in aegirine II.

13. The Ilmenite-Pegmatite Body of the First Western Stream of Alluaiv

There are a great many schlieren-like pegmatitic bodies on the western slope of Alluaiv in the stream bed at the edge of the forest zone. These pegmatites occur in an area of 20×100 m in the foyaites of the differentiated complex near the contact between the alkali massif and the gneisses. The largest of these bodies (8×3 m) is here described from the findings of I. P. Tikhonenkov.

The foyaites that contain the pegmatitic bodies differ from ordinary foyaites in that their texture is more macrocrystalline and in having a higher aegirine content. Their composition is fundamentally altered in a 25-30 cm thick zone at the contact with the pegmatite: the loparite and nepheline content is increased (to 50-70 per cent) and the microcline content is reduced. In addition there are large quantities of eudialyte, ramsayite and ilmenite in the foyaites at the contact.

The pegmatite is separated from the nepheline rock just described by a narrow strip of a mesocratic rock that has a higher aegirine and lower nepheline and loparite content than the foyaites. The contact between the mesocratic rock and the pegmatite is indistinct owing to gradual reduction in the amount of aegirine and increase in the microcline content between the country rock and the centre of the pegmatitic body.

This pegmatitic body is genetically associated with foyaites, of which it is a facies formation. The presence of a comparatively large amount of mangan-ilmenite in the country rocks and in the pegmatitic vein probably indicates partial contamination, since this mineral is not typical of the greater part of the Lovozero massif and is found only where there has been contamination of the nepheline-syenite magma by the country rocks.

It should be noted that the presence of early replacement albite is typical of this pegmatitic body and of the pegmatitic horizon. It does not normally occur in phase pegmatites in the rocks of the massif.

The pegmatitic body is oval and its outlines are irregular. Three concentric zones can be distinguished between the margin and the centre: (1) the outer microcrystalline zone, (2) intermediate macrocrystalline zone and (3) the central block zone.

The 10-20 cm thick microcrystalline zone is composed of microcline, nepheline and aegirine; there is an increase in the manganilmenite, eudialyte and ramsayite content. Maximum grain size does not exceed 1 cm. The 30-40 cm macro-crystalline zone consists of the same minerals, but there is a reduction in the amount of nepheline, manganilmenite, eudialyte and ramsayite. The dimensions of microcline segregations increase to $10 \times 5 \times 1$ cm. The dimensions of individual units in the central (block) zone reaches 50-60 cm along the long axis. The zone is composed mainly of microcline and arfvedsonite, with a lesser amount of aegirine II, sodalite and natrolite.

The main minerals of the pegmatitic body are microcline and albite (approxi-mately 50 per cent), nepheline, sodalite and natrolite (approximately 15 per cent), aegirine (approximately 10 per cent), arfvedsonite (approximately 10 per cent) and eudialyte (approximately 10 per cent). Ramsayite, manganilmenite, loparite, astrophyllite and neptunite also occur.

Nepheline occurs in the first two zones, where its content reaches 30 per cent. It forms hexagonal crystals or greenish-grey oval grains. They do not exceed 0·5 cm in cross-section in the contact area, but reach 3-4 cm in the intermediate zone. Nepheline often contains inclusions of aegirine I crystals and is found to be idiomorphic to microcline. Natrolite forms pseudomorphs after nepheline. The nepheline crystals that are most replaced by natrolite are those that are poikilitically enclosed in aegirine (Fig. 67).

Microcline forms tabular crystals of a greenish-grey colour that is due to the many inclusions of fine-acicular aegirine I crystals usually orientated along the cleavage. The length of the microcline crystals varies from 0·5 cm round the

FIG. 67. Poikilitic nepheline inclusions (light) replaced by natrolite in macrocrystalline aegirine. ×46. Without analyser

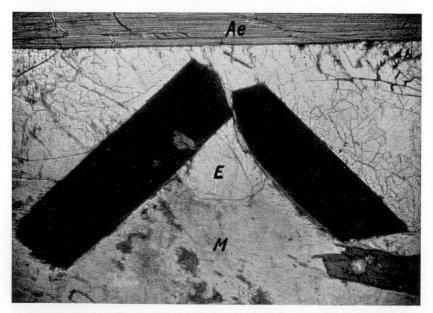

FIG. 68. Relationship of manganilmenite (black) to microcline (M) and eudialyte (E); Ae—aegirine. ×10. Without analyser

contacts to 30-50 cm in the central zone. Small microcline crystals are usually included in large aegirine I crystals. At the same time large microcline crystals contain aegirine I inclusions, and interpenetration is observed. Microcline appears as a later mineral than manganilmenite, arfvedsonite and nepheline. Eudialyte and ramsayite usually fill the interstices between its crystals or penetrate into them along fissures. Microcline is replaced by albite and sodalite both from the periphery of the segregations and along cleavage cracks.

Albite replaces microcline, often leaving only isolated relics of microcline crystals in the central zone. Albite develops along cleavage cracks as long narrow strips. When microcline crystals are somewhat poorly albitized the albite in them takes the form of isolated irregular areas of up to 0.1×0.1 mm with polysynthetic twinning.

In addition to polysynthetic albite there is lath albite replacing microcline from the edges of its crystals; this gives rise to accumulations of up to 2×2 mm. The dimensions of each lath are up to 0.2×0.01 mm. Lath albite is later than polysynthetic albite.

Aegirine has two generations. Aegirine I is confined to the outer and intermediate zones, where it forms large dark-green crystals up to 8-10 cm long and small acicular crystals enclosed in segregations of leucocratic minerals. Small nepheline and microcline crystals are sometimes included in large aegirine crystals and in their turn contain inclusions of fine-acicular aegirine I crystals. It is evident that these three minerals were formed at about the same time and that the crystallization of aegirine I began slightly before the crystallization of nepheline and ended when the microcline was beginning to crystallize.

There are small quantities of *aegirine II* in the central zone, where it forms radiate-fibrous bundles of up to 1.5×1.5 cm in area, filling the interstices between early minerals.

Arfvedsonite forms large black prismatic crystals (up to 20 cm long) in the central zone included in the peripheral parts of microcline crystals. It sometimes contains inclusions of regular aegirine I crystals. Secondary arfvedsonite developing after aegirine I is found in the outer zone.

Eudialyte is mainly developed in the outer zone as pink and reddish-brown aggregations with a cross-section of up to 10-15 cm. This is a late mineral of the pegmatitic body that fills the interstices between segregations of microcline, nepheline, aegirine I, manganilmenite and arfvedsonite. Zirfesite and catapleiite normally partly replace it. The replacement begins along fissures and then spreads to the whole mass.

Dark-brown xenomorphic segregations of *ramsayite* (up to 2×2 cm in cross-section) fill the interstices between early minerals chiefly in the intermediate zone. Its inclusions in eudialyte are regular in form.

In addition to primary ramsayite the pegmatitic body contains brownish-yellow secondary ramsayite formed on manganilmenite. Irregular ilmenite relicts are often found in this ramsayite.

Manganilmenite occurs mainly in the outer zone as irregular segregations or black tabular crystals of up to $6 \times 4 \times 0.3$ cm. The only inclusions are nepheline. Its cracks are sometimes filled with aegirine and ramsayite, the latter of which corrodes its crystals. Manganilmenite is often included in the peripheral parts of microcline and eudialyte crystals (Fig. 68).

Astrophyllite is present in very small amounts, intimately associated with secondary ramsayite. Its dark-brown tabular segregations (up to 0.5×0.5 cm) are xenomorphic to secondary ramsayite.

Small quantities of *loparite* occur as crystals with a cross-section of up to 3 mm in the contact zone. Loparite crystallized later than nepheline and contains nepheline grains, but earlier than microcline and eudialyte. Its crystals are normally included in microcline, eudialyte, manganilmenite, ramsayite and aegirine I.

Natrolite is normally found as a replacement of nepheline. It forms small druses of prismatic crystals (up to 0.5 cm long) in cavities.

Neptunite occurs extremely rarely in intimate association with natrolite developing on nepheline, forming irregular segregations of up to 0.2×0.2 mm.

Elpidite forms fine-acicular crystals up to 0.1 mm long that fill the cracks in eudialyte or are intimately associated with zirfesite. It is apparently formed simultaneously with zirfesite in the replacement of eudialyte.

Typical Features of the Pegmatites of the Differentiated Complex

One of the most typical features that distinguish the pegmatites of the differentiated complex from those of other complexes is the existence of facies pegmatitic horizons. These horizons are located beneath horizons of nearly monomineralic rocks (urtites and ijolite-urtites) that are the normal products of the differentiation of the magma by crystallization and emanation. The great extent of the pegmatitic horizons (tens of kilometres), their conformability with the general layering of the rocks in the complex, the absence of intrusive contacts in most cases, the regular association of specific rock horizons with the roofs and their absence in those areas of the massif where differentiation is poorly developed or has been destroyed by large xenoliths of the roof and intrusions of poikilitic syenites, all indicate that the pegmatitic melt was formed during the general differentiation of the magma.

The question that naturally arises is how the volatile compounds essential for the formation of pegmatites beneath urtitic horizons were concentrated. The following conclusion can be drawn from an analysis of the data. During the crystallization of the urtites and ijolite-urtites, which took place from above downwards, all the components of the magma not involved in the crystal lattice of nepheline, including the volatile compounds, were forced downwards by the almost monomineralic crystallizing mass. At the same time the nepheline horizons that were forming could have served as barriers for the volatile compounds rising from below. In this way quite thick magma horizons enriched in volatile compounds and rare elements could have been formed as a result of crystallization and emanation. The increased content of volatiles retarded the crystallization process in these horizons, while the overlying and underlying rocks continued to crystallize. As the already-crystallized rocks cooled they fissured, the direction of the fractures usually coinciding with the general direction of the layering. The injection of part of the pegmatitic melt from the pegmatitic horizon along these fissures gave rise to a whole series of pegmatitic veins and apophyses, although the main mass of the melt crystallized *in situ*.

There is relatively less of the zirconium minerals (eudialyte) and more of the niobium and titanium minerals (murmanite, lomonosovite, ramsayite, aenigmatite, etc.) in the pegmatites of the differentiated complex than in those of the eudialytic lujavrite complex. Very small amounts of the beryllium mineral eudidymite are also found.

Zoning is poorly displayed in most of the pegmatites. Its usual expression is to be found in the fact that the contact zones are mainly composed of leucocratic minerals (microcline and nepheline) while the central parts are composed of aegirine. Eudialyte is frequently found in the contact zones. The grain size of the minerals usually increases from the contacts in towards the central parts of the pegmatites.

Differentiation does not normally proceed as far as the formation of mono-mineralic zones. Where differentiation is greatest the central sectors may contain replacement zones made up of a fine-grained complex of albite that sometimes contains admixtures of natrolite, analcite, chabazite and clay minerals. Rare minerals such as elpidite, labuntsovite and eudidymite are found in this association.

The four main types of texture that determine the zonal structure of the pegmatites of the differentiated complex are pegmatoid, porphyritic, fine-block and microcrystalline.

A pegmatoid structure is usually found in undifferentiated pegmatites and in the peripheral zones of differentiated pegmatites. This texture is due to the presence of pegmatoid intergrowths of the main minerals that separated at about the same time.

The porphyritic texture is typical of the intermediate melanocratic zones of differentiated pegmatites; on rare occasions it occurs in the central parts of un-differentiated pegmatites. This texture is due to the presence of large pheno-crysts (3-50 cm in length) in a fine-grained groundmass, in which the grain size does not exceed 0·5-1 cm, when the volume of phenocrysts is considerably less than the volume of the groundmass. The phenocrysts are usually microcline and nepheline and less frequently eudialyte, murmanite and ramsayite. The ground-mass is made up of the same minerals and fine-acicular aegirine II.

The block texture is most often found in the central zones of the differentiated pegmatites. These zones are composed of large prismatic microcline crystals that are frequently elongated from the contact planes to the centre, or of pegmatoid intergrowths of microcline and arfvedsonite, the interstices between which are filled with aegirine II containing inclusions of eudialyte, murmanite, ramsayite and other non-ferrous minerals. Thus there is a time difference in the formation of block textures between early leucocratic minerals (microcline and nepheline) and later minerals (aegirine and rare-metal minerals).

The microcrystalline texture is found in replacement zones. It is due to the formation of monomineralic microcrystalline (to cryptocrystalline) aggregates or polymict aggregates in which grain size does not usually exceed tenths of a millimetre and rarely attains 0·5-1 mm.

There are three paragenetic mineral associations in the pegmatites of the differentiated complex that differ both in mineralogical composition and in the time of formation: (1) nepheline-microcline; (2) aegirine; and (3) natrolite-albite. The names given to these associations are those of the dominant minerals.

In addition to nepheline and microcline the first includes aegirine I, loparite and, in parts, arfvedsonite, lamprophyllite and eudialyte. All these minerals, which are located in the peripheral zones of the pegmatites, are earlier than aegirine II. The aegirine association includes eudialyte, ramsayite, murmanite, aenigmatite and, in places, lamprophyllite, in addition to aegirine II. All these minerals crystallized earlier than aegirine II, which fills the interstices between them. The third association is a group of replacement minerals, consisting of albite, natrolite, analcite, chabazite, neptunite and a series of rare minerals including eudidymite, labuntsovite and elpidite. It is extremely interesting to note the presence of quartz in this association, since this is an unusual mineral for nepheline syenites and one that has not previously been encountered under similar conditions in the Lovozero massif. Primary quartz has been described (Flink, 1901) in the pegmatites of nepheline syenites in Greenland, where it is associated with the same minerals (epididymite, elpidite, etc.). The appearance of quartz in a late mineral association of a pegmatite horizon is clearly due to the concentration of fluorine, chlorine and carbon dioxide compounds in late solutions, leading to the formation of sodium halides, carbonates and bicarbonates and to the separation of free silica and the formation of quartz. It is also in this association that we encounter chalcedony, apparently formed by the destruction of nepheline, for the first time in the Lovozero massif.

It should be noted that the mineral associations indicated above are somewhat tentatively identified and that there is some variation in each pegmatitic body. In relation to their content in the pegmatitic bodies such minerals as arfvedsonite, lamprophyllite, ramsayite and eudialyte, may be found in either the nepheline-microcline or the aegirine association. When the main elements of which these minerals are composed are present in large quantity in the pegmatitic melt they will separate from the melt at an earlier stage and be incorporated in an earlier mineral association.

All the minerals of the first two associations crystallize successively and there is very little indication of replacement between them or none at all. The minerals of the third paragenetic association (the replacement association) were either crystallized directly from the residual pegmatitic melt or were formed in the replacement of early minerals. The most highly-developed replacement processes in the pegmatites of the differentiated complex are the albitization of microcline and the natrolitization of nepheline. To a lesser extent there is replacement of aegirine by arfvedsonite, of murmanite by belyankinite and of manganilmenite by ramsayite and astrophyllite.

* * * *

Four stages can be provisionally distinguished in the formation of the pegmatites of the differentiated complex (Fig. 69).

Nepheline, aegirine I, eucolite, loparite, manganilmenite and a considerable part of the microcline crystallized in the first stage. Lamprophyllite, arfvedsonite and part of the eudialyte and ramsayite separate at this stage in some pegmatites.

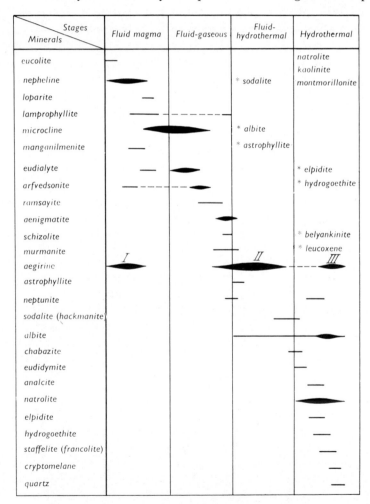

FIG. 69. Diagram of the sequence of crystallization in the pegmatites of the differentiated complex; the asterisk indicates the beginning of the replacement process; I, II, III—aegirine generations

The first of these minerals to crystallize in most cases is aegirine I, which forms inclusions of regular crystals in nepheline, microcline and other minerals. Nepheline, early eudialyte and lamprophyllite, which are idiomorphic to microcline, form after aegirine I. Microcline crystallizes after nepheline; early arfvedsonite and ramsayite separate at the end of its crystallization period. Early arfvedsonite, ramsayite and late eudialyte form inclusions of regular crystals in the margins of microcline segregations.

The typical feature of the second stage is crystallization of late eudialyte and frequently of ramsayite, late arfvedsonite, aenigmatite and murmanite. They are all xenomorphic to microcline. Aegirine II, which fills the interstices between all the minerals mentioned, began to crystallize at the end of this stage.

The main mass of aegirine II crystallizes with sodalite in the third stage and the replacement of microcline by albite and nepheline by sodalite begins.

The main mass of the albite, natrolite, analcite and chabazite is formed in the fourth stage in addition to a series of minerals containing rare elements such as beryllium (eudidymite), zirconium (elpidite), titanium (neptunite, labuntsovite) etc. All these minerals are intimately associated with albite or form cavities in it.

In the last stages of the hydrothermal process the high-temperature pegmatitic minerals were greatly altered and replaced; a number of secondary minerals appeared. Thus, nepheline was replaced by natrolite, hydrargillite, kaolinite and montmorillonite; microcline by albite; eudialyte by catapleiite, elpidite and nontronite; murmanite by belyankinite; ramsayite and murmanite by leucoxene; arfvedsonite by hydrogoethite, etc.

Hybrid pegmatites are found in addition to pure pegmatites in the differentiated complex. These will be discussed below.

CHAPTER THREE

THE PEGMATITES OF THE POIKILITIC SYENITE COMPLEX

IT has already been shown that the poikilitic nepheline-sodalitic syenite complex is richest in readily volatile compounds. The increased content of volatile matter, including rare-metal compounds, in the magma of the poikilitic syenites gave rise to a more extensive and clearly manifested pegmatitic process. Although the poikilitic syenites do not account for more than 5-6 per cent of the total area of the massif, a great many pegmatitic bodies are genetically associated with them. More than 36 extensive pegmatitic bodies have been discovered (14 of which cover hundreds of square metres), in addition to the small schlieren-like pegmatitic formations (see Fig. 5) which are usually less than 1 m and only occasionally a few metres across.

The pegmatites of the poikilitic syenite complex are found on the north-eastern and north-western slopes of Karnasurt, on the northern slope of Lepkhe-Nel'm, on the left side of the Chinglusuai valley, on the ridge between the first and second cirques of Raslak—on Kedykvyrpakhk, on the north-eastern slope and the plateau of Mannepakhk, on the eastern slope of Malyi Punkaruaiv, on the southern slope of Kuivchorr, in the upper reaches of the Chivruai valley and in the upper reaches of the Koklukhtiuai valley. The possibility is not excluded that pegmatites of this complex may be found in other districts of the massif, where there are poikilitic syenite outcrops. The pegmatites are most abundant on the extreme north-eastern spur of Karnasurt (between the Second Eastern stream and Flora).

The pegmatites of the complex include both facies and phase formations, the former predominating. It should be noticed that the poikilitic syenites and especially their hackmanitic varieties are, in essence, the pegmatitic facies of the Lovozero alkaline massif, as is shown by their macrocrystalline structure, the abundance of volatile compounds, poikilitic texture, and the presence in them of a great number of clearly-defined facies macrocrystalline pegmatitic segregations. Moreover, in the apical parts of poikilitic sodalite-syenite intrusions, especially at the contacts with the country rocks of the differentiated complex, one can sometimes find pegmatitic facies from which vein pegmatites run into the country rocks.

The facies pegmatites are normally similar in chemical and mineralogical composition to the parent rocks. They are small irregular bodies that merge gradually with the parent rocks. Their mineralogical composition is usually orthoclase (60-80 per cent), nepheline or sodalite (20-80 per cent), eudialyte (10-30 per cent), aegirine I (10-20 per cent), ramsayite (3-5 per cent, sometimes as much as 20 per cent) and murmanite. The pegmatitic bodies vary in size from a few tens of square centimetres to several tens of square metres and sometimes attain several hundred square metres. Zonal structure is not usually apparent. The main minerals crystallized at about the same time in the early stages of the pegmatitic process and late hydrothermal processes are very little in evidence in these pegmatites.

The facies pegmatites differ from the parent rocks in the larger dimensions of the mineral components, the absence of poikilitic texture in the orthoclases, the predominance of one of the main rock-forming minerals (hackmanite, microcline or aegirine) and the increased content of one or more rare-metal minerals (eudialyte, murmanite, lomonosovite, ramsayite, chinglusuite and others).

On the rare occasions when the facies pegmatites were formed from the crystallization of large volumes of pegmatitic melt greatly enriched with volatile compounds, their chemical and mineralogical composition differs considerably from that of the parent rocks. Such pegmatitic bodies pass through all the stages in the pegmatitic process, from the early stage of the formation of equigranular zones to the hydrothermal stage, and are frequently differentiated, though the differentiation does not normally proceed as far as the formation of monomineralic zones.

The phase pegmatites include veins and irregular stock-like pegmatitic bodies formed by the injection of the pegmatitic melt along spaces caused by dislocations and weakened contact zones into crystallized parts of the parent rocks or into rocks of other complexes. The intrusive contacts are sharp and there is considerable contact-alteration of the country rocks. When phase pegmatites are emplaced in the rocks of the differentiated complex and of the eudialytic lujavrite complex one usually finds margins, mainly of aegirine-rich, eudialytic or microcline-sodalite-rich composition, at the contacts, owing to the interaction between the pegmatitic melt and the country rocks. Reaction rims are not found at the contacts between phase pegmatites and poikilitic syenites, because of the similarity in chemical and mineralogical composition between the pegmatitic melt and the parent rock.

Great thickness and zonal structure are typical of large phase pegmatitic bodies, which reach a size of 60×40 metres. Their main minerals, in addition to nepheline aegirine and orthoclase, are hackmanite, natrolite, analcite, ussingite and albite. In addition to titanium, zirconium and niobium minerals, rare-metal minerals of common occurrence include rare-earth and thorium minerals (steenstrupine, erikite, karnasurtite, nordite and others), lithium minerals (polylithionite and tainiolite) and beryllium minerals (epididymite, chkalovite, leucophane and beryl) as well as minerals that are absent from the parent rocks or present only in trace amounts. The large phase pegmatites are richest in mineral species. They have been found to contain more than 120 minerals, i.e. almost all the minerals found in the Lovozero alkali massif. They usually differ considerably in chemical and mineralogical composition from the parent rocks owing to the different initial composition of the pegmatitic melt, the higher degree of differentiation and the important part played by late (hydrothermal) processes. The hackmanite-natrolite and natrolite-albite pegmatitic bodies of Karnasurt, the orthoclase-natrolite pegmatitic body of Lepkhe-Nel'm and others described below are typical examples of phase pegmatites.

14. THE ORTHOCLASE-AEGIRINE PEGMATITIC BODY OF LEPKHE-NEL'M

There is a 16×13 m orthoclase-aegirine schlieren-like body (Fig. 70) in the centre of the northern slope of Lepkhe-Nel'm approximately 200 m below the

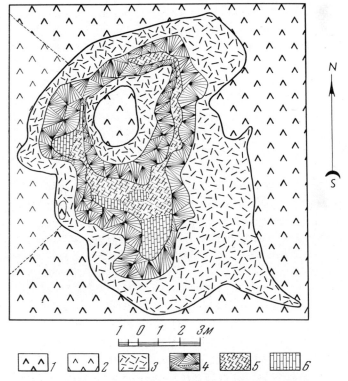

FIG. 70. Diagram of the orthoclase-aegirine pegmatitic body of Lepkhe-Nel'm (after Semenov and Ivanov)

1. poikilitic hydrosodalite-syenite; 2. poikilitic nepheline-syenite; 3. outer pegmatoid zone; 4. intermediate ortho-clase-aegirine zone; 5. natrolite; 6. orthoclase

upper brow of the rocky outcrops. It was first discovered by Semenov, whose findings are taken into account here. The country rocks are poikilitic nepheline- and hydrosodalite-syenites into which the pegmatites gradually merge. In the central part of the body there is a large outcrop (up to 3 m across) of poikilitic hydrosodalite-syenite that is apparently an outcrop of the country rocks adjacent to the lower wall of the body.

This pegmatitic body is a facies formation of the poikilitic syenite. The presence of two block zones (see below) indicates partial differentiation of the pegmatitic melt.

There is clearly-defined dual concentric zoning in the pegmatitic body. Three zones can be distinguished from the periphery and from the central outcrop of the country rocks to the axial part of the annular pegmatite outcrop: (1) an outer equigranular zone, (2) an intermediate macrocrystalline orthoclase-aegirine zone and (3) a central block orthoclase-natrolite zone. The first two zones outline the outer boundary between the pegmatitic body and the country rocks and the central outcrop of these rocks, while the orthoclase-natrolite zone is developed only in the southern part of the pegmatitic body (see Fig. 70).

The thickness of the outer equigranular zone varies from 1 m in the western part of the body to 3 m in the eastern. It is composed mainly of orthoclase (50 per cent), nepheline (20 per cent) and aegirine I (30 per cent). It gives way gradually to the intermediate orthoclase-aegirine zone. This zone (which is approximately 1 m thick) is composed of orthoclase (approximately 30 per cent) and green fibrous aegirine II (approximately 60 per cent). One finds also ramsayite, lamprophyllite and eudialyte. The central zone of the pegmatitic body (up to 2 m thick) is composed in the main of orthoclase and natrolite and has a block structure. Large orthoclase blocks are included in a monomineralic mass of macrocrystalline and drusy white natrolite. Segregations of most of the rare-metal minerals are associated with the natrolite areas.

Orthoclase, nepheline, aegirine and natrolite are the main minerals of the pegmatitic body and there are subordinate amounts of ramsayite, lamprophyllite, eudialyte, neptunite and others.

Orthoclase is most widely distributed in the central zone, where it forms monomineralic blocks of up to 1.5×1.5 m. In the outer and intermediate zones it is represented by tabular crystals of up to $10 \times 5 \times 1$ cm and the dimensions of its segregations increase from the periphery to the central part of the pegmatitic body. The colour of the orthoclase is grey and bluish-green. The grey tint is typical of the contact zone, while the bluish-green is found in the central zone.

This is an early mineral of the pegmatitic body. It contains inclusions of idiomorphic aegirine I and nepheline crystals, while the remaining minerals are confined to the interstices between its segregations. Orthoclase is replaced by natrolite, which is most widely manifested in the central zone.

Nepheline occurs only in the outer zone, where it is represented by greenish crystals with a cross-section of up to 2 cm. Crystals of it are usually found in aegirine II and less frequently in the peripheral parts of orthoclase crystals. Nepheline, in its turn, contains inclusions of well-formed aegirine I crystals; it is sometimes spreusteinized and replaced round its border by chalcedonic natrolite.

Aegirine is found mainly in the outer and intermediate zones, where it is represented by two generations. Aegirine I occurs in the outer zone as slender-prismatic black crystals of up to 5 cm in length and 0.5×0.3 cm in cross-section. It is the earliest mineral and is usually present as inclusions in orthoclase and nepheline. Aegirine II is developed mainly in the intermediate zone, where it forms fibrous aggregates, that are usually radiating but sometimes fibrous-diverse. It fills the interstices between segregations of orthoclase, lamprophyllite, ramsayite, eudialyte, etc.

Ramsayite is found mainly in the intermediate zone as irregular dark brown segregations of up to 10×7 cm. It is normally included in fibrous aegirine II and is xenomorphic to orthoclase crystals.

Lamprophyllite, like ramsayite, is a typical rare-metal mineral of the intermediate zone. It forms tabular crystals, and less frequently radiate-fibrous aggregates, up to $15 \times 4 \times 2$ cm. Lamprophyllite crystals are usually included in aegirine II.

Eudialyte is seen in the outer and intermediate zones as equant brownish-red segregations up to $4 \times 3 \times 3$ cm, included in aegirine II. In the outer zone eudialyte contains inclusions of idiomorphic aegirine I crystals. It is replaced by catapleiite and zirfesite.

Neptunite is encountered in the central zone as irregular segregations of up to 2×1 cm, and less frequently as small well-bounded crystals with a cross-section of up to 0.5 cm. It is dark red or nearly black in colour. Neptunite is present in natrolite either as inclusions or filling cavities. One sometimes finds secondary neptunite that has developed in schizolite, eudialyte and ramsayite. This neptunite usually fills cracks in these minerals or forms fringes round them.

Apatite is present in considerable quantities in the central zone, where it forms yellowish-green prismatic crystals of up to 3 cm in length and 0.5×0.5 cm in cross-section. One also comes across light green and dark blue apatite spherulites and blue and colourless apatite as prismatic crystals and $1.5 \times 1 \times 1$ cm irregular segregations. Apatite is intimately associated with tainiolite, staffelite [francolite] etc.

Sphalerite occurs in the central zone as irregular segregations up to 1.5-2 cm in length and 0.2-0.3 cm thick. It is typically found as an intergrowth with orthoclase and is seen less frequently as inclusions in natrolite. The colour of sphalerite varies, but it is usually black and brown and less frequently yellow and greenish-blue. The mineral is unstable and oxidizes readily to give rise to limonite, sauconite and calamine.

Galena, which is much less common than sphalerite, is represented by irregular leaden-grey segregations of up to 1 cm included in natrolite. It is sometimes replaced from the periphery by cerussite.

Natrolite is widely distributed in the central zone as coarse-prismatic monomineralic segregations measuring 1.5×1 m. It also forms clearly-defined crystals in cavities in coarse-prismatic natrolite and compact segregations of fibrous structure. It is usually white, but small crystals are sometimes water-clear.

Natrolite is a late mineral of the pegmatitic body. It contains inclusions of

apatite, neptunite, sphalerite, galena and other minerals. Such minerals as tainiolite, polylithionite, staffelite [francolite], vernadite, sauconite and halloysite fill
cavities and cracks in it.

Besides the minerals mentioned here, this pegmatitic body contains minute
quantities of microcline, sodalite, analcite, arfvedsonite, loparite, pyrochlore, etc.

15. The Orthoclase-Natrolite Pegmatitic Body of Lepkhe-Nel'm

The orthoclase-natrolite pegmatitic body in the central area of the northern
slope of Lepkhe-Nel'm, approximately 100 m above the body just described, was

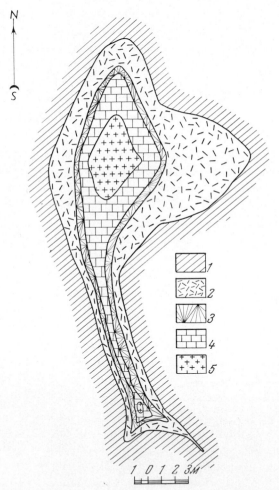

Fig. 71. Diagram of the orthoclase-natrolite
pegmatitic body of Lepkhe-Nel'm (after Semenov)

1. poikilitic hydrosodalite-syenite; 2. outer equigranular zone; 3. orthoclase-aegirine zone; 4. orthoclase zone; 5. natrolite nucleus

first discovered by Semenov and is here described from his data. It is emplaced in poikilitic hydrosodalite-syenites that are more leucocratic than ordinary hydro-sodalite-syenites and that have a coarser-grained texture.

The pegmatitic body is of irregular lenticular shape and meridional trend. Its length is 26 m. The thickness increases to 13 m in a bulge in the northern part and tapers to 2 m towards the south (Fig. 71).

Symmetrical zoning is quite clearly manifested in the pegmatitic body. The following zones can be distinguished between the walls and the axial region: (1) contact; (2) orthoclase-aegirine; (3) orthoclase, and (4) natrolite.

The equigranular contact zone, varying between 30 cm and 5·5 m in thickness, is composed in the main of aegirine I, orthoclase and nepheline. The length of the greyish-yellow prismatic orthoclase crystals may reach 10 cm. Nepheline forms greenish-grey crystals up to 3 cm across and 5 cm long that are idiomorphic to orthoclase. Black prismatic crystals of aegirine I as much as 5 cm long and $0·5 \times 0·4$ cm in cross-section occur as inclusions in the nepheline and the orthoclase. There are small quantities of eudialyte, loparite, and sphene in this zone.

The orthoclase-aegirine zone, which reaches a thickness of 0·7 m, is far more enriched with eudialyte and lamprophyllite than the contact zone. The orthoclase in it forms light-grey crystals up to $50 \times 20 \times 10$ cm, the interstices between which are filled with fibrous dark-green aegirine II. The longest dimension of the eudialyte, ramsayite and lamprophyllite segregations does not normally exceed 5 cm. These minerals are concentrated in the interstices between orthoclase crystals and are contained in aegirine II.

The orthoclase zone, which reaches a thickness of 3 m, is almost entirely composed of large block light-grey orthoclase. The individual crystals are often orientated perpendicular to the contact and extend from the contact zone through the orthoclase-aegirine zone into the orthoclase zone. In such cases the length of the orthoclase crystals may be more than a metre for a width that varies from a few centimetres in the peripheral zone to several tens of centimetres in the central zone, where they seem to merge and form a monomineralic zone.

The 5×3 m natrolite zone (the nucleus) in the central area of the bulge is mainly composed of macrocrystalline natrolite. Segregations of analcite, apatite, halloysite, sauconite, schizolite and polylithionite, are confined to the natrolite nucleus.

Besides the minerals mentioned above, arfvedsonite, ramsayite, staffelite [francolite], sphalerite and other minerals are found in the pegmatitic body.

Unlike the orthoclase-aegirine pegmatitic body already described, differentiation has been more complete in this body, and the orthoclase has crystallized as a monomineralic zone, while natrolite and analcite have formed separate small nuclei in the axial region of the body.

16. The Apatite-Bearing Orthoclase-Natrolite Pegmatitic Stock of Lepkhe-Nel'm

This pegmatitic stock was first discovered and studied in 1951 by Semenov, whose findings are taken into consideration in this description. It lies on the northern slope of Lepkhe-Nel'm facing Seid"yavr approximately 200 m above the lake and 180 m to the east-south-east of the orthoclase-aegirine body.

The pegmatitic body is emplaced in aegirine-lujavrites. The irregular oval outcrop, the greatest diameter of which is approximately 30 m and the smallest

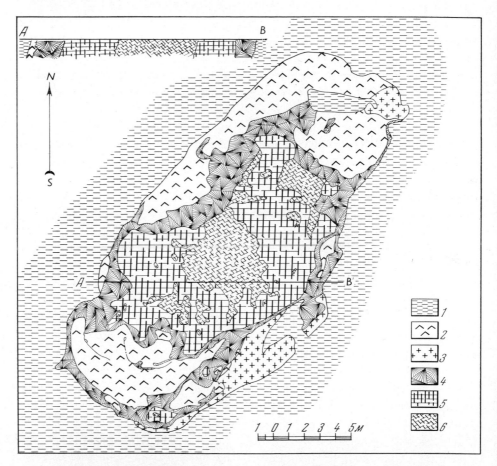

Fig. 72. Diagram of the apatite-bearing orthoclase-natrolite pegmatitic stock (after Semenov and Ivanov)

1. aegirine-lujavrite; 2. poikilitic syenite; 3. contact microcline zone; 4. ortho-clase-aegirine zone; 5. orthoclase zone; 6. natrolite zone

approximately 15 m (Fig. 72), is of south-westerly trend. There is a sharp magmatic contact between the pegmatitic stock and the enclosing lujavrites. The lujavrite horizon is slightly domed over the pegmatites. The trachytoid structure of the lujavrites is cut across by the contact. The lujavrites are greatly natrolitized at the contact, near which microcline is found to be replaced by orthoclase and albite and aegirine by arfvedsonite.

A great many large xenoliths of greatly altered and reworked poikilitic syenite (up to 3×5 m) are known to exist in the northern and southern parts of the pegmatitic body. In the north-western and northern parts of the pegmatite there are sharp contacts between the enclosing lujavrites and the poikilitic syenite xenoliths, and there is great alteration and loss of trachytoid texture in the lujavrites at the contact. The contacts between the lujavrites and the poikilitic syenites and pegmatite are very steep (from 50° in the southern part of the body to 70° in the northern part) and they dip to the south-east. It is clear that the pegmatitic melt broke through the apical area of a column-like intrusion of poikilitic syenite in the lujavrite and penetrated along the contact between the poikilitic syenite and the lujavrites.

Concentric zoning is clearly defined in this pegmatitic stock. There are the following zones between the periphery and the centre: (1) contact microcline; (2) block orthoclase-aegirine; (3) orthoclase; and (4) natrolite (see Fig. 72). There are gradual transitions from one to another of the first three zones.

The contact zone is to be seen only in the south-eastern part of the pegmatitic stock. Its thickness varies between 20 cm in the southern part and 1·5 m in the south-western part. It consists largely of microcline but contains small amounts of eudialyte, sphene and certain other minerals.

It is interesting to note that a microcline fringe can be seen in the southern part of the pegmatitic stock round a lujavrite xenolith and bordering on the ortho-clase-aegirine zone.

The orthoclase-aegirine zone, which can be traced along the periphery of the pegmatitic stock, bounds all the poikilitic syenite xenoliths. Its thickness varies from 0·1 to 2 m. This zone has a block structure. It is half composed of large orthoclase crystals, the interstices between which are filled with radiate-fibrous felted aegirine, which accounts for approximately 30 per cent of the zone. The remaining 20 per cent of the zone consists of nepheline, arfvedsonite, eudialyte, lamprophyllite, etc.

Nine-tenths of the orthoclase zone, the thickness of which varies between 1·5 and 4 m, consists of large orthoclase crystals. There are small amounts of late aegirine, with eudialyte and lamprophyllite inclusions, in the interstices between the orthoclase crystals.

The 4×6 m natrolite zone (the nucleus) occupies the central area of the pegmatitic stock. It is nine-tenths made up of natrolite. The specific minerals are apatite, tainiolite, polylithionite, schizolite, staffelite [francolite], neptunite, leucophane, clay minerals of the montmorillonite group (sauconite) and halloysite. There are also small quantities of vernadite, quartz and a series of hydrous silico-phosphates of the rare earths.

The main minerals of the pegmatitic body are orthoclase (approximately 40 per cent), natrolite (approximately 20 per cent) and aegirine (approximately 20 per cent). The following accessory minerals are worth mentioning: eudialyte (approximately 5 per cent), microcline (approximately 5 per cent), nepheline (approximately 5 per cent), arfvedsonite, lamprophyllite, apatite, staffelite [franco-lite], tainiolite, polylithionite, leucophane, hydrargillite and vernadite.

Orthoclase accounts for 40-50 per cent of the pegmatitic body. The size of its bluish-grey crystals varies from $8 \times 5 \times 1.5$ cm in the peripheral parts of the block zone to $2.4 \times 0.7 \times 0.4$ m in the orthoclase zone. They are usually orientated from the periphery to the centre of the pegmatite, and the same crystal frequently passes all through the block zone, gradually increasing in width and thickness. Near the natrolite zone one finds areas, or small isolated transparent bluish crystals, of orthoclase ('moonstone') with distinct iridescence on the cleavage surfaces.

Orthoclase is one of the earliest minerals to separate. All the remaining minerals except arfvedsonite are confined to the interstices between the orthoclase crystals or enclosed in their borders (eudialyte, lamprophyllite and apatite). Inclusions of arfvedsonite crystals are also found in the central parts of orthoclase crystals. Near the central zone the orthoclase is greatly replaced by natrolite, as is shown by the irregular, etched contours of the natrolite zone and the existence of orthoclase relicts in its marginal parts. The orthoclase has been much altered to clay minerals.

Microcline occurs only in the outer zone, where it accounts for approximately 80 per cent of the volume. Its light-cream tabular crystals, reaching lengths of up to 5 cm, are closely packed and orientated approximately perpendicular to the contact. Microcline is the earliest mineral to have separated. Sphene and eudialyte are normally xenomorphic to it.

Nepheline is present in large amounts in the block zone, especially at its margin. It forms greenish-grey idiomorphic crystals up to 30 cm, the brownish-grey and reddish-brown colour of which is due to strongly-manifested replacement processes. There is an increase in the dimensions of the segregations between the periphery and the centre of the pegmatitic body.

Nepheline separated later than orthoclase, since it is found in the interstices between orthoclase crystals. Idiomorphic crystals of it are usually included in fibrous aegirine II.

The reddish-brown tint of the nepheline near the orthoclase zone is due to its marked zeolitization, the degree of which increases from the margins to the centre. The nepheline is sometimes entirely replaced by zeolite. Fringes (up to 3 cm thick) of greyish-brown chalcedonic natrolite are found round such pseudo-morphs. Hydrargillite and montmorillonite are sometimes present in the central parts of replaced nepheline crystals.

Aegirine is represented only as a late precipitate. Aegirine II, which is the main mineral of the block zone, occurs as dense felted segregations of radiate-fibrous structure and greyish-green colour that fill the interstices between the crystals of microcline, nepheline, eudialyte, astrophyllite and other minerals in the zone. Aegirine III is encountered in small amounts in natrolite cavities in the central zone, as acicular crystals and bluish-green radiate-fibrous segregations with a cross-section of up to 1.5 cm, or as veinlets in the quartz-clay rock of the central zone. In addition to aegirine III, acmite is found in natrolite cavities as cinnamon-brown or reddish segregations of sheaf-like appearance with a cross-section of up to 0·7 cm. Both aegirine III and acmite are late minerals and are associated with the minerals of the replacement complex.

Arfvedsonite is found mainly in the block zone and less frequently in the orthoclase and natrolite zones. Its regular black crystals vary in size from microscopic size to $2 \times 2 \times 3$ cm, and are included in orthoclase, nepheline, eudialyte, aegirine II, natrolite and other minerals.

Eudialyte is abundant in the periphery of the block zone. In the northern part of the pegmatite there are nests and bands of fine-grained feldspathic eudialyte-

FIG. 73. Replacement of eudialyte (black) by catapleiite (light). ×46. Crossed nicols

rock up to 1 m wide, 70-80 per cent of which is eudialyte. In other regions of the pegmatite the eudialyte forms idiomorphic reddish-pink crystals with a cross-section up to 3 cm included in nepheline and in aegirine II or in the borders of orthoclase crystals. Large irregular eudialyte segregations with a cross-section up to 10×15 cm are found in aegirine II. They are normally greatly altered and replaced by eucolite, catapleiite (Fig. 73) and zirfesite.

Lamprophyllite is found mainly in the block zone as reddish-brown tabular segregations up to $15 \times 4 \times 3$ cm or as radiate-fibrous crystal growths that may be as much as 10 cm long and $0·3 \times 1$ cm in cross-section. Lamprophyllite crystals are usually included in aegirine II and less frequently in eudialyte and nepheline. Lamprophyllite is replaced by yellow ochreous leucoxene.

Apatite is widely distributed in the natrolite zone, where it forms light-green idiomorphic hexagonal-prismatic crystals varying from a few millimetres in length to $12 \times 6 \times 6$ cm, or aggregates of small irregular grains. In the northern part of the body there is a small zone of almost monomineralic fine-grained apatite-rock. As well as green apatite, one finds also white, bluish and dark-brown apatite. (See Part 3, 'Mineralogy', for a description of these varieties.)

Green prismatic apatite formed earlier than natrolite, as is shown by its idiomorphism to natrolite. Other apatite varieties are usually confined to natrolite cavities and are later.

Natrolite forms prismatic crystals up to $20 \times 10 \times 10$ cm in the central zone and microcrystalline monomineralic segregations. It is often found to contain orthoclase relicts of irregular shape and regular arfvedsonite crystals. At the contacts between the intermediate and central zones natrolite occurs in cavities as free-growing crystals of pseudotetragonal habit.

There are small amounts of *staffelite* [francolite] in the central zone, in natrolite or aegirine II cavities, as columnar encrusting segregations, dark-brown to brown, yellow and white in colour and up to $0.8 \times 0.1 \times 0.1$ cm in size, or crusts up to 1 mm thick. Staffelite spherulites with a diameter up to 0.3 cm are found less frequently. Normally it is intimately associated with montmorillonite, sauconite and the alteration-products of schizolite, and it is one of the last minerals to separate.

Tainiolite and polylithionite are concentrated in the northern part of the central zone, where they are intimately associated with clay minerals. They form white, greenish, cream or dark-brown to brown, foliaceous, tabular or sheaf-like segregations with a diameter between 2 mm and 1 cm. These minerals usually fill the cracks in natrolite and less frequently in orthoclase; during alteration they are converted into an argillaceous mass greasy to the touch.

Hydrargillite is usually present in spreustein pseudomorphs after nepheline, as small scattered flakes. White transparent hydrargillite crystals up to 0.5 cm in cross-section are sometimes found in the centres of these pseudomorphs.

Vernadite is found in the central zone in association with brown apatite and schizolite. It forms irregular black segregations up to 10×10 cm with the lustre of pitch. It is often formed in the replacement of schizolite, and usually fills cavities and spaces in natrolite.

Halloysite is present in large quantities in the central zone, where it fills cavities in natrolite together with polylithionite and staffelite. It is sometimes found in the central parts of spreustein pseudomorphs after nepheline as soft rounded aggregations. The colour is brownish-pink or brown.

Neptunite forms dark-red crystals up to $0.5 \times 0.3 \times 0.3$ cm that are intimately associated with manganese minerals in the clay subzone.

Besides the minerals listed above, this pegmatitic body contains minute amounts of analcite, kupletskite, pyrochlore, hydrogoethite, cerussite, leucophane, sphalerite, galena, molybdenite, chlorite, quartz, opal, fluorite, etc.

It can be seen that abundance of orthoclase and the presence of magnesian and calcium minerals (tainiolite, montmorillonite, halloysite and apatite) are typical of this body. This all indicates that the initial pegmatitic melt was richer in potassium, magnesium and calcium than the melt from which the Karnasurt pegmatites originated.

17. THE TAINIOLITE PEGMATITIC BODY OF LEPKHE-NEL'M

This body was first discovered and studied in 1951 by Semenov, whose findings are taken into consideration here. It lies on the northern slope of Lepkhe-Nel'm 90 m to the south-west of the orthoclase-natrolite pegmatitic stock and is emplaced in poikilitic nepheline-sodalite-syenites approximately 30 m from their contact with the aegirine-lujavrites of the differentiated complex.

It should be noted that this pegmatitic body lies in a transitional zone between poikilitic nepheline- and sodalite-syenites and that its north-eastern part is emplaced in poikilitic nepheline-syenites with orthoclase and hydrosodalite, while its south-western part is bedded in poikilitic sodalite (hackmanite)-syenites with

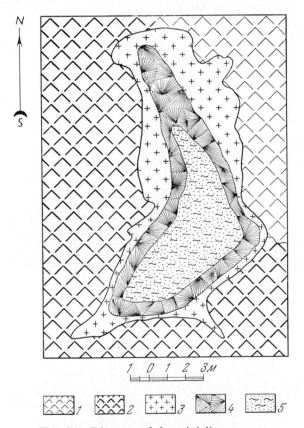

FIG. 74. Diagram of the tainiolite pegmatitic body (after Semenov)

1. poikilitic hydrosodalite-syenite; 2. poikilitic sodalite-syenite; 3. outer equigranular zone; 4. feldspathic aegirine zone; 5. replacement zone

microcline. These poikilitic syenite varieties merge gradually with each other through intermediate varieties containing nepheline in conjunction with sodalite and orthoclase in conjunction with microcline.

The pegmatitic body is a facies formation that crystallized where the pegmatitic melt accumulated in the poikilitic syenites. It is an irregular southward-stretching body (Fig. 74) approximately 18 m long and up to 10 m wide. It reaches its greatest width in the southern part of the pegmatitic body and tapers off to the north.

There are gradual transitions between the country rocks and the pegmatitic body. Near the pegmatite there is a zone more than 1 m thick in which the poikilitic syenites are inequigranular in texture and enriched in places with eudialyte, aegirine II or non-poikilitic orthoclase, the segregations of which reach a length of 8 cm and a thickness of more than 1 cm.

Three zones are clearly visible between the margins and the centre: (1) outer fine-grained; (2) intermediate macrocrystalline (block) feldspar-aegirine; and (3) central natrolite zone (see Fig. 74).

The outer fine-grained zone, which is 0·5 m thick in the southern part of the pegmatite and up to 2 m in the northern part, is composed mainly of orthoclase, aegirine I, nepheline and eudialyte. There are smaller quantities of lamprophyllite, ramsayite and loparite. There is a gradual increase in the dimensions of the mineral segregations from the periphery to the centre. Near the feldspar-aegirine zone the orthoclase segregations reach a length of 20 cm and a width of 6 cm, while in the peripheral parts they are 2 cm long and 0·5 cm thick. Some parts of the zone are eudialyte-enriched.

The orthoclase-aegirine zone, which merges gradually with the fine-grained zone, consists primarily of orthoclase (up to 40 per cent) and aegirine II (up to 30 per cent). There are smaller amounts of nepheline, eudialyte, ramsayite, and other minerals. The central zone (approximately 7 × 3 m) is composed mainly of clay minerals, in which halloysite predominates (up to 30 per cent). Other minerals widely distributed in it include prismatic natrolite (20 per cent), tainiolite, polylithionite, apatite (5 per cent), late microcrystalline orthoclase (5 per cent), staffelite [francolite], neptunite, schizolite (15 per cent), sphene, sulphides and other minerals, including especially manganese minerals and the hydrous silicophosphates of the rare earths.

The main minerals of the pegmatitic body are orthoclase, nepheline, aegirine, eudialyte, natrolite and clay minerals. There are lesser quantities of polylithionite, lamprophyllite, ramsayite, apatite, kupletskite, loparite, etc.

Orthoclase forms thick-tabular light-grey and bluish-grey semi-transparent crystals varying from 2 cm in length and 0·5 cm in thickness in the peripheral zone to up to 20 × 6 × 5 cm in the intermediate zone. This is an early mineral of the pegmatitic body. It normally contains inclusions of idiomorphic nepheline, loparite, aegirine I and eudialyte crystals and is, in its turn, included in a felted aggregate of aegirine II. Late orthoclase occurs in the cavities of the natrolite zone as tabular light-cream crystals up to 0·7 × 0·5 × 0·2 cm.

Orthoclase is quite often altered to an aggregate of clay minerals, and less frequently replaced by natrolite. The process of natrolitization is especially marked in the central zone. In these cases the natrolite replaces orthoclase from the periphery of the crystals or fills cracks in them.

Nepheline is present mainly in the fine-grained and less frequently in the intermediate zone as greenish-grey and grey segregations with a rounded or hexagonal cross-section up to 3 cm. It is one of the earliest minerals. Its idiomorphic crystals are included in orthoclase and, in their turn, contain inclusions of aegirine I crystals.

In the late stages it is replaced by natrolite. This process is particularly widespread in the intermediate zone, where natrolite forms fibrous pseudomorphs after nepheline enclosed in a felted mass of aegirine II.

There are three generations of *aegirine*. Aegirine I forms long-prismatic black crystals a few millimetres long in the borders of the peripheral zone and up to 4 cm long and 0.7×0.5 cm in cross-section in its central part. This is the earliest mineral of the pegmatitic body. Its idiomorphic crystals are usually included in nepheline, orthoclase, eudialyte and other minerals.

In the intermediate zone aegirine II forms felted segregations in the interstices between crystals of orthoclase, nepheline, eudialyte and other high-temperature rare-metal minerals. Idiomorphic inclusions of eudialyte and ramsayite and pseudomorphs of fibrous natrolite after nepheline are found in aegirine II.

Aegirine III is sometimes found in cracks in orthoclase crystals as yellowish-green spherulites with a diameter up to 0.4 cm.

Small amounts of *loparite* are found only in the outer zone as small black crystals with an average cross-section of 1-2 mm and rarely 4 mm. This is a very early mineral of the pegmatitic body; its idiomorphic crystals are usually included in orthoclase, nepheline and eudialyte.

In the outer zone and especially at the contact between this zone and the intermediate zone *eudialyte* quite often forms practically monomineralic areas. It occurs as reddish-pink equant segregations or well-formed crystals up to 1-2 cm and occasionally as much as 15 cm in cross-section. The large crystals are associated with aegirine II and orthoclase.

Eudialyte separated later than nepheline and aegirine I but earlier than aegirine II, lamprophyllite and ramsayite. Its segregations usually contain inclusions of aegirine I and, in their turn, are included in orthoclase, in the marginal parts of nepheline, and in ramsayite, lamprophyllite and aegirine II.

Eudialyte is often replaced by eucolite, catapleiite and zirfesite. The first two are developed mainly in the central part of the pegmatitic body, while zirfesite occurs also in the border zone. The replacement of eudialyte has usually been progressive. The initial development of eucolite replacement is followed by catapleiite. Eucolite is most often developed at the borders of the pseudomorphs, while the central zones consist of catapleiite. Zirfesite develops from eudialyte under surface conditions.

Lamprophyllite is most typical of the outer zone, where it forms reddish-brown bladed crystals or radiating tufts up to 5 cm long and $1·3 \times 1·5$ cm in cross-section. Large accumulations of lamprophyllite (up to $20 \times 15 \times 10$ cm) consisting of variously-orientated packets of crystals (up to 13 cm long and 4×4 cm in cross-section) are found in some regions of the pegmatitic body nearer the centre. Lamprophyllite separated later than eudialyte and nepheline. It sometimes forms intergrowths with orthoclase.

Kupletskite occurs rarely in the southern part of the outer zone, where it is intimately associated with eudialyte. Its finely scaly dark-brown to black segregations reach sizes of $0·5 \times 0·3$ cm.

Small amounts of *ramsayite* are found as irregular dark-brown segregations up to $2 \times 1 \times 1$ cm, xenomorphic to lamprophyllite. Well-formed crystals are occasionally found included in orthoclase. Ramsayite is often replaced by vinogradovite, which develops round the borders of its segregations and occasionally fills cracks in it. It is also replaced by neptunite and white radiate-fibrous sphene.

Natrolite is found mainly in the central zone as relicts up to $10 \times 7 \times 5$ cm in a fine-grained mass of tainiolite, polylithionite and clay minerals. The colour is white. It is normally represented by variously-orientated bladed crystals, some of which are as much as 7 cm long and 2×2 cm in cross-section.

Tainiolite forms brown tabular crystals in the central zone, pseudohexagonal in shape and measuring up to $3 \times 3 \times 0·5$ cm. Large lepidolite crystals have a zonal structure; their cores, which are stained dark-brown, consist of tainiolite, while the peripheral (lighter) parts are polylithionite. Tainiolite and polylithionite zones sometimes alternate in the same crystal. The tainiolite is intimately associated with schizolite, polylithionite and apatite.

Polylithionite is found in the central zone as compact finely scaly segregations filling the interstices between tainiolite aggregations. It sometimes fills cracks up to 1 cm wide through orthoclase and natrolite and forms margins up to $1·5$ cm thick round orthoclase crystals. The colour is usually white, less frequently brown and greenish-blue.

Apatite occurs in the central zone. Several varieties can be distinguished by the colour and form of the segregations. Green and yellowish-green apatite, which forms short-prismatic crystals up to $10 \times 6 \times 6$ cm, is the most widely distributed. This apatite sometimes forms quite large monomineralic areas. On rare occasions the prismatic apatite is replaced by a lower-temperature fine-grained aggregate of brown apatite.

Besides prismatic apatite, greenish and brownish-grey tabular apatite occurs quite commonly in the pegmatitic body; the tabular segregations reach dimensions of $5 \times 5 \times 3$ cm. In the central zone yellowish-grey, sky-blue, blue, violet, spherulitic and pale-green apatite varieties are found much less frequently.

Labuntsovite is found rarely in the central zone as brown prismatic crystals up to $1 \times 0·2 \times 0·1$ cm in the leaching cavities of earlier minerals. It is typically in paragenetic association with tainiolite, tabular apatite and halloysite.

Halloysite forms large, practically monomineralic brownish-yellow and brown segregations ($5 \times 5 \times 4$ cm, rarely $50 \times 50 \times 30$ cm) in the central zone. It normally contains inclusions of apatite, tainiolite and the other minerals of the zone, and fills the interstices between natrolite crystals.

In addition to the minerals here described, the pegmatitic body contains minute amounts of analcite, arfvedsonite, sphene, neptunite, pyrochlore, vernadite, sphalerite, staffelite [francolite], schizolite, galena, calamine, sauconite, etc.

18. The Orthoclase-Analcite Pegmatitic Vein of Kuivchorr

This vein was first discovered by Semenov, whose data are taken into account in the present description. It lies roughly in the centre of the south-eastern slope of Kuivchorr, 600-700 m from the mouth of the Koklukhtiuai valley.

The pegmatitic vein can be traced down the slope at an azimuth of 160° for approximately 170 m and dips steeply to the north-east at an angle of approximately 70°, with almost parallel sharp contacts. The thickness varies between 3 and 6 m. In the central part of the body there is a xenolith of fine-grained rock, approximately 3 × 0·4 m, that follows the direction of the strike of the vein. A branch up to 1·5 m thick from the upper part of the vein can be traced to the north parallel to the main body (Fig. 75).

The northern part of the pegmatitic vein is emplaced in fine- and medium-grained dense nepheline rocks, containing pyrrhotite, which were probably formed by recrystallization of xenoliths of Devonian rocks enclosed in the foyaites of the differentiated complex. There then follows a wide outcrop of ijolitic poiki-litic nepheline-syenite, underneath which there is a vast xenolith of dark-grey to black very dense Devonian rocks, followed by the lujavrites of the differentiated complex. Below the lujavrites the slope of Kuivchorr is covered with vegetation.

The pegmatitic vein cuts through all the rocks above. Its contacts with the country rocks are sharply intrusive. The genetic link of the vein with the poikilitic syenites is indicated by the complete analogy between its chemical and minera-logical composition and structure and that of the Lepkhe-Nel'm pegmatites.

There is symmetrical zoning in the main pegmatitic body, especially in its thicker parts. The following zones can be distinguished between the contacts and the axial region (see Fig. 75): (1) outer equigranular; (2) aegirine; (3) orthoclase-analcite; and (4) replacement (albite) zone. The same zoning can be seen round the xenolith in the upper part of the vein.

The outer zone is between 0·3 and 1 m thick at the eastern contact and between 0·3 and 1·5 m thick at the western. The main minerals are orthoclase (40 per cent), nepheline (30 per cent), aegirine I and II and eudialyte. The accessory minerals include lamprophyllite, apatite, loparite and zircon. The equigranular zone gives way gradually to the aegirine zone by an increase in the content of aegirine II.

The aegirine zone is composed in the main of dark-green fibrous aegirine with a subordinate amount of orthoclase, eudialyte and zircon. There are minute

LAM M

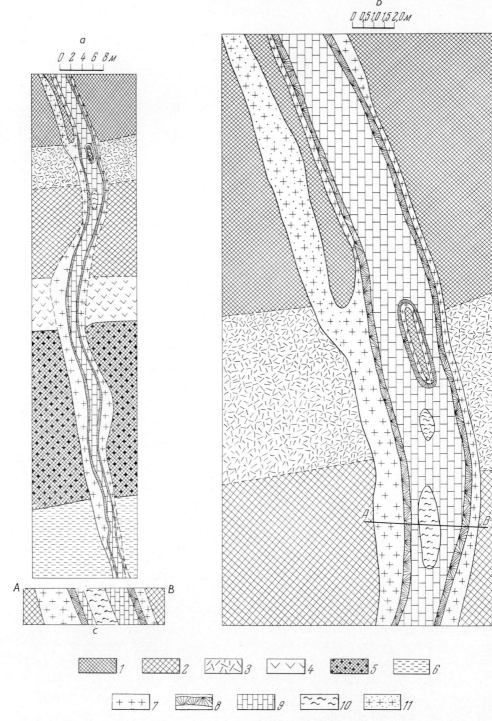

FIG. 75. Diagram of the orthoclase-analcite pegmatitic vein; a—general view; b—upper part; c—section along the line A-B (after E. I. Semenov)

1. fine-grained nepheline-syenite; 2. medium-grained nepheline-syenite; 3. foyaite; 4. poikilitic nepheline-syenite; 5. xenoliths of Devonian rocks; 6. lujavrite; 7. outer zone; 8. aegirine zone; 9. orthoclase-analcite zone; 10. replacement zone; 11. fine-grained albitized pegmatite

quantities of ilmenite and fluorite. The thickness of the zone ranges from 0·3 to 1 m. It forms a single central zone where the vein pinches.

The aegirine II zone is followed by the orthoclase-analcite zone, the transition between them being gradual. The orthoclase-analcite zone reaches a thickness of 2·5 m in swells, but is absent from pinches. The axial part of the zone, which reaches a thickness of 1·5 m, is almost entirely replaced by analcite. There are smaller amounts of aegirine II and eudialyte.

The replacement (albite) zone is found only in the thickest part of the vein as several small lenses up to 4 m long and 1 m wide. It is composed mainly of albite, analcite, natrolite and apatite, with a small amount of epididymite, tainiolite, zircon, sphene, ilmenite, fluorite and other accessory minerals.

The branch vein is an equigranular pegmatite consisting mainly of orthoclase, nepheline, aegirine I, eudialyte and loparite. The orthoclase here forms white tabular crystals up to $7 \times 7 \times 1$ cm. The nepheline and eudialyte occur as xenomorphic segregations in the interstices between orthoclase crystals. The nepheline is often entirely replaced by fibrous natrolite. Loparite and black acicular aegirine I form inclusions in eudialyte, nepheline and orthoclase.

The main minerals of the pegmatitic body are orthoclase, nepheline, aegirine, albite, analcite and eudialyte. The auxiliary and accessory minerals include lamprophyllite, apatite, loparite, zircon, sphene, ilmenite, fluorite, epididymite and tainiolite.

Orthoclase forms thick-tabular greyish-white crystals from 10 cm in length and 2×5 cm in cross-section in the equigranular pegmatite zone to 80 cm in length and 6×10 cm in cross-section in the orthoclase-analcite zones. It is an early mineral of this pegmatitic body. Its crystals are usually included in aegirine II and contain inclusions of aegirine I, nepheline, loparite and ilmenite.

The replacement of orthoclase by analcite is widespread, especially in the orthoclase-analcite zone, where the greater part of the orthoclase has been so replaced. Natrolite and albite develop on it in addition to analcite.

Nepheline is found only in the outer zone as greenish-grey hexagonal crystals with a cross-section up to 2 cm. It is one of the earlier minerals of the zone. It is usually found as idiomorphic inclusions in the marginal parts of orthoclase crystals or as irregular segregations in the interstices between them. Nepheline crystals often contain inclusions of aegirine I, loparite and ilmenite. The greater part of the nepheline has been spreusteinized or replaced by fine-fibrous natrolite.

There are two generations of *aegirine*. Aegirine I is developed only in the outer zone, where it is found as acicular black crystals varying between fractions of a millimetre in length and $1 \times 0·2 \times 0·1$ cm. It is an earlier mineral of the pegmatitic body. Inclusions of its crystals are found in such early minerals as nepheline, orthoclase and eudialyte. Aegirine II is developed mainly in the second zone and less commonly in the equigranular zone. It forms radiating finely-fibrous dirty-green bundles with a diameter up to 20 cm in the interstices between nepheline, aegirine I, orthoclase and eudialyte segregations.

Eudialyte is developed mainly in the outer zone, where it accounts for 30 per cent of its volume in some regions; it is rarely found in the other zones. Its rounded and hexagonal segregations reach a size of 5×5 cm; the colour is reddish-brown. The largest segregations are typical of the outer zone. Eudialyte most often fills the interstices between orthoclase and nepheline crystals. It contains inclusions of loparite and aegirine I and, in its turn, is included in aegirine II. It is often replaced by eucolite forming reddish-pink fine fringes. Zirfesite develops from it under surface conditions.

Lamprophyllite occurs mainly in the outer zone as tabular crystals up to $3 \times 0.7 \times 0.2$ cm and radiate-fibrous rosettes of brownish-yellow crystals with a radius up to 12 cm in aegirine II.

Loparite is found in the outer zone, where it is represented by idiomorphic crystals (combinations of cube and octahedron) included in all the minerals except aegirine I, which is earlier.

Ilmenite is found in accessory quantities in all zones of the pegmatitic body. Its thin tabular black crystals (up to $2 \times 2 \times 0.1$ cm) are usually included in orthoclase, analcite and albite. In the central zone it is greatly replaced by limonite or rutile-leucoxene.

Brookite is found in the outer zone as black isometric crystals with a cross-section up to 0.4×0.2 cm. It is sometimes confined to pseudomorphs of brown leucoxene on lamprophyllite, in which case its dimensions are up to 2×2 cm.

Zircon is found in minute quantities in the outer zone; it is more widely distributed in the central zone, where it is associated with albite, epididymite and apatite. It forms light- and dark-brown dipyramidal crystals with a cross-section up to 1 cm. In the outer zone it occurs as small crystals on the walls of leaching cavities.

Albite is widely distributed in the central part of the body, where it forms practically monomineralic white and brownish-pink segregations up to 4×1 m. It consists chiefly of the fine-grained variety; spherulites and the thin tabular varieties are found less frequently. Its intimate association with epididymite, tainiolite, sphene and apatite is typical.

Apatite occurs in the outer zone as light-green prismatic crystals with a cross-section up to 0.5 cm. In the central zone it is represented by brown ochreous coral-like segregations with a cross-section up to 5×5 cm. These segregations are made up of randomly intertwined long-prismatic crystals up to 3 cm in length and 0.3×0.2 cm in cross-section. Blue and violet apatite is sometimes found. The blue variety forms irregular segregations with a cross-section up to 1×0.4 cm in the central part of the pegmatite. Violet apatite is intimately associated with blue apatite and forms irregular segregations with a cross-section up to 0.3 cm.

Analcite is a main mineral of the orthoclase-analcite zone and is less common in the equigranular zone, where it forms a fine-grained white and creamy-white mass in the interstices between acicular segregations of aegirine II. It is found less frequently in the cavities of this zone as rounded globular segregations or equant crystals with a diameter up to 1 cm. In the orthoclase-analcite zone it forms white, practically monomineralic segregations up to 2×2 m. The greater part of the analcite is formed by the replacement of orthoclase, but in the outer zone it is apparently primary.

Epididymite is characteristic of the albite zone, where it forms white spherulites with a diameter up to 1·5 cm in intimate association with albite, apatite and zircon in a dense ochreous aggregate of brown fine-grained albite (Fig. 76). Epididymite is also found as irregular segregations up to $5 \times 1·5 \times 0·5$ cm, and

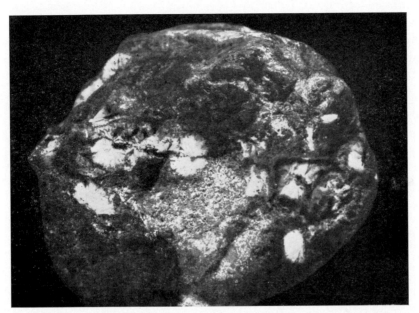

FIG. 76. Spherulites of epididymite (light) in fine-grained albite. Natural size

less frequently as spherulites up to 2 cm in diameter in cavities of orthoclase replaced by analcite.

Biotite occurs in the central zone as brownish-black tabular crystals up to $1 \times 1 \times 0·3$ cm, mainly as a secondary mineral on arfvedsonite. In some cases complete pseudomorphs after arfvedsonite are found. Manganiferous chlorite sometimes develops on biotite to form brown radiate segregations.

Fluorite occurs in all zones as countless small irregular violet segregations with a cross-section up to 0·2 cm.

Besides the minerals described above, the pegmatitic body also contains accessory amounts of natrolite, catapleiite, kupletskite, sphene, pyrochlore, tainiolite, hydromuscovite, staffelite [francolite], hydrogoethite, hydrargillite, sphalerite, sauconite, halloysite, etc.

19. The Microcline-Sodalite Pegmatitic stock of Malyi Punkaruaiv

The microcline-sodalite pegmatitic body lies on the north-eastern slope of Malyi Punkaruaiv approximately 100 m above the forest zone. The mountain slope in this district is made up of greatly sodalitized foyaites, lujavrites and urtites of the differentiated complex with a large number of facies and phase pegmatitic formations, of which this pegmatitic body is the largest. It was first discovered in 1951 by Borodin and is here described from his data.

Approximately 100 m to the south-east of the microcline-sodalite pegmatite the foyaites are pierced by a large intrusion of poikilitic syenite that extends for 150 m along the slope. The afforested lower part of the slope is also made up of

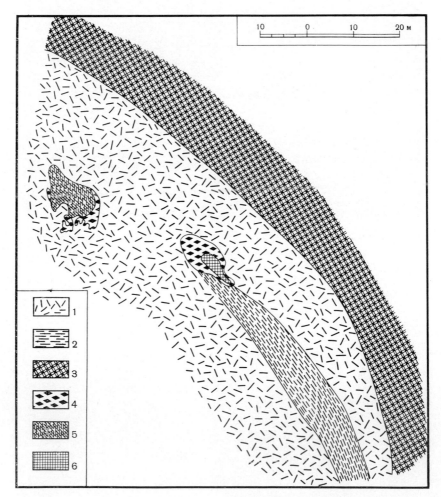

Fig. 77. Geological relations of the microcline-sodalite and ussingite pegmatitic bodies of Malyi Punkaruaiv (after Borodin)

1. foyaite; 2. lujavrite; 3. fine-grained nepheline-syenite; 4. eudialytic pegmatite zone; 5. microcline-sodalite zone; 6. ussingite zone

poikilitic syenite. Thus the pegmatitic body is emplaced in foyaites (Fig. 77) that appear to be compressed between two intrusions of poikilitic syenite.

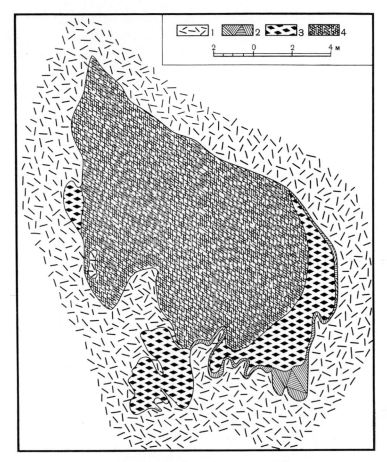

Fig. 78. Sketch of the microcline-sodalite peg-matite of Malyi Punkaruaiv (after Borodin)

1. foyaite; 2. aegirine zone; 3. eudialyte zone; 4. micro-cline-sodalite zone

The microcline-sodalite pegmatitic body is irregular in shape. It is slightly elongated towards the north-west (Fig. 78) and has an area of 16×8 m. There are sharp contacts between the pegmatite and the foyaites. The country rocks are highly sodalitized at the contact and enriched in eudialyte, ramsayite and arfvedsonite: there are great variations in their composition and texture at different places along the contact. The southern contact is sinuous owing to injections of pegmatite into the foyaites. Foyaite xenoliths of various shapes and sizes are found in the contact zone of the pegmatitic body, the largest being 80×30 cm.

It is highly probable that this pegmatitic body is genetically associated with poikilitic syenites and is injected into the foyaites. The existence of a genetic link between the pegmatitic body and the poikilitic syenites is indicated by the presence of a large amount of sodalite in it, which is either absent from the pegmatites of other rock complexes or present only in minute amounts.

The structure of the pegmatitic body varies in different parts. In the south-eastern area there is some zoning; three zones can be distinguished here between the margins and the centre: (1) aegirine; (2) eudialyte, and (3) microcline-sodalite (see Fig. 78). The microcline-sodalite zone accounts for the main mass of the pegmatite and comes directly into contact with the foyaites in the northern, north-eastern and western parts of the body.

The aegirine zone can be traced for approximately 18 m. Its thickness ranges between 10 cm and 2 m. It is made up in the main of fine-acicular aegirine and ussingite. Microcline, murmanite, neptunite, ramsayite, eudialyte and schizolite are also found. Except for neptunite, all these minerals form idiomorphic inclusions in aegirine or ussingite and fill the interstices between microcline crystals. Neptunite is usually confined to leaching cavities in aegirine and ussingite, where it forms idiomorphic crystals. The aegirine zone gives way gradually to the eudialyte zone by an increase in eudialyte content and a decrease in aegirine and ussingite.

The eudialytic zone is made up of a macrocrystalline monomineralic aggregate of brownish-red eudialyte with a subordinate amount of aegirine, loparite and microcline. Its thickness varies between a few centimetres where it peters out in the eastern part and 3 m in the southern part. In the southern and south-eastern parts of the pegmatitic body this zone gives way gradually to the microcline-sodalite zone.

The microcline-sodalite zone is approximately four-fifths microcline: the interstices between its crystals are filled with a monomineralic mass of sodalite. Where the zone makes direct contact with the foyaites, the microcline crystals are orientated roughly perpendicular to the contacts. Nepheline, eudialyte, arfved-sonite, ramsayite, aegirine and murmanite are also found in this zone. All these minerals, except nepheline, fill the interstices between microcline crystals and are idiomorphic to sodalite.

The main minerals of the pegmatitic stock are microcline, sodalite, eudialyte and aegirine. There are lesser amounts of arfvedsonite, murmanite, ramsayite, loparite, schizolite, neptunite, natrolite, ussingite, etc.

Nepheline is usually found in the microcline-sodalite zone, where greenish-grey prismatic crystals up to $3 \times 2 \times 2$ cm, almost invariably containing microscopic inclusions of aegirine I and arfvedsonite, form inclusions in eudialyte and microcline. It is replaced by sodalite, natrolite and albite.

Microcline occurs in the microcline-sodalite zone as prismatic grey crystals up to $30 \times 15 \times 10$ cm. In the eudialyte zone it forms well-shaped crystals that are idiomorphic to eudialyte. The cross-hatched twinning typical of microcline can be seen in thin sections. In the marginal parts of the crystals there are inclusions of idiomorphic nepheline, aegirine I, and, less frequently, arfvedsonite. Microcline is replaced by albite.

Arfvedsonite is represented in the microcline-sodalite zone by well-formed elongate-prismatic black crystals, often gathered into radiating aggregates ('suns').

The crystals reach a size of $7 \times 3 \times 1.5$ cm. Together with eudialyte, arfvedsonite fills the interstices between microcline crystals, and segregations of it are often included in eudialyte.

Aegirine makes up the aegirine zone and is represented by small acicular crystals up to 2 mm long and 0·2 mm wide that usually form compact radiating or felty aggregates filling the interstices between microcline crystals or forming nodular bundles in the ussingite mass. Small amounts of aegirine I occur as microscopic crystals included in nepheline and microcline.

Eudialyte forms regular crystals up to $3 \times 3 \times 2$ cm in the aegirine zone or dense macrocrystalline brownish-red aggregates in the interstices between the crystals of microcline and arfvedsonite in the eudialyte and microcline-sodalite zones.

Murmanite is found mainly in the ussingite areas of the aegirine zone and, less frequently, in the central part of the pegmatitic body. It is represented by brown or brownish-pink tabular segregations with a bronze chatoyancy along cleavage planes (up to $3 \times 2 \times 0.5$ cm). It usually fills the interstices between microcline and arfvedsonite crystals. It is earlier than ussingite, since it forms idiomorphic inclusions in it. In some cases there is apparently splintering of tabular segregations of murmanite included in ussingite, or some crystals are bent.

Ramsayite has been noted in various parts of the pegmatitic body as idiomorphic dark-brown crystals. Large segregations (up to $5 \times 2.5 \times 1.5$ cm) are normally found in the microcline-sodalite zone, while they do not exceed 3 cm in cross-section in the marginal parts of the body. Ramsayite frequently forms phenocrysts in eudialyte and sodalite, and together these three minerals fill the interstices between microcline crystals.

Loparite is found in some parts of the eudialyte zone as clusters of small crystals (up to 1-2 mm across). Usually included in eudialyte, it is found less frequently in arfvedsonite. It should be noted that most of the loparite grains have been crushed and that they form regular angular fragments apparently cemented by eudialyte and arfvedsonite.

Schizolite occurs in the aegirine zone as black prismatic crystals that are greatly altered and converted to a soft ochreous mass.

Neptunite is represented by regular, well-formed dark-red crystals, druses of which are found in the aegirine zone on the walls of cavities apparently formed by the leaching of sodalite, natrolite and ussingite. The cross-section of individual crystals does not exceed 1-1·5 cm.

Sodalite forms grey macrocrystalline segregations of irregular shape and up to 10×5 cm in area filling the interstices between crystals of other minerals or replacing nepheline as pseudomorphs.

Natrolite occurs as grey macrocrystalline segregations up to $7 \times 5 \times 3$ cm or radiate-fibrous growths in the borders of the microcline-sodalite zone. It fills the interstices between microcline and arfvedsonite crystals and is also developed after sodalite. The replacement of natrolite by ussingite is observed.

Ussingite is found in some parts of the aegirine zone as dense fine-grained masses of a light-violet colour. It contains inclusions of idiomorphic crystals of almost all the other minerals of the pegmatite and is normally deposited round late aegirine nodular concretions. There are frequent cases of the development of ussingite on microcline, sodalite and prismatic natrolite.

Differentiation did not proceed in this pegmatitic body as far as the formation of monomineralic zones. The body is a typical example of pegmatites with a block microcline-sodalite structure.

20. The Ussingite Pegmatitic Body of Malyi Punkaruaiv

The ussingite pegmatitic body lies on the north-eastern slope of Malyi Punkaruaiv approximately 150 m to the south-east of the microcline-sodalite pegmatite (see Fig. 77). It is the largest of five ussingite bodies of Malyi Punkaruaiv

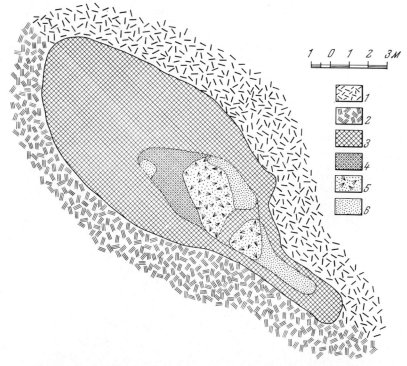

FIG. 79. Diagram of the ussingite pegmatitic body of Malyi Punkaruaiv (after Borodin)

1. foyaite; 2. mesocratic nepheline-syenite; 3. eudialyte zone; 4. eudialyte-ussingite zone; 5. aegirine-ussingite zone; 6. ussingite zone

in the original bedding. The ussingite bodies were discovered by Gerasimovskii and later studied by Borodin, whose data have been used in the present work.

The pegmatitic body is lens-shaped and strikes at 325°. Its dimensions are approximately 15 × 6 m.

The country rocks consist of foyaites and lujavrites of the differentiated complex. The pegmatitic body is emplaced where one of the lujavrite horizons in contact with the foyaite to the east and with the melanocratic nepheline syenite to the west (Fig. 77) peters out. There are quite sharp contacts between the pegmatitic body and the country rocks; alteration round the veins is shown by the enrichment of the country rocks with eudialyte, murmanite and sodalite.

Two zones can be distinguished in the pegmatitic body: (1) a eudialyte or peripheral zone and (2) an ussingite or central zone (see Fig. 79).

The eudialyte zone is 80-90 per cent eudialyte. Its thickness varies from 0·5 m in the south-eastern part to 6 m in the north-western part. In addition to eudialyte, it contains aegirine, schizolite, erikite, murmanite, ussingite, ramsayite and neptunite. These minerals are unevenly distributed. They are all xeno-morphic to eudialyte and are arranged in the interstices between its crystals.

There is a marked diminution in the amount of eudialyte (to 30-40 per cent) in the immediate vicinity of the contact with the country rocks. Here nepheline accompanies eudialyte as a major mineral. The thickness of the nepheline fringe does not exceed 10 cm.

In the north-western area the eudialyte zone does not make direct contact with the country rock. At the contact of this part of the pegmatite aegirine predominates (up to 70 per cent) and there are lesser quantities of ussingite (15-20 per cent), eudialyte (up to 5 per cent), schizolite and murmanite (up to 5 per cent). Texturally this part of the pegmatite differs greatly from the remainder of the outer zone. It is composed of nodular concretions of aegirine II apparently cemented by massive ussingite. Aegirine is represented by a dense felt-like mass consisting of small fine-acicular crystals scarcely visible without a microscope. The remaining minerals form inclusions in both aegirine and ussingite.

The ussingite zone is approximately 8 m long and 4 m wide. Its south-eastern part is made up mainly of ussingite (up to 60 per cent) in addition to microcline and sodalite (25-30 per cent) in approximately equal amounts. There are lesser quantities of natrolite (up to 5 per cent), murmanite and schizolite (up to 5 per cent). The accessory minerals include steenstrupine, galena, sphalerite, chkalovite, erikite, neptunite, arfvedsonite and aegirine. Chkalovite and steenstrupine, which are absent from the other parts of the pegmatite, are characteristic.

The abundance of sodalite, microcline and macrocrystalline natrolite relicts in the ussingite gives a mottled effect to the groundmass of this part of the zone: irregular areas of violet or pink ussingite alternate with greenish or transparent sodalite segregations, or with white or grey microcline. Segregations of chkalovite and sulphides and their alteration-products are associated with the contact between the ussingite and the eudialyte zones.

The central part of the zone differs from the south-eastern in that there is less ussingite, sodalite and microcline. The total amount of these minerals decreases to 50-60 per cent, while the aegirine content increases to 30-35 per cent. This part of the zone has a finer grain and a well-marked porphyritic texture. The small acicular crystals of aegirine (up to 1 cm long) are distributed randomly in a micro-cline-sodalite-ussingite mass. The fine-grained rock contains separate larger segregations of schizolite, erikite, murmanite, arfvedsonite, neptunite and eudialyte, which are rather unevenly distributed and are sometimes concentrated in particular areas. This part of the ussingite zone gives way gradually to both the ussingite and the eudialyte zones.

The north-western part of the zone is considerably enriched in eudialyte and is somewhat transitional between the ussingite and eudialyte zones. Here the ussingite is represented by isolated segregations in a coarse-grained eudialyte aggregate. There is no difference in the content of accessory minerals between this and the other parts of the ussingite zone.

The main minerals of the pegmatitic body are eudialyte, 35-40 per cent, ussingite (partly sodalite and natrolite), 25-30 per cent and aegirine, 15-20 per cent. There are smaller but persistent amounts of microcline, murmanite, schizo-lite, erikite, neptunite, arfvedsonite and nepheline and sporadic occurrence of chkalovite, galena, sphalerite, ramsayite, steenstrupine, etc. The main minerals are unevenly distributed in the body of the pegmatite. Eudialyte and aegirine are located mainly in the peripheral regions, while ussingite, natrolite and sodalite are found in the central part.

Nepheline occurs chiefly at the contact with the country rocks as small (1.5×1 cm) crystals of square or rectangular section. It is earlier than eudialyte and murmanite, which fill the interstices between its grains. It is replaced by sodalite and natrolite.

Microcline is confined to the ussingite and aegirine-ussingite regions of the central zone. In the south-eastern part it is found as monocrystalline segregations of up to $15 \times 10 \times 10$ cm, while in the aegirine-ussingite part it is represented by small prismatic crystals up to 3-4 cm long, which are usually entirely replaced by ussingite. The colour of the microcline is white or light-grey. Tabular segrega-tions of murmanite that form intergrowths with microcline in the border of the zone are found in the interstices between its crystals.

Arfvedsonite is represented by black elongated crystals up to $12 \times 1 \times 0.8$ cm, mainly in the ussingite and aegirine-ussingite regions of the central zone. Its idiomorphic crystals are included in ussingite and microcline and sometimes in eudialyte and murmanite.

There are two generations of *aegirine*. Aegirine I occurs as small acicular and prismatic crystals, varying in size between a few hundredths of a millimetre and 2-3 cm, in the aegirine-ussingite and ussingite regions of the central zone. Its crystals form inclusions in various (early and late) minerals. Aegirine II is de-veloped in the contact region of the eudialyte zone as felted segregations filling the interstices between other minerals or forming nodular concretions.

Eudialyte is confined mainly to the outer zone. It is represented by crystals up to 5-7 cm in cross-section or by dense macrocrystalline aggregations. The colour varies from pink to dark reddish-brown in unaltered material. On alteration it is converted to a fine aggregate mixture, yellow, dark-brown or brown. Zoning can be seen in many eudialyte grains in thin sections (Fig. 80).

Eudialyte is one of the early minerals to separate. Ramsayite, schizolite and

FIG. 80. Zoning in eudialyte. ×90. Crossed nicols

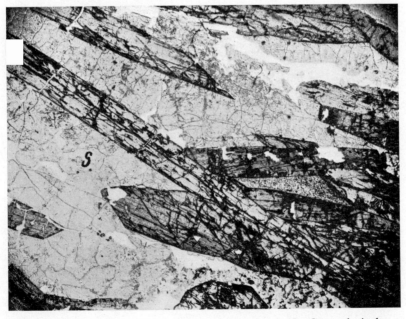

FIG. 81. Schizolite crystals (dark) in sodalite (S). ×10. Crossed nicols

aegirine II fill the interstices between its crystals in the eudialyte zone. Eudialyte inclusions are found in murmanite and ussingite (the ussingite zone). Eudialyte is replaced by zirfesite along joints.

Murmanite forms tabular segregations up $5 \times 3 \times 1.5$ cm. The colour is a light violet-pink in fresh material and brown in altered crystals. There is a whole range of intermediate shades between these two colours depending upon the extent to which the murmanite is altered. In the borders of the ussingite zone at its contact with the eudialyte, the murmanite loses colour and ranges from yellow and light-cream to silvery-white varieties. Tabular crystals of murmanite normally form inclusions in ussingite or fill the interstices between eudialyte and microcline crystals. Inclusions of arfvedsonite and aegirine I crystals are found in murmanite.

Ramsayite is found only in the eudialyte zone as small brown crystals with a cross-section up to 0·5 cm. It is normally confined to areas of acicular aegirine II crystals filling the interstices between eudialyte grains.

Schizolite occurs mainly in the central zone. Two varieties can be distinguished morphologically: one is represented by comparatively large elongate-prismatic crystals up to 5 cm long, the dark-brown or black colour of which is due to the advanced alteration of the mineral; the other consists of short-prismatic crystals

FIG. 82. Schizolite inclusions (dark) in ussingite

or irregular yellowish-grey and light-brown segregations. The second variety has scarcely been affected by alteration processes.

Unaltered schizolite is confined to the aegirine-ussingite zone, where it forms idiomorphic inclusions in sodalite and ussingite (Fig. 81). In its turn it frequently contains inclusions of aegirine I crystals. Altered schizolite is found in various parts of the pegmatitic body, but its largest and best-formed crystals are found in the ussingite zone, where they occur as inclusions in ussingite (Fig. 82).

Neptunite is normally represented by well-formed dark-red crystals up to $5 \times 3 \times 2$ cm. It is found as inclusions in ussingite confined to those parts of the pegmatitic body where the process of ussingitization is displayed (Fig. 83). It contains inclusions of aegirine I and less frequently of eudialyte.

Erikite is found as crystals of square or rectangular section (up to 3×2 cm), greenish-yellow in colour. It occurs mainly in the ussingite zone, where it forms idiomorphic inclusions in ussingite. It contains inclusions of schizolite and murmanite crystals.

Chkalovite is found at the contact of the ussingite and eudialyte zones as a few white aggregations up to $20 \times 12 \times 10$ cm in ussingite. No crystals have been

Fig. 83. Neptunite crystals (dark) in ussingite

found. Rarely, it contains inclusions of schizolite and arfvedsonite in the peripheries of large aggregations.

Steenstrupine is found in ussingite as ovoid or equant dark-brown and black grains with a cross-section up to 3 cm.

Sphalerite is developed as separate grains or aggregates of tabular crystals that form distinctive intergrowths ('fir trees'). Some of the crystals are 2-3 cm long. The colour is various shades of yellow or brown. The interstices between these sphalerite crystals in the aggregates are filled by ussingite.

Galena is found sporadically in various parts of the ussingite zone as irregular segregations up to 1-2 cm across included in ussingite.

Natrolite forms macrocrystalline segregations or fine-grained saccharoidal white aggregates up to $7 \times 3 \times 3$ cm. The shape of the macrocrystalline natrolite segregations is usually irregular owing to replacement by ussingite or by a fine-grained sodalite-ussingite aggregate. Fine-grained saccharoidal natrolite is later than ussingite, which it corrodes.

Sodalite is found as separate grains with a cross-section up to 1-2 cm, or as dense masses up to 10×10 cm in ussingite. The colour is light grey, sometimes with a yellowish tinge. There are also large amounts of sodalite in the fine-grained complex of replacement minerals, forming patches among ussingite or fringes round the crystals of sphalerite, natrolite, microcline and other minerals. These dense porcellanous segregations are an association of microscopically small segregations of sodalite, ussingite and natrolite. The development of this association is clearly due to the simultaneous separation of these minerals.

Ussingite usually forms compact massive segregations in various shades of violet-pink in the central part of the pegmatitic body. Poorly-formed crystals are found less frequently in miarolitic cavities in the pegmatite. Ussingite is one of the last minerals to separate. It fills the interstices between all the minerals except fine-grained natrolite and sodalite.

Belovite occurs as well-formed light-yellow crystals in ussingite: the crystals have the form of hexagonal prisms, the largest of which measures $1·5 \times 0·5 \times 0·5$ cm.

The genetic link between the ussingite pegmatitic body and the pegmatites of the poikilitic syenite complex is shown by the presence in it of such minerals as sodalite, ussingite and natrolite, and of minerals of the rare earths, thorium and beryllium (erikite, steenstrupine and chkalovite) as well as by the proximity of poikilitic syenite outcrops.

21. The Natrolite-Albite Pegmatitic Vein of Karnasurt

This vein, which was first discovered in 1938 by local geologists, is of great interest owing to the diversity of the minerals that it contains. It lies in the centre of the north-eastern slope of Karnasurt approximately 800 m to the east of the middle reaches of the Second Eastern stream. To the north and west of the vein

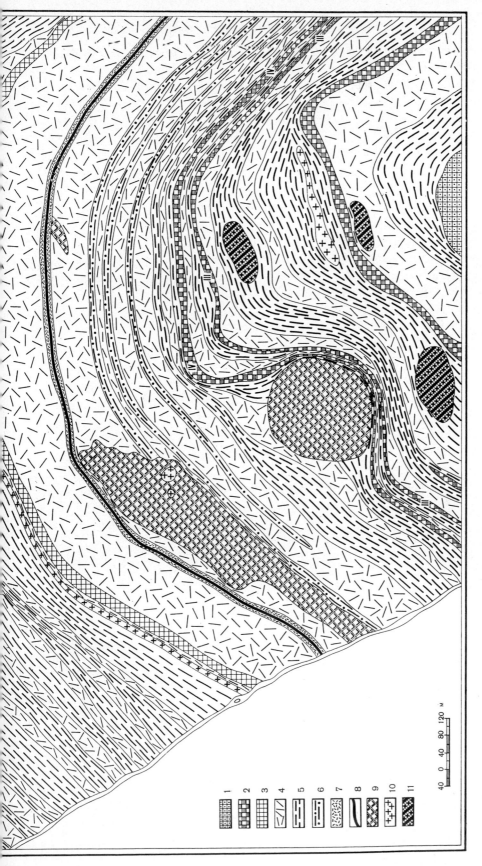

Fig. 84. Diagrammatic geological map of the north-eastern slope of Karnasurt (after Kozhanov)

1. eudialytic lujavrite; 2. urtite; 3. ijolitic urtite; 4. foyaite; 5. aegirine-lujavrite; 6. hornblende-lujavrite; 7. juvite; 8. malignite; 9. poikilitic sodalite-syenite; 10. pegmatites; 11. metamorphosed sedimentary rocks

[The units of scale of this map have been changed from Km in the original Russian to m—compare figs. 4 and 5.—Eds.]

there are intrusions of poikilitic sodalite-syenite that disturb the regular layering of the rocks of the differentiated complex in this part of the massif (Fig. 84).

The pegmatitic vein is revealed as outcrops of bedrock and many areas of large block rubble *in situ* over an area of approximately 100 × 50 m. The abundance of white natrolite makes it clearly visible on the grey ground of the country rocks. This is a sheet vein; the strike is 60°, the dip 7-8° to 330°. The thickness, which is not constant, varies between 1 and 2·5 m (Fig. 85).

Ten metres to the north of this vein a thin pegmatitic vein of similar composition underlying the lujavrites of the lower wall of main pegmatitic vein reaches the surface. This is clearly an apophysis of the main vein.

Aegirine reaction zones are a feature of the sharp contacts between the pegmatitic vein and the country rocks, the latter being mesocratic aegirine-lujavrites enriched in eudialyte and murmanite in the roof of the vein. Natrolitization and

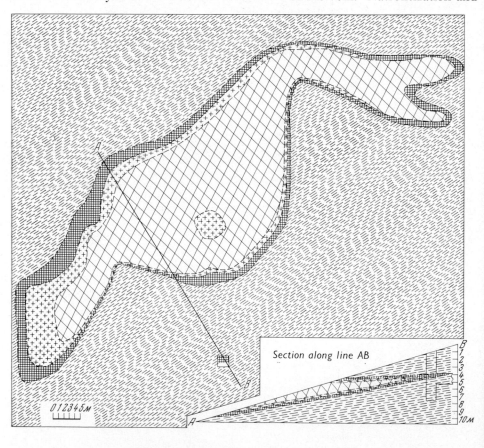

Fig. 85. Diagram of the natrolite-albite pegmatitic vein (after Kuz'menko)

1. lujavrite; 2. fine-grained zone of the pegmatitic vein; 3. coarse-grained zone; 4. large block hackmanite-natrolite-albite zone

albitization processes are apparent in the lujavrites near the contact (extending more than a metre from the contact). Nearer the contact with the pegmatitic vein the process of natrolitization in the lujavrites is intensified. At the contact and for approximately 0·5 m the nepheline is entirely replaced by natrolite. Microcline has been preserved only as relicts in natrolite.

At the lower wall of the vein there are small lenticles with an area of up to 30 × 15 cm in the lujavrites composed of large-prismatic white natrolite and crypto-crystalline brownish-pink albite. These formations have no direct connexion with the pegmatitic vein, but their leaders are orientated towards the contact of the vein and they are evidently apophyses of it that were injected into the lujavrites in the late stages of pegmatite formation.

The sharp contact between the pegmatite and the enclosing lujavrites, the existence of an aegirine fringe at the contact, disturbance of the trachytoid struc-ture in the lujavrites at the contact with the pegmatite and their high natrolitization all indicate that this vein was formed by the injection of the pegmatitic melt into the aegirine-lujavrites along a fracture parallel to the layering.

Since the vein has been uncovered by erosion almost along its dip surface it appears on the ground surface as a sweeping irregular ellipse approximately 30 m wide (see Fig. 85). A symmetrical zonal structure can be observed, the following zones being distinguished between the contacts and the centre: (1) the aegirine fringe contact zone; (2) a fine-grained pegmatite zone; (3) a medium- and coarse-grained pegmatite zone, and (4) a central zone of large block pegmatite (Fig. 86).

The aegirine fringe contact zone can be traced most clearly at the lower surface of the vein. Its thickness ranges from between 2 and 10 cm on the lower side to between 1 and 5 cm on the upper side. It is made up of fine-acicular dark-green aegirine (40-90 per cent), microcline (5-10 per cent) and natrolite (5-20 per cent) and contains a large amount of eudialyte in places. The colour of the fringe is dark green owing to the abundance of aegirine.

The fine-grained zone consists of aegirine (30 per cent), arfvedsonite (15 per cent), microcline (25 per cent) and natro-lite (25 per cent). The accessory minerals

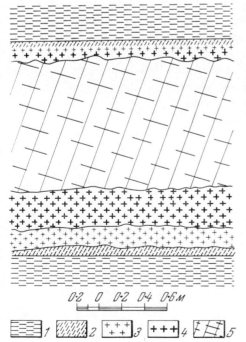

FIG. 86. Diagrammatic profile of the natro-lite-albite pegmatitic vein (after Kuz'menko)

1. aegirine-lujavrite; 2. aegirine fringe of the vein;
3. fine-grained zone; 4. medium- and coarse-grained zone; 5. large block zone

are eudialyte, schizolite, manganosteenstrupine, hydrocerite and nenadkevichite. The grain size of the minerals varies between fractions of a millimetre and 7 mm in cross-section. The thickness of the zone is 10-20 cm on the lower side and 1-2 cm on the upper side.

The medium- and coarse-grained pegmatite zone is 20-50 cm thick on the lower side and 5-10 cm on the upper side. Like the previous zone, with which it merges gradually, this zone is made up in the main of microcline (30 per cent), aegirine (20 per cent), arfvedsonite (10 per cent) and natrolite (30 per cent). There is a reduction in the aegirine and arfvedsonite content, eudialyte disappears and the content of schizolite, manganosteenstrupine, nenadkevichite and hydrocerite increases. Most of the dark-coloured minerals are confined to the interstices between microcline crystals.

Because of the reduction in the aegirine and arfvedsonite inclusions the microcline gradually takes on its natural creamy-grey colour inwards from the contacts towards the axis of the vein. The texture of the zone gradually becomes more macrocrystalline in the same direction. The dimensions of the microcline crystals increase gradually from a long axis of 7 mm in the fine-grained pegmatite zone to $10 \times 7 \times 5$ cm near the central zone.

Except for beryllium minerals, the main mass of the rare-metal minerals is confined to this zone, especially to its more central parts; their amount is considerably less at the upper than at the lower side. Galena, sphalerite, analcite, hydrargillite and other minerals are also found in this zone. The zone is greatly enriched in murmanite in the south, where the vein is split and peters out.

The central zone (more than a metre thick) is large block pegmatite consisting of microcline, hackmanite, natrolite and albite, the two last-mentioned minerals accounting for approximately 70 per cent of its volume. The accessory minerals include epididymite, schizolite, manganchlorite, murmanite, sphalerite and neptunite.

In the eastern part of the pegmatitic vein the albite is intimately associated with late microcline and fine-acicular aegirine that form a finely aggregated polymict mixture of the replacement complex. The minerals of this complex corrode and replace prismatic natrolite and fill cracks in it.

The main minerals of the pegmatitic body are natrolite (approximately 40 per cent), albite (approximately 20 per cent), hackmanite (approximately 20 per cent), microcline (approximately 10 per cent), aegirine (approximately 10 per cent) and arfvedsonite (approximately 3 per cent).

The accessory minerals are represented by schizolite, manganosteenstrupine, nenadkevichite, manganchlorite, hydrocerite, neptunite, eudialyte, murmanite and epididymite. There is a small quantity of sphalerite, galena and other minerals. The vein has been so greatly altered by hydrothermal processes that it is now difficult to establish the structure in the early stages of its development.

Microcline is found in the fine-, medium- and coarse-grained zones as well as in the marginal parts of the central zone. The dimensions of its crystals vary between $5 \times 3 \times 1$ mm at the vein contacts and $20 \times 10 \times 5$ cm in the border regions of the central zone. The form of the crystals is thick tabular. The colour is creamy-yellow and sometimes grey, while near the contacts it is dark-green to black owing to the large quantity of arfvedsonite and aegirine inclusions. It varies between opaque and semitransparent. Small fragments are white and transparent.

Microcline was one of the earliest minerals of the pegmatitic vein to separate. The accumulation of aegirine and arfvedsonite in the border regions of microcline crystals and in the interstices between them indicates that its crystallization began a little later than the beginning of the crystallization of the dark-coloured com-

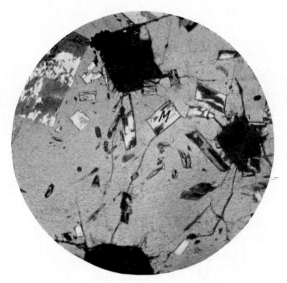

FIG. 87. Inclusions of microcline (M) and manganosteenstrupine (black) in natrolite.   × 20. Crossed nicols

ponents and ended when the main mass of these components was beginning to separate.

The microcline was greatly replaced by natrolite and albite in the hydrothermal stage. The great development of natrolitization in the vein masks all the preceding processes. Natrolite replaces microcline, forming continuous monocrystalline individuals. Such individuals often contain idiomorphic well-bounded microcline crystals (Fig. 87) in addition to irregular microcline relicts with etched and corroded outlines. The microcline was slightly pelitized in the supergene stage.

There is a large amount of *hackmanite* in this vein. It is concentrated in the central zone in the south-western and central parts of the vein, which contain very little else. Its segregations (up to 3 × 4 m in area) are irregular and much replaced near the surface by a fine-grained aggregate of natrolite containing a little hydrargillite. The colour of hackmanite varies from bright pink with a violet tinge to beet-red on a fresh fracture. When exposed to the light it rapidly becomes sky-blue or grey. There is a strong smell of hydrogen sulphide when it is fractured. Hackmanite separated later than microcline and fills the interstices between its crystals.

Fɪɢ. 88. Replacement of large-prismatic natrolite (in the cente—light) by albite. Half size

In the hydrothermal stage, hackmanite was replaced by a fine-grained aggregate of natrolite and hydrargillite (bergmannite) and chalcedonic natrolite. The latter mineral often forms veinlets in hackmanite. In some places the replacement of hackmanite by natrolite has been so intensive that only irregular relicts remain.

This pegmatitic vein differs from the other pegmatitic bodies in that the *aegirine* was crystallized without interruption, and it is therefore impossible to separate the generations. It was the first mineral to crystallize from the pegmatitic melt, but its main mass crystallized later than microcline. In the contact fringe and in the outer zone its main mass crystallized earlier than microcline, in which it forms idiomorphic inclusions. In the medium-grained pegmatite zone aegirine is also present as inclusions in microcline and in the interstices between its crystals. Towards the central zone there is a continuous decline in the number of aegirine inclusions in the microcline and a relative increase in the amount in the interstices between microcline crystals. The aegirine crystals are normally tenths of a millimetre long, occasionally reaching several millimetres in length; but only at the contact, where aegirine forms a practically monomineralic rock in places, do they increase to this size. The colour of the aegirine is dark-green to black.

The replacement zone contains very late aegirine mixed with fine-grained natrolite and albite in cracks in coarse-prismatic natrolite or in miarolitic cavities in the medium- and coarse-grained pegmatite zone.

Arfvedsonite, like aegirine, is concentrated in the marginal zones of the vein, where it forms small idiomorphic black crystals in microcline and other minerals. The crystals are prismatic, varying in length between a few tenths of a millimetre and 2 mm, and rarely more.

Arfvedsonite began to crystallize a little later than the beginning of aegirine crystallization and then separated with it, as is shown by the occasional idiomorphism of aegirine in relation to arfvedsonite.

Aegirine and arfvedsonite are not affected by replacement processes.

There are four varieties of *natrolite*, which together account for not less than 40 per cent of the volume of the pegmatitic vein: (1) coarse prismatic; (2) granular; (3) foliaceous or radiate fibrous, and (4) cryptocrystalline (chalcedonic), all of which are most developed in the central zone.

Coarse prismatic natrolite forms irregular monocrystalline individuals up to 1 m across, the dominant cleavage being prismatic, the colour of which is white and, less frequently, light pink. It probably crystallized from high temperature solutions in the interstices between hackmanite and microcline segregations in the hydrothermal stage and partly replaced these segregations. This natrolite is earlier than the albite. Fine grained albite fills geodes and cracks in it and replaces it (Fig. 88). In some parts of the vein coarse-prismatic natrolite gradually gives way to the foliaceous and granular varieties.

Granular natrolite occurs as randomly orientated, somewhat elongated rounded grains. The length of the long axis varies between tenths of a millimetre and 2 mm. This natrolite is more typical of the medium- and fine-grained pegmatite.

Foliaceous natrolite forms fine-grained segregations in which the separate grains have the most varied shape, as is generally typical of zeolites. The grain size varies between hundredths of a millimetre and 1 mm. The commonest type of grain is 0·1-1 mm across, foliaceous with highly dissected edges and fan extinction. There is also natrolite forming radiate-fibrous bundles of tabular crystals, grains of the most diverse and bizarre form with irregular extinction, globular hemispherical segregations with fan extinction, and so on. Foliaceous natrolite was formed mainly by the replacement of hackmanite. It is usually considerably altered and contaminated with brown oxides, and therefore presents different shades of brown in thin sections.

Cryptocrystalline natrolite is an extremely distinctive variety very similar to chalcedony. It forms veinlets varying in thickness from microscopic dimensions

FIG. 89. An albite geode

to 10 cm in altered hackmanite. These veinlets are irregular and sinuous and often looped. The colour is grey, brown, dark-brown, wine-yellow, lilac, pale-pink and light-violet. It is semitransparent to opaque. The opaque varieties are white and dull. The colour of chalcedonic natrolite is variable and usually banded or mottled in a fashion reminiscent of the colour of agates and jaspers. Cryptocrystalline natrolite has a fibrous structure at contacts between its veinlets and hackmanite, the fibres being perpendicular to the contact.

Albite is concentrated exclusively in the central zone. It forms large, irregular, fine-grained segregations (up to 0·7 × 0·5 m) that are white, pink and brownish-grey, or small tabular and elongated prismatic crystals up to 2-3 mm long in miarolitic cavities, sometimes forming radiate-fibrous rosettes (Fig. 89). Small albite crystals have a slightly greasy to vitreous lustre. Three varieties of albite are distinguished by the form of the segregations: (1) tabular; (2) foliaceous, and (3) granular.

Clearly defined simple and polysynthetic twins are typical of tabular albite crystals (up to 3 mm long and 1 mm thick). The plates are variously orientated, and intersect each other or are assembled in radiate-fibrous fan rosettes. Grains of foliaceous albite are irregular, with the most diverse and often greatly dissected contours reminiscent of leaf shapes. In this albite the twins are indistinctly defined and the composition planes are not sharp. Extinction is usually fanned and sometimes irregular. Grain size varies between a few tenths of a millimetre and 1 mm, rarely greater. Granular albite forms a fine-grained (to cryptocrystalline) aggregate. Grain size varies between thousandths of a millimetre and 0·3 mm. The shape of the grains is irregular and rounded. The texture of the segregations is inequigranular. Bands of coarser-grained albite merging gradually with the fine-grained groundmass are sometimes found.

Albite began to crystallize in the hydrothermal stage, after the formation of the greater part of the coarse-prismatic natrolite, and continued to separate until the end of this stage. It replaces microcline and, in part, hackmanite, as well as prismatic natrolite, and fills the interstices between segregations of these minerals. Veinlets of fine-grained brown albite are found in prismatic natrolite.

The albite was slightly pelitized in the supergene stage.

Epididymite is concentrated in the margins of the central zone, in the western end of the pegmatitic vein, where it forms irregular segregations with a cross-section up to 15 cm and veinlets up to 3 cm thick, mainly at the contacts between prismatic natrolite and albite. The structure of the epididymite aggregates is finely scaly to cryptocrystalline. The colour is white, less frequently light-cream and greyish-blue. In the process of alteration it is replaced by beryllite or converted into a fine-grained aggregate of clay minerals with an increased beryllium content.

Schizolite is widely distributed in this vein, but has not been preserved in a fresh state. It is replaced by black manganese hydroxides that can easily be crumbled with the fingernail. It has been totally leached in places, leaving behind only regularly bounded cavities. Schizolite segregations vary in size from 0·5 mm long to $7 \times 2 \times 1$ cm. The form of the segregations is tabular and the cross-section has the shape of a greatly elongated rhomb truncated at both sides. In the central zone schizolite is represented only in the marginal parts as completely altered idiomorphic crystals in microcline with a cross-section up to 6×1 cm.

Schizolite is one of the earliest minerals. It crystallized earlier than microcline, since it forms quite regular idiomorphic crystals in it, but later than early aegirine and arfvedsonite. When schizolite is included in natrolite there is often a fringe of greyish-brown albite (up to 2 mm thick) round it. It is clear from thin sections that this albite is the fine-fibrous variety and that the fibres are perpendicular to the schizolite faces.

Manganosteenstrupine is found in the medium- and coarse-grained pegmatite zone as black segregations of between 0·5 mm and 3 cm in cross-section that are usually irregular. It fills the interstices between microcline crystals, and occurs as crystals of square or pentagonal form in natrolite. Manganosteenstrupine was replaced by hydrocerite under the influence of late solutions.

There is a fair amount of *nenadkevichite* in the vein. The majority is concentrated in the lower wall, in the medium- and coarse-grained pegmatite zone, where its content reaches 10-15 per cent in places. It forms regular tabular crystals with parallel faces varying from a few millimetres long to $4 \times 2.5 \times 0.4$ cm. The colour is dark-brown, brown, brownish-pink to pink and sometimes chestnut-pink.

Nenadkevichite is apparently an early mineral. It forms idiomorphic tabular segregations in microcline and intergrowth textures with it. It is corroded by foliaceous albite and natrolite. Relicts of it in foliaceous albite have strongly-etched outlines and are contaminated with brown alteration products. It is replaced by a yellow ochreous mineral that is most probably leucoxene.

Eudialyte is found at the contacts with the enclosing lujavrites and in the fine-grained pegmatite zone: monomineralic areas of eudialyte rock are found at the vein contact. Eudialyte is represented by grains of up to 0.5 cm in diameter, reddish-brown in colour and almost entirely altered and converted into a brown friable mass consisting of zirfesite and catapleiite.

Murmanite is concentrated in the southern tapering end of the vein, where it forms almost monomineralic accumulations with a cross-section of more than 10 cm in places. Unaltered varieties are lilac-pink and altered varieties yellowish or brownish. The crystals measure up to 2×2 cm. In the central part of the vein murmanite occurs sporadically in natrolite as large tabular crystals up to 5 cm in length and 2 mm in thickness, almost entirely replaced by leucoxene.

Murmanite is antipathetic to nenadkevichite. Nenadkevichite is absent from places where there are large accumulations of murmanite or is present only in very small amounts. Nearer the centre of the vein the murmanite declines and the amount of nenadkevichite increases.

The murmanite crystallized fairly early. It forms finely scaly inclusions in microcline and altered hackmanite in association with arfvedsonite.

Sphalerite is present in small quantities as tabular aggregates, less frequently as small crystals (with a cross-section up to 2 mm) along cracks in hackmanite. The dimensions of the tabular aggregates vary between fractions of a millimetre and 0.5 cm thick and up to 1.5 cm long. The colour varies from cream through pale-yellow and waxy-yellow to wine-yellow; semitransparent to transparent. Sphalerite is a late mineral. It is intimately associated with fine-grained natrolite filling the cracks in hackmanite.

Galena is present in minute amounts in the southern part of the vein near the tapering region. It forms segregations up to 12 mm long and approximately 5 mm wide or cubes with a cross-section up to 7 mm showing eminent cubic cleavage. It is normally included in fine-grained natrolite that replaces leucocratic minerals in the fine- and medium-grained pegmatite zones.

Minute quantities of *manganchlorite* occur as radiate-fibrous aggregates with a diameter between 0·1 and 3 cm. The colour is light-brown, brown and dark-brown to black. The lustre is silky for the brown variety and pitch-like for the black variety. The structure is fine-fibrous or felted but massive in the black variety. This mineral is always associated with fine-grained albite, in which it forms radiate-fibrous rosettes and fills cracks.

Hydrocerite is usually found in the medium- and coarse-grained pegmatite zone, where it is a secondary mineral that forms on manganosteenstrupine. The colour is light-yellow to copper-yellow. Hydrocerite segregations have a fine-grained structure similar to that of ochreous aggregates.

There is a considerable amount of *neptunite*. It occurs in reddish-brown earthy crusts and powdery coatings on aegirine II that are a fine-grained neptunite aggregate cemented with manganese hydroxides. It is sometimes found as small black crystals with a diameter up to 1·5 mm in cavities on the faces of microcline. Thin fragments have a cherry-red translucence, while the powder is reddish-brown.

It is always associated with secondary minerals formed during the destruction of titanium and manganese minerals. It also is probably secondary, formed during the alteration of murmanite, eudialyte, schizolite and other minerals.

Erikite occurs as irregular finely scaly segregations or fills leaching cavities of up to $5 \times 3 \times 2$ cm between microcline crystals in the coarse-grained pegmatite zone. The colour is tobacco-green. The flakes are hexagonal, between 0·01 and 0·03 mm in diameter.

There are minute quantities of *beryllite*. It fills leaching cavities up to 4 cm in diameter in brown albite or develops on epididymite. Macroscopically it is a white friable clay mineral very similar to minerals of the kaolin group. Under a binocular microscope it can be seen that it forms small spherulites and soft white encrustations of fibrous structure with a silky lustre. This is one of the late minerals, formed by the alteration of epididymite that occurs in it as relicts.

Analcite is present in minute quantities as irregular aggregations up to 3×2 cm, or as dirty-white trapezohedral crystals up to $4 \times 4 \times 3$ cm in the coarse-grained zones. It separated earlier than albite, which fills cracks in it.

Considerable quantities of *hydrargillite* are found as a component of berg-mannite. It forms extremely small white tabular segregations of irregular shape and veinlets in foliaceous natrolite. These segregations and veinlets are tenths of a millimetre long and can be seen only under the microscope. The polysynthetic twins, which are typical, form a chain in the veinlets in such a way that the composition faces run approximately along the contacts. Hydrargillite crystallized together with the foliaceous natrolite that replaces hackmanite.

In mineralogical composition the pegmatitic body is very similar to the poikilitic sodalite-syenites and also to the hackmanite-natrolite pegmatitic stock described below, which is directly associated with the poikilitic syenites. Its genetic link with the poikilitic syenites is indicated both by this fact and by the presence of poikilitic syenite outcrops near the pegmatite.

The pegmatitic body has a higher concentration of the rare earths, thorium, niobium, titanium, manganese, phosphorus, zinc, lead, beryllium and gallium than the parent poikilitic syenites; except for gallium, all these elements form separate minerals.

22. THE HACKMANITE-NATROLITE PEGMATITIC STOCK OF KARNASURT

This stock, which was first discovered by Kozhanov in 1947, lies in the centre of the north-eastern slope of Karnasurt approximately 0·8 km to the east of the lower reaches of the Second Eastern stream.

The pegmatitic body is emplaced at the contact between the rocks of the differentiated complex (foyaites and lujavrites) and the poikilitic sodalite-syenites.

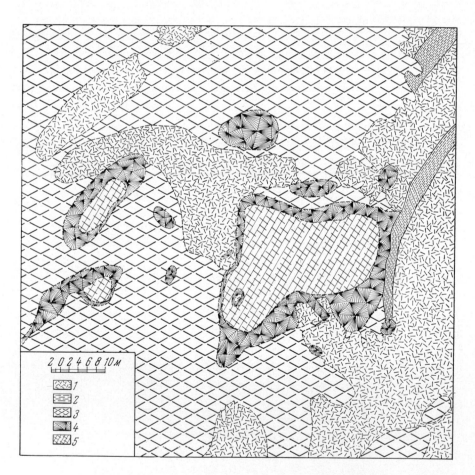

FIG. 90. Diagram of the hackmanite-natrolite pegmatitic stock (after Kuz'menko)

1. foyaite; 2. lujavrite; 3. poikilitic sodalite-syenite; 4. outer aegirine zone; 5. inner hackmanite-natrolite zone

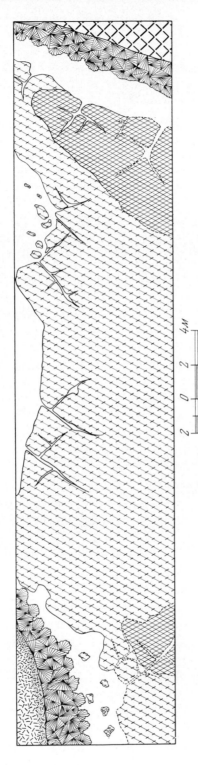

Fig. 91. Diagram of the structure of a swell in the hackmanite–natrolite stock (compiled by Kuz'menko)

1. foyaite; 2. altered foyaite; 3. poikilitic sodalite-syenite; 4. outer aegirine zone; 5. prismatic natrolite; 6. hackmanite; 7. intermediate zone of hydrothermal replacement

This contact is intrusive and there are countless poikilitic syenite apophyses up to 10 m long and 2 m thick in the foyaites. A great many irregular foyaite xenoliths up to 50 m long and 20 m wide are found in a zone approximately 100 m wide in the poikilitic syenites at the contact.

The pegmatitic body is exposed at the surface as five bedrock outcrops and four areas of block rubble *in situ* (Fig. 90). Judging by their similar mineralogical composition and structure all these outcrops are parts of one irregular pegmatitic body with extensive pinches and swells and many apophyses in the country rocks. The largest swell is exposed at the surface as an irregular 55 × 40 m oval.

The pegmatitic body strikes south-west to north-east and dips south-east. The angle of dip of the contact varies between 15° and 45° on the upper side and between 40° and 80° on the lower side.

The pegmatitic stock can be seen from 5-6 km away, the abundance of white natrolite in the float making it plainly visible against the grey ground of the rocks.

The contact between the pegmatitic stock and the poikilitic sodalite-syenites and foyaites is sharp because of the rapid change in mineralogical composition and the advanced natrolitization in the country rocks. The syenites are coarser-grained at the contact and enriched with early aegirine. Arfvedsonite develops on aegirine. The natrolite in the poikilitic syenite forms a fine-grained aggregate that replaces sodalite and microcline; at the contact the sodalite is entirely replaced by natrolite and microcline is preserved only as relicts. The amount of natrolite begins to decline within 3·5 m of the contact. At the contact with the pegmatitic body the foyaites are considerably altered and enriched in sodalite, eudialyte and late fibrous aegirine II. The thickness of the altered zone is 10-15 cm.

This hackmanite-natrolite pegmatitic stock was almost certainly formed by the accumulation of readily volatile and readily fusible components in the apical region of the poikilitic sodalite-syenite intrusion. This accumulation retarded the crystallization of the poikilitic sodalite-syenite. This led to the injection of the residual pegmatitic melt into the weakened zone of the contact between the poikilitic sodalite-syenites and the foyaites where it crystallized as a stock.

The structure of the hackmanite-natrolite pegmatitic body is concentrically zonal in the swells. The cross-section of the thickest swell (Fig. 91) reveals four zones: (1) an outer aegirine zone; (2) an intermediate hackmanite zone; (3) a central natrolite zone, and (4) a replacement zone.

The thickness of the outer zone varies between 0·7 m in the north-western part of the swell to 1 m in the south-eastern part. It is four-fifths composed of aegirine II. Large crystals of microcline, aegirine I, altered eudialyte, murmanite and hackmanite are sporadically distributed in the mass of fibrous aegirine II. These minerals are unevenly distributed. They are most completely represented in the western part of the body. The last three minerals are not found in the east, where the content of aegirine I is also very small.

The character of radiate-fibrous bundles of aegirine II at the inner side of the outer zone indicates that it grew into an open cavity. The surfaces of these bundles are highly smoothed, as if 'licked round' by late solutions, and covered with a crust of fine-crystalline neptunite, a yellow ochreous mineral (a rare-earth silico-phosphate) or by black manganese hydroxides. Small cavities filled with druses of fine-acicular dark-green third-generation aegirine, natrolite, sauconite or montmorillonite are found in the dense mass of felted aegirine.

The intermediate zone is made up of large irregular monocrystalline blocks of hackmanite occurring as relics in natrolite. The size of the hackmanite segregations varies from a few centimetres across to $3 \times 2 \times 2$ m. At the contact between the natrolite and the replacement zone minerals, hackmanite is always replaced by a light-blue or light-green fine-grained aggregate of natrolite and hydrargillite. Monomineralic segregations of massive pink natrolite containing small geodes (with a cross-section up to 5 cm), strewn with natrolite, chabazite and hydrargillite microcrystals, are found in the central parts of some relics.

The localization of the relics and large hackmanite blocks in the peripheral parts of the central natrolite zone and in the replacement zone, and their absence from the central region of the natrolite zone, indicate that the hackmanite originally formed a compact monomineralic zone that was subsequently replaced by natrolite and later minerals.

The central (39×19 m) zone is composed mainly of large-prismatic natrolite (up to 80 per cent) on which minerals of the montmorillonite group develop. There are also small amounts of karnasurtite.

The replacement zone lies at the contact between the aegirine zone and hackmanite and natrolite zone. It is made up of a fine-grained aggregate of late microcline and chalcedonic natrolite, with micaceous and clay minerals from the montmorillonite group, containing large relics of hackmanite and prismatic natrolite as inclusions. The micaceous minerals are epididymite and polylithionite. The clay minerals form a soft, colloidal, white, pink, yellowish, greenish and bluish mass replacing natrolite. Neptunite, psilomelane and late silicophosphates of the rare earths and thorium are also associated with the replacement zone. The thickness of the zone varies between 10-20 cm and 1·5 m; its outlines are irregular, it peters out in places and in others forms countless branches and veinlets in the hackmanite and prismatic natrolite of the central zone (see Fig. 91).

It is interesting to note that an aegirine zone and a replacement zone associated with the contacts between the aegirine and central zones are developed round xenoliths of poikilitic sodalite-syenite in the pegmatitic body, as well as at the contact between the pegmatite and the country rocks.

The impression given is that the replacement zone was formed as a result of the crystallization of residual hydrothermal solutions squeezed out into the aegirine zone by the monomineralic prismatic natrolite crystallizing in the central region. These late hydrothermal solutions interacted both with the aegirine of the outer zone and especially with the natrolite and hackmanite of the central zone.

The main minerals of the pegmatitic stock are aegirine (approximately 17 per cent), microcline (approximately 8 per cent), hackmanite (approximately 20 per cent) and natrolite (approximately 53 per cent). The accessory minerals (approximately 2 per cent) include eudialyte, murmanite, polylithionite, epididymite, montmorillonite, psilomelane, karnasurtite, neptunite, chabazite and hydrargillite.

Aegirine is concentrated exclusively in the outer zone, where it is represented by two generations. There is a small, unevenly distributed amount of aegirine I (3-5 per cent). The main mass is confined to places where the pegmatitic body peters out. It forms idiomorphic black prismatic crystals varying from micro-scopic dimensions to $8 \times 0.9 \times 0.8$ cm. Aegirine I is one of the earliest minerals, as is shown by its idiomorphism to all the remaining minerals and by the presence of small inclusions of its regular prismatic crystals in early microcline and other minerals.

Aegirine II forms an extremely fine-fibred felted aggregate in the outer zone (see Fig. 91). Its radiate-fibrous bundles reach a diameter of 35 cm in some cases. Crystals of aegirine I are sometimes found in these bundles as centres round which the aegirine II grew. The colour of aegirine II is greyish-green to dark-green. Aegirine II fills the interstices between segregations of aegirine I, microcline, eudialyte and murmanite, and was evidently one of the last minerals to crystallize in the outer zone. Radiate-fibrous bundles of aegirine II are sometimes covered near the surface by psilomelane, neptunite or a yellow ochreous mineral (a hydrous rare-earth silicophosphate). Sometimes the interstices between aegirine II fibres are filled with fine-grained natrolite or psilomelane.

Eudialyte is concentrated exclusively in the outer zone, where its content does not exceed 3 per cent. It forms rounded aggregates with an area between a few square millimetres and 3×4 cm. The colour of the eudialyte ranges from creamy-yellow through yellowish-brown to chestnut-brown. It is usually included in aegirine II or fills the interstices between microcline crystals; inclusions of it are found less frequently in the borders of microcline crystals. Eudialyte apparently separated at the end of the period in which microcline crystallized. It is usually greatly replaced by zirfesite, catapleiite and manganese hydroxides.

There are two generations of *microcline*: early and late. Early microcline is found exclusively in the outer zone, of which it forms approximately 15 per cent by volume. It forms creamy-grey thick-tabular crystals up to $2 \times 4 \times 10$ cm in aegirine II, containing inclusions of very small idiomorphic aegirine I crystals and considerably replaced by fine-grained natrolite and albite.

Late microcline is concentrated in the replacement zone (up to 40 per cent) as irregular aggregates varying in size from a few centimetres in cross-section to 1×7 m in area. The texture of the aggregates is very fine-grained and the grain size does not exceed tenths of a millimetre. This microcline separated later than prismatic natrolite, as is shown by the existence of veinlets of it in natrolite and by the presence of natrolite relicts in late microcline.

There is a considerable quantity of *murmanite* (up to 2 per cent) in the outer zone, where it occurs as tabular aggregations up to $7 \times 4 \times 0.7$ cm in aegirine II. The colour is brown, chestnut-brown, pinkish-brown and sometimes black. This is a comparatively early mineral. It fills the interstices between segregations of early microcline, with which it occasionally forms intergrowths. Murmanite is usually greatly altered.

Hackmanite is found in large quantities in the intermediate zone as relicts in natrolite. Small quantities are found in the outer zone as equant aggregates with a cross-section up to 1·5 cm in aegirine II, sometimes entirely replaced by natrolite or bergmannite.

The fresh form of hackmanite has been preserved in the intermediate zone. Its colour on a fresh fracture is beet-red or various shades of pink. It rapidly loses its colour when exposed to the light and becomes pale blue or pale green. It is always replaced by bergmannite* at the boundary with prismatic and chalcedonic natrolite.

Natrolite forms a fine-grained aggregate that replaces hackmanite and, in part, microcline, in the outer zone. In the central zone it is represented by a white, transparent large-prismatic variety that is greatly fissured and converted in places into fine gritty particles contained in a white clayey mass. Other varieties of natrolite found in this zone include white fine-grained natrolite, pink radiate-fibrous natrolite and chalcedonic natrolite.

The structure of fine-grained natrolite segregations is granular, foliaceous, fanned or fibrous and the grain size does not exceed 0·1 mm. It is sometimes contaminated by brown oxides and clay particles. It is formed during the replacement of hackmanite.

Chalcedonic natrolite occurs in the outer and central zones. In the former it is found as a cryptocrystalline aggregate secondary to hackmanite and in the latter it forms countless veinlets between microscopic thickness and 20 cm in altered hackmanite. The colour is white, creamy, grey-brown, bluish-grey and light-chocolate, and bands of different colour are usually parallel to the contacts of the veinlets. It is semitransparent. The structure of this variety of natrolite is crypto-crystalline and between crossed nicols one can see fibrous, feathery, undulating or mottled extinction: it merges gradually with prismatic natrolite.

Coarse-prismatic natrolite separated later than hackmanite, which it replaces, but earlier than late microcline, polylithionite, epididymite and other minerals of the replacement complex. Late microcline replaces prismatic natrolite and fills fissures in it.

The fine-grained variety of natrolite is usually intimately associated with the minerals of the replacement complex and is later than coarse-prismatic natrolite.

Polylithionite forms irregular segregations with a diameter up to 20 cm in the replacement zone and veinlets of between 0·5 and 5 cm thick in prismatic natrolite in the marginal parts of the central zone. It is a typical feature that karnasurtite and psilomelane are associated with it in the form of films and powdery coatings along fissures in a compact aggregate of polylithionite. Fresh varieties of poly-lithionite are bright pink or cream, while altered varieties are light-pink or light-cream to white. This mineral is concentrated in the replacement zone near aggregates of late microcline, where it replaces prismatic natrolite and fills cracks

---

* Bergmannite is a mixture of fine-grained natrolite, hydrargillite and relict hackmanite contaminated with brown or grey alteration products. The natrolite in it forms irregular segregations of fibrous, feathery or foliaceous structure and accounts for approximately 90 per cent of the total mass of the bergmannite.

in it (Fig. 92). The structure of polylithionite segregations is microcrystalline finely-scaly to cryptocrystalline.

Polylithionite is a late mineral, as is shown by the irregular form of its aggregates and by the presence of veinlets of it in prismatic natrolite. During alteration it is converted into a soft clayey mass, greasy to the touch.

Epididymite is quite widely distributed. Like polylithionite it forms irregular aggregates in the borders of the central zone and in the replacement zone, varying

Fig. 92. Interrelationship of polylithionite (grey) and prismatic natrolite (light). ×20. Crossed nicols

in size from a few centimetres in cross-section to $2 \times 10 \times 5$ cm. Macroscopically there are three textural varieties of epididymite to be distinguished: micaceous, fine-crystalline and dense porcellanous, of which the latter is the most widely distributed. It can be seen under the microscope that these varieties merge gradually one into another.

The structure of the porcellanous variety is cryptocrystalline. The grain size is measured in thousandths and hundredths of a millimetre. The structure of the fine-crystalline variety is coarser-grained, the grain size being tenths and hundredths of a millimetre. In some parts it merges gradually with micaceous epididymite, which forms irregular areas in the fine-crystalline and porcellanous varieties. The size of these crystalline areas varies between a few millimetres and 10 cm in cross-section.

The colour of epididymite is white and the lustre is vitreous. The separate flakes vary from fractions of a millimetre to 2 mm in cross-section. Epididymite is colourless in thin sections. It forms simple and less frequently polysynthetic twins with diffuse composition planes. It is usually intimately associated with fine-grained natrolite, polylithionite and other minerals of the replacement zone and apparently crystallized in the last stage of formation of the pegmatitic body.

Psilomelane is concentrated in the replacement zone, where it forms rounded or irregular concretions with a cross-section up to 10 cm and films on the surfaces of aegirine II rosettes. The colour is black with a bluish tinge; in thin sections it is black and opaque. It apparently separated later than aegirine II from manganese-enriched solutions.

Karnasurtite is found in the replacement and central zones. Most of it is concentrated in the south-western end of the stock. The colour is honey-yellow to light yellow in altered specimens. It is usually intimately associated with the minerals of the replacement complex, especially with polylithionite, which replaces it from the periphery. However, idiomorphic karnasurtite segregations sometimes occur as inclusions in prismatic natrolite. In the process of alteration it is converted into a creamy-yellow ochreous mass of hydrous silicophosphates of the rare earths.

There are considerable quantities of *neptunite* as earthy crusts and powdery coatings on aegirine II or as large accumulations of small reddish-brown grains cemented with psilomelane. The form of its segregations and their association with the inner side of the aegirine zone, where the late-hydrothermal solutions that form the replacement mineral complex were crystallized, indicate that this is one of the late minerals.

There are considerable quantities of *chabazite* in the central zone, where it lines the walls of miarolitic cavities as small rhombohedral white transparent crystals or crystal aggregates, or forms a fine-grained aggregate that fills fissures in hackmanite, prismatic natrolite and late microcline. Its crystals reach 1 mm in cross-section. Chabazite is one of the late minerals.

Hydrargillite is present in considerable quantities. It is a component of bergmannite, in which it forms small irregular aggregates and veinlets. It is found less frequently as white transparent tabular crystals between a few millimetres and $0.7 \times 0.7 \times 0.4$ cm in miarolitic cavities in natrolite. Hydrargillite is a late mineral.

Besides the minerals already mentioned the pegmatitic body also contains a further series of minerals belonging to the rare-earth group of hydrous silicophosphates, and chlorite, montmorillonite, zincian montmorillonite, etc. The hackmanite-natrolite body differs from the parent rocks in having a higher concentration of lithium, the rare earths, thorium, niobium, titanium, beryllium, manganese, phosphorus, gallium and water, as is shown by the presence of the natural minerals of these elements, most of which are confined to the central zone and the replacement zone. An increased gallium concentration can be seen in all the main rock-forming minerals of the central zone and the replacement zone—hackmanite, natrolite, late microcline, etc.

SPECIAL FEATURES OF THE PEGMATITES OF THE POIKILITIC SYENITE COMPLEX

The pegmatites of the poikilitic syenite complex have the following characteristic features:

1. Spatial proximity and direct connexion with poikilitic syenite intrusions. The pegmatites of this complex are exclusively developed in areas where there are large outcrops of poikilitic syenite and are either emplaced directly in these rocks, with which they sometimes merge gradually, or in rocks of other complexes enclosing poikilitic syenites and near contacts with them.

2. Great thickness of the pegmatitic bodies, large dimensions of the mineral units and marked differentiation of the pegmatitic melt, revealed in distinct zoning and the formation of monomineralic zones of the main minerals in the best-developed pegmatitic bodies.

3. The great diversity of the main pegmatite-forming minerals. In addition to microcline, aegirine, arfvedsonite and eudialyte, which are the main minerals in the pegmatites of other complexes, hackmanite, natrolite, ussingite and albite, which are accessory minerals in the pegmatites of other complexes, are here main pegmatite-forming minerals.

4. An increased content of thorium, the rare earths, beryllium, lithium, manganese, zinc and gallium. In addition to the zirconium, titanium and niobium minerals (ramsayite, murmanite, lamprophyllite, loparite, sphene and others) typical of the pegmatites of other complexes, the rare-metal minerals here include the minerals of lithium (tainiolite, polylithionite), beryllium (epididymite, chkalovite, leucophane and beryllite), thorium (steenstrupine and manganosteenstrupine), the rare earths (steenstrupine, manganosteenstrupine, hydrocerite, erikite, nordite, karnasurtite, etc.) and manganese (psilomelane, vernadite, schizolite and chinglusuite), which are either absent from other pegmatites or present in very small quantities.

5. Strongly-developed replacement processes, because of differentiation and the increased concentration of readily volatile compounds, especially chlorine, sulphur and water. Minerals of the replacement stage are widely distributed in the pegmatites of this complex. These minerals include natrolite, ussingite, albite, late zeolites (chabazite and analcite), micas and micaceous minerals (tainiolite, polylithionite and epididymite).

Except for the first, these features are typical only of the most developed pegmatites of the poikilitic syenite complex and not of all. Nearly all facies bodies and the majority of the small phase bodies have a simple mineralogical composition, which is close to that of the parent rocks. Such pegmatites are not differentiated and their structure is usually equigranular. The main minerals in them crystallized at the same or approximately the same time. In the central parts of the larger pegmatitic bodies of this type there is some tendency to differentiation: the dimensions of the mineral units increase and there is a rise in the content of zirconium, titanium and niobium minerals.

In far fewer of the large facies and vein pegmatitic bodies (1·5-2 m thick) there is a block zone, composed largely of orthoclase and fibrous aegirine with eudialyte, ramsayite, lamprophyllite and murmanite, in addition to the outer equigranular zone. Such pegmatites are richest in zirconium, titanium and niobium minerals. Orthoclase was usually the first to crystallize, forming large crystals or large monomineralic accumulations (blocks). The rare-metal minerals are concentrated in the interstices between orthoclase crystals. A fine-fibrous mass of aegirine fills the interstices between crystals of orthoclase and the rare-metal minerals.

In the central parts of the larger oval pegmatitic bodies with an area of 10×20 m there is an additional block zone of feldspathic-hackmanitic or feldspathic-natrolitic composition. A feldspathic-hackmanitic zone is found only in pegmatites that are genetically associated with poikilitic hackmanite-syenites.

In addition to eudialyte, murmanite, lamprophyllite and ramsayite, the rare-metal minerals in these pegmatites sometimes include small amounts of rare-earth and thorium minerals—steenstrupine, manganosteenstrupine, rare-earth apatite and other minerals. The orthoclase-aegirine pegmatitic body on the northern slope of Lepkhe-N'elm is an example of a triple-zoned pegmatite of this type.

In addition to the outer equigranular and block feldspathic-aegirine zones, the central parts of some of the largest stock-like and lens-shaped pegmatitic bodies that cover hundreds of square metres contain monomineralic feldspathic (rarely hackmanitic) and natrolitic zones. A monomineralic feldspathic zone is clearly revealed in the pegmatites of the central region of the massif, genetically associated with nepheline and nepheline-sodalite varieties of poikilitic syenites (the pegmatites of Lepkhe Nel'm and Kuivchorr). A feldspathic zone is usually absent from the Karnasurt pegmatites, which are genetically associated with poikilitic hackmanite-syenites extremely rich in sodium, chlorine and sulphur, but there is a clearly manifested monomineralic hackmanite zone. A natrolite nucleus is typical of all fully differentiated pegmatites.

In some of the largest pegmatitic bodies of the poikilitic syenite complex, the chemical and mineralogical composition of which is more complex, five zones can be distinguished between the margin and the centre: (1) a zone of equigranular structure; (2) a block zone composed of feldspar and aegirine; (3) a monomineralic zone of orthoclase or hackmanite; (4) a natrolite nucleus, and (5) a replacement zone.

The replacement mineral complex usually consists of a microcrystalline aggregate of late orthoclase or albite, microcrystalline and cryptocrystalline natrolite, chabazite, analcite, ussingite, hydrargillite and fine-crystalline aggregates of micaceous and mica-like minerals (tainiolite, polylithionite, epididymite, etc.). It is generally confined either to the central parts of the pegmatitic bodies (the tainiolitic body of Lepkhe-Nel'm and the orthoclase-analcite pegmatitic vein on Kuivchorr) or to the contacts of the central natrolitic zones with the feldspathic-aegirine zones (hackmanite-natrolite stock of Karnasurt), or is randomly distributed as irregular segregations and veinlets in the prismatic natrolite of the central zone (the natrolite-albite vein on Karnasurt). All the lithium and beryllium mineralization is confined to the replacement mineral complexes, as are the late silicophosphates of the rare earths and thorium. The replacement zone is so extensively developed in some pegmatitic bodies that it is difficult to establish their initial structure (the tainiolite pegmatitic body of Lepkhe-Nel'm).

On the basis of our account we can distinguish four paragenetic mineral associations in the pegmatites of the poikilitic syenite complex: (1) the nepheline (sodalite)-microcline-aegirine association of the equigranular zones, which is similar in composition to the parent rock; (2) the feldspathic-aegirine association containing zirconium, titanium and niobium minerals; (3) the hackmanite-natrolite association containing rare-earth and thorium minerals, and (5) an association of replacement stage minerals containing lithium and beryllium minerals and the hydrous silicophosphates of the rare earths.

The mineralogical composition of the best-developed pegmatites of the poikilitic syenite complex is more intricate than that of the pegmatites of other complexes. More than 120 mineral species have been discovered in them. The pegmatites of Karnasurt and the central region of the massif (Lepkhe-Nel'm) are the most highly mineralized.

There are characteristic features of mineralogical composition in the pegmatites of the complex in different areas of the massif. Unlike the pegmatites of the central region of the massif, the pegmatites of Karnasurt, which are genetically associated with the poikilitic hackmanite-syenites, are marked by absence of nepheline, a lower content of early orthoclase and a higher content of niobium minerals in the first and second paragenetic mineral associations, abundance of hackmanite and prismatic natrolite, stronger signs of replacement processes and the occurrence of a large quantity of late orthoclase among the minerals of the replacement complex. Typical features of the pegmatites of the central region of the massif, genetically associated with the poikilitic nepheline-syenites, include the presence of nepheline in the first paragenetic association, predominance of potassium minerals (orthoclase) over sodium minerals (natrolite, albite and others), absence of hackmanite and a higher content of calcium and magnesium minerals (apatite, sphene, tainiolite, montmorillonite and others).

The less-developed pegmatites of Malyi Punkaruaiv have an abundance of ussingite, less rare-metal minerals and no lithium minerals.

In the valley of the Chinglusuai there are small facies pegmatites that are, in essence, composed of the first paragenetic association. Typical features are the absence of zoning and the presence of minerals unstable in the presence of water —villiaumite and lomonosovite, which indicates that there was little water in the pegmatitic melt solution. There are few signs of replacement processes in them.

These differences in the mineralogical composition of the pegmatites of different districts are reflected in the alteration of the earlier separated main paragenetic mineral associations which have their own specific features in each case.

*   *   *   *

Four stages corresponding to the paragenetic mineral associations can be distinguished in the formation of the pegmatitic bodies of the poikilitic syenite complex (Fig. 93).

Aegirine I, nepheline, early sodalite, arfvedsonite, and in part eudialyte, schizolite, nenadkevichite and lamprophyllite crystallized in the first stage and microcline also began to crystallize. Small undifferentiated pegmatites and the outer equigranular zones of large zonal pegmatitic bodies were formed during this stage. The crystallization process usually began with the separation of aegirine I and arfvedsonite, most of which crystallized at the contacts between the pegmatites and the country rocks; aegirine separated earlier than arfvedsonite, as is shown by its idiomorphism to arfvedsonite.

There is scarcely any aegirine I in the pegmatites of the central region of the massif (Lepkhe-Nel'm) in which potassium minerals predominate over sodium minerals, and the formation of the pegmatitic bodies began with the crystallization of microcline.

The high potassium content of the pegmatitic melt and additional assimilation of potassium from the microcline of the country rocks usually leads to the formation of microcline reaction rims at the contact between the apical parts of the pegmatitic bodies and the country rocks. Nepheline, which crystallized earlier than orthoclase in the other pegmatites, separates later in these pegmatitic bodies and is usually confined to the interstices between orthoclase crystals.

The greater part of the orthoclase crystallized in the second stage, in addition to the minerals of titanium, niobium and zirconium (eudialyte, ramsayite, lamprophyllite and murmanite). Aegirine II crystallized a little later and, in part, simultaneously with the rare-metal minerals already mentioned. This stage is represented by the formation of the block feldspathic-aegirine or monomineralic feldspathic and aegirine zones.

In some pegmatitic bodies from which monomineralic feldspathic-aegirine zones are absent (the natrolite-albite zone of Karnasurt) no break can be seen between the crystallization periods of aegirine I and aegirine II. Aegirine I and arfvedsonite, which began to crystallize earlier than microcline, continued to separate throughout the period of its crystallization and considerably later.

The third stage is marked by the crystallization of the greater part of the sodalite (hackmanite), by the continued crystallization of aegirine II and by the formation of rare-metal and thorium minerals (steenstrupine, chinglusuite and, in part, nordite).

Coarse-prismatic natrolite, apatite and karnasurtite crystallized in the fourth (hydrothermal) stage, and the replacement zones were formed. During the crystallization of natrolite water began to play a great part in the formation of the pegmatites, and there was solution and replacement of the earlier crystallized leucocratic minerals (orthoclase and hackmanite) by natrolite or analcite. The alumina liberated in the replacement of hackmanite by zeolites is taken up in hydrargillite, which forms a dense aggregate (bergmannite) with fine-grained natrolite. During this period the leucocratic minerals of the outer fine-grained

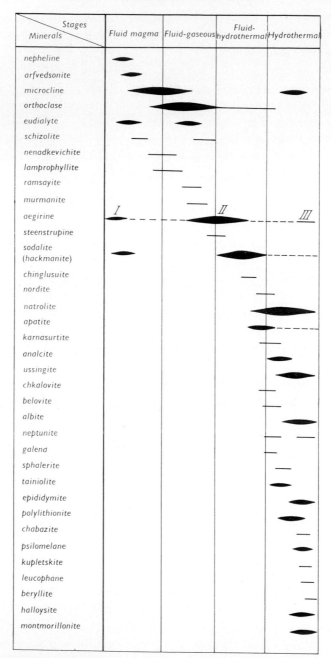

FIG. 93. Diagram of the order of crystallization of minerals in the pegmatites of the poikilitic syenite complex

and medium-grained zones of the pegmatitic bodies, and of the contact fringes and country rocks for a distance of more than a metre from the pegmatite contacts, are also replaced by natrolite.

Fine-grained albite or ussingite, which corrode and replace prismatic natrolite and other higher-temperature leucocratic minerals, fill fissures in them and also form monomineralic masses, began to crystallize, in the replacement process, after the formation of the greater part of the coarse-prismatic natrolite, when most of the water from the pegmatitic melt was already combined. At lower temperatures the crystallization of microcrystalline natrolite and albite proceeded almost simultaneously, and their cryptocrystalline varieties were formed. In some pegmatitic bodies genetically associated with the sodalitic varieties of poikilitic syenite, fine-grained microcline crystallized instead of albite in the fourth stage (the hackmanite-natrolite stock on Karnasurt).

After the greater part of the pegmatitic solution had crystallized as natrolite, albite, analcite, ussingite, or microcline, beryllium, niobium, rare earths, phosphorus, fluorine, manganese, zinc and lithium were highly concentrated in the small volume that remained. This led to the formation of epididymite, tainiolite, polylithionite and other minerals.

Under low-temperature conditions late-hydrothermal solutions brought about the further decomposition and leaching of accessory minerals and their replacement by secondary products. Large quantities of manganese, titanium, thorium, the rare earths, beryllium and other elements were freed during the alteration of schizolite, eudialyte, epididymite and manganosteenstrupine, and there was formation of neptunite, kupletskite, deposition of free manganese hydroxides and formation of beryllite, hydrocerite, erikite, psilomelane and clay minerals of the halloysite and montmorillonite groups with an enhanced content of zinc, zirconium, niobium, titanium and the rare earths.

HYBRID PEGMATITES

WE know of several dozen hybrid pegmatitic bodies in the Lovozero massif. They occur in districts of the massif where there are a great many xenoliths of Devonian rocks. A distinctive calcium paragenesis is typical of the minerals in the rocks and pegmatites of these districts. The rocks and pegmatites contain considerable quantities of apatite, sphene, manganilmenite, zircon and biotite, while the minerals typical of alkaline rocks and pure pegmatites (ramsayite, lamprophyllite, murmanite, etc.) are absent or present only in very small amounts. One mineral of the eudialyte group to be found is eucolite.

Hybrid pegmatites are formed by the assimilation of the country rocks of the massif by a pegmatitic melt injected into fissures. In addition to hybrid pegmatites, the Lovozero massif also contains what are known as contaminated pegmatites, formed by assimilation of the country rocks by the apical part of the alkaline intrusion, which served as a focus of formation of the pegmatitic melt. Alteration in the composition of the foci was connected with alteration in the composition of the parent magma.

It is interesting that hybrid pegmatites in the Lovozero massif were formed under the influence of assimilation of both gneissose granites and basic rocks, and it is very important that the results of this assimilation were similar. Thus, for example, zircon and ilmenite appear in both cases instead of eudialyte and complex titanosilicates. This is because eudialyte and complex titanosilicates are stable only under definite physical and chemical conditions in a strictly defined range of equilibria when the content of alkalis in the magma is high. The addition of small amounts of silica makes them unstable and zircon and ilmenite are formed in their place. They also became unstable on assimilation of rocks rich in iron, magnesium and calcium but poor in alkalis.

Hybrid pegmatites varying in thickness between a few centimetres and one metre usually cut xenoliths of Devonian rocks or are emplaced in gneissose granites near the contacts with the massif (Ninchurt, Flora, Vavnbed, etc.). The main minerals of these pegmatites are orthoclase, aegirine, albite, zircon and manganilmenite. The accessory minerals include sphene, apatite, hornblende and genthelvite.

Contaminated pegmatites are found mainly in the rocks of the differentiated and poikilitic syenite complexes where there are roof xenoliths of Devonian rocks. They are most widely distributed in the central part of the massif in the vicinity of Ninchurt and in the valleys of the Koklukhtiuai, Suoluai and Ankisuai. A whole group of distinctive pegmatites that contain minerals typical of both pure and hybrid pegmatites is associated with the rocks of the differentiated complex in this district. There are also slight signs of contamination in the pegmatites of Lepkhe-Nel'm and Kuivchorr (described above) which are genetically associated with poikilitic syenites.

23. THE FELDSPATHIC-ZIRCON VEINS OF FLORA

Feldspathic-zircon pegmatitic veins emplaced in a xenolith of Devonian augite-porphyrite were discovered in the summer of 1948 on the northern slope of Flora. The xenolith (approximately 500 m²) is ellipsoidal (Fig. 94). It lies at the contact between the porphyritic lujavrite of the eudialytic lujavrite complex and the

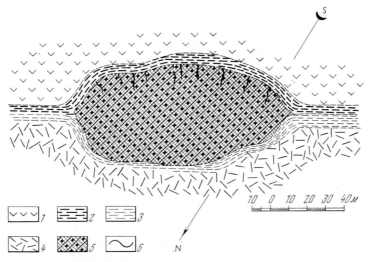

FIG. 94. Diagram of augite-porphyrite xenolith on Flora (constructed by Es'kova)

1. eudialytic lujavrite; 2. porphyritic eudialytic lujavrite; 3. mesocratic aegirine-lujavrite; 4. foyaite; 5. augite-porphyrite; 6. pegmatite

mesocratic aegirine-lujavrite of the differentiated complex. It is interesting to note that the trachytoid texture of the enclosing lujavrites follows the outlines of the xenolith. At the contact between the xenolith and the alkaline rocks there are small lenticular pegmatitic bodies with apophyses into the interior of the xenolith. The contact between the pegmatites and the country rocks is sharp. The minera-logical composition of the pegmatites is that usually found in pure alkaline peg-matites. The pegmatitic segregations reach a size of 0·5 × 0·4 m.

The pegmatitic apophyses in the augite-porphyrite are typical examples of hybrid pegmatites. The pegmatitic melt was injected into the xenolith along fissures that existed only in its southern part, i.e. from the side in contact with the porphyritic eudialytic lujavrite and perpendicular to the contact. There are some 20 small apophyses, varying in thickness from fractions of a centimetre to 10-15 cm in this part of the xenolith. Their length sometimes reaches 10-15 m. The contact between the pegmatite and the country rocks is sharp and straight. The augite-porphyrite is bleached at the contact with the larger apophyses. In the immediate vicinity of the contact, the porphyrites have been entirely reworked and consist in the main of alkaline rock minerals—nepheline, aegirine, hornblende and sodalite. Further from the contact the effect of the pegmatitic melt on the country rock is seen to decline: there is a decrease in the amount of the typical alkaline minerals aegirine and nepheline. Titanomagnetite, which is typical of the unaltered country rocks, is almost absent from the replacement zone.

Small veins do not give rise to alterations in the country rocks.

These pegmatitic veins, which are leucocratic and medium-grained, can be distinguished clearly against the dark background of the country rocks by their

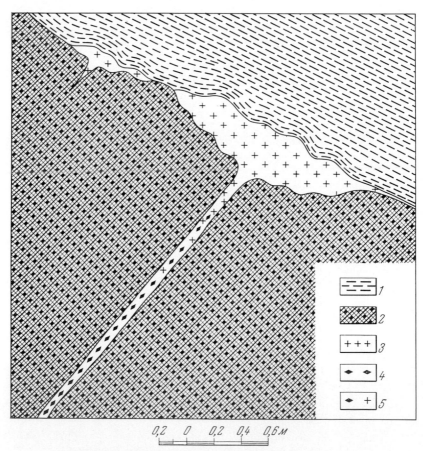

Fig. 95. Relationship between hybrid and pure pegmatites (after Es'kova)

1. porphyritic eudialytic lujavrite; 2. Devonian augite-porphyrite;
3. pure alkali pegmatite; 4. hybrid pegmatite; 5. transitional zone

white colour. The structure of the largest veins is symmetrically zonal. The contact zone is composed of orthoclase (40-50 per cent), manganilmenite (20-30 per cent), zircon (20-25 per cent) and aegirine I (3-5 per cent), the last three being included in the orthoclase. The size of the aegirine and manganilmenite crystals decreases from the vein contacts to their central parts. The orthoclase and zircon crystals increase in size in the same direction.

The central zone, which is up to 5 cm thick (and on rare occasions 10 cm) consists in the main of orthoclase (up to 90 per cent) with a small quantity of

Fig. 96. Orientated arrangement of feldspar crystals in hybrid pegmatitic veins. ×10. Crossed nicols

sodalite, genthelvite and apatite, the sodalite and genthelvite being found in the axial part of the veins. Eudialyte grains are also sometimes found in this part. There is therefore an increase in orthoclase content and a decrease in the content of zircon, manganilmenite and aegirine between the walls of the veins and their axial parts.

Zoning is absent from the smaller pegmatitic veins, and their mineral segregations are smaller than in the more extensive bodies. They usually contain less manganilmenite and zircon, and more aegirine.

In some cases one finds gradual transitions from hybrid to pure pegmatites. This type of picture can be seen in one apophysis, which is 10 cm thick near the pegmatitic lens and 3-5 cm thick further along the strike and approximately 5 m long (Fig. 95). For the first 0·5 m the apophysis has the same mineralogical composition as the lenticular body of which it forms a branch. There then follows a part whose mineralogical composition is intermediate between the pure and hybrid pegmatites. Hybrid pegmatite minerals (zircon, manganilmenite and orthoclase) make their appearance. It is interesting that in the transitional zone these minerals lie near the contact with the Devonian rocks and run perpendicular to the walls. Pure pegmatite minerals (microcline, aegirine and eudialyte) lie nearer the centre of the vein. Murmanite and lamprophyllite are absent from the transitional zone. Deeper into the xenolith the pegmatitic vein becomes a typical example of hybrid pegmatites.

The main minerals of the feldspathic-zircon veins are orthoclase (40-90 per cent), zircon (1-20 per cent), manganilmenite (up to 30 per cent) and aegirine (up to 10 per cent). Sodalite, eudialyte, genthelvite, apatite, natrolite and albite are sometimes present.

Orthoclase is found as white tabular crystals running perpendicular to the walls (Fig. 96). The crystals, which are frequently twinned, reach sizes of $2 \times 0.5 \times 0.2$ cm.

Orthoclase formed later than manganilmenite, zircon, apatite, aegirine and hornblende, and encloses idiomorphic crystals of them.

Zircon is widely distributed in pegmatites of this type. Comparatively rarely it forms clearly dipyramidal crystals, but it is usually found as aggregates of these crystals. The crystals vary between 0.1 and 0.6 cm across; the cross-section of the aggregate may reach 1.5×2 cm. The colour is light brown, less frequently light chestnut. The greater part of the zircon is confined to the contact zones; its quantity decreases away from the contacts and it is absent from the central sectors of the largest pegmatitic veins.

Zircon is an early mineral in these pegmatites. Idiomorphic inclusions of it are found in orthoclase, aegirine and hornblende. Fine tabular segregations of manganilmenite are included in zircon crystals, while apatite is xenomorphic to it. There is an interesting relationship between zircon and eudialyte. Eudialyte is of extremely rare occurrence in feldspathic-zircon veins. When it is present, its segregations are usually concentrated towards the central parts of some pegmatitic bodies where zircon is not found. When there are small amounts of zircon in conjunction with eudialyte, the latter is always xenomorphic to the zircon.

Manganilmenite is intimately associated with zircon. It is normally found round the walls of the pegmatitic veins (up to 20-30 per cent) and less frequently in the central parts (3-5 per cent). Its pitch-black fine-tabular crystals are arranged perpendicular to the vein walls throughout their thickness. The flakes vary between 0.3×0.5 and 2.5×2 cm for a thickness of between 0.1 and 2 mm. This is the earliest mineral of the feldspathic-zircon veins, and idiomorphic crystals of it are included in orthoclase, aegirine, hornblende and zircon.

Aegirine occurs as long-prismatic dark-green crystals in the contact zones of the larger pegmatitic veins and is frequently found in the central parts of thin veinlets (1-2 cm). Its crystals, which may be as large as $2 \times 0.4 \times 0.1$ cm, decrease in size from the vein contacts to the axial regions. The amount of aegirine in the contact zones does not exceed 3-5 per cent. Its crystals run perpendicular to the walls, are normally included in orthoclase, and in their turn contain inclusions of zircon (Fig. 97), manganilmenite and apatite crystals.

Hornblende is found in intimate intergrowth with aegirine in the contact zones, where its quantity does not exceed 1 per cent. It forms elongated black crystals up to $1 \times 0.2 \times 0.1$ cm, usually included in orthoclase. It sometimes replaces aegirine. Its crystals enclose idiomorphic crystals of apatite, zircon and manganilmenite.

Genthelvite is found extremely rarely in the central parts of some pegmatitic veins in intimate association with sodalite. It forms irregular segregations with an area of up to 1×0.5 cm, and more frequently with a cross-section of 0.2 cm,

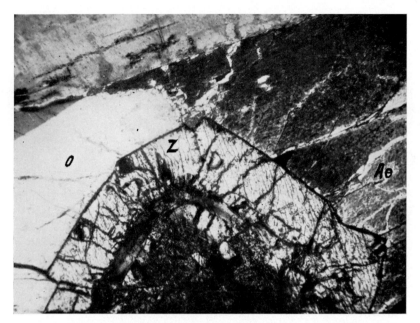

FIG. 97. Relationship of zircon (Z) to aegirine (Ae) and orthoclase (O). × 46. Without analyser

ranging from almost colourless to bluish- and emerald-green. The colourless varieties are rare.

Apatite is always present, though in very small quantities, as lath-like slightly greenish-white crystals no more than 0.1 cm long but sometimes reaching 0.5×0.1 cm in cross-section. Apatite crystals are usually included in orthoclase, aegirine and hornblende. Apatite is xenomorphic to zircon and manganilmenite, and grows round them.

Sodalite is found only in the central parts of some of the largest veins, as dark-grey and dark greenish-grey crystals up to 1 cm across. Its content does not exceed 1 per cent. Two varieties of sodalite can be distinguished by time of crystallization. The first is represented by idiomorphic crystals included in orthoclase. Such sodalite has rectilinear outlines. There is no replacement of orthoclase by sodalite. The second variety fills interstices between orthoclase crystals, replacing them from the periphery. Natrolite develops on sodalite.

Eudialyte is found as small reddish-brown irregular segregations in the central parts of some of the larger pegmatitic veins. The grains may reach 0.5×0.3 cm, but are usually smaller. It fills the interstices between orthoclase and zircon crystals, and is replaced along cracks by zirfesite.

Natrolite is found only in thin sections and then in small amounts. It forms a fine-grained aggregate of grains that develop on sodalite and less frequently on orthoclase. Replacement of sodalite usually begins from the periphery of sodalite segregations, though less frequently natrolite penetrates along cracks into their central sectors.

24. The Pegmatoid Metasomatic Zone of Vavnbed

A pegmatoid metasomatic zone that is also characterized by ilmenite-zircon mineralization forms an outcrop on the northern slopes of Vavnbed and Alluaiv. It has not as yet been studied in full detail. The zone is associated with the contacts between the massif and the enclosing gneissose granites and is up to or more than 100 m wide. It is composed mainly of pegmatoid feldspathic-aegirine rocks with separate pegmatitic and albitized areas. One pegmatitic area uncovered in a trench on the northern slope of Vavnbed has the following mineralogical composition: orthoclase, aegirine, albite, zircon, manganilmenite, ramsayite, etc.

There are separate *orthoclase* areas consisting of tabular grey crystals and clusters of small crystals. The crystals, which vary between $3 \times 2 \times 0.5$ and $12 \times 8 \times 6$ cm, are often strongly corroded along the faces by aegirine and albite. Outgrowing microcrystals of natrolite are found on the faces of some crystals.

In thin sections the orthoclase is found to be strongly sericitized. The edges of its grains are zeolitized.

Albite forms large areas of a dense white sugary appearance, small cavities in which contain well-bounded albite crystals of up to 0.5×0.5 mm. It is evident under the microscope that the sugary albite consists of finely-twinned grains with occasional larger or smaller orthoclase relicts indicating the replacement of the orthoclase by albite.

There are three generations of *aegirine*. Aegirine I is found as large crystals (with a cross-section of up to 1 cm) included in orthoclase. Fine-acicular crystals of aegirine II up to 2-3 mm long form nests in sugary albite. There are small (0.5 cm) acicular crystals of aegirine III at the contacts between the aegirine and albite aggregations. They grow out in different directions from the walls of small cavities. Transparent albite crystals sometimes grow from an aegirine III needle.

Manganilmenite is represented by tabular segregations in feldspathic areas and by well-formed crystals in cavities among albite. The tabular segregations reach dimensions of $3 \times 2 \times 0.3$ cm.

Large amounts of *zircon* are found as well-bounded dipyramidal crystals in cavities among albite. The crystals vary between a few millimetres and 1.5 cm across. Twins are sometimes found. The margins of zircon usually contain a great many inclusions of albite, which give the edges of the grains an irregular outline.

Very little *ramsayite* is found. It usually fills the interstices between orthoclase crystals.

If we compare the pegmatoid zone of Vavnbed with the feldspathic-zircon pegmatites of Flora we see that there are differences as well as common features. Zircon and manganilmenite, for example, are early minerals in the feldspathic-zircon veins of Flora, while zircon is a late mineral in the pegmatoid zone of Vavnbed and manganilmenite is represented by both early and late varieties. The central zones of the hybrid pegmatites on Flora are composed largely of orthoclase with a little sodalite, genthelvite and natrolite, and there are very few signs of replacement processes. There is slight sodalitization of orthoclase and development of natrolite on sodalite. Albitization is strongly developed in the pegmatoid zone of Vavnbed and the large amounts of aegirine II here present are not found in the feldspathic-zircon veins of Flora.

25. The Feldspathic Aegirine-Apatite Pegmatoid Vein of the Koklukhtiuai Valley

This vein was discovered by Borodin in 1949 and is here described from his data. It is emplaced in rocks of the differentiated complex (Fig. 98) at a contact with a Devonian xenolith. No regular layered structure can be seen in this region of the differentiated complex owing to the large number of xenoliths. The greater part of the pegmatoid vein intersects foyaites, but the upper part is injected into mesocratic aegirine-lujavrites. The vein is 35-40 cm thick in the foyaites, 50-60 cm in the lujavrites and approximately 35 m long.

A number of veinlets run from this vein along a system of joints of north-westerly strike (320°) running parallel to the vein.

Since the foyaites and lujavrites at the contacts with the pegmatite are strongly natrolitized, spreusteinized and pelitized they have become pinkish-grey. Ilmenite is an accessory mineral found in the foyaites of this district.

This pegmatitic body is composed in the main of two mineral associations: an early microcline-aegirine and a late aegirine-apatite association. The zonal structure of the vein (a central apatite zone and a contact aegirine-microcline zone) is due to the presence of the two associations.

The pegmatoid structure of the aegirine-microcline zones is characterized by the growth of large aegirine and feldspar crystals (up to 5 cm long). The aegirine content is approximately 60 per cent in the immediate vicinity of the contact with the foyaites, but nearer the centre it falls to 25-30 per cent and there is a corresponding increase in the potassium feldspar content. Small amounts of ilmenite, nepheline and zircon are found in this zone. The thickness of the contact zones varies between 5 and 15 cm, in direct relation to the total thickness of the vein.

The central zone is made up mainly of apatite, which forms radiate growths of small prismatic crystals, and of aegirine, which occurs as elongate-prismatic crystals up to 10 cm long. The content of ilmenite and zircon is higher in this zone than in the contact zones.

There is a slight variation in quantitative mineralogical composition along the strike of the vein. Thus, for example, there are approximately equal amounts of aegirine, potassium feldspar and apatite in the lower part of the vein bedded in

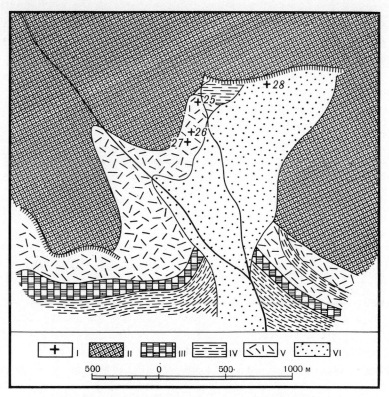

FIG. 98. Geological sketch map of the Koklukhtiuai valley (after Borodin)

I—pegmatite; II—eudialytic lujavrite; III—urtite; IV—lujavrite; V—foyaite; VI—diluvial deposits

foyaites, whereas there is a noticeable decline in apatite and zircon in the upper part of the vein and the aegirine content increases. In the upper part of the vein, which is bedded in lujavrites, the aegirine and potassium feldspar crystals in the central apatite zone are typically orientated parallel to the contact. Moreover, feldspar is absent from the zone along the walls, which consists of a dense mass of macrocrystalline aegirine.

The central apatite zone is absent from the thin apophyses that run from the master vein. These apophyses consist of orthoclase and aegirine, containing grains of ilmenite, zircon and apatite.

The main minerals of the vein are aegirine (30-60 per cent), orthoclase (25-30 per cent), apatite (5-30 per cent), nepheline (up to 5 per cent), ilmenite (3-5 per cent) and zircon (3-5 per cent).

Potassium feldspar is developed mainly in the outer zone, where it forms prismatic crystals up to $5 \times 3 \times 2$ cm or dense macrocrystalline segregations, the dark-brown colour of which is due to pelitization. It is an early mineral and contains inclusions of idiomorphic ilmenite, nepheline, pyrochlore and aegirine I crystals. Apatite, zircon and other minerals are markedly xenomorphic to it.

Aegirine is represented by two generations. Aegirine I is found as elongate-prismatic black crystals (up to 4-5 cm long) intergrown with orthoclase. It is an early mineral and its degree of idiomorphism is less only than that of ilmenite. The greater part clearly crystallized simultaneously with orthoclase. Separate aegirine I crystals are not infrequently more idiomorphic than orthoclase, or are included in it. Aegirine II is present mainly in the central zone as small prismatic or acicular crystals, sometimes forming radiate-fibrous aggregations, in the interstices between crystals of aegirine I, potassium feldspar and nepheline. It is idiomorphic to apatite and zircon.

Apatite is developed in the central zone as small prismatic crystals of up to 2 cm in length gathered into radiate-fibrous growths. The colour is white, sometimes with a slight greenish tinge. The fact that radiated aggregates of apatite crystals usually fill the interstices between potassium feldspar and aegirine indicates that it separated later.

Ilmenite is found mainly in the central zone as fine iron-black tabular crystals up to 2 cm long with a metallic lustre. It is markedly idiomorphic to all the other minerals and forms inclusions both in late minerals and in such early minerals as potassium feldspar and nepheline.

Zircon is developed mainly in the central zone of the vein, where it is bedded in foyaites. It forms irregular segregations and, less often, incomplete light-brown crystals in natrolite or in the interstices between apatite and potassium feldspar segregations. Idiomorphic inclusions of aegirine II, ilmenite and apatite are found quite often in zircon segregations.

Pyrochlore is found primarily in the central zone, where it forms small reddish-brown crystals, up to 1 mm across, and accumulations of grains. It is an early mineral, and well-formed crystals are found as inclusions in potassium feldspar, aegirine II, apatite and zircon.

Nepheline is represented by prismatic crystals included in aegirine II and apatite in the interstices between orthoclase segregations. At later stages in the formation of the pegmatitic body nepheline has been strongly replaced by natrolite. Complete pseudomorphs of natrolite after nepheline are found near the central zone.

Natrolite forms pseudomorphs after nepheline or compact irregular segregations of a pinkish-grey colour in the interstices between other minerals. These segregations are usually fine-grained and not infrequently contain inclusions of other minerals.

In addition to the minerals described above, small quantities of albite, biotite and arfvedsonite are found in the pegmatitic body.

26. THE AEGIRINE-APATITE VEIN OF THE KOKLUKHTIUAI VALLEY

This pegmatitic body, like the previous one, is described from the data of Borodin. It lies in the Eastern Cirque of the Koklukhtiuai valley 300 m to the south of vein 25 in the upper part of the differentiated complex (see Fig. 98). It is a steeply-dipping vein up to 30 cm thick. Its thickness is not maintained, but decreases from north-west to south-east until the vein peters out. The vein can be traced for 20 m along the strike, which is north-west (315°) and the angle of dip is approximately 85°.

The vein intersects trachytoid foyaites that contain two large xenoliths of Devonian rocks, and the north-western and south-eastern ends of the vein cut the xenoliths. The foyaites, which are contaminated, include sphene, manganilmenite, apatite and biotite. Microcline is greatly pelitized and nepheline natrolitized. The contact between the pegmatite and foyaites is sharp.

The structure of the pegmatitic vein is symmetrically zonal. Two zones can be distinguished between the margins and the centre: (1) an aegirine zone and (2) an apatite zone.

The aegirine zone, which is approximately 10 cm thick, is found at the walls of the vein immediately along its contacts with the enclosing foyaites. It is almost entirely composed of aegirine I, in which manganilmenite crystals are found. There is no special orientation of the aegirine crystals relative to the contact. The apatite zone, which is up to 15 cm thick, lies in the centre of the vein and is made up of a dense fine-grained mass of white sugary apatite containing separate crystals of aegirine I and manganilmenite.

The structure of the vein changes where it intersects the Devonian xenoliths. Here the aegirine zone is absent and the vein is composed chiefly of sugary apatite, which contains separate crystals of aegirine I and manganilmenite. There is a thin zone of leucocratic essentially natrolitic rock with inclusions of separate crystals of manganilmenite, biotite and, less frequently, zircon, at the contact between the vein and the Devonian rocks.

The main minerals of the pegmatitic vein are aegirine (60 per cent), apatite (25-30 per cent) and manganilmenite (up to 10 per cent). There are trifling amounts of natrolite, zircon and biotite.

Aegirine is represented only by the early generation, mainly in the aegirine zone. It forms monomineralic aggregates of dark-green and black columnar-prismatic crystals. It occurs in the central zone as isolated crystals included in the sugary apatite mass. The largest aegirine crystals are 10 cm long with a cross-section of 2×2 cm. Aegirine I is the earliest mineral of the pegmatitic body. Well-formed crystals of it are included in apatite; they are idiomorphic to manganilmenite.

Manganilmenite is found in the contact zone as iron-black thick-tabular or tabular crystals with a cross-section up to 12×8 cm and a thickness up to 3 cm. Its xenomorphic segregations fill interstices between aegirine I crystals in the aegirine zone. In the central zone it is represented by idiomorphic crystals in a fine-grained mass of apatite.

Apatite forms monomineralic areas in the central zone consisting of small prismatic crystals that often form radiate segregations. The colour is white with a greenish tinge. It is a late mineral of the pegmatitic body and contains inclusions of idiomorphic aegirine I and manganilmenite crystals.

Natrolite is mainly developed at the contact between the xenolith of Devonian rocks and the north-western and south-eastern ends of the pegmatitic vein, and forms pinkish-grey fine-grained monomineralic segregations. It contains inclusions of idiomorphic apatite, biotite and aegirine crystals.

Biotite is intimately associated with natrolite, in which it forms well-defined brown crystals up to 1 cm across and irregular segregations with an area up to 3×1.5 cm. Biotite crystals sometimes contain inclusions of idiomorphic apatite.

Zircon is found in association with natrolite and biotite, and forms light-brown dipyramidal crystals up to 1 cm across. Crystals are normally included in natrolite and contain inclusions of idiomorphic apatite. This pegmatitic vein is similar to the preceding feldspathic-aegirine-apatite vein in mineralogical composition, internal structure and genesis. It differs from the latter in the total absence of feldspar, nepheline, aegirine II and pyrochlore, and in containing less zircon, manganilmenite and natrolite.

27-28. The Natrolite Veins of the Koklukhtiuai Valley

In 1949 Borodin discovered two very interesting veins composed largely of natrolite in the Koklukhtiuai valley. One of them lies in the middle part of the valley near the aegirine-apatite pegmatitic vein 26 (see Fig. 98). This vein lies at the contact between a Devonian xenolith and the foyaites of the upper part of the differentiated complex, and is elongated with one of its ends in the rocks of the Devonian xenolith. The foyaites are found at the upper wall and the rocks of the xenolith at the lower wall. The vein is 10 m long and up to 3·5 m thick. The contact with the foyaites is sharp and irregular, and the foyaites are strongly natrolitized at the contact.

The second natrolite body 28 (see Fig. 98) is situated in the eastern part of the Koklukhtiuai valley in the sheer faces of the cirque and is inaccessible to direct examination. It is a lens up to 6×2 m at the contact between a pegmatoid foyaite and a Devonian xenolith. The foyaites fill fissures in the Devonian xenolith to form lenticular bodies and veins.

Neither of the natrolitic bodies is zonal. They are composed mainly of natrolite (90 per cent) with a little aegirine I, ilmenite, apatite, biotite, zircon and thomsonite.

Natrolite is present as radiate-fibrous growths of milky-white or transparent slender-prismatic crystals up to $5 \times 0.5 \times 0.5$ cm. The centres of the growths are often composed of microcrystalline pinkish-grey natrolite. This mineral was one of the last to separate. It fills interstices between other minerals and contains them as inclusions.

Small quantities of *aegirine* are found as macrocrystalline segregations with an area up to 3×1.5 cm, or as spherulites of fine black acicular crystals included in the natrolite mass.

Apatite is found as small short-columnar crystals that form compact pale-green irregular segregations included in the natrolite. The apatite crystals are not more than 0·5 cm long and 1·5 mm across.

Biotite is found with aegirine as tabular segregations up to 2 cm across or as poorly-formed brownish-black crystals.

Ilmenite is represented in small amounts as irregular black grains measuring up to 0·5 cm across with a metallic lustre.

Zircon is found, very rarely, as separate poorly-formed light-brown dipyramidal crystals up to 0·7 mm long included in natrolite.

Thomsonite lines the walls of geodes in the natrolite and is formed by the replacement of natrolite. Its white sheaf-like segregations of fine-acicular crystals are usually altered near the surface.

These natrolite bodies have a mineralogical composition peculiar to late stages in the formation of alkaline pegmatites and are, in essence, hydrothermal vein formations. The presence of minerals typical of contaminated pegmatites, such as apatite, zircon, manganilmenite, pyrochlore, biotite and thomsonite, indicates that the natrolite bodies are genetically akin to the previously described apatite pegmatites of this district.

According to Borodin, natrolite body 27 extends right up to the central zone of vein 26 and may possibly be an apophysis that was split off at a late stage during the formation of the central natrolite zone of this vein.

CHARACTERISTIC FEATURES OF HYBRID PEGMATITES

The following are the main features that distinguish hybrid pegmatites from pure pegmatites:

1. Direct connexion with xenoliths of Devonian augite-porphyrites or with the Archean gneissose granites surrounding the Lovozero alkali massif.

2. Abundance of orthoclase, aegirine and albite and absence of nepheline, sodalite and natrolite in the main pegmatite-forming minerals.

3. Abundance of zircon and manganilmenite and the presence of sphene and genthelvite among the rare-metal minerals.

4. Absence of eudialyte, murmanite, lamprophyllite and other minerals typical of pure pegmatites.

The development of a distinctive calcium-magnesium mineral association in hybrid pegmatites and the presence of zircon is due to enrichment of the pegmatitic melt with titanium, iron, manganese, calcium and magnesium by assimilation of the Devonian roof.

*   *   *   *

One can provisionally distinguish four stages in the formation of hybrid pegmatites (Fig. 99). Manganilmenite, zircon, apatite, aegirine I, hornblende and part of the orthoclase crystallized in the first stage. Manganilmenite, which is included in all the other minerals, was the first to separate. The slightly later formation of zircon and apatite is indicated by the idiomorphic inclusions of manganilmenite crystals in these minerals. Apatite crystals contain inclusions of idiomorphic zircon. Aegirine I and hornblende, which crystallized after apatite, contain inclusions of manganilmenite, zircon and apatite crystals, and are them-

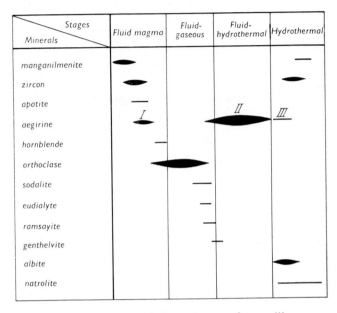

FIG. 99. Diagram of the sequence of crystallization in hybrid pegmatites

selves present as idiomorphic inclusions in orthoclase. The first stage in pegmatite formation, in which the contact zones are formed, terminates with the crystallization of orthoclase. In hybrid pegmatites emplaced in gneissose granites most of the zircon crystallized in the last stage.

The feldspathic zones of the pegmatitic veins are formed in the second stage. Early sodalite, the idiomorphic crystals of which are included in orthoclase, was the first to crystallize in these zones. Other minerals (genthelvite, ramsayite and eudialyte) normally fill the interstices between orthoclase crystals.

The aegirine II of the central parts of large pegmatitic veins emplaced in gneissose granites was crystallized in the third stage. The formation of the pegmatitic bodies ends (the fourth stage) with the crystallization of albite, aegirine III and natrolite, and sometimes late zircon and manganilmenite, in the central zones. The small quantities of natrolite usually replace sodalite from the periphery of the grains, and often penetrate along cracks into their interiors.

At the contact between aggregates of sugary albite and aegirine in the central zones of the veins one often finds cavities, the walls of which are lined with fine crystals of albite, aegirine III, manganilmenite or zircon, the last two not being found in the same cavity. The albite and zircon microcrystals and the well-formed manganilmenite crystals were probably formed at a later stage than the sugary albite and aegirine II.

Besides the microcline, nepheline, aegirine and natrolite found in pure pegmatites, contaminated pegmatites also contain such minerals as ilmenite, pyrochlore, apatite, biotite and zircon, which do not occur in pure pegmatites. Such minerals as murmanite, ramsayite, lamprophyllite and eudialyte, on the other hand, are absent from them. Also, the fact that there is more aegirine I than aegirine II in

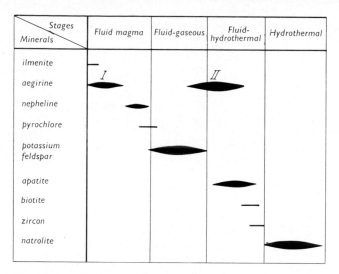

FIG. 100. Diagram of the sequence of crystallization in contaminated pegmatites

these pegmatites indicates that there was a higher iron concentration in the pegmatitic melt during the early stages of the pegmatitic process.

It should be noted that such minerals as apatite, ilmenite, zircon, biotite and sphene are found also in the alkali rocks near the Devonian xenoliths. It is highly probable that contaminated pegmatites are derivatives of a contaminated alkali magma enriched with calcium, iron and magnesium by assimilation of the roof of the massif.

The order of crystallization of the minerals in contaminated pegmatites is as follows (Fig. 100): ilmenite, aegirine I, nepheline and part of the pyrochlore, the well-formed crystals of which are found in microcline, crystallized in the first stage.

Microcline, which with aegirine I makes up the outer zones, separated in the second stage. The microcline fills the interstices between aegirine I crystals. It is usually xenomorphic to pyrochlore, ilmenite and nepheline and idiomorphic to apatite and zircon.

Late minerals, belonging chiefly to the central parts of the veins, crystallized in the third stage. Aegirine II, the earliest mineral of this stage, forms inclusions of idiomorphic crystals in apatite and zircon. Apatite, biotite and zircon separated later as a fine-grained complex.

In the fourth stage natrolite was formed after nepheline and crystallized as dense segregations in some parts of the pegmatitic bodies. Sometimes natrolite filled fissures in the rocks and formed natrolite veins.

CHAPTER FIVE

CLASSIFICATION AND GENESIS OF PEGMATITES

Structural and Paragenetic Classification

SEVERAL students of the pegmatites of the Lovozero alkali massif (Gerasimovskii, Kostyleva, Bonshtedt-Kupletskaya, Labuntsov, Gutkova and Shcherbina) have put forward classifications of the pegmatites based on mineralogical composition (Table 26). They distinguish some types by the main minerals (feldspar-aegirine, aegirine-microcline, albite and so on), some by the rare-metal minerals (lamprophyllite-murmanite, lamprophyllite-eudialyte with ramsayite and murmanite) and some in relation to both rock-forming and rare-metal minerals (microcline with aegirine and eudialyte and so on). It is evident that, since the large pegmatitic bodies with a well-defined zonal structure and highly intricate mineral complex were not known when these classifications were evolved, they failed to take into account these features in the diversity of the pegmatites.

Classification of the alkaline pegmatites of the Lovozero massif solely by their mineralogical composition is incapable of reflecting a number of their characteristic genetic properties, especially properties of structure and texture, that are of great importance for classification and for an understanding of the genesis of the pegmatites.

When a classification based on mineralogical composition fails to indicate the percentage content of the minerals we have no objective criteria for distinguishing between pegmatite types. It is difficult to distinguish between types on this basis because of the presence of the same rock-forming minerals and, in some cases, the same rare-metal minerals, in all the pegmatitic bodies.

Therefore, in classifying the pegmatites, we have to take account both of the mineralogical composition and of other and more obvious attributes observed directly under natural conditions. These attributes include the structure and texture of the pegmatitic bodies, from which one can give a more complete description of the pegmatite types and, which is very important, a more complete account of the course of their formation (Vlasov, 1946, 1947, 1951-1953, 1956; Kuz'menko, 1957).

All the minerals in the pegmatites of the Lovozero massif can be grouped into six paragenetic associations:

(1) nepheline-aegirine I-microcline-eudialyte;
(2) nepheline-aegirine I-microcline with eudialyte;

(3) sodalite-nepheline-aegirine I-microcline-eudialyte with Zr, Ti, Nb and rare-earth minerals;

(4) feldspar-aegirine II with Zr, Ti and Nb minerals;

(5) hackmanite-natrolite with rare-earth and Th minerals;

(6) natrolite-analcite-ussingite-albite with late microcline and Li and Be minerals.

The chemical and mineralogical composition of the first three associations corresponds to the three rock complexes of the massif: the first to the eudialytic lujavrites, the second to the rocks of the differentiated complex and the third to the poikilitic syenites. These associations sometimes form complete small undifferentiated pegmatitic bodies.

The remaining three associations are typical of the more highly differentiated pegmatites and reflect further stages in the development of the pegmatitic process.

TABLE 26 Classification of the pegmatites of the Lovozero massif (Gerasimovskii, 1939)

The Lovozero tundra (Bonshtedt, Kostyleva, Labuntsov and Gutkova)	South-western part of the Lovozero tundra (Shcherbina)	Lovozero tundra (Kostyleva)	Lovozero tundra (Gerasimovskii)
1. Aegirine-feldspar with ramsayite and eudialyte	1. Aegirine-feldspar with ramsayite and eudialyte	1. Aegirine-microcline	1. Microcline with aegirine and eudialyte
2. Lamprophyllite-murmanite	2. Lamprophyllite-murmanite	2. Lamprophyllite-murmanite	2. Lamprophyllite-eudialyte with ramsayite and murmanite
3. Schizolite-ussingite	—	3. Sodalite-ussingite 4. Albite 5. Ilmenite-orthoclase	3. Sodalite-ussingite 4. Albite 5. Feldspar with ilmenite and sphene 6. Feldspar with eudialyte and sphene 7. Microcline with lamprophyllite 8. Zeolite
	3. Aegirine-eudialyte	—	
	4. Aegirine-feldspar	—	
	—	6. Eudialyte-ramsayite	Gerasimovskii includes these types in the microcline with aegirine and eudialyte type
	5. Aenigmatite-feldspar	—	
4. Analcite (sodalite)-aegirine with neptunite	—	7. Neptunite	
5. Aegirine-natrolite	—	—	

They make up separate zones in the pegmatites or form independent mineral complexes.

The pegmatites of the Lovozero massif can be combined into four groups by structural and textural features: (1) fine-grained undifferentiated pegmatites; (2) block pegmatites; (3) completely differentiated pegmatites; and (4) differentiated and extensively replaced pegmatites.

The varied relationships of the paragenetic mineral associations to each other and to texture and structure define each separate pegmatite type. One can distinguish 14 textural and paragenetic types among the pegmatites of the massif, each of which has a given texture (or structure) and a specific paragenesis consisting of one or more paragenetic mineral associations (Table 27). Since, in the development of the pegmatitic process, the rôle of the previous associations is reduced with the appearance of each new paragenetic association, only the main minerals and those rare-metal minerals typical of the most highly-developed association are given in the name of the pegmatite type. This is done for the sake of brevity.

TABLE 27 Structural and paragenetic pegmatite types

Pegmatite groups	Eudialytic lujavrite and differentiated complexes	Poikilitic syenite complex
Fine-grained un-differentiated	I. Nepheline-aegirine (I)-microcline-eudialyte II. Nepheline-aegirine (I)-microcline	III. Sodalite-nepheline-aegirine (I)-microcline-eudialyte with lomonosovite, chinglusuite and nordite
Block	IV. Microcline-aegirine (II) with eudialyte, ramsayite, lamprophyllite and murmanite	V. Microcline-aegirine (II)-sodalite with eudialyte, ramsayite and murmanite VI. Orthoclase-aegirine (II)-natrolite with eudialyte, lamprophyllite and apatite
Completely differentiated	VII. Microcline-aegirine with eudialyte, ramsayite, lamprophyllite and murmanite	VIII. Orthoclase-aegirine (II)-natrolite with eudialyte, kupletskite, murmanite, apatite and steenstrupine
Differentiated and extensively replaced	IX. Microcline-aegirine-natrolite-albite with eudialyte, ramsayite, lamprophyllite and murmanite	X. Orthoclase-analcite-albite with apatite, polylithionite and leucophane XI. Orthoclase-aegirine-natrolite with tainiolite, steenstrupine and leucophane XII. Microcline-aegirine-ussingite with steenstrupine, chkalovite, belovite and erikite XIII. Hackmanite-natrolite-albite with nenadkevichite, manganosteenstrupine, hydrocerite, epididymite and beryllite XIV. Hackmanite-natrolite-microcline with polylithionite, karnasurtite and epididymite

THE GROUP OF FINE-GRAINED UNDIFFERENTIATED PEGMATITES covers an extremely large number of small facies and phase pegmatitic bodies (from a few square decimetres to several metres) that are genetically and spatially connected with distinct rock complexes. Typical features of these pegmatites include the small size of the minerals of which they are composed, simple mineralogical composition and absence of zoning (Fig. 101). Fine-grained undifferentiated pegmatites are subdivided into three types on the basis of the paragenetic associations of which they are composed:

I. *The nepheline-aegirine I-microcline-eudialyte type.* This type includes the majority of the small facies and phase pegmatitic bodies of the eudialytic lujavrite complex. Pegmatites of this type, which are represented by nests and thin veins and veinlets, are made up of the first paragenetic mineral association, that is

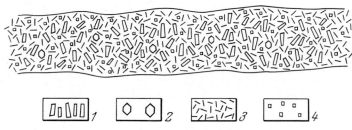

FIG. 101. Fine-grained undifferentiated pegmatite type

1. microcline; 2. nepheline; 3. aegirine I; 4. eudialyte

similar in composition to the eudialytic lujavrites and eudialytites. They consist in the main of minerals of the eudialyte group with a subordinate amount of nepheline, aegirine I and microcline. Small quantities of arfvedsonite, ramsayite and lamprophyllite are sometimes present.

II. *The nepheline-aegirine I-microcline type.* This embraces most of the facies and small phase pegmatitic bodies of the differentiated complex, in which, in essence, only the fine-grained zone is developed, if one disregards the contact fringe around the injected pegmatites. Pegmatites of this type are very close in composition to the corresponding parent rocks and are composed of the second paragenetic mineral association, consisting in the main of nepheline, microcline and aegirine I with a subordinate amount of eudialyte and sometimes arfvedsonite. In some cases there are small quantities of ramsayite, lamprophyllite and minerals of the lomonosovite-murmanite group, also found in the rocks of the massif. The minerals vary in size, but the maximum does not normally exceed 10 cm. Pegmatites of the second type differ from those of the first in having a considerably lower eudialyte content.

III. *The sodalite-nepheline-aegirine I-microcline-eudialyte type with lomonosovite, chinglusuite and nordite.* This type, which is widespread among the pegmatites of the poikilitic syenite complex, has a texture similar to that of the first and second type described above. On the other hand it has the essentially distinct third paragenetic mineral association, in which sodalite and, in a number of cases, rare-earth minerals appear, owing to the genetic connexion between pegmatites of this type and a more mineralized rock complex. This type includes most of the small facies and phase pegmatitic bodies of the poikilitic syenite complex, which are similar in composition to the parent rocks and are composed of sodalite (10-30 per cent), aegirine I (10-20 per cent), microcline (30-60 per cent) and eudialyte (10-20 per cent). In some cases they contain considerable quantities of nepheline, ramsayite, lamprophyllite, lomonosovite, murmanite, chinglusuite and nordite. Their texture is fine-grained. Grain size does not normally exceed 10 cm. There is scarcely any sign of differentiation. The pegmatites of the Chinglusuai valley are an example of this type.

THE BLOCK PEGMATITE GROUP includes most of the large facies and phase pegmatitic bodies that consist of two or three zones. Besides an outer fine-grained

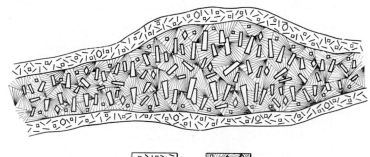

$_1$ $_2$

FIG. 102. Block feldspar-aegirine type

1. fine-grained zone; 2. block feldspar-aegirine zone

zone composed of one of the first three paragenetic associations and playing a secondary rôle in the composition of the pegmatites, they have an inner block zone composed of the fourth paragenetic mineral association. The greater part of the volume of the pegmatitic bodies is accounted for by this zone. In addition to the fourth paragenetic association, the fifth (hackmanite-natrolite) often appears in the block pegmatites of the poikilitic syenite complex.

Three structural and paragenetic types are distinguished in block pegmatites by reference to the minerals of which the block structures are formed:

IV. *The microcline-aegirine II type with eudialyte, ramsayite, lamprophyllite and murmanite.* This type includes pegmatitic bodies whose groundmass is composed of early orthoclase and fibrous aegirine II with a lesser amount of eudialyte, murmanite, ramsayite, lamprophyllite, aenigmatite and other minerals. The greater part of the zirconium, titanium and niobium minerals in the pegmatites of the massif belong to this paragenetic association. A considerable hiatus between the formation of the main minerals is typical of the microcline-aegirine block zones. Under the quieter conditions of a slow fall in temperature, when there are considerable quantities of compounds of high heat capacity, and sufficient volumes involved, the main minerals crystallize more slowly and form large monomineralic aggregations (blocks).

Microcline crystallizes first as huge crystals up to $2 \times 0.5 \times 0.4$ m or as blocks of up to $3 \times 1.5 \times 1$ m, the interstices between which are filled with aegirine II (Fig. 102). The greater part of the rare-metal minerals are concentrated in the interstices between microcline crystals and are less frequently found as idiomorphic inclusions in the edges of microcline crystals. The maximum size of the rare-metal mineral segregations does not normally exceed 10 cm. The pegmatites of Kedykvyrpakhk and a number of the Flora veins are typical.

There are varieties intermediate between the fine-grained pegmatites and the type described, in which microcline has already segregated as large crystals and the remaining minerals form a relatively fine-grained mass that fills the interstices between them.

V. *The microcline-aegirine II-sodalite type with eudialyte, ramsayite and murmanite.* This type embraces the lenticular bodies of the poikilitic syenite complex,

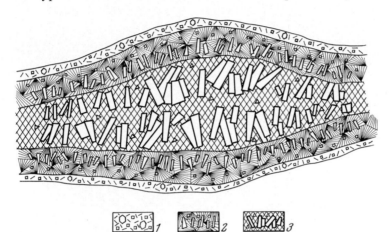

FIG. 103. Block microcline-sodalite type

1. fine-grained zone; 2. block feldspar-aegirine zone; 3. block microcline-sodalite zone

which cover areas of tens (and sometimes hundreds) of square metres and differ from the previous type by the presence of the fifth paragenetic mineral association. In addition to the outer fine-grained zones, they sometimes include fine-grained essentially aegirine or essentially eudialyte zones and have a clearly-defined block microcline-sodalite (hackmanite) zone, the structure of which includes the fourth and fifth paragenetic mineral associations. This zone, which accounts for the main volume of the pegmatitic bodies, is made up of 70-80 per cent of large microcline crystals (up to 30 cm), the interstices between which are filled with practically monomineralic sodalite (Fig. 103).

The rare-metal minerals include zirconium, titanium, niobium and the rare earths (ramsayite, lamprophyllite, murmanite, loparite and neptunite). Minerals of the replacement complex (natrolite and ussingite) appear. The microcline-sodalite pegmatitic body of Malyi Punkaruaiv is an example of this type.

VI. *The orthoclase-aegirine II-natrolite type with eudialyte, lamprophyllite and apatite.* This type includes large oval bodies of between 100 and 200 m² that are genetically associated with the nepheline-bearing varieties of poikilitic syenite. In addition to an outer fine-grained zone of similar composition to the parent rocks they include two block zones (orthoclase-aegirine and orthoclase-natrolite) made up of the fourth and fifth paragenetic mineral associations. Approximately 30 per cent of the orthoclase-aegirine zone is large orthoclase crystals (30-50 cm) the interstices between which are filled by aegirine II, to which the greater part of the zirconium, titanium and niobium minerals is confined. Approximately 70 per cent of the orthoclase-natrolite zone in the central parts of the pegmatitic bodies is large (1·5 × 1·5 m) blocks of orthoclase, the interstices between which

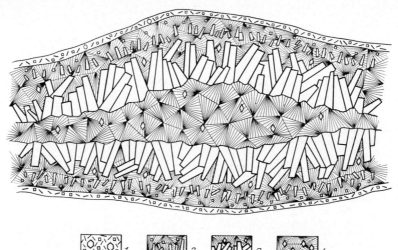

FIG. 104. Completely differentiated microcline-aegirine type

1. fine-grained zone; 2. block feldspar-aegirine zone; 3. practically monomineralic feldspar zone; 4. aegirine zone

are filled by coarse-prismatic natrolite with rare-earth apatite and steenstrupine. Thus, unlike the previous types, a later association of minerals consisting of coarse-prismatic natrolite and rare-earth minerals is widely represented in these pegmatites. The orthoclase-natrolite pegmatitic body of Lepkhe-Nel'm is an example of this type of pegmatite.

THE COMPLETELY DIFFERENTIATED PEGMATITES of the Lovozero massif are to be found in the large pegmatitic bodies of the poikilitic syenite complex, in which the main minerals (microcline and aegirine) form monomineralic zones. Well-defined completely differentiated bodies are not found among the pegmatites of the differentiated and eudialytic lujavrite complexes. We have therefore provisionally assigned only a few of the largest pegmatitic bodies of these complexes to this group (see Type VII). Two structural and paragenetic types can be distinguished in completely differentiated pegmatites in relation to the main minerals of which the monomineralic zones are composed:

VII. *The microcline-aegirine type with eudialyte, ramsayite, lamprophyllite and murmanite.* This type embraces the most completely differentiated bodies of the eudialytic lujavrite complex and the differentiated complex, in which, in addition

to fine-grained and block feldspar-aegirine zones, there are almost monomineral
feldspar (up to 80 per cent microcline) and aegirine (up to 80 per cent aegirine)
zones. Aegirine and the rare-metal mineral complex are concentrated in the
central part (Fig. 104). Niobium minerals, especially murmanite, play the major
part among the rare-metal minerals (zirconium, titanium and niobium minerals).
The processes of natrolitization, ussingitization and albitization are somewhat
more developed in these bodies, i.e. minerals of the sixth paragenetic association
appear. Some parts of the pegmatitic horizon and the pegmatites of the Sengis"yavr

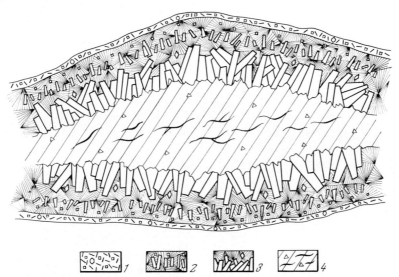

FIG. 105. Completely differentiated orthoclase-aegirine-natrolite
type

1. fine-grained zone; 2. block feldspar-aegirine zone; 3. monomineralic
feldspar zone; 4. monomineralic natrolite zone

cirque and the upper reaches of the Tyul'bn'yunuai valley are examples of pegmatites of this type.

There are transitional varieties between the Class VII completely differentiated
pegmatites and Class IV block types, in which differentiation of the rock-forming
minerals is more clearly revealed than in the Class IV type and there is an increase
in the content and diversity of titanium and niobium minerals in addition to the
appearance of minerals of the replacement complex (natrolite, albite and ussingite).
The vein in the Tyul'bn'yunuai valley ('Bear's Den' vein) is one of these transitional varieties.

VIII. *The orthoclase-aegirine II-natrolite type with eudialyte, kupletskite, murmanite, apatite and steenstrupine.* This includes the largest pegmatitic bodies of
the poikilitic syenite complex, to be measured in hundreds of square metres, in
which the main minerals form clearly-defined monomineralic zones. They have
a four-zone structure in which the following zones can be distinguished between
the margins and the centre: (1) a fine-grained zone; (2) a block zone of feldspar-
aegirine or essentially aegirine composition; (3) a monomineralic orthoclase zone;

and (4) a central nucleus of prismatic natrolite (Fig. 105). Unlike the pegmatites previously described, the fifth paragenetic mineral association consisting of natrolite with rare-earth and thorium minerals (steenstrupine and rare-earth apatites) forms a separate zone in pegmatites of this type.

The pegmatites here described differ from block pegmatites in that the main minerals are more separated both in space and by time of formation, zirconium, titanium and niobium minerals are represented by a more varied complex, there is a large amount of rare-earth apatite and, in some cases, there are small amounts of a replacement complex consisting of albite, fine-grained natrolite and halloysite with lithium and beryllium minerals (epididymite, polylithionite, tainiolite, leucophane and others). The orthoclase-natrolite pegmatitic body containing apatite and the orthoclase pegmatitic body on the northern slope of Lepkhe-Nel'm are typical examples of such pegmatites.

The following six pegmatite types (IX, X, XI, XII, XIII and XIV) comprise the group of DIFFERENTIATED AND EXTENSIVELY REPLACED PEGMATITES. They include isolated spheroidal pegmatitic bodies of greater than usual thickness, in which there is a clearly-defined zone made up of the sixth paragenetic mineral association (the replacement complex) in addition to the fine-grained, block and mineral zones.

The minerals of the replacement association are represented by late orthoclase, albite, fine-crystalline and cryptocrystalline natrolite, analcite and ussingite with a lesser amount of chabazite, hydrargillite and fine-crystalline aggregates of micaceous and mica-like minerals (tainiolite, polylithionite, epididymite and others). A series of clay minerals, especially sauconite, zincian montmorillonite and halloysite, also belong to this association. Note that late orthoclase, albite, fine-grained natrolite, analcite and ussingite, the main minerals of the replacement association, are not always found together. One or two of these minerals usually predominate and only small quantities of the others are found. All the minerals of the replacement complex are of fine-grained and cryptocrystalline structure and form large practically monomineralic aggregates or mineral mixtures.

In some cases the minerals of the replacement complex form independent zones confined to the central parts of the pegmatitic bodies or to the margins of monomineralic natrolite zones; in other cases they are irregularly distributed in the natrolite, and sometimes in the hackmanite and feldspar zones, which they replace and in which they form veinlets (see the description of the replacement zones in the Karnasurt pegmatites and those of the central part of the massif).

Extensively replaced pegmatites can be divided into the following structural and paragenetic types in relation to the main minerals that form the monomineralic zones and making allowance for the mineral that predominates in the replacement complex and for the typical rare-metal minerals:

IX. *The microcline-aegirine-natrolite-albite type with eudialyte, ramsayite, lamprophyllite and murmanite.* This type includes the most developed pegmatitic bodies of the eudialytic lujavrite and differentiated complexes. In addition to fine-grained, block and almost monomineralic zones of feldspar-aegirine composition, they include a replacement zone consisting of fine-grained natrolite and albite (Fig. 106). They also contain a very diverse selection of zirconium, titanium and niobium minerals, and, in some cases, beryllium minerals.

It should be noted that completely differentiated and extensively replaced pegmatites are poorly developed in the rocks of the eudialytic lujavrite and differentiated complexes.

X. *The orthoclase-analcite-albite type with apatite, polylithionite and leucophane.* Like all the following, this pegmatite type is found only in the pegmatites of the poikilitic syenite complex.

There are four zones between the walls and the axial part in these pegmatites: (1) a fine-grained zone with eudialyte; (2) an essentially aegirine block zone with

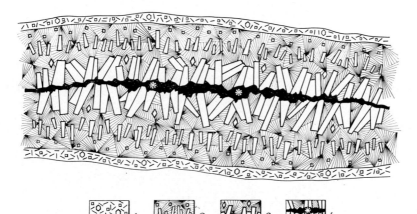

FIG. 106. Differentiated and extensively replaced microcline-aegirine-natrolite-albite type

1. fine-grained zone; 2. block microcline-aegirine zone; 3. practically monomineralic microcline zone; 4. natrolite-albite replacement zone

orthoclase and zirconium, titanium and niobium minerals; (3) a monomineralic orthoclase zone; and (4) an analcite replacement zone with albite and natrolite cores and minerals of the rare earths, thorium, lithium and beryllium. The pegmatitic vein on Kuivchorr is an example of this type.

XI. *The orthoclase-aegirine-natrolite type with tainiolite, steenstrupine and leucophane.* In pegmatites of this type there is a widely-distributed complex of replacement minerals, consisting of fine-grained natrolite, halloysite and tainiolite with polylithionite and beryllium minerals in addition to the fine-grained, block and monomineralic (orthoclase and natrolite) zones. In some cases the monomineralic zones have been replaced by minerals of this complex except for a few small relicts. The tainiolite pegmatitic body of the northern slope of Lepkhe-Nel'm is an example of this type.

XII. *The microcline-aegirine-ussingite type with steenstrupine, chkalovite, belovite and erikite.* Pegmatites of this type have three zones. The outer fine-grained zone is made up mainly of eudialyte with a lesser amount of nepheline, microcline, aegirine I and other minerals, forming segregations of a few centimetres. The second zone is made up mainly of aegirine II with a lesser amount of microcline and zirconium, titanium and niobium minerals. The microcline segregations reach a size of 15 cm. The third or block zone, composed of microcline, hackmanite and natrolite, remains only as irregular relics owing to the intensive development of an ussingite replacement zone. The latter forms the central parts of the pegmatitic bodies and occurs as nests in other zones. Rare-earth beryllium and thorium mineralization (steenstrupine, belovite, erikite and chkalovite) is confined to this zone. The ussingite pegmatitic body of Malyi Punkaruaiv is an example of this type of pegmatite.

XIII. *The hackmanite-natrolite-albite type with nenadkevichite, mangano-steenstrupine, hydrocerite, epididymite and beryllite.* Three- or four-zone structures

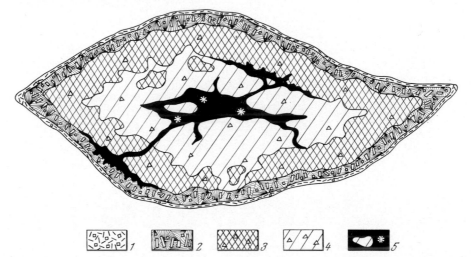

Fig. 107. Differentiated and extensively replaced hackmanite-natrolite-microcline type

1. fine-grained zone; 2. block microcline-aegirine zone; 3. monomineralic hackmanite zone; 4. monomineralic natrolite zone; 5. natrolite-microcline replacement zone

are found in such pegmatites. The outer zone is fine-grained and made up of microcline, hackmanite, aegirine and eudialyte with minerals of titanium, niobium, the rare earths and thorium (murmanite, nenadkevichite, manganosteenstrupine and hydrocerite). The second zone has a block structure and is made up of hackmanite and coarse-prismatic natrolite, with the hackmanite forming blocks of up to 2×1.5 m and the natrolite filling the interstices between them as a monocrystalline mass. Rare-earths and thorium minerals and sulphides are also present. In some of the pegmatitic bodies this zone is divided into two, a monomineralic hackmanite and a natrolite zone, in which case the central part of the pegmatitic body is a natrolite zone. In these pegmatites the replacement zone is made up of fine-grained albite with a lesser amount of fine-grained and chalcedonic natrolite, hydrargillite, chabazite and clay minerals; lithium and beryllium mineralization (epididymite, eudidymite, beryllite and polylithionite) is typical. The replacement zone develops either in the central part of the body or at the contacts between hackmanite and natrolite segregations, where it replaces both these minerals. In the latter case it is distributed throughout the hackmanite-natrolite zone. The natrolite-albite pegmatitic vein of Karnasurt is an example of this type.

XIV. *The hackmanite-natrolite-microcline type with polylithionite, karnasurtite, rhabdophane and epididymite.* This includes the most fully developed stock-like pegmatitic bodies, the thickness of which runs to tens of metres. They have the following zones: (1) an outer fringe of fine-grained structure, consisting of hack-

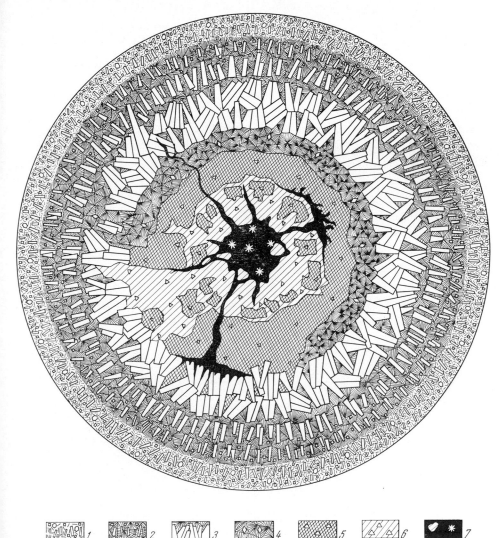

FIG. 108. Diagram of the alkali pegmatitic process and the formation of pegmatite types

1. fine-grained complex (zone) of minerals consisting of nepheline, microcline (sodalite), aegirine I and eudialyte; 2. feldspar-aegirine complex with the minerals of titanium, zirconium and niobium; 3. monomineralic feldspar zone; 4. monomineralic aegirine zone with titanium, zirconium and niobium minerals; 5. hackmanite zone with minerals of the rare earths and thorium; 6. natrolite zone with minerals of the rare earths and thorium; 7. replacement mineral complex with minerals of the rare earths, thorium, lithium, beryllium and zinc

manite, aegirine and microcline with eudialyte; (2) an essentially aegirine zone with a lesser amount of microcline, eudialyte, hackmanite, arfvedsonite and murmanite; (3) a monomineralic or block hackmanite zone; (4) a central natrolite monomineralic zone with rare-earth and thorium minerals; (5) a replacement zone made up mainly of fine-grained late microcline with a lesser amount of natrolite, chabazite, hydrargillite and montmorillonite (Fig. 107). The epididymite, karna-surtite, polylithionite and rhabdophane are confined to this zone.

The hackmanite-natrolite stock of Karnasurt is an example of this type.

There are intermediate links in both mineral composition and structural and textural attributes between the pegmatite types described above. Thus, for example, hackmanite and natrolite are typical of the pegmatites of the poikilitic nepheline-sodalite-syenite complex. These minerals are, however, also found in the more or less developed pegmatites genetically associated with eudialytic lujavrites, and natrolite is often present in the pegmatites of the differentiated complex.

The appearance of even small amounts of the minerals typical of more complex types in the simpler pegmatites indicates that there is a common line of evolution amongst the alkali magmas and their derivatives the pegmatites. This tendency is revealed in the formation of later mineral associations containing volatile compounds of sulphur, chlorine and water. Small quantities of such minerals are formed at late stages in the simple pegmatites.

Complex pegmatites begin to form at lower temperatures, and the main minerals that make up the greater part of their volume are from late associations. It follows from the description of paragenetic mineral associations and pegmatite types that the pegmatitic process develops in stages (Fig. 108) in which new mineral associations appear and the rôle of early associations is reduced (as far as total disappearance).

The Genesis of the Pegmatites

Explanation of the genesis of alkali pegmatites, as of pegmatites in general, reduces itself in essence to an explanation of the factors governing the concentration of volatile compounds in the magma. The beginning, for any reason, of a concentration of volatile compounds in the magma is also the beginning of the development of a pegmatitic process. Not every concentration of volatiles will, of course, lead to the development of a pegmatitic melt-solution. This concentration will often remain at a stage at which the relatively volatile-enriched melt-solution will give rise not to pegmatites but to coarse-grained rock facies that are intermediate links between the ordinary rocks and pegmatites. Only in some favourable cases will the concentration of volatiles reach a level at which the melt-solution will form facies or, in the case of tectonic disturbances, phase pegmatites.

The rôle of volatiles in the formation of the pegmatites of the Lovozero alkali massif is vast. The most complex and highly-developed pegmatitic bodies carry the greatest quantity of minerals containing chlorine, sulphur and water. The most complex pegmatites associated with the poikilitic syenites are characterized by the presence of large amounts of hackmanite, natrolite, analcite, ussingite and other volatile-containing minerals.

One can conclude from an analysis of the mode of occurrence of the pegmatitic bodies and from their chemical and mineralogical composition that emanation and [fractional] crystallization were the two main factors governing the genesis of the pegmatites (Vlasov, 1956₂).

The accumulation of chlorine, sulphur and water compounds in some parts of the Lovozero alkaline intrusion before or during its crystallization retarded crystallization of part of the magma and gave rise to characteristic melts that later crystallized as pegmatites.

The rôle of emanation processes in the formation of the pegmatites can be illustrated from the poikilitic syenites and associated pegmatites. The poikilitic nepheline-sodalite-syenites are the crystallization products of extensive magma foci of similar physical and chemical properties and composition to pegmatitic melts. The injection of this magma into the upper horizons of the massif led to additional concentration of readily volatile compounds in the apical parts of the active intrusions. This led to the development of even more volatile-enriched pegmatitic melt-solutions from which the most complex and highly-developed textural and structural pegmatite types were later formed. The rôle of emanation processes in pegmatite formation is shown also by the presence of distinctive pegmatitic facies at the contact between the Lovozero alkali massif and the gneisses, and also at the contact between the poikilitic sodalite-syenites and the other rocks of the massif.

The fact that pegmatitic bodies and whole horizons of pegmatites are associated with the floors of urtite and ijolite-urtite horizons, indicates the rôle of the crystallization factor in pegmatite formation. Observe that the crystallization and the emanation factors were operative in the formation of pegmatites bedded beneath the urtite horizons. The formation of thick nepheline horizons that did not include volatiles and readily-fusible compounds in their composition led to the concentration of these compounds below the floors of the horizons and to the development of the pegmatitic process. At the same time the urtite horizons acted as screens for the volatile compounds ascending from below.

Tectonics had a great influence on the formation of the pegmatites. When the pegmatitic melt remained *in situ* it gave rise to pegmatitic bodies with a relatively simple mineralogical composition and textural and structural features. When the pegmatitic melt was injected into more or less vertical fissures and cavities of different forms there was further redistribution and concentration of volatile compounds in the upper parts of the vein bodies.

The pegmatites of the Lovozero alkali massif differ quite fundamentally in mineralogical composition from the parent rocks. This is largely due to the presence of increased quantities of readily-volatile compounds in the pegmatites. The presence of large amounts of chlorine, sulphur and water lowered the crystallization temperature of the minerals and gave rise, for example, to the formation of sodalite, hackmanite and natrolite instead of nepheline, and of murmanite instead of lomonosovite.

Analysis of the data shows that there are a number of causes of the diversity of the pegmatitic bodies: the composition of the parent magma, the level of its saturation with volatiles, the nature and composition of the volatiles, form, volume, the composition of the country rocks and so on.

The time at which the pegmatitic melt is injected into the fissures is of particular importance in pegmatite formation. This is a process intimately associated with tectonic events. The pegmatitic melts were injected at different stages in the evolution of the pegmatitic foci. Where injection took place at an early stage in development, when the concentration of volatiles including rare-metal compounds was still slight, simple pegmatites little different from the country rocks were formed in thin veins. When pegmatitic foci were dissected by fissures at a late stage in their formation pneumatolytic-hydrothermal solutions or hydrothermal solutions giving rise to metasomatism were separated. The field for the development of the pegmatitic process lies between these extreme cases. Absence of tectonic thrusts during the early stages in the evolution of pegmatitic foci prevented the development of the pegmatitic process and led to the formation of pegmatoid facies in the rocks. The content and nature of the readily-volatile compounds in the Lovozero alkali massif and the volumes and shapes of the pegmatitic bodies led to the development of a diverse complex of pegmatitic formations ranging from thin veins that were little different from the parent rocks to large bodies of extremely complex chemical and mineralogical composition and zonal structure, such as the hackmanite stock on Karnasurt.

The chemical composition of the solutions and the form and dimensions of the cavities in which they were contained affected the crystallization of the pegmatites. Thus, pegmatitic solutions, poor in volatiles, injected into thin fissures, crystallized rapidly and with very little differentiation, to give rise to single-zone bodies of simple mineralogical constitution similar in composition to the parent rocks. The picture is quite different when a volatile-enriched pegmatitic melt was injected into a large cavity. The presence of a large quantity of volatile compounds of high heat capacity and the relatively small cooling surface of the rounded bodies retarded the crystallization of the melt-solutions; the slow and undisturbed growth of the minerals led, in some cases, to the formation of monocrystalline zones and aggregates. There was a further concentration of rare-metal and readily-volatile compounds in the solution during crystallization. At a certain stage in the process these late solutions reacted with the previously separated minerals to give rise to an extremely interesting complex of replacement minerals.

Four main stages can be distinguished in the formation of the Lovozero massif pegmatites (Fig. 109). The demarcation of these stages is purely provisional, since it is extremely difficult to find precise boundaries for the stages in the single continuous process of pegmatite formation. Nevertheless, the boundaries of these stages can be established from a study of the age relationships of the minerals and their composition, and one can even distinguish subdivisions within each stage.

Nepheline, aegirine I, arfvedsonite and part of the microcline were formed in the first stage of pegmatite formation. Early sodalite also separated at this stage in the pegmatites of the poikilitic syenite complex. These minerals did not, of course, crystallize simultaneously, but at intervals corresponding approximately to the period of formation of one of the main rock-forming minerals.

The greater part of the early orthoclase crystallized in the second stage, sometimes as large monomineralic aggregates (blocks or practically monomineralic

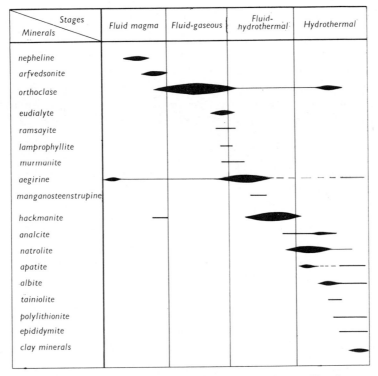

Minerals \ Stages	Fluid magma	Fluid-gaseous	Fluid-hydrothermal	Hydrothermal
nepheline	━			
arfvedsonite	━			
orthoclase	━━━		━	
eudialyte		━		
ramsayite		│		
lamprophyllite		│		
murmanite		│		
aegirine	━	━━	━ ━ ━ ━	
manganosteenstrupine		─		
hackmanite	│	━━		
analcite			━	
natrolite			━━	
apatite			━ ─ ─ ─	
albite			━	
tainiolite			─	
polylithionite			─	
epididymite			─	
clay minerals			━	

FIG. 109. General outline of the sequence of crystallization of the main and characteristic minerals in the alkali pegmatites of the Lovozero massif

zones). Monomineralic feldspar zones are formed only in pegmatites that are richer in potassium than in sodium, and in the absence of sulphur and chlorine. At the end of the period in which early orthoclase crystallized the greater part of the high-temperature rare-metal minerals of zirconium, titanium and niobium, and of the eudialyte, ramsayite, lamprophyllite, murmanite and other minerals, separated.

The third stage is marked by the formation of minerals containing volatiles: fluorine, sulphur and the hydroxyl group. The first to crystallize was fine-fibrous aegirine, which fills the interstices between the high-temperature rare-metal minerals and early potassium feldspar. Hackmanite zones are also formed at this stage in the pegmatites of the poikilitic syenite complex and early rare-earth and thorium minerals separate (steenstrupine, manganosteenstrupine, chinglusuite and nordite).

In the fourth (hydrothermal) stage the minerals that formed were in the main those containing water. Marked decomposition and replacement of all the previously-formed minerals are typical of this stage.

Large-prismatic natrolite, which fills the central parts of completely differentiated pegmatitic bodies as a monocrystalline mass, crystallized in the first phase of this stage. Rare-earth apatite separated during the formation of large-prismatic natrolite and some silicophosphates of niobium, the rare earths and thorium began to crystallize.

The replacement mineral complex was formed during the second part of the stage. These minerals are represented by late orthoclase, albite, analcite, ussingite, chalcedonic natrolite, chabazite, epididymite, polylithionite, tainiolite and other minerals. Some clay minerals, namely sauconite, zincian montmorillonite and halloysite, were apparently formed at the close of this part of the stage. The halloysite contains rare elements intimately associated with the minerals enumerated above. The minerals of this complex replace early potassium feldspar, hackmanite and prismatic natrolite, and fill fissures in them. The composition of the replacement complexes is largely dependent on the initial composition of the pegmatitic melt. Thus, for example, late fine-crystalline microcline is found only among the replacement minerals in those pegmatitic bodies in which there is a great predominance of sodium over potassium, or, in other words, in which the concentration of potassium in the early stages of the pegmatitic process was insufficient for the formation of early microcline. Owing to the abundance of sodium in these pegmatites the hackmanite crystallized earlier than the greater part of the microcline, which separated after prismatic natrolite, in the replacement stage as a fine-grained aggregate.

Increase in the beryllium and lithium concentration in the completely differentiated pegmatites of the poikilitic syenite complex during the replacement stage led to the formation of independent beryllium (epididymite and leucophane) and lithium (polylithionite and tainiolite) minerals. In pegmatites poor in calcium and magnesium the lithium was taken up in polylithionite (potash mica) and the beryllium in epididymite (the sodium mineral of Karnasurt). In calcium- and magnesium-enriched pegmatites the lithium was taken up in magnesium mica (tainiolite) and the beryllium in the calcium mineral leucophane (Lepkhe-Nel'm). It is interesting to note that an increase in the silicon concentration that takes place during the pegmatitic process can be seen towards the close. This indicates the general tendency to differentiation in the rocks.

All the stages here indicated are not, of course, clearly manifested in all the pegmatites. The development of most of the facies and small phase pegmatites is ended, in the main, in the first stage. The second and third stages are often poorly exhibited in such pegmatites. The beginning of the fourth stage is clearly indicated in some pegmatitic bodies by the formation of central natrolite zones. All four stages are fully expressed only in the thick spheroidal pegmatites of the poikilitic syenite complex, in which the differentiation of the pegmatitic melt-solution proceeded farthest.

PART THREE

MINERALOGY

INTRODUCTION

MORE than 130 mineral species and varieties have now been found in the Lovozero alkali massif. About 60 of these contain rare elements: zirconium, niobium, titanium and elements of the rare-earth group, thorium, lithium and beryllium. No other massif in the world is known to contain such a wealth and variety of minerals. The nearest to the Lovozero in this respect are the alkali massifs of Khibiny in the Kola peninsula, the Langesund Fiord in Southern Norway and the Kangerdluarsuk and Narsarsuk in Greenland, but their mineralogy is much poorer.

More than 50 of the minerals known from the Lovozero massif are either lacking from other massifs or present only in very small amounts. Such minerals as chkalovite, nordite, lovozerite, seidozerite, chinglusuite, metaloparite, lomonosovite, beliankinite, gerasimovskite, hydrosodalite, nenadkevichite, karnasurtite, kupletskite, vinogradovite, labuntsovite, belovite, manganosteenstrupine, hydrocerite, beryllite and others have been found only in the Lovozero. Loparite, murmanite, ramsayite, rinkolite, lovchorrite, narsarsukite, tainiolite, polylithionite, schizolite, steenstrupine, erikite, ussingite, manganilmenite, villiaumite, hackmanite, zirfesite, elpidite, titan-låvenite, lamprophyllite, astrophyllite, neptunite, aenigmatite, leucophane, epididymite, eudidymite and others occur in other alkali massifs, but in considerably smaller amounts.

Mineralization is more advanced in the Lovozero pegmatites than in the other rocks of the massif. The alkali rocks contain not more than 50 different mineral species, whereas nearly all the minerals found in the massif are represented in the pegmatites genetically associated with them. Both in the pegmatites and in the other rocks the number and variety of mineral species increase, from the eudialytic lujavrite complex, through the differentiated complex to the youngest, the poikilitic syenite complex.

120 Lovozero minerals are described in this book. We have provisionally classified them into three main groups: (1) principal rock-forming minerals, (2) rare-metal minerals and (3) secondary and accessory minerals (Table 28).

The principal rock-forming minerals include chiefly nepheline, microcline and aegirine, which make up nine-tenths of the main rock and pegmatite mass. In some rock varieties the main rock-forming minerals are sodalite, hydrosodalite, natrolite and arfvedsonite. In the pegmatites nepheline is present in much smaller amounts than in the other rocks, and hydrosodalite is lacking; on the other hand, natrolite, ussingite, analcite and albite are extensively developed, forming fairly thick monomineralic zones in a number of the fully-differentiated pegmatitic

TABLE 28 Classification

Group		Aluminosilicates		Silicates		Zirconium silicates
		anhydrous	hydrous	anhydrous	hydrous	
Main rock-forming minerals		Nepheline Microcline Orthoclase Albite Sodalite Hackmanite	Hydro-sodalite Ussingite Natrolite Analcite	Aegirine Arfved-sonite	—	—
Rare-metal minerals	Zirconium minerals	—	—	Zircon	—	Eudialyte Mesodialyte Eucolite Lovozerite Catapleiite Zirfesite Elpidite Titan-låvenite Seidozerite
	Titanium and niobium minerals	—	—	—	—	—
	Rare-earth and thorium minerals	—	—	Nordite Thorite	Steen-strupine Mangano-steen-strupine Karna-surtite Hydrocerite	—
	Lithium minerals	—	Poly-lithionite Hydro-poly-lithionite	—	Tainiolite Hydro-tainiolite Ferro-tainiolite	—

of Lovozero minerals

Titanoniobium silicates	Niobo-titanates, titanates and niobates	Oxides and hydroxides	Halides	Sulphides, sulphosalts and arsenides	Phosphates and silico-phosphates	Carbonates and sulphates
—	—	—	—	—	—	—
—	—	—	—	—	—	—
Lomonosovite Murmanite Nenadkevichite Ramsayite Lamprophyllite Astrophyllite Kupletskite Mangan-neptunite Aenigmatite Narsarsukite Chinglusuite Labuntsovite Vinogradovite Epistolite	Loparite Meta-loparite Pyrochlore Sphene	Mangan-ilmenite Rutile Brookite Anatase Pyro-phanite Ulvöspinel Belyankin-ite Gerasi-movskite	—	—	—	—
Rinkolite Lovchorrite	—	—	—	—	RE Apatite Belovite Erikite and other silico-phosphates	—
—	—	—	—	—	—	—

TABLE 28

Group	Aluminosilicates		Silicates		Zirconium silicates
	anhydrous	hydrous	anhydrous	hydrous	
Beryllium minerals	—	—	Chkalovite Genthelvite	Leucophane Epididymite Eudidymite Beryllite Gel-bertrandite Sphaero-bertrandite Karpinskyite	—
Secondary and accessory minerals	Natro-davyne	Cancrinite Biotite Hydro-muscovite Chabazite Celadonite Thomson-ite Chlorites Spodio-phyllite Allophane Thuringite Chloro-phyllite Beidellite	Acmite Aegirite-augite Cato-phorite	Pectolite Schizolite Apophyllite Calamine [hemi-morphite] Mont-morillonite Zn-mont-morillonite Sauconite Halloysite Kaolinite Nontronite Hisingerite	—

bodies. In some of the rocks rare-metal minerals (eudialyte, apatite and others) act as rock-forming minerals.

The second group comprises minerals in which rare elements are the main components: zirconium, niobium, titanium, rare earths, thorium, lithium and beryllium. This group is further divided into subgroups, according to the pre-dominant rare element or group of rare elements. Only about 20 species of the rare-metal minerals have been found in the non-pegmatitic rocks of the massif, against more than 50 in the pegmatites.

The third group comprises minerals containing hardly any rare elements and occurring in the massif only in small amounts. Most of these minerals are present only in the pegmatites.

In terms of chemical [anionic] radicals the Lovozero minerals fall into ten groups (see Table 28).

More than 200 full chemical analyses, more than 250 qualitative spectro-graphic analyses, more than 70 Debye-Scherrer powder patterns and numerous partial determinations by quantitative spectrographic and roentgenochemical methods have been used in preparing the following description of the minerals. Heating and dehydration curves, together with interplanar spacings, are generally

(continued)

Titanoniobium silicates	Niobo-titanates, titanates and niobates	Oxides and hydroxides	Halides	Sulphides, sulphosalts and arsenides	Phosphates and silico-phosphates	Carbonates and sulphates
—	—	—	—	—	—	—
—	—	Quartz Chalcedony Opal Natro-opal Hydro-goethite Psilo-melane Crypto-melane Vernadite Pyrolusite Hydrar-gillite Boehmite Cuprite	Villiaumite Fluorite	Molybden-ite Sphalerite Pyrite Marcasite Chalco-pyrite Galena Covellite Pyrrhotite Löllingite	Staffelite [francolite] Mangano-staffelite Calcio-ferrite Poly-sphærite	Calcite Cerussite Ancylite Jarosite

given in the descriptions of new or little-known minerals. The refractive indices of most of the minerals were determined by the immersion method.

CHAPTER ONE

PRINCIPAL ROCK-FORMING MINERALS

The principal minerals of the Lovozero massif include nepheline, microcline, aegirine, arfvedsonite, orthoclase, albite, sodalite, hackmanite, hydrosodalite, ussingite, natrolite and analcite. All these minerals are aluminosilicates or silicates (see Table 28).

1. Nepheline

Na[AlSiO$_4$]; hex.; sp.gr. 2·55—2·65; H. 5·5—6

In the Lovozero massif nepheline usually forms irregularly circular grains, a few millimetres (rarely as much as 1 cm) in diameter. In the pegmatites it is represented by hexagonal prismatic crystals measuring from $1 \times 1 \times 2$ to $5 \times 5 \times 10$ cm or by large irregularly-shaped masses up to 30 cm in diameter. Crystals with good faces rarely occur. The crystals have a characteristic hexagonal prism m (10$\bar{1}$0) and a pinacoid c (0001). The colour is grey, greenish-grey or light grey. Altered varieties have a brown or red-brown coloration. The fracture is uneven. The lustre is greasy. In thin fragments nepheline is semi-transparent. Cleavage perceptible only in thin sections along (0001) and (10$\bar{1}$0). Colourless in transmitted light. Optically uniaxial, negative; sometimes slightly anomalously biaxial. Straight extinction. Low birefringence. The refractive indices of the rock and pegmatitic nephelines are similar:

	No	Ne	No – Ne
Rock nepheline	1·535—1·547	1·533—1·545	0·002—0·003
Pegmatitic nepheline	1·533—1·548	1·529—1·545	0·003—0·004

Nepheline is soluble in concentrated HCl and HNO$_3$. Recalculating the results of the chemical analysis shown in Table 29 we see that the composition of nepheline can be reduced to the formula (Na, K) AlSiO$_4$, some excess of silicon being observable. E. I. Semenov reports that 0·001 per cent of beryllium oxide was detected in the nepheline by chemical assay.

In addition to the elements chemically determined, gallium (0·01 per cent), strontium, titanium and copper have been found spectrographically in pegmatitic nepheline from various parts of the massif (Alluaiv, Lepkhe-Nel'm and Flora and the River Tyul'bn'yunuai). Barium is present in pegmatitic nepheline from Lepkhe-Nel'm and the upper reaches of the Tyul'bn'yunuai. Lanthanum and yttrium have been detected in nepheline from the ijolitic urtites and pegmatites of the First Western stream on Alluaiv and the upper reaches of the Tynl'bn'yunuai.

The nepheline content in the Lovozero alkali massif varies from 2 to 95 per cent in the non-pegmatitic rocks (Table 30) and from 0 to 20 per cent in the pegmatites. The differentiated and the eudialytic lujavrite complexes have roughly the same average content of this mineral, but its distribution in space and time varies greatly with the degree of differentiation of the rocks (see Part One, Chapter Five). No regular distribution pattern can be observed in the rocks of the poikilitic syenite complex. In the nepheline-bearing varieties of the poikilitic syenite, in which the nepheline content sometimes amounts to 75 per cent, the nepheline-rich parts form irregularly-shaped pockets.

In the pegmatites nepheline occurs mainly in small undifferentiated and un-replaced bodies, and also in peripheral bodies, more rarely in block zones of large pegmatitic bodies, in all the complexes, except in pegmatites genetically connected with hackmanite-bearing varieties of poikilitic syenite, where nepheline is lacking. In small, unzoned pegmatitic bodies it forms large phenocrysts and is present in small amounts in the fine-grained groundmass.

Nepheline separates at different times in different rocks and pegmatites, appearing earlier in rocks with a high nepheline content (urtites, ijolite-urtites, poikilitic nepheline-syenites) than in nepheline-poor rocks.

In the urtites and ijolite-urtites nepheline forms irregularly-shaped segregations closely adjacent to one another, the interstices between them being filled with other minerals, including microcline (Fig. 110). It often forms poikilitic inclusions in microcline, aegirine, arfvedsonite and other minerals. Poikilitic

TABLE 29 Chemical composition of nepheline from Malyi Punkaruaiv pegmatite

Constituent	Content, %	Atomic proportions	Calculation of atomic ratios		
SiO_2	45·17	0·752	0·752	1·19	−1
TiO_2	trace	—	—	—	—
ZrO_2	0·02	—	—	—	—
Al_2O_3	32·29	0·634			
Fe_2O_3	0·77	0·010	0·646	1·02	−1
FeO	0·14	0·002			
MnO	0·003	—			
MgO	0·05	0·001			
CaO	0·20	0·004			
BaO	nil	—	0·619	0·98	−1
SrO	trace	—			
Na_2O	15·74	0·508			
K_2O	4·99	0·106			
H_2O	0·13	—	—	—	—
Other	0·33	—	—	—	—
—	—	0 =2·684	2·684	4·23	−4
Total	99·83	—			
Analyst	Smirnov, 1935				
Reference	*Minerals of the Khibiny and Lovozero tundras* (1937)				

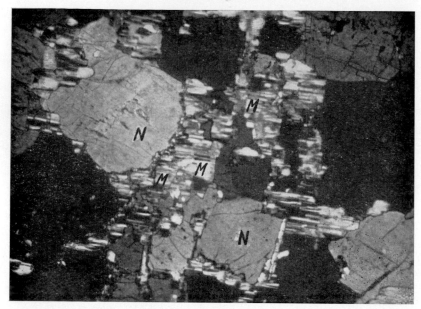

Fig. 110. Albitized microcline (M) filling interstices between nepheline
(N).   ×46. Crossed nicols

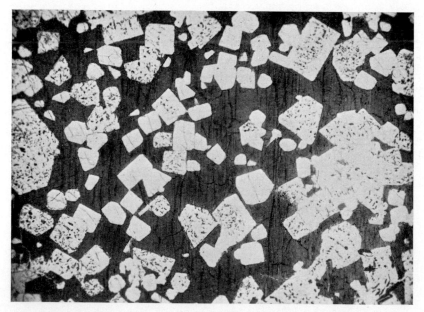

Fig. 111. Poikilitic inclusions of nepheline (light) in arfvedsonite (dark).
×10. Without analyser

FIG. 112. Nepheline (N) in interstices between microcline laths (M). ×46. Crossed nicols

FIG. 113. Replacement of nepheline (dark) by natrolite. ×46. Crossed nicols

TABLE 30 Nepheline content in Lovozero Rocks

Differentiated complex	Content, per cent	Eudialytic lujavrite complex	Content, per cent	Poikilitic syenite complex	Content, per cent
Upper division of complex:		Eudialytic lujavrites:		Poikilitic sodalite-syenites	2·1- 3·4
Foyaites	9·5-21·0	Melanocratic	23·4-30·2	Poikilitic nepheline-syenites	40·0-75·0
Urtites	4·0-63·2	Mesocratic	19·1-22·8	Poikilitic hydrosodalite-syenites	5·5-10·0
Aegirine-lujavrites	8·4-28·4	Leucocratic	17·7-18·9		
Hornblende-lujavrites	15·3-24·5	Porphyritic lujavrites	19·6-41·0		
Malignites	24·3-41·2	Porphyritic juvites	27·9-32·4		
Middle division of complex:		Porphyritic foyaites	19·7-25·5		
Foyaites	16·6-44·7				
Urtites	51·8-65·3				
Aegirine-lujavrites	15·7-21·4				
Hornblende-lujavrites	29·8-30·3				
Lower division of complex:					
Foyaites	15·4-23·9				
Urtites	66·2-95·1				
Aegirine-lujavrites	18·3-25·7				

texture is most characteristic of the poikilitic nepheline-syenites. The poikilitic inclusions of nepheline are irregularly-shaped if they are included in potassium feldspar, but when enclosed in aegirine, arfvedsonite (Fig. 111) and other minerals have good crystallographic outlines.

In the foyaites, on the other hand, which have the lowest nepheline content of all the rocks in the massif, nepheline crystallizes after microcline. In these rocks the nepheline grains are usually included among large laths of microcline and are xenomorphic towards it (Fig. 112).

In the aegirine-, hornblende- and eudialytic lujavrites the nepheline has in part crystallized earlier than the microcline, although the main body of it has separated out either after or at the same time as microcline. Most of the irregular nepheline segregations in these rocks occur in the interstices between parallel laths of microcline and are cemented by acicular aegirine II. Occasionally nepheline inclusions are found in microcline; in the aegirine-lujavrites stratigraphically below the urtites the number of such inclusions increases towards the urtite contact.

In most of the pegmatitic bodies nepheline has crystallized at a very early stage in the pegmatitic process and therefore occurs in their border zones. The ortho-clase pegmatites in the central part of the massif (Lepkhe-Nel'm), which are very rich in potassium, are an exception to this rule, their potassium feldspar having begun to crystallize earlier than their nepheline. Pegmatitic nepheline often contains inclusions of aegirine I and occasionally of arfvedsonite crystals, which are sometimes orientated parallel to the crystal faces.

In the later stages of formation of the massif nepheline is replaced by sodalite, natrolite, ussingite, cancrinite, spreustein, montmorillonite, hydrargillite and hydromuscovite. Sodalitization, natrolitization and spreusteinization are the most advanced of these alteration processes. The replacement of nepheline by sodalite is typical of the rocks and pegmatites in the poikilitic syenite complex and of the sodalitized foyaites in the differentiated complex. Natrolitization is very evident in the rocks and pegmatites of all the complexes. The nepheline is re-placed by fine-grained, finely-fibrous and cryptocrystalline natrolite, which some-times forms radiate-fibrous margins (Fig. 113). In the pegmatites, pseudomorphs of spreustein (which is a finely-crystalline mixture consisting mainly of natrolite with an admixture of hydrargillite, diaspore and opaque colloidal matter) often form after nepheline. The hydrargillite segregations in spreustein are never larger than 0.1×0.1 mm. Spreustein is usually very inhomogeneous in com-position and contaminated with various ochreous materials.

Hydromuscovite replacement of nepheline occurs mainly in the rocks and pegmatites in the upper part of the differentiated complex and in the fracture zones on Karnasurt, where it is associated with fine-grained natrolite, replacing nepheline and microcline. Montmorillonite develops from nepheline only in large pegmatitic bodies, in which late stages of replacement are clearly apparent, and sometimes forms pseudomorphs from it along with hydrargillite. Replace-ment of nepheline by ussingite and cancrinite is rare.

2. Microcline

$KAlSi_3O_8$; tric.; sp.gr. 2·5—2·6; H.6—6.5

Microcline is the principal rock-forming mineral in the Lovozero rocks and pegmatites. Only in the urtites and orthoclase pegmatites in the central part of the massif is it reduced to small amounts or absent.

In the non-pegmatitic rocks microcline forms lath-like crystals, elongated along (001), of a white or greenish and light-grey colour, measuring $1 \times 0·6 \times 0·1$ cm in the foyaites and lujavrites of the differentiated and eudialytic lujavrite complexes, to $20 \times 5 \times 4$ cm in the rocks of the poikilitic syenite complex.

In the pegmatites microcline is represented by two generations, one early, one late. The early microcline forms tabular segregations, measuring $5 \times 3 \times 1$ mm

FIG. 114. Character of microcline twinning. ×20. Crossed nicols

at the contacts of the pegmatitic bodies with the country rocks, to $70 \times 20 \times 10$ cm in the block feldspar-aegirine zones. The colour is white, creamy-yellow, creamy-grey, grey, greenish or sometimes, near the contacts, dark-green owing to the presence of large amounts of microscopic inclusions of aegirine I and arfvedsonite. Opaque to semi-transparent; in small fragments, white, transparent. Lustre on cleavage planes vitreous. Specific gravity 2·53.

Late microcline forms monomineralic finely-crystalline segregations in the large, completely replaced pegmatites genetically connected with poikilitic hackmanite-syenites of Karnasurt, where it is closely associated with other minerals of the replacement zone. These segregations are irregularly-shaped and measure from 3-5 cm in diameter to $4 \times 0·7$ m. They are cream-coloured. Individual laths vary in length from 0·1 to 0·3 mm.

In transmitted light microcline is colourless. The characteristic cross-hatched twinning does not appear. The twinning of the microcline from the alkali rocks

TABLE 31 Optical orientation of microcline

Rock	Co-ordinates of indicatrix axes						2 V
	c ⊥ (001)			c ⊥ (010)			
	Ng	Nm	Np	Ng	Nm	Np	
Differentiated complex:							
Foyaites	78-83°	12-15°	80-83°	16-19°	81-83°	74-76°	-72-84°
Urtites	79-83°	12-16°	75-81°	18-20°	82-84°	73-74°	-74-78°
Aegirine-lujavrites	80-85°	10-15°	79-85°	17-19°	82-84°	73-75°	-74-82°
Hornblende-lujavrites	81-83°	12-14°	80-84°	18-20°	81-84°	73-75°	-76-78°
Malignites	80-82°	14-16°	80-83°	19-20°	83-85°	72-75°	-72-76°
Pegmatites:							
Flora	79°	12°	86°	—	—	—	-78°
Kitkuai valley	72°	20°	75°	—	—	—	-84°
Kitkn'yun	70°	10°	86°	—	—	—	-84°
Eudialytic lujavrite complex:							
Eudialytic lujavrites	85-87°	10-13°	79-82°	17-19°	80-83°	74-76°	-76-80°
Pegmatites:							
Tyul'bn'yunuai valley	83°	13°	82°	—	—	—	-84°
Kedykvyrpakhk	75°	15°	85°	—	—	—	-82°
Poikilitic syenite complex:							
Poikilitic sodalite-syenites	80-85°	12-15°	81-83°	18-19°	80-81°	75-76°	-70-76°
Poikilitic nepheline-syenites	83-85°	13-14°	82-84°	17-18°	81-83°	73-75°	-74-78°
Pegmatites:							
Karnasurt	78°	14°	83°	—	—	—	-83°
Malyi Punkaruaiv	78°	18°	86°	—	—	—	-68°

and pegmatites of the Lovozero tundras is a special case of penetration twinning, where the separate individuals of the twinning have the shape of bands and patches in sections parallel to (001) but are fusiform or string-like in other sections. This twinned structure is reminiscent of perthite or chequer-albite (Fig. 114). The twinning is usually on the Albite law ($BNg = 18°$; $BNm = 82°$; $BNp = 74°$), but is occasionally, in the pegmatites, on the Baveno law.

Optically biaxial, negative. Elongation negative. Pronounced cleavage along (001), poor along (010) and (110). $2V$ varies from $-60°$ to $-84°$. The optic axial plane is almost perpendicular to (010). Angle between Nm axis and ψ (001) $= 10$-$16°$. The Fedorov stage measurements are shown in Table 31 and the refractive indices in Table 32.

As can be seen from the figures the optical properties of the microcline are very similar, whether it comes from the rocks or from the pegmatites.

The chemical composition of microcline is readily reduced to the theoretical formula $KAlSi_3O_8$. Rock microcline contains more soda (Table 33) than pegmatitic microcline, because of its strong albitization. The high iron content in some microcline samples is apparently due to the presence of very small aegirine inclusions in them.

In addition to the elements determined chemically, manganese, titanium, gallium and copper have been detected by the spectrographic method (10 tests) in microcline from various parts of the massif. In some samples the following were also found: beryllium (in foyaites and pegmatites from the Tyul'bn'yunuai valley and Malyi Punkaruaiv), lead (in pegmatites from Malyi Punkaruaiv and in the foyaites), silver (in pegmatites from Karnasurt), molybdenum (in foyaites and late microcline from Karnasurt pegmatites), zirconium (in pegmatites from the upper reaches of the Tyul'bn'yunuai and from Malyi Punkaruaiv), scandium (in Karnasurt pegmatites) and lanthanum (in Malyi Punkaruaiv pegmatites).

The microcline content varies from nil in the urtites to 85 per cent in the foyaites and from 10 to 60 per cent in the pegmatites. The largest amounts of microcline have been found in foyaites from the differentiated complex, particularly in its well-layered parts (Table 34).

In the three-component stratal groups of this complex, as well as in the eudialytic lujavrites, the distribution of microcline follows a definite pattern (see Part One,

TABLE 32 Refractive indices of microcline

Microcline	Ng	Nm	Np	Ng-Np	Determined by
From rocks	1·524	—	1·517	0·007	Vorob'eva
From pegmatites:					
(a) early, Karnasurt	1·525	1·522	1·518	0·007	Present authors
early, Mannepakhk	1·5275	—	1·5217	0·0058	Gerasimovskii
early, Koklukhtiuai valley	1·5236	—	1·5187	0·0049	,,
early, Tyul'bn'yunuai valley	1·5230	—	1·5171	0·0057	,,
(b) late, Karnasurt	1·525	1·522	1·517	0·008	Present authors

TABLE 33 Chemical compositions of microclines

Constituent	From albitic natrolite pegmatite vein, Karnasurt (early microcline)			From natrolitic hackmanite pegmatite stock, Karnasurt (late microcline)		From pegmatite, Punkaruaiv*		From aegirine-lujavrite, Punkaruaiv†		From foyaites, Vavnbed‡	
	per cent	Atomic proportions	Calculation of atomic ratios	per cent	Atomic proportions	per cent	Atomic proportions	per cent	Atomic proportions	per cent	Atomic proportions
SiO_2	64·18	1·0686	1·0686 2·99 —3	64·28	1·0701	63·87	1·063	65·00	1·082	64·40	1·072
TiO_2	—	—	—	nil	—	—	—	—	—	—	—
Al_2O_3	18·38	0·3606	} 0·3634 1·01 —1	18·93	0·3714	18·58	0·364	19·75	0·386	19·67	0·386
Fe_2O_3	0·22	0·0028		0·11	0·0014	0·71	0·008	0·25	0·004	0·17	0·002
FeO	trace	—		trace	—	trace	—	—	—	—	—
MnO	0·22	0·0055		0·06	0·0015	0·16	0·004	0·03	0·001	0·04	0·001
MgO	0·62	0·0111	} 0·3734 1·01 —1	0·10	0·0018	0·14	0·003	0·20	0·004	0·50	0·009
CaO	—	—		—	—	—	—	0·08	—	0·01	—
SrO	—	—		—	—	—	—	0·05	—	—	—
BaO	—	—		—	—	—	—	—	—	—	—
Na_2O	0·69	0·0222		1·80	0·0580	1·27	0·040	3·18	0·104	3·56	0·114
K_2O	15·76	0·3346		14·78	0·3138	15·20	0·322	11·72	0·248	11·04	0·236
P_2O_5	—	—		0·06	—	—	—	—	—	0·42	0·046
H_2O^+	0·27	0·0300		0·11	0·0122	—	—	0·15	0·016	—	—
H_2O^-	0·12	2·8923	O = 2·8923 8·09 —8	0·10	—	0·33	—	—	—	—	—
Other	—	—	—	—	—	—	—	—	—	—	—
Total	100·46			100·33		100·26		100·41		99·81	
Specific gravity	2·53			2·56							
Analyst	Kazakova, 1949			Vladimirova		Vladimirova		Moleva		Moleva	

* Gerasimovskii's data
†‡ Vorob'eva's data

Chapter Five). In the poikilitic syenites microcline is distributed extremely unevenly; in some parts it forms pockets, in others it is lacking altogether.

In the equigranular undifferentiated pegmatites early microcline is distributed
throughout the rock mass, the size of the segregations increasing from periphery
to centre. In the large zoned pegmatitic bodies it is usually localized in the outer
fine-grained and block feldspathic-aegirine zones.

The principal part of the microcline is one of the earliest minerals in the
rocks and pegmatites. The presence of numerous inclusions of idiomorphic

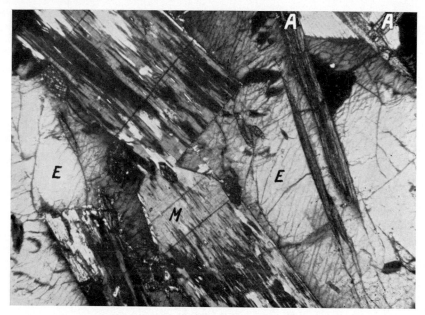

Fig. 115. Interrelationship of microcline (M) and aegirine (A) with
eudialyte (E). ×46. Crossed nicols

aegirine and arfvedsonite crystals in it and the accumulation of these minerals at
the extremities of the microcline segregations and in the interstices between
them indicate that microcline began to crystallize some time after the dark-
coloured components began to separate out and ended when the main mass of
these components had begun to crystallize.

Compared with eudialyte, lamprophyllite and ramsayite, microcline is in
general idiomorphic (Fig. 115). Sometimes, however, instances of the entrapping
of these minerals in the marginal parts of the microcline have been noted.

At late stages in the formation of the rocks and pegmatites early microcline
has been replaced by albite, sodalite, natrolite, hydromuscovite, ussingite and
cancrinite, the commonest processes being albitization, sodalitization and natrolitization. Albitization of microcline can be observed in all the complexes and is
particularly widespread in the more leucocratic rock varieties. In the pegmatites,
the replacement of microcline by albite occurs only in large bodies in which the
late hydrothermal stage of replacement is clearly expressed. Sodalitization is

TABLE 34 Feldspar content in Lovozero rocks

Differentiated complex	Content, per cent	Eudialytic lujavrite complex	Content, per cent	Poikilitic syenite complex	Content, per cent
Upper division of complex:		Eudialytic lujavrites:		Poikilitic sodalite-syenites	10·0-48·0
Foyaites	54·8-85·0	Melanocratic	30·5-38·9	Poikilitic nepheline-syenites	15·0-35·0
Urtites	0·0-11·5	Mesocratic	39·7-43·0	Poikilitic hydrosodalite-syenites	20·0-45·0
Aegirine-lujavrites	28·4-59·7	Leucocratic	45·7-55·3		
Hornblende-lujavrites	25·8	Porphyritic lujavrites	24·6-41·02		
Malignites	9·36-29·19	Porphyritic juvites	22·75-27·27		
Middle division of complex:		Porphyritic foyaites	47·29-60·52		
Foyaites	29·0-51·8				
Urtites	4·0-14·0				
Aegirine-lujavrites	38·0-46·4				
Hornblende-lujavrites	31·61				
Lower division of complex:					
Foyaites	55·7-67·8				
Urtites	0·0-8·9				
Aegirine-lujavrites	34·6-45·3				

found only in the non-pegmatitic rocks of the massif and is most apparent in the poikilitic sodalite-syenites and near their outcrops in the rocks of other complexes. Natrolitization has developed very extensively in all the rocks and in most of the pegmatites. The replacement of microcline by natrolite is most evident in rocks of the upper part of the differentiated complex and also near pegmatitic bodies in the rocks of all complexes. In the pegmatites the replacement of early microcline by natrolite is observed in large zoned bodies, where the natrolite forms independent zones.

The replacement of microcline by hydromuscovite is observed in the rocks and pegmatites of the upper part of the differentiated complex and is particularly developed in the central parts of the three uppermost foyaitic horizons, where hydromuscovite is closely associated with natrolite replacing nepheline and microcline.

Ussingitization of microcline is widespread in the foyaites and lujavrites of the middle and lower parts of the differentiated complex, where the natrolitization process is poorly developed or completely absent. In the poikilitic sodalite-syenites and the sodalitized foyaites individual microcline segregations are replaced by ussingite to the extent of 20-30 per cent. In the pegmatites ussingitization of microcline is most apparent in bodies emplaced in the upper part of the differentiated complex and near the outcrops of poikilitic syenites.

Cancrinitization of microcline is extremely rare, except in the non-pegmatitic rocks, and can be detected only under the microscope.

Late microcline crystallized after prismatic natrolite at the late hydrothermal stage, as is shown by the presence of late microcline streaks in prismatic natrolite and by its replacement of the latter. It is closely associated with polylithionite, which replaces it.

3. Orthoclase

$KAlSi_3O_8$; mon.; sp. gr. 2·5—2·6; H. 6—6·5

Orthoclase is the characteristic mineral of the contaminated rocks and pegmatites in the poikilitic syenite complex of the central part of the massif (Lepkhe-Nel'm, Kuivchorr and others), the porphyritic rocks of the eudialytic lujavrite complex and the hybrid pegmatites. It is present also in appreciable amounts in

Fig. 116. Moonstone (natural size)

the malignites and juvites and is occasionally found in the aegirine-lujavrites and foyaites (Eliseev and Nefedov, 1940).

In the rocks of the poikilitic syenite complex orthoclase occurs as lath-like segregations measuring $5 \times 2 \times 1$ cm. In the porphyritic rocks of the eudialytic lujavrite complex it forms phenocrysts in the fine-grained groundmass, measuring up to $1 \times 0.5 \times 0.2$ m. In the contaminated pegmatites of the poikilitic syenite complex in the central part of the massif and also in the hybrid pegmatites, ortho-clase occurs in the form of prismatic segregations measuring up to $1.5 \times 0.6 \times 0.2$ m and forms monomineralic zones up to 2 m thick.

Orthoclase is white, grey or bluish-grey. The white and grey varieties are opaque, the bluish-grey semi-transparent to transparent. In the transparent varieties a distinct iridescence is noticeable on the cleavage (moonstone; Fig. 116). Lustre vitreous. Fracture uneven. Specific gravity of the pegmatitic orthoclase, according to Gerasimovskii, 2.553. Cleavage distinctly expressed along (001) and poorly along (010). Unlike microcline, orthoclase does not possess a characteristic twinned structure but contains a large amount of very small perthitic ingrowths of albite of extremely bizarre shapes.

Orthoclase is characterized by a slightly different optical orientation from microcline and by highly variable optical properties (Table 35).

Extinction is straight in the (001) section with respect to the (010) cleavage. Optically biaxial, negative. The refractive indices, according to Semenov and Gerasimovskii, are: $Ng = 1.524\text{-}1.529$; $Nm = 1.522$; $Np = 1.518\text{-}1.520$; $Ng\text{-}Np = 0.006\text{-}0.009$.

Because of its variable optical properties and, in particular, the small optic axial angle, Vorob'eva (1937) took this mineral to be anorthoclase, while Gerasi-movskii, Nefedov and Eliseev distinguish anorthoclase as well as orthoclase. In our opinion, however, given the general lack of constancy in the optical properties, the small angle of the optic axes is an inadequate criterion by which to classify

TABLE 35 Optical orientation of orthoclase

Rock	Co-ordinates of indicatrix axes						2V
	Ng	Nm	Np	Ng	Nm	Np	
	$c \perp (001)$			$c \perp (010)$			
Hybrid pegmatite, Flora	87°	10°	80°	—	—	—	−60°
Contaminated pegmatite (after Gerasimovskii)	86-89°	4-6°	85-88°	—	—	—	−69°
Porphyritic lujavrite	85-86°	7-9°	83-86°	7-8°	85-87°	84-85°	−50-52°
Porphyritic juvite	86-88°	5-9°	85-87°	—	—	—	−48-55°
Porphyritic juvite (after Nefedov)	88°	6°	88°	—	—	—	−86°
Poikilitic nepheline-syenite	87-88°	5-7°	85-86°	—	—	—	−49-53°
Poikilitic hydrosodalite-syenite	86-89°	6-9°	84-87°	4-7°	86-89°	83-85°	−50-55°
Malignite (Eliseev, 1940)	86-90°	4-6°	86-88°	0-2.5°	88-90°	88-90°	−76-86°

these varieties of K-Na feldspar as anorthoclase. The term should surely be kept for K-Na feldspars in which sodium predominates over potassium. Such feldspars have not been found among the Lovozero alkali feldspars.

Recalculation of the chemical analyses given in Table 36 shows that the composition of orthoclase agrees well with the theoretical formula. In addition to the constituents found by chemical analysis, titanium, beryllium and zirconium were detected spectroscopically. S. A. Borovik established rubidium (<0.001 per cent) and gallium (0.001 per cent) in orthoclase from the Suoluaiv pegmatites by quantitative spectrographic analysis.

In chemical composition orthoclase differs from microcline in its higher sodium content, which is particularly evident when the pegmatitic varieties of these two minerals are compared. The difference is apparently due to the presence of perthitic ingrowths of albite in the orthoclase; these do not occur in the pegmatitic microcline.

In the ordinary alkali rocks of the massif orthoclase occurs in small amounts. The largest concentrations are found in rocks of the poikilitic syenite complex, although it is the principal rock-forming mineral only in the hydrosodalite- and nepheline-bearing varieties of these rocks and is completely lacking in the sodalite-syenites, where microcline is represented. The intermediate nepheline-sodalite varieties of poikilitic syenites contain both microcline and orthoclase. In the case of the hybrid pegmatites orthoclase is the principal rock-forming mineral.

In the pegmatites, orthoclase, like microcline, is usually localized in the peripheral parts, where it forms either zones of block structure together with aegirine II

TABLE 36   Chemical compositions of orthoclase

Constituent	From natrolitic orthoclase pegmatite of Lepkhe-Nel'm				From Suoluaiv pegmatite	From river Ankisuai poikilitic nepheline-syenite
	%	atomic proportions	calculation of atomic ratios			
SiO_2	63·40	1·0556	1·0556	3·06-3	65·16	65·20
TiO_2	trace	—		—	trace	—
Al_2O_3	19·02	0·3732			20·98	19·71
Fe_2O_3	0·16	0·0020			0·61	0·15
FeO	—	—			—	—
MnO	0·00	—	0·3809	1·10-1	trace	—
MgO	0·23	0·0057			0·28	0·06
CaO	0·72	0·0128			0·78	0·52
SrO	—	—			—	—
BaO	0·21	0·0013			—	—
Na_2O	2·48	0·0800	0·3845	1·11-1	4·51	4·45
K_2O	13·68	0·2904			8·43	9·80
H_2O	—	—			—	—
—	—	O = 2·8790	2·8790	8·35-8	—	—
Total	99·90		—		100·75	99·89
Analyst	Veprintseva, 1953				Isakov	Moleva
Investigator	Semenov				Gerasimovskii	Vorob'eva

and high-temperature rare-metal minerals or monomineralic zones (see the description of the orthoclase pegmatites in the central part of the massif).

Rock orthoclase is usually later than nepheline, which forms inclusions in it, but earlier than aegirine II, which fills in the interstices between its segregations. In the orthoclase pegmatites of the central part of the massif the orthoclase ground-mass crystallized after nepheline in the form of monomineralic zones. In relation to aegirine II and the high-temperature rare-metal minerals—lamprophyllite, ramsayite, eudialyte and others—orthoclase is idiomorphic.

At later stages in the formation of the massif orthoclase was replaced by albite, natrolite, analcite and sodalite.

4. Albite
NaAlSi$_3$O$_8$; tric.; sp.gr. 2·5—2·6; H. 6—6·5

Albite is extensively developed in the Lovozero massif. In the non-pegmatitic rocks it can be detected only under the microscope. In the fully differentiated pegmatites, in which the late hydrothermal stage of replacement is very apparent, albite is one of the principal minerals in the replacement complex. In the small pegmatitic bodies it is represented in very small amounts as a mineral formed in the process of replacement of the early potassium feldspars, microcline and orthoclase.

Four varieties of albite can be distinguished in the Lovozero massif, differing in their habit and the time of their formation: (1) albite-perthite; (2) polysynthetic; (3) lath; and (4) granular.

Perthitically-intergrown albite (exsolution perthite) is observed in very small amounts, chiefly in the orthoclase of the poikilitic syenites and their associated pegmatites as minute, randomly scattered segregations of irregular shape, visible only under the microscope (Fig. 117).

Polysynthetic albite forms irregularly-shaped segregations in microcline, arranged parallel to the long side of the microcline crystal or along its cleavage (Fig. 118). It usually replaces potassium feldspar to the extent of 30-40 per cent, but pseudomorphs of it after microcline are sometimes found. This albite is characteristic only of the non-pegmatitic rocks in the massif. It is particularly extensively developed in the rocks of the differentiated and poikilitic syenite complexes and is less characteristic of the eudialytic lujavrites. It is commonest in the hydrosodalitic varieties of poikilitic syenite and also in the foyaites of the

TABLE 37 Refractive indices of albite

Albite	Ng	Nm	Np	Ng-Np
From albite-natrolite-pegmatite vein, north-eastern slope of Karnasurt	1·538	1·532	1·528	0·010
From natrolitic pegmatite of Karnasurt mine region	1·535	—	1·525	0·010
From Vavnbed hybrid pegmatite	1·534	—	1·523	0·011
From pegmatite (Gerasimovskii's data)	1·537	1·529	1·526	0·011

Fig. 117. Perthitic intergrowths of albite (dark) in orthoclase.   ×90. Crossed nicols

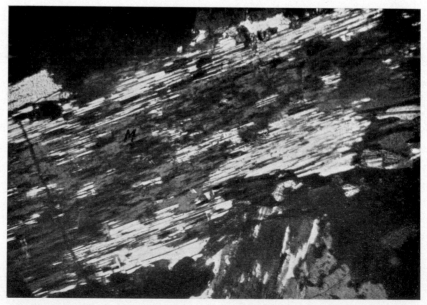

Fig. 118. Replacement of microcline (M) by polysynthetically twinned albite (light). (Dark—late sodalite.)   ×46. Crossed nicols

FIG. 119. Segregation of lath albite. ×46. Crossed nicols

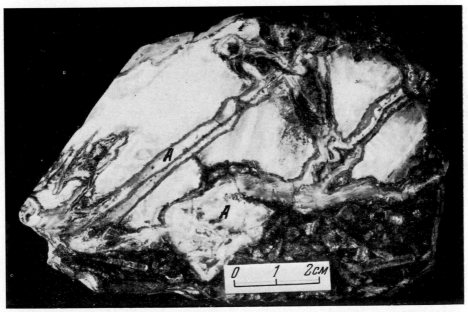

FIG. 120. Streaks of cryptocrystalline pink albite (A) in prismatic natrolite

differentiated complex, the degree of albitization increasing with depth. It occurs in negligible amounts in the pegmatites, and then only in the pegmatitic horizons of the differentiated complex.

Lath albite is represented by coarsely twinned lath-like crystals up to 0·2-0·5 mm long, usually occurring in the interstices between nepheline and microcline and replacing the peripheral parts of these minerals (Fig. 119). Occasionally its laths, orientated in various directions, are to be seen in microcline.

Lath albite is present in concentrations of 1-5 per cent in all the rocks of the massif, its content increasing with the age of the leucocratic rocks. In the pegmatites, such albite rarely occurs. It is present in large quantities in the eucolite-ramsayite pegmatitic body of Flora, where it is one of the main minerals, along with aegirine and arfvedsonite, of the fine-grained groundmass of the vein body and together with aegirine fills up interstices between segregations of other minerals. In addition, albite inclusions are found in eudialyte, ramsayite and arfvedsonite, where they sometimes make up 50-60 per cent of the mineral volume. Segregations of light-coloured minerals are resorbed by this albite from the periphery. Where there is a high content of albite inclusions the minerals have skeletal shapes and look like open-work grids, with the result that the shape and dimensions of the albitic intergrowths vary and no pattern at all can be found in the disposition of the intergrowths.

Granular albite is characteristic only of the pegmatites. It usually forms monomineralic segregations of irregular shape, from 2×3 to 30×50 cm and streaks in prismatic natrolite, or forms whole zones in the large pegmatitic bodies on Karnasurt, Kuftn'yun, Flora and other mountains.

Segregations of such albite, sometimes with a concentrically banded structure, resemble concretions with inner cavities filled with clay material and in some cases lined with small crystals of albite. In the small pegmatite apophyses this albite forms mantles round natrolite at the contact with the country rocks, or streaks in the natrolite, and partially replaces it (Fig. 120). In the cavities of certain pegmatitic bodies albite forms rosettes of plate-like crystals up to 7 mm in diameter (see Fig. 89) or elongate-prismatic crystals up to 2 mm long.

TABLE 38 Optical orientation of

Rock	Polysynthetic albite						
	DoNg	DoNm	DoNp	PNg	PNm	PNp	2V, twinning law, plagioclase No.*
Foyaite	71°	20°	88°	19°	71°	87°	+71°, Carlsbad, No. 1-2
Juvite	—	—	—	—	—	—	—
Urtite	'18°'	'72°'	86°	18°	72°	86°	+75-85°, Albite, No. 4
Aegirine-lujavrite	71°	20°	87°	20°	71°	87°	+70 +85°, Carlsbad, No. 2
Hornblende-lujavrite	70°	20°	88°	20°	69°	87°	+70°, Carlsbad, No. 2
Eudialytic lujavrite	67°	23°	89°	25°	67°	84°	+80°, Carlsbad, No. 1
Poikilitic syenite	73°	17°	89°	17°	73°	88°	+72-78°, Carlsbad, No. 2-4

[* Refers to the divisions of

Under the microscope it can be seen that the shapes of individual segregations of granular albite vary greatly. In the main they form a very fine-grained to crypto-crystalline aggregate, in which the grain size varies from a few thousandths to 0·3 mm; the grains are of an irregularly circular shape. The fabric of the segregations is inequigranular. Sometimes zones and individual areas of lath-like or plate-like albite can be seen in the groundmass, with gradual transitions to a finely-granular groundmass.

The colour is white, pale pink, pink, cream and brownish-grey. The coloured varieties are characteristic of the pegmatites. The lustre is vitreous in the small crystals but dull in the dense aggregates. In thin sections albite is colourless. Optically biaxial, positive. Cleavage well-marked along (001) and (010). The refractive indices of granular albite from pegmatites in different parts of the massif are similar (Table 37).

Polysynthetic albite is usually twinned on the Carlsbad law, the co-ordinates of the twinning axis with the indicatrix axes are: $DoNg = 67\text{-}73°$, $DoNm = 17\text{-}23°$, $DoNp = 86\text{-}89°$. The optic axial angle varies from $+72$ to $+85°$ (Table 38, wherein numbers 1-4 correspond to 1 per cent intervals of anorthite content). Lath albite is twinned on the Albite law. The co-ordinates of the twinning axis with the indicatrix axes are: $DoNg = 17\text{-}21°$, $DoNm = 69\text{-}74°$, $DoNp = 84\text{-}89°$; $2V$ varies from $+70$ to $+80°$ (see Table 38: numbers 0-3 denote 1 per cent intervals of anorthite content).

As can be seen from Table 39 the chemical composition of albite corresponds to the theoretical formula $NaAlSi_3O_8$.

Strontium, gallium, phosphorus, beryllium, manganese, barium, copper, zinc, titanium, lead, zirconium, vanadium and silver were detected in pegmatitic albite from different parts of the massif by the spectrographic method (9 determinations), beryllium, copper, manganese, strontium and titanium being present in samples from all the complexes. It is worth noting that the albite from pegmatites of the poikilitic syenite complex contains more gallium and beryllium than does the pegmatitic albite from other complexes. In two specimens of pegmatitic albite from the poikilitic syenite complex on Karnasurt A. S. Dudykin determined

albite from Lovozero rocks

			Lath albite			
DoNg	DoNm	DoNp	PNg	PNm	PNp	2V, twinning law, plagioclase No. *
19°	71°	84°	19°	72°	87°	+80°, Albite, No. 0
19°	72°	89°	19°	72°	89°	+70-74°, Albite, No. 1
—	—	—	—	—	—	—
20°	70°	88°	19°	69°	87°	+72-78°, Albite, No. 2-3
21°	69°	87°	22°	68°	85°	+80°, Albite, No. 2
17°	74°	88°	17°	73°	87°	+72°, Albite, No. 2
18°	72°	88°	18°	72°	88°	+69-76°, Albite, No. 1

the plagioclase series. Eds.]

0·0002 and 0·1 per cent of beryllium respectively, by the quantitative spectro-graphic method. Lead, zinc, silver and phosphorus are rare, occurring exclusively in pegmatitic albite from the poikilitic syenite complex. Barium and zirconium are present in albite from the hybrid pegmatites as well as from the poikilitic syenite complex, but vanadium occurs only in the former.

Albite-perthite, formed by the exsolution of K-Na feldspars, was the earliest to separate. Polysynthetic albite, which some investigators have called replace-ment perthite, is later. It replaces potassium feldspar from its borders or along the cleavage cracks. Lath albite, which is still later, is often localized in the inter-stices between segregations of potassium feldspar and nepheline and replaces these from their borders. Granular albite seems to have crystallized at the late hydrothermal stage, after precipitation of the main mass of coarsely-prismatic natrolite. It replaces earlier potassium feldspars, prismatic natrolite and, in part, hackmanite.

In the non-pegmatitic rocks of the massif polysynthetic and lath albite are replaced by sodalite, natrolite and, occasionally, ussingite and cancrinite. At the hypergene stage albite is slightly pelitized.

TABLE 39 Chemical composition of albite from albitic natrolite-pegmatite vein on north-eastern slope of Karnasurt

Constituent	Content, per cent	Atomic proportions	Calculation of atomic ratios		
SiO_2	68·03	1·1327	1·1327	2·9	−3
Al_2O_3	20·00	0·3924	0·3936	1·0	−1
Fe_2O_3	0·10	0·0012			
MgO	0·05	0·0012			
CaO	0·15	0·0027			
Na_2O	11·12	0·3586	0·4061	1·0	−1
K_2O	0·94	0·02			
Li_2O	0·02	0·0014			
H_2O^+	0·20	0·0222			
H_2O^-	0·05	—			
—	—	O = 3·0608	3·0608	7·9	−8
Total	100·66		—		
Specific gravity	2·60				
Analyst		Kazakova, 1949			

5. Sodalite (hackmanite)

$Na_8 [AlSiO_4]_6 (Cl, S)_2$; cub.,; sp.gr. 2·2—2·3; H. 5·5—6

Both sodalite proper and its sulphur-bearing variety, hackmanite, are repre-sented in the Lovozero massif, the former in the non-pegmatitic rocks of the differentiated complex and the eudialytic lujavrite complex and the latter in the rocks and pegmatites of the poikilitic syenite complex.

Sodalite forms irregular grains measuring up to 0·5 × 0·2 cm in cross-section, irregularly-shaped segregations up to 0·5 × 0·7 cm, or poorly-outlined dodecahedra up to 4 cm in diameter. In the pegmatites it forms irregularly-shaped relics in natrolite, and blocks measuring from a few square centimetres to $3 \times 2 \times 2$ m.

The sodalite is pale yellow or grey with a greenish tint and the hackmanite is bright-pink with a violet tinge to beet-red on the fresh fracture. It quickly loses its colour in the light and becomes sky-blue or grey, but under ultraviolet light, and in the dark, the colour of hackmanite is restored. Sodalite is opaque, hackmanite semi-transparent. The lustre is greasy to vitreous. Fracture conchoidal to uneven. Specific gravity of hackmanite: 2·285-2·286 (Gerasimovskii, 1934, 1936₂). Cleavage perfect in two directions. On fracturing hackmanite gives off a strong odour of hydrogen sulphide, but the smell quickly vanishes in the air. Fluoresces with a bright orange light.

When heated to about 1000° for three hours hackmanite acquires a green colour, varying from yellowish to emerald-green and greenish-blue tints. The decomposed parts are light-blue. Coloration acquired during heating does not subsequently disappear.

TABLE 40 Chemical compositions of pegmatitic hackmanite and sodalite

| Constituent | Hackmanite | | | | | Sodalite Uel'kuai valley |
| | Tavaiok valley | | | Punkaruaiv | Karnasurt | |
	per cent	Atomic proportions	Calculation of atomic ratios			
SiO₂	36·99	0·6010	0.6010 5.89-6	36·69	36·78	37·85
Al₂O₃	31·77	0·6232	}0·6252 6·11-6	31·40	32·42	31·08
Fe₂O₃	0·17	0·0020		0·85	—	0·51
FeO	—	—	—	—	—	0·34
MgO	—	—	—	0·03	0·45	0·14
CaO	0·05	0·0009	}0·8377 8·20-8	0·19	1·07	0·34
Na₂O	25·84	0·8336		25·96	22·65	22·27
K₂O	0·16	0·0032		0·23	—	0·43
H₂O⁺	—	—	—	0·30	1·68	1·06
H₂O⁻	—	—	—	0·04	0·97	0·44
S total	0·39	0·0121	}0·1937 1·90-2	0·38	0·38	0·02
Cl	6·44	0·1816		5·64	5·47	4·88
Insoluble residue	—	—	—	—	—	1·28
		O=2·4562	2,4562 24·05-24			
Total	101·81		—	101·71	101·87	100·64
−O=2Cl	−1·64		—	−1·39	−1·40	−0·97
	100·17		—	100·32	100·47	99·67
Specific gravity	2·32-2·33			2·285-2·286	—	—
Analyst	Borgström, 1936			Vladimirova	Krutetskaya	Nesterova
Reference	L. Borgström, (1901, 1936)			Minerals of Khibiny and Lovozero tundras (1937)	—	Gerasimovskii (1939)

TABLE 41 Sodalite (hackmanite) content in Lovozero rocks

Differentiated complex	Content, per cent	Eudialytic lujavrite complex	Content, per cent	Poikilitic syenite complex	Content, per cent
Upper division of complex:		Eudialytic lujavrites:		Poikilitic sodalite-syenites	45-71·6
Foyaites	0-15·3	Melanocratic	—	Poikilitic nepheline-syenites	0-1·5
Urtites	0-7·4	Mesocratic	0·1-0·8	Poikilitic hydrosodalite-syenites	0·8-1·0
Aegirine-lujavrites	0-2·5	Leucocratic	0·7-2·5		
Hornblende-lujavrites	3·0	Porphyritic lujavrites	0·5-6		
Malignites	0·23-10·08	Porphyritic foyaites	4·8-10·1		
Middle division of complex:					
Foyaites	0-6·4				
Urtites	0·2-1·9				
Aegirine-lujavrites	1·8-7·0				
Hornblende-lujavrites	2·07				
Lower division of complex:					
Foyaites	3·8-7·5				
Urtites	0·4-1·2				
Aegirine-lujavrites	0·5-3·5				

In thin sections sodalite is colourless, or yellowish to yellowish-brown owing to secondary products. The mineral is isotropic. The refractive index of pegmatitic hackmanite as determined by the immersion method is 1·483-1·487; that of rock hackmanite, according to Vorob'eva, is 1·486-1·488.

Hackmanite and sodalite are readily soluble in concentrated HCl without heating and in HNO_3 on heating.

According to Borneman and Moleva the sulphur content in pegmatitic hackmanite from Malyi Punkaruaiv may amount to 1·10-1·13 per cent. Vlodavets

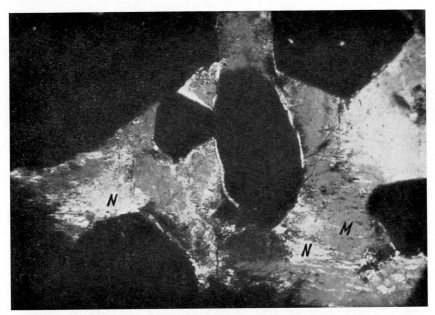

FIG. 121. Early sodalite (black) in microcline (M); N—natrolite. ×20. Crossed nicols

determined 0·043 per cent of gallium oxide on a separate sample of hackmanite from a natrolitic-hackmanite stock from Karnasurt by chemical assay.

Recalculation of the chemical analyses of hackmanite from the Tavaiok valley (Table 40) show that its composition corresponds to the theoretical formula $Na_8[AlSiO_4]_6 (Cl, S)_2$. A certain deficiency in alkalis and the presence of water in other samples of hackmanite analysed seems to be due either to contamination of the sample by natrolite or to partial leaching of sodium from the hackmanite.

Strontium, manganese, zirconium, titanium, lithium, barium, nickel, beryllium and copper were detected spectrographically in hackmanite from the pegmatites of Malyi Punkaruaiv and Karnasurt and from the Tyul'bn'yunuai valley. The spectrographic analysis showed a higher gallium content in pegmatitic hackmanite from the poikilitic syenite complex than in that from pegmatites of other complexes. Only the hackmanite from pegmatites in the poikilitic syenite complex contains lithium. Hackmanite from the Karnasurt pegmatites, which are genetically connected with the poikilitic sodalite-syenites, was found by the quantitative spectrographic method to contain 0·0006 per cent of beryllium (analyst L. N. Idichenko).

The sodalite content in the non-pegmatitic rocks of the massif varies from 0 to 72 per cent (Table 41). Hackmanite is present in large amounts in the poikilitic sodalite-syenites. In the differentiated complex it is concentrated mainly in the foyaites of the upper part (up to 15·3 per cent), the sodalite content in the foyaites increasing as the differentiation becomes more advanced. In each three-component stratal group there is a regular increase in the sodalite content from

FIG. 122. Replacement of nepheline (N) and microcline (M) by sodalite (black). ×46. Crossed nicols

the aegirine-lujavrites and urtites to the foyaites. In the rocks of the differentiated complex there is much less sodalite near the surface, because of the heavy natrolitization of the leucocratic minerals, including sodalite.

In the pegmatites the largest amounts of hackmanite (up to 20 per cent) are found in bodies genetically connected with the sodalitic varieties of poikilitic syenite. In the pegmatites of the other rock complexes and of the poikilitic nepheline-syenites hackmanite is present in negligible amounts.

As regards time of separation, an early and a late sodalite can be distinguished in the rocks of the massif. Early sodalite occurs only in the poikilitic sodalite-syenites, in the form of poikilitic intergrowths in microcline. These intergrowths are usually of irregular shape, but grains of regular shape can occasionally be found (Fig. 121). This sodalite seems to have separated at roughly the same time as, or slightly later than, nepheline, for instances are known where it is idiomorphic towards the latter. In the poikilitic syenites early sodalite probably took the place of nepheline, and formed instead of it, in a medium rich in volatile elements, particularly sulphur and chlorine.

Late sodalite is more widely distributed in the non-pegmatitic rocks. It separated after nepheline, microcline, early sodalite, polysynthetic and lath albite, filling up the interstices between these (Fig. 122). Replacement of these minerals by sodalite can be observed; in the case of microcline the replacement is selective, the albitized varieties being the most intensively sodalitized.

In the pegmatites, hackmanite seems to have crystallized after early microcline and after the main mass of aegirine II. It fills up interstices between microcline

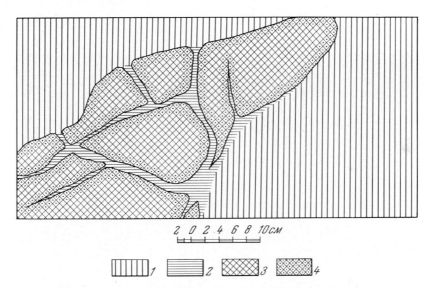

2 0 2 4 6 8 10см

FIG. 123. Streaks of chalcedonic natrolite in hackmanite

1. prismatic natrolite; 2. chalcedonic natrolite; 3. hackmanite;
4. hackmanite replaced by bergmannite

crystals and forms monomineralic zones near the central parts of the pegmatitic bodies. At the hydrothermal stage hackmanite is replaced by a fine-grained aggregate of natrolite and hydrargillite (bergmannite) or by monomineralic natrolite, which form streaks in it and replace it from the periphery. In a number of cases only irregularly-shaped relicts of the hackmanite have been preserved, owing to natrolitization (Fig. 123).

Ussingite, cancrinite and analcite have also developed from sodalite and hackmanite. The replacement of sodalite by ussingite is more characteristic of the pegmatites than of the non-pegmatitic rocks (see description of the pegmatites from Malyi Punkaruaiv, the Tyul'bn'yunuai valley and others). Cancrinitization of sodalite has been noted only in the non-pegmatitic rocks, this process being most extensively developed in the rocks of the poikilitic syenite complex (Malyi Punkaruaiv, Ninchurt and others). The replacement of sodalite by analcite, according to Gerasimovskii, occurs rarely in certain pegmatitic bodies in the col at the head of the northern branch of the river Tavaiok, the Angvundaschorr and Sengischorr cirques and elsewhere.

6. Hydrosodalite
$$2Na\,[AlSiO_4]\,.\,H_2O$$

Hydrosodalite is one of the principal rock-forming minerals of the poikilitic nepheline- and hydrosodalite-syenites (Ninchurt, Mannepakhk, Lepkhe-Nel'm, Punkaruaiv and others), where its content varies from 40 to 70 per cent. It is absent from the pegmatites.

In colour it is dark-grey to black. The shape of the crystals is irregular in feldspar (Fig. 124) and aegirine, but similar to the shape of nepheline crystals

FIG. 124. Poikilitic enclosure of hydrosodalite (dark) in orthoclase. × 10. Crossed nicols

(square and hexagonal in section) in arfvedsonite, mesodialyte and other minerals. The mineral is isotropic. A finely-aggregate structure can be detected under the microscope. The colour is dark-brown to black. In Gerasimovskii's opinion (1940₃) the dark colour is due to numerous inclusions of aegirine I. The refractive index ($N = 1.487$-1.490) is near to that of sodalite (Gerasimovskii's data).

In chemical composition hydrosodalite resembles sodalite (Table 42), but differs from it in having a lower soda content, an almost complete absence of chlorine and more silica and water. Gerasimovskii believes hydrosodalite to be a variety of sodalite in which the alkalis have been partially, and the chlorine almost entirely, replaced by a hydroxyl group. Recalculation of the chemical analysis showed that hydrosodalite has a formula near to nepheline, $2Na\,[AlSiO_4]\,.\,H_2O$, and is distinguished from it by the presence of water. In the formula for hydro-sodalite there is one molecule of water to two molecules of nepheline. Hydro-sodalite is thus an intermediate variety between nepheline $Na[AlSiO_4]$ and hydronepheline $Na[AlSiO_4] \cdot H_2O$, in which there is one molecule of water to one molecule of nepheline. Hydrosodalite is formed by a process of replacement of nepheline, as is shown by the presence of nepheline relicts in it. Complete pseudo-morphs of hydrosodalite after nepheline are often found. The replacement of nepheline by hydrosodalite occurred during a post-magmatic stage, when water began to play a large part as one of the agents of mineralization at lower tem-peratures (Gerasimovskii, 1940[3]).

7. Ussingite

$Na_2 AlSi_3O_8 (OH)$; tric.; sp.gr. 2·46; H. 6—7

Ussingite is a characteristic mineral in the rocks and pegmatites of the poikilitic syenite complex and in pegmatites emplaced in the sodalitized foyaites of the upper part of the differentiated complex. It occurs in small quantities as a replace-ment mineral in the rocks and pegmatites of other complexes, and can be dis-tinguished only under the microscope. Ussingite from the Lovozero tundras was studied in detail by Gerasimovskii (1937[1]), on whose information we have drawn for the description given here.

Ussingite occurs in the non-pegmatitic rocks of the massif in the form of very small segregations visible only under the microscope. In the pegmatites it some-

TABLE 42 Chemical composition of hydrosodalite*

Constituent	Content, per cent	Atomic proportions	Calculation of atomic ratios		
SiO_2	41·05	0·6831	0·6831	2·18	− 2
TiO_2	nil	—			
Al_2O_3	28·36	0·5564			
Fe_2O_3	0·64	0·0080			
FeO	nil	—	0·5695	1·82	− 2
MnO	0·05	0·0007			
MgO	0·18	0·0044			
CaO	0·60	0·0106			
SrO	nil	—			
Na_2O	19·02	0·6134	0·6550	2·09	− 2
K_2O	1·46	0·0310			
H_2O^+	5·40 ⎫	0·7382			
H_2O^-	1·25 ⎭				
F	nil	—	0·7861	2·51	− 2
Cl	0·16	0·0045			
S	1·38	0·0434			
—	—	O = 2·8742	2·8742	9·19	− 9
Total	99·55		—		
Analyst		Moleva			

* Vorob'eva's data

0   1   2 CM

FIG. 125. Ussingite crystals in geode

FIG. 126. Ussingite streaks (U) in microcline (M).   × 46. Crossed nicols

times forms streaks in microcline, up to 2 mm thick, and occasionally large segregations up to 30 cm in diameter, composed of a dense, monomineralic, fine-grained
aggregate, pink with a violet or lilac-blue tint. In the ussingitic pegmatite of
Malyi Punkaruaiv it makes up the entire central zone, in the form of a monomineralic aggregate or in admixture with natrolite and late aegirine. In the
miarolitic cavities of monomineralic ussingite segregations one sometimes finds
ussingite crystals of pseudocubic habit, up to 1 cm in diameter (Fig. 125).

The lustre is slightly greasy to vitreous and slightly nacreous on the cleavage
planes. Cleavage imperfect. Fracture uneven. Colourless in thin sections.
Characterized by high interference colours of pure quality, by which it is readily
distinguished from other minerals, but in the sections normal to Ng it has a grey
interference tint and is almost indistinguishable from cancrinite.

Twins are sometimes found. Optically biaxial, positive. Refractive indices:
$Ng=1\cdot545$, $Nm=1\cdot509$, $Np=1\cdot504$, $Ng\text{-}Np=0\cdot041$; $2V=35\text{-}36°$ (according to
Gerasimovskii).

The refractive indices of ussingite from the poikilitic sodalite-syenites, according to Vorob'eva, are as follows: $Ng=1\cdot543$, $Np=1\cdot506$, $Ng\text{-}Np=0\cdot037$; $2V=38°$.

TABLE 43 Chemical compositions of ussingite (per cent)

| Constituent | Punkaruaiv | | | | Alluaiv | Greenland |
	Analysis 1	Analysis 2	Average of two analyses	Atomic ratios		
SiO_2	59·30	59·15	59·225	0·986 2·9	59·17	58·74
Al_2O_3	17·30	17·15	17·225	0·340 1·0	17·67	17·73
CaO	0·33	0·28	0·305	0·006 ⎫		
Na_2O	19·09	19·08	19·085	0·616 ⎬ 1·9	19·66	19·91
K_2O	0·90	0·83	0·865	0·018 ⎭		
H_2O^+	3·40		3·40	0·378 ⎫	3·80	⎫ 4·19
H_2O^-	0·30		0·30	— ⎬ 1·1		⎭
S	0·08	0·09	0·085	0·003 ⎬	—	—
Cl	0·05	0·04	0·04	0·001 ⎭	—	—
F	nil		—	—		
				$O=3\cdot006$ 8·84		
Total	100·75	100·32	100·53	—	100·30	100·57
$-O=(Cl_2,S)$	$-0\cdot06$	$-0\cdot06$	$-0\cdot06$	—	—	—
	100·69	100·26	100·47	—	—	—
Specific gravity	2·457	2·460			—	2·495
Analyst	Gerasimovskii				Vrevskaya	Christensen
Reference	Gerasimovskii (1937₁)				*Minerals of Khibiny and Lovozero tundras* (1937)	O. Böggild (1914)

Cleavage perfect along (001) and imperfect along (110). According to Gerasimovskii the cleavage and twin measurements are $B_2Ng = 87°$, $B_2Nm = 85°$, $B_2Np = 6°$, $P_1Ng = 36°$, $P_1Nm = 54°$, $P_1Np = 89\text{-}90°$, $P_2Ng = 64°$, $P_2Nm = 76°$, $P_2Np = 40°$. Twinning plane (010).

Ussingite is readily soluble in HCl and HNO_3 and soluble with difficulty in H_2SO_4. It gelatinizes with HCl and HNO_3. Recalculation (Table 43) of the chemical analysis shows that its composition corresponds to the formula $Na_2AlSi_3O_8(OH)$.

In the ussingite from the Malyi Punkaruaiv pegmatites (two samples) and the upper reaches of the Tyul'bn'yunuai valley (one sample), gallium, zirconium, strontium, magnesium, manganese, iron, nickel, titanium, beryllium, copper, lithium, barium, lead and zinc were detected by the spectrographic method. N. V. Lizunov determined a content of 0·031 per cent of gallium by quantitative spectrographic analysis of pegmatitic ussingite from Malyi Punkaruaiv.

In the non-pegmatitic rocks ussingite forms by replacement of microcline, sodalite and, in part, nepheline. In the poikilitic sodalite-syenites individual segregations of microcline are replaced by ussingite to the extent of 20-30 per cent; ussingitization is extensively developed in the foyaites and lujavrites of the middle and lower parts of the differentiated complex, where natrolitization is poorly developed or does not occur at all.

In the pegmatites ussingite has been found in small quantities in the Chinglusuai and Tyul'bn'yunuai river valleys, in the Second Raslak cirque, in the southern cirque of Alluaiv and in the valley of the Second Eastern stream on Karnasurt, as a fine-grained aggregate formed by the replacement of microcline and sodalite. Ussingite is present in small amounts in the pegmatites of Malyi Punkaruaiv. Ussingite is one of the latest minerals. It fills up fissures in early microcline (Fig. 126), albite, hackmanite and prismatic natrolite and replaces them round their margins. In the ussingitic pegmatitic body of Malyi Punkaruaiv, relics of sodalite and prismatic natrolite can be observed in the ussingite making up the central zone. These facts indicate that the ussingite has crystallized in the replacement of sodalite, microcline, prismatic natrolite and, in part, nepheline, under the influence of late hydrothermal solutions.

8. Natrolite

$Na_2 [Al_2Si_3O_{10}] . 2H_2O$; orthorhomb.; sp.gr. 2·21—2·26; H. 5·5

Natrolite is widely distributed in the Lovozero alkali massif, its content varying from 0 to 90 per cent in the non-pegmatitic rocks and from 2 to 60 per cent in the pegmatites. Six varieties can be distinguished, differing in shape and conditions of formation: (1) coarsely-prismatic; (2) finely-prismatic; (3) finely-granular; (4) chalcedonic; (5) radiate-fibrous; and (6) acicular.

The coarsely-prismatic natrolite forms huge blocks measuring tens of cubic metres or makes up whole zones measuring hundreds of cubic metres (see description of Karnasurt pegmatites). Such monomineralic segregations usually possess excellent prismatic cleavage and can be readily split into separate pieces

(Fig. 127). In certain pegmatites (Lepkhe-Nel'm) the central zones are represented not by a monocrystalline natrolite mass but by growths of pseudotetragonal crystals with pyramidal terminations. The size of the crystals varies from 1 to 10 cm in length and from 0·3 × 0·3 to 6 × 6 cm in cross-section.

The natrolite crystals are usually elongated along the z axis and bounded chiefly by the forms p (111) and m (110); pinacoids a (100) and b (010) are occasion-

FIG. 127. Coarsely prismatic natrolite. 1/6·25 natural size

ally found. The commonest habit of prismatic natrolite crystals is shown in] Fig. 128.

The central zeolitic zones of the pegmatites are sometimes made up entirely of finely-prismatic natrolite in the form of a thin columnar continuous milk-white mass. Completely transparent crystals of finely-prismatic natrolite also occur, growing on the walls of cavities in these zones.

Fine-grained natrolite replaces nepheline, microcline, hackmanite and other minerals both in the rocks and in the pegmatites, forming streaks up to 2 cm thick. In the natrolitic hackmanite stock on Karnasurt, fine-grained natrolite

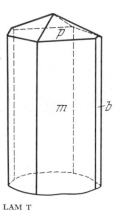

forms monomineralic massive segregations of irregular shape and bright pink colour, measuring 10 × 5 to 20 × 30 cm in the hackmanite. The commonest grain shapes are oval with irregular contours, foliated with heavily indented margins, and spherical, with radial extinction (Fig. 129). The diameter varies from some hundredths of a millimetre to 2 mm.

The chalcedonic natrolite bears a strong outward resemblance to chalcedony, for which it was mistaken by some earlier investigators. It forms streaks, ranging from micro-

FIG. 128. Crystal of natrolite (after Labuntsov)

FIG. 129. Spherical segregations of natrolite.   × 90. Crossed nicols

FIG. 130. Extinction of chalcedonic natrolite.   × 46. Crossed nicols

scopic dimensions to 20 cm in thickness, in altered pegmatitic hackmanite and
in the urtites. These streaks are of irregular shape, sinuous and somewhat loop-
shaped. At their borders the natrolite has a fibrous structure, the fibres being
arranged perpendicular to the contacts. In addition, the chalcedonic natrolite,
both in the rocks and in the pegmatites, forms fringes around nepheline segregations, when the fibres are arranged perpendicular to the surfaces of the nepheline
grains. It also forms streaks in nepheline and occasionally microcline. In the
central parts of the large streaks of finely-fibrous chalcedonic natrolite there is
sometimes a coarse-grained rosette of natrolite with wavy extinction. The texture
of the variety we are describing is fine-grained or fibrous. When the stage is

FIG. 131. Colour-banding of chalcedonic natrolite (N)

rotated at various angles between crossed nicols a very great variety of patterns
can be seen, resembling the frost patterns on windows (Fig. 130).

Radiate-fibrous natrolite has been found only in the natrolitic hackmanite
pegmatitic stock on Karnasurt, where it forms monomineralic pink segregations
in altered hackmanite, measuring up to $10 \times 10 \times 20$ cm and made up of closely-
appressed spherulites of long-prismatic small crystals. The spherulites are 1-
1·5 cm in diameter, the individual crystallites being 1-2 mm long and 0·1-0·2 mm
wide. Acicular natrolite occurs in almost all the rocks and pegmatites but in
small amounts. It forms small crystals in miarolitic cavities and in leaching cavities
along with chabazite and aegirine III. The habit of the crystals is long-prismatic
or, more rarely, short-prismatic. They are 0·5-5 mm in length and 0·1-1 mm in
diameter.

More often than not, natrolite is white; more rarely it is greyish, bluish or
pale pink. The radiate-fibrous and fine-grained varieties sometimes have a

bright pink colour. The chalcedonic natrolite occurs in a wide variety of colours —milk-white, grey, bluish-grey, cinnamon, brown, light chocolate, wine-yellow, lilac, pale pink, pale violet and other colours. The coloration is uneven, mostly striated or patchy, as in agates and jaspers. In the striated varieties bands of different colour usually lie parallel to the borders of the streaks (Fig. 131). The lustre is vitreous, but greasy in the chalcedonic varieties. Some varieties of chalcedonic natrolite (the milk-white and those with cinnamon tones) are matt. The matt varieties are opaque, the others semi-transparent to transparent. Fracture uneven. Brittle. Specific gravity: 2·222—2·226 (Gerasimovskii's data). The coloured varieties of chalcedonic and radiate-fibrous natrolite have a higher specific gravity (2·247). The specific gravity of the milk-white chalcedonic natrolite is 2·214.

The varieties are not distinguishable by optical properties. In transmitted light natrolite is colourless. Optically biaxial, positive. Elongation positive. Straight extinction. In the well-crystallized varieties perfect cleavage can be observed along (110) and imperfect along (010). The co-ordinates of the perfect cleavage with the indicatrix axes are as follows: $PNg = 89° 00'$, $PNm = 59° 00'$, $PNp = 31° 00'$; $2V = 60\text{-}66°$.

The refractive indices of the rock and the pegmatitic natrolite are similar, varying within narrow limits (Table 44).

X-ray powder photographs of four varieties of natrolite—prismatic, chalcedonic, white opalescent and pink fine-grained—were prepared by N. N. Sludskaya, using Debye's method. The powder patterns obtained proved similar to one another.

Natrolite is readily soluble and gelatinizes in hydrochloric, nitric and sulphuric acids. Chemical analyses are shown in Table 45. In addition, M. E. Kazakova determined water by the direct method in chalcedonic and opalescent natrolite

TABLE 44   Refractive indices of natrolite

Natrolite	Ng	Nm	Np	$Ng - Np$	Investigator
Fine-grained, from poikilitic nepheline-syenite	1·490	—	1·479	0·011	Vorob'eva
Fine-grained, from Alluaiv pegmatite	1·491	—	1·480	0·011	Tikhonenkov
Chalcedonic, from horizon IV urtite	1·487	—	1·475	0·012	Present authors
Chalcedonic, from Kedykvyrpakhk pegmatite	1·489	—	1·481	0·008	Slepnev
Coarse-prismatic, from Karnasurt pegmatite	1·489	1·482	1·480	0·009	Present authors
Fine-prismatic, from Koklukhtiuai valley pegmatite	1·488-1·491	—	1·478-1·481	0·009-0·010	Borodin

from the natrolitic hackmanite stock on Karnasurt and obtained the following results:

Natrolite	$H_2O + (\%)$	$H_2O - (\%)$
Chalcedonic	8·84	0·30
Opalescent (milk-white)	8·88	0·44

The figures given show that the water content in the different varieties of natrolite is similar.

Recalculating the chemical analyses we find that the composition of natrolite is expressed by the theoretical formula $Na_2 [Al_2Si_3O_{10}] . 2H_2O$. In the coarsely-prismatic natrolite from an albitic natrolite pegmatitic vein on Karnasurt, Kazakova determined 0·02 per cent of gallium oxide. In coarsely-prismatic natrolite from a natrolitic hackmanite of the pegmatitic stock on Karnasurt Lizunov detected 0·04 per cent of metallic gallium, by the quantitative spectrographic method, and

TABLE 45   Chemical compositions of pegmatitic natrolite

Constituents	Coarse-prismatic natrolite, Karnasurt						Chalcedonic natrolite, Karnasurt		Fine-prismatic natrolite, Chivruai valley*	
	%	Recalculated to 100%	Atomic proportions	Calculation of atomic ratios			%	Atomic proportions	%	Atomic proportions
SiO$_2$	46·72	47·12	0·7845	0·7845	3·01	– 3	47·30	0·7376	47·45	0·790
TiO$_2$	nil	—	—				trace		nil	—
Al$_2$O$_3$	26·51	26·74	0·5246	} 0·5272	2·03	– 2	27·92	0·5478	27·40	0·536
Fe$_2$O$_3$	0·20	0·20	0·0026				0·18	0·0022	0·25	0·004
FeO	nil	—	—		—		nil	—	—	—
RE$_2$O$_3$	—	—	—		—		—	—	nil	—
MnO	nil	—	—		—		trace	—	—	—
MgO	0·12	0·12	0·0003				nil	—	—	—
CaO	0·24	0·24	0·0043	0·5346	2·09	– 2	0·48	0·0085	0·07	0·001
Na$_2$O	15·95	16·09	0·5190				13·60	0·4388	15·45	0·498
K$_2$O	0·52	0·52	0·0110				0·83	0·0176	0·42	0·008
H$_2$O$^+$	8·88	8·95	0·9936	0·9936	3·82	– 4	9·50	1·0546	9·16	1·018
H$_2$O$^-$	0·20	—	—		—		0·20	—	—	—
P$_2$O$_5$	0·08	—	—		—		—	—	—	—
S	—	—	—		—		—	—	nil	—
Cl	—	—	—		—		—	—	trace	—
Other	0·49	—					—	—	—	—
			O = 3·1272	3·1272	12·03	– 12	—	—	—	—
Total	99·91	99·98					100·01	—	100·20	—
Specific gravity							2·247		—	
Analyst	Pokrovskaya, 1948						Kazakova, 1948		Vladimirova	

* Gerasimovskii's data

0·028 per cent of gallium in the granular natrolite from pegmatites of Malyi Punkaruaiv. L. N. Indichenko determined 0·0003 per cent of beryllium, again by quantitative spectrographic analysis, in the acicular natrolite from Karnasurt pegmatites and 0·003-0·007 per cent of beryllium in the fine-grained natrolite replacing hackmanite.

Barium, strontium, manganese, titanium, copper, molybdenum, lanthanum, arsenic, lead, cobalt, chromium, silver, zinc, vanadium, yttrium and tin were

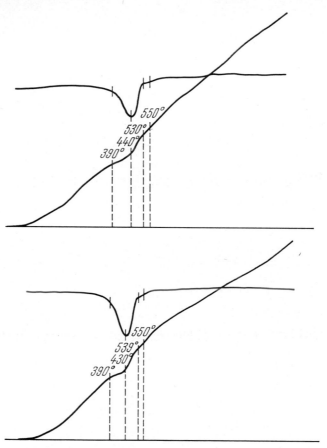

FIG. 132. Thermal analysis curves of prismatic (top) and chalcedonic (bottom) natrolite

detected by the spectrographic method in different varieties of pegmatitic natrolite (fourteen samples). It is noteworthy that a higher gallium content, as well as arsenic, lead, tin, cobalt, molybdenum and chromium are observed in Karnasurt pegmatites genetically connected with poikilitic sodalite (hackmanitic)-syenites. Rare earths are present in natrolite from pegmatites from the differentiated complex (Alluaiv and the Koklukhtiuai valley).

Comparison of the spectrographic analyses of different varieties of natrolite shows that the quantity of trace elements in them diminishes from the higher- to the lower-temperature varieties.

The heating curves for the prismatic and chalcedonic natrolite are similar (Fig. 132).

Of the six varieties of natrolite described, the most extensively developed in the non-pegmatitic rocks of the Lovozero massif are the fine-grained and the chalcedonic, while the coarsely-prismatic and fine-grained are the commonest varieties in the pegmatites.

The largest amounts of natrolite are found in the differentiated complex, where the natrolite content follows a regular pattern of increase from bottom to top (Table 46).

In the three-component stratal groups the natrolite content increases towards the urtite-lujavrite contact. Natrolite replaces 70-95 per cent of the urtite over

FIG. 133. Interrelationship of prismatic natrolite (light) and microcline. Natural size

a zone 1·5-2 m thick; in the lujavrites it replaces almost all the leucocratic minerals. Above and below this zeolitized zone the amount of natrolite gradually diminishes. In the foyaites natrolite has usually developed at the lower surfaces of the horizons, at the urtite contact. In the uppermost stratal group of the differentiated complex natrolitization has developed fairly strongly in the foyaites, near the contact with the porphyritic lujavrites. In the hornblende-lujavrites natrolite is concentrated mainly at the contacts with the foyaites.

In the poorly-layered (middle) part of the differentiated complex and in the rocks of the eudialytic lujavrite complex no clearly-defined pattern can be observed in the natrolite distribution, except that the natrolite content usually increases from the melanocratic to the leucocratic varieties of these rocks. In addition, a higher natrolite content is observed in all the rocks of the differentiated and eudialytic lujavrite complexes at contacts with intrusions of poikilitic syenite.

In the rocks of the poikilitic syenite complex the natrolite content is found to increase from the sodalitic to the nepheline-bearing and hydrosodalitic varieties and also towards the contacts with pegmatites. In the sodalitic varieties natrolite is most extensively developed in surface outcrops.

In the pegmatites natrolite is ubiquitous, but most abundant in the fully

FIG. 134. Streaks of brown albite in prismatic natrolite (light)

TABLE 46 Natrolite content in Lovozero rocks

Differentiated complex	Content, per cent	Eudialytic lujavrite complex	Content, per cent	Poikilitic syenite complex	Content, per cent
Upper division of complex:		Eudialytic lujavrites:		Poikilitic sodalite-syenites	0-6·7
Foyaites	0-25·4	Melanocratic	2·8-4·3	Poikilitic nepheline-syenites	0·5-10·3
Urtites	6·4-90·1	Mesocratic	5·4-7·7	Poikilitic hydrosodalite-syenites	3·8-15·4
Aegirine-lujavrites	0·8-33·4	Leucocratic	6·8-9·5		
Hornblende-lujavrites	6·5				
Malignites	4·5-23·6	Porphyritic lujavrites	3·3-9·3		
Middle division of complex:		Porphyritic foyaites	5·2-7·5		
Foyaites	0-16·9				
Urtites	6·6-13·6				
Aegirine-lujavrites	2·2-4·7				
Hornblende-lujavrites	4·0				
Lower division of complex:					
Foyaites	0-1·8				
Urtites	0-2·3				
Aegirine-lujavrites	0·3-1·8				

differentiated and intensively replaced bodies, chiefly in the poikilitic syenite complex, in which all its varieties are represented. Natrolite is one of the latest minerals to crystallize. In the non-pegmatitic rocks it forms in the process of replacing nepheline, microcline, sodalite, albite, cancrinite and ussingite and fills up fissures in them. In the pegmatites different varieties of natrolite have crystallized at different temperatures. The variety of habit sometimes observed in natrolite segregations occurring in a single pegmatitic body (the natrolitic hackmanite stock on Karnasurt) is due to the stability of this mineral under a variety of conditions, and to its long period of formation. The highest-temperature natrolite is the coarsely-prismatic variety, which separated under the undisturbed conditions of relatively high temperatures, forming the central parts of the pegmatitic bodies, filling up the interstices between microcline crystals and welding the fissures in them (Fig. 133). It crystallized earlier than late microcline, albite and other minerals of the replacement stage. Fine-grained albite fills up the fissures in prismatic natrolite and replaces it (Fig. 134).

Compact, radiate-fibrous and chalcedonic natrolite are characteristic of the replacement zones. They are more rarely to be found in other pegmatite zones too, where they develop from nepheline, early potassium feldspar and hackmanite. Finely-acicular natrolite crystallized after compact natrolite during the period when these minerals were leached.

9. Analcite

Na $[AlSi_2O_6] . H_2O$; cub.; sp.gr. 2·22—2·29; H. 5

Analcite is a fairly common mineral in the pegmatites, where it usually occurs in the central zeolitic zones (Karnasurt) or the zeolitized parts of external equigranular and feldspathic-aegirine zones (Lepkhe-Nel'm, Kitkn'yun, Kuftn'yun, Sengischorr and others. It forms irregularly-shaped segregations measuring up to $7 \times 5 \times 4$ cm or trapezohedral crystals measuring $3 \times 2 \times 3$ mm to $7 \times 5 \times 4$ cm (Fig. 135). In a pegmatitic vein on Kuivchorr it completely replaces some individual regions of an almost monomineralic feldspathic zone. It sometimes forms during the alteration of nepheline and sodalite. The texture of the analcite aggre-

TABLE 47 Interplanar spacings of analcite

Line no.	I	d	Line no.	I	d	Line no.	I	d
1	8	5·54	13	3	2·01	25	3	1·448
2	4	4·81	14	6	1·902	26	5	1·417
3	2	4·47	15	5	1·867	27	6	1·362
4	5	3·76	16	7	1·741	28	4	1·308
5	10	3·40	17	3	1·714	29	4	1·287
6	1	3·21	18	3	1·692	30	2	1·277
7	8	2·92	19	1	1·667	31	3	1·267
8	6	2·68	20	1	1·618	32	6	1·225
9	6	2·48	21	4	1·594	33	5	1·187
10	4	2·41	22	1	1·562	34	4	1·170
11	5	2·22	23	2	1·448	35	5	1·123
12	2	2·10	24	4	1·481	36	4	1·069

gates is finely-granular. The colour is white, dirty-white, grey with a brownish tint, yellow and pinkish. The lustre is vitreous. Cleavage cubic, perfect. Fracture uneven. Opaque, translucent in thin fragments.

In thin sections analcite is usually colourless, occasionally slightly brown. In some cases polysynthetic twins can be seen. Optically isotropic, sometimes slightly anisotropic. Refractive indices: $N = 1.485—1.490$. Table 47 shows the interplanar spacings.

Analcite dissolves in concentrated HCl, HNO_3 and H_2SO_4. Table 48 shows the chemical analysis of a yellow variety from the Kitkn'yun pegmatites, made on Semenov's material.

Recalculation of the chemical analysis gives the conventional formula for analcite—Na $[AlSi_2O_6]$. H_2O. Gallium, strontium, manganese, iron and titanium have been detected by the spectrographic method in analcite from pegmatites on Lepkhe-Nel'm, Kuftn'yun and Kitkn'yun.

In the non-pegmatitic rocks of the massif analcite occurs rarely and in negligible amounts, exclusively as a secondary mineral after nepheline in the poikilitic nepheline-syenites of the central part of the massif.

In time of separation analcite is near to prismatic natrolite. The central parts of some of its crystals are made up of transparent natrolite. This seems to indicate replacement of prismatic natrolite by analcite. In other cases analcite displays idiomorphism in relation to natrolite (see Fig. 135). Compared with fine-grained albite analcite is the earlier, for albite fills up fissures in the analcite and interstices between its crystals. In an analcitic orthoclase pegmatitic body on Kuivchorr the analcite replaces orthoclase as a fine-grained aggregate forming pseudomorphs from it.

Analcite seems to have separated during the period when prismatic natrolite crystallized but before the crystallization of albite, finely-crystalline natrolite, micaceous minerals and other minerals of the replacement complex.

TABLE 48 Chemical composition of analcite

Constituent	Content, per cent	Atomic proportions	Calculation of atomic ratios		
SiO_2	52·47	0·875	0·888	2·04	− 2
BeO	0·33	0·013			
Al_2O_3	24·77	0·480	0·480	1·10	− 1
CaO	0·73	0·013			
MgO	0·06	0·002	0·397	0·91	− 1
Na_2O	10·52	0·338			
K_2O	2·10	0·044			
H_2O^+	7·98	0·886	0·886	2·04	− 2
H_2O^-	1·56	—			
		O = 3·132	3·132	7·20	− 7
Total	100·52	—		—	
Analyst		Kazakova			

10. Aegirine

NaFe $[Si_2O_6]$; mon.; sp.gr 3·38—3·55; H. 6—6·5

Of the pyroxene group, aegirine, aegirine-augite and acmite are represented in the Lovozero massif. Aegirine-augite and acmite occur rarely and in negligible amounts. Aegirine, one of the principal minerals in the massif, is widespread in all the rocks and pegmatites.

Three generations of aegirine, aegirine I, aegirine II and aegirine III, can be distinguished in the rocks and pegmatites.

Aegirine I forms elongate-prismatic crystals, from microscopic dimensions in the non-pegmatitic rocks to $15 \times 2 \times 2$ cm in the pegmatites. Small acicular crystals, measuring tenths and hundredths of a millimetre, are usually included in nepheline, sodalite, hydrosodalite and early potassium feldspars in the rocks and in the external equigranular pegmatite zones. Large elongate-prismatic crystals of aegirine I occur only in the pegmatites. Sometimes it forms radial concretions of long, black, prismatic crystals orientated roughly perpendicular to the contacts (Kedykvyrpakhk, Kitkuai valley).

In the contaminated pegmatites of the differentiated complex, in the upper reaches of the Koklukhtiuai, aegirine is represented exclusively by elongated

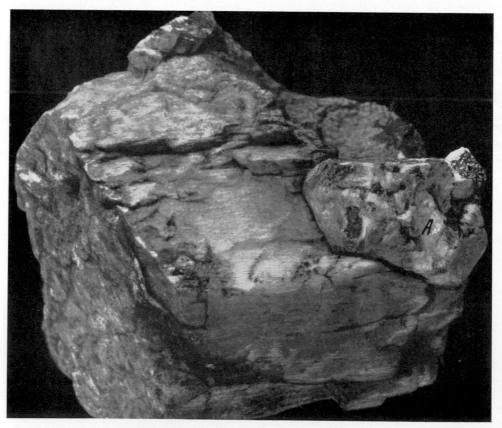

FIG. 135. Analcite crystal (A) in natrolite

prismatic crystals of the first generation, forming continuous coarsely-crystalline segregations in vein selvages, while in the apatite-enriched central part of the pegmatite it can be seen in the form of individual crystals, idiomorphic with respect to apatite.

The colour of aegirine I is dark green to black; the powder is dark green. In thin sections it is grass-green to colourless in small crystals. In the poikilitic hydrosodalite-syenites of Lepkhe-Nel'm one finds zonal crystals of aegirine in which the central part is made up of aegirine-augite. Fracture uneven. Lustre vitreous. Cleavage perfect along (110). Specific gravity 3·385 (Gerasimovskii's figures).

Aegirine I crystals are elongated along the z axis. In transverse section they are compressed along the x axis. The principal crystallographic forms are a (100) and m (110). Crystals terminated by s ($1\bar{1}1$) faces rarely occur.

The second generation includes all the macroscopically visible aegirine in the non-pegmatitic rocks and the groundmass of the pegmatitic aegirine. In the lujavrites it forms accumulations of finely-acicular crystals filling up interstices between segregations of microcline and nepheline and occasionally of mesodialyte (Fig. 136). Individual crystals reach a size of 0·5 cm along the long axis.

Large prismatic crystals of aegirine II also occur, measuring $1·5 \times 0·2$ cm in the foyaites and urtites of the differentiated complex to $10 \times 2 \times 0·5$ cm in the poikilitic syenites, with a large number of poikilitic inclusions of nepheline, primary sodalite and, more rarely, microcline (Fig. 137).

In the pegmatites aegirine II forms matted-fibrous segregations of radiate-

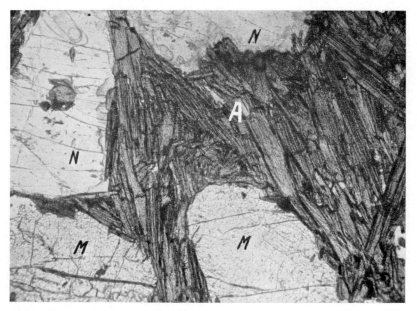

FIG. 136. Interrelationship of aegirine II (A) with nepheline (N) and mesodialyte (M). ×46. Without analyser

fibrous texture up to 35 cm in diameter, which sometimes make up 80 per cent of the feldspathic aegirine zone and fill interstices between microcline, nepheline, eudialyte and other high-temperature rare-metal minerals. Aegirine II is greyish-green to dark green. Opaque. Specific gravity 3·452 (Gerasimovskii's figures).

Aegirine III forms fine-acicular crystals up to 2-5 mm (rarely up to 3 cm) in length, lining the walls of leaching cavities or filling in miarolitic cavities in the rocks, and in the aegirine II of the feldspathic aegirine zones in the pegmatites, in the form of druses. The colour is green to light-green. Fine-acicular crystals of aegirine III, up to 1 mm in length, occur as an invariable constituent of aggregates formed in the process of alteration of early dark-coloured minerals. The finely-fibrous aegirine closely associated with minerals of the replacement complex in the large pegmatitic bodies should, it seems, also be classified as third generation. In thin sections aegirine appears in various shades of green or yellowish-green. Elongation negative. Optically biaxial, negative. Pleochroism: Ng—from greenish-yellow to straw-yellow, Nm—yellowish-green, Np—from grass-green to dark green, sometimes with a blue tint. Absorption: $Np>Nm>Ng$. Extinction angle $c:Np=2\text{-}8°$, sometimes more; $2V$ 60-68° for pegmatites and 68-73° for non-pegmatitic rocks (Table 49).

Refractive indices of aegirine from various rocks: $Ng=1\cdot795—1\cdot799$, $Np=1\cdot745—1\cdot752$, $Ng\text{-}Np=0\cdot047—0\cdot050$.

Aegirine partly dissolves in concentrated HCl, HNO_3 and H_2SO_4 on heating.

Recalculation of the chemical analysis (Table 50) shows that aegirine contains 65-66 per cent of the acmite molecule ($NaFeSi_2O_6$), 9-14 per cent of the heden-

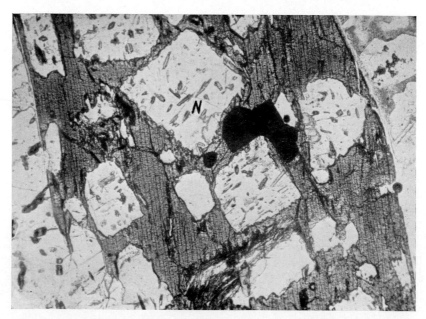

FIG. 137. Aegirine crystal with poikilitic inclusions of nepheline (N) and loparite (black).   ×46. Without analyser

bergite molecule ($CaFeSi_2O_6$) and about 3 per cent of the diopside molecule ($CaMgSi_2O_6$). In terms of the predominant components we can write the chemical formula for aegirine as m $NaFeSi_2O_6 \cdot n$ $CaFeSi_2O_6 \cdot p$ $CaMgSi_2O_6 \cdot g$ $NaAlSi_2O_6$.

If we compare the analysis of rock aegirine with that of pegmatitic aegirine we find that the latter contains more ferric and less ferrous oxide. According to P. A. Volkov's data rock aegirine of the first and second generations contains 0·03-0·04 per cent and pegmatitic aegirine 0·01 per cent of vanadium oxide.

In six samples of pegmatitic aegirine I from different parts of the massif strontium, barium, beryllium, tin, lead, copper, zinc and nickel were detected by the spectrographic method. In twelve samples of aegirine II beryllium, chromium, lithium, barium, strontium, lead, tin, copper, zinc, niobium, nickel, cobalt and molybdenum were detected by the same means. Lithium, nickel, cobalt and molybdenum are present only in aegirine II from non-pegmatitic rocks. The spectrographic analyses indicate that trace elements are present in appreciably greater amounts in aegirine II than in aegirine I.

The maximum aegirine content is found in the aegirine-lujavrites of the differentiated complex and in the porphyritic lujavrites of the eudialytic lujavrite complex (Table 51). A number of recurrent features can be observed in the distribution of aegirine in the rock in these complexes (see Part One, Chapter Five).

In the well-layered parts of the differentiated complex there is a regular alternation of aegirine-rich and aegirine-poor horizons. The lowest aegirine content in each stratal group occurs in the upper and central parts of the urtite horizon. Towards the floor of this horizon the aegirine content increases, to reach a peak in the roof of the underlying aegirine-lujavrite horizon, after which it gradually diminishes towards the floor of the lujavrite horizon and the underlying foyaites and so on.

The aegirine concentration in the roof of the aegirine-lujavrite horizon depends on the degree of differentiation of the rocks. The urtites and foyaites in the poorly-differentiated parts of the complex invariably contain more aegirine than those in the well-layered parts.

In the eudialytic lujavrites and in the porphyritic rocks of this complex the aegirine distribution pattern indicated above is less apparent. In the poikilitic

TABLE 49 Optical orientation of aegirine from Lovozero rocks

Rock	Co-ordinates of indicatrix axes			cNp	2V
	Ng	Nm	Np		
		$c \perp (110)$			
Urtite	47°	44°	86°	6°	−71°
Foyaite	42°	48°	86°	4°30′	−71°
Hornblende-lujavrite	46°	42°	84°	7°	−69°
Eudialytic lujavrite	46°	46°	88°	3°	−68°
Poikilitic sodalite-syenite	43°	47°	89°	3°30′	−73°

TABLE 50   Chemical compositions of aegirines

Constituent	Aegirine I, Lovozero tundra	Aegirine II from aegirine-lujavrites of Punkaruaiv differentiated complex		Aegirine II from poikilitic-sodalite syenites		Aegirine II from rocks in Sengisyavr pass		Aegirine II from pegmatite of 2nd Raslak cirque		Aegirine III, Sengischorr	
	per cent	per cent	Atomic proportions	per cent	Atomic proportions	per cent	Atomic proportions	per cent	Atomic proportions	per cent	Atomic proportions
SiO_2	51·82	50·76	0·8452	51·96	0·8651	52·43	0·873	52·22	0·869	52·48	0·874
TiO_2	not det.	2·64	0·0330	2·70	0·0330	3·48	0·044	2·32	0·029	1·80	0·023
ZrO_2	,, ,,	not det.	—	not det.	—	0·47	0·004	0·80	0·006	not det.	—
ΣRE_2O_3	,, ,,	,, ,,	—	,, ,,	—	0·09	—	0·07	—	,, ,,	—
Al_2O_3	0·60	2·19	0·0428	2·17	0·0428	0·96	0·018	0·95	0·018	1·81	0·036
Fe_2O_3	21·02	22·66	0·2838	23·07	0·2888	24·21	0·304	25·36	0·318	28·58	0·358
FeO	8·14	3·45	0·0480	2·51	0·0349	2·26	0·031	1·31	0·018	1·35	0·019
MnO	1·00	0·59	0·0083	0·49	0·0069	0·79	0·011	0·55	0·008	1·40	0·019
MgO	1·47	2·32	0·0575	2·13	0·0528	1·59	0·039	2·07	0·051	0·67	0·017
CaO	3·01	4·02	0·0716	2·70	0·0482	1·38	0·025	3·60	0·064	1·12	0·019
Na_2O	11·87	10·64	0·3432	12·00	0·3870	10·57	0·340	10·00	0·322	9·37	0·302
K_2O	0·85	0·18	0·0038	0·06	0·0012	0·74	0·016	0·14	0·008	1·13	0·024
H_2O^+	0·50	0·04	0·0044	0·12	0·0132	0·56	0·062	not det.	—	0·22	0·024
H_2O^-	not det.	0·52	—	0·32	—	—	—	,, ,,	—	not det.	—
Cl	,, ,,	trace	—	not det.	—	0·07	—	,, ,,	—	,, ,,	—
F	,, ,,	not det.*	—	,, ,,	—	not det.	—	,, ,,	—	,, ,,	—
P_2O_5	,, ,,	nil	—	,, ,,	—	,, ,,	—	,, ,,	—	,, ,,	—
V_2O_5	,, ,,	0·24	—	present	—	0·03	—	,, ,,	—	,, ,,	—
Total	100·28	100·25		100·23		99·63		99·39		99·93	
Analyst	Fosberg, 1890	Moleva, 1938–1939				Vladimirova				Neumarck, 1931	
Reference	Ramsay (1890)	From Vorob'eva's data				From Gerasimovskii's data				Minerals of Khibiny and Lovozero tundras (1937)	

* In addition, 0·3 per cent F was determined in aegirine II

syenites aegirine occurs typically in pockets; alongside regions rich in aegirine (tawites) one finds parts in which there is no aegirine at all.

The aegirine content in the pegmatites varies from 10 to 75 per cent. Its main mass is represented by aegirine II. Aegirine I is characteristic only of the small undifferentiated pegmatitic bodies and external fine-grained zones of the large fully-differentiated pegmatites.

The aegirine groundmass in the non-pegmatitic rocks is later (aegirine II) than nepheline and microcline, as is evident from its occurrence in the interstices between these minerals. Aegirine I forms small idiomorphic inclusions in microcline and nepheline; it must therefore have crystallized before these minerals.

In the pegmatites aegirine I crystallized first. Its idiomorphism in comparison with all the other minerals and the presence of small inclusions of regular prismatic aegirine I crystals in early microcline, nepheline, eudialyte, aegirine II and other minerals are evidence of this. Aegirine II crystallized mainly after the formation of nepheline, early potassium feldspars and the high-temperature dark minerals, and fills up the interstices between these minerals. The interstices between aegirine II fibres are sometimes filled with fine-grained natrolite, ussingite or psilomelane.

Aegirine III crystallized at the late hydrothermal stage, as is evident from its close association with various ochreous decomposition products and crystals of the finely-acicular natrolite that fill up the leaching cavities. Aegirine III often develops in the fissures in other minerals, filling these along with natrolite (Fig. 138). In certain pegmatitic bodies, for example in the albite-natrolite vein on

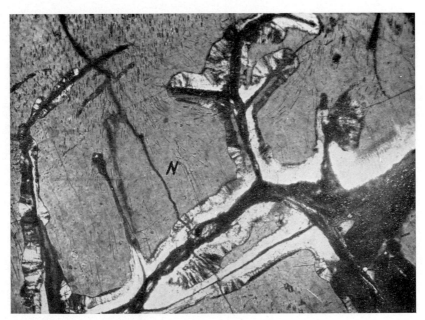

Fig. 138. Replacement of nepheline (N) by natrolite (light) and aegirine III (dark) along fissures

TABLE 51 Aegirine content in Lovozero rocks

Differentiated complex	Content, per cent	Eudialytic lujavrite complex	Content, per cent	Poikilitic syenite complex	Content, per cent
Upper division of complex:		Eudialytic lujavrites:		Poikilitic sodalite-syenites	0-4·5
Foyaites	4·7-8·4	Melanocratic	23·9-28·4	Poikilitic nepheline-syenites	3·5-15·7
Urtites	4·3-20·1	Mesocratic	19·6-23·0	Poikilitic hydrosodalite-syenites	4·5-8·5
Aegirine-lujavrites	11·8-45·3	Leucocratic	11·2-14·5		
Hornblende-lujavrites	3·7	Porphyritic lujavrites	24·3-50·1		
Malignites	13·7-30·1	Porphyritic juvites	16·2-16·5		
Middle division of complex:		Porphyritic foyaites	3·9-10·8		
Foyaites	8·8-14·6				
Urtites	5·6-19·5				
Aegirine-lujavrites	13·8-27·4				
Hornblende-lujavrites	12·5				
Lower division of complex:					
Foyaites	4·6-9·3				
Urtites	2·4-23·0				
Aegirine-lujavrites	20·3-35·1				

Karnasurt, no interruptions in the crystallization of aegirine have been established.

The process of replacement of aegirine by arfvedsonite is widely developed. In the late hydrothermal and hypergene stage aegirine is replaced by chlorite, celadonite and nontronite. Surface conditions produce marked bleaching of aegirine II, which pales to a greenish-yellow and decays.

Acmite was found by Semenov (1953) in the Lepkhe-Nel'm pegmatites genetically connected with the poikilitic nepheline-sodalite-syenites. It forms radial growths of reddish-brown acicular crystals measuring $2 \times 1 \times 1$ cm in natrolite and analcite cavities in the central parts of the pegmatitic bodies.

Aegirine-augite occurs along with aegirine in the poikilitic nepheline- and hydrosodalite-syenites. It is distinguished from aegirine by its oblique extinction (10-12°) and pleochroism in several yellower tones.

11. Arfvedsonite

$Na_3(Fe, Mg)_4 (Al, Fe) [Si_4O_{11}]_2(OH, F)_2$; mon.; sp.gr. 3·21—3·25; H. 6

In the non-pegmatitic rocks of the massif arfvedsonite forms either fine-prismatic crystals, for example in the hornblende-lujavrites, or xenomorphic segregations, typical of most of the rocks. The crystals reach sizes of $0·5 \times 0·01$ cm and the segregations are of irregular shape, $0·1 \times 0·2$ cm. In the pegmatites the crystal sizes vary from 0·2-2 mm for small inclusions in microcline to $20 \times 5 \times 1·5$ cm for large crystals found in coarse-grained parts of the pegmatites. The habit of the crystals is long-prismatic, elongated along the z axis. Sometimes the arfvedsonite in pegmatites forms radiate-fibrous accumulations, 2-3 cm in diameter. The colour is black with a dark green outline. The lustre is vitreous. Cleavage perfect prismatic (110). Fracture uneven. Opaque.

The mineral is optically biaxial, negative. Elongation negative. Extinction angle $c : Np$ varies from 7-35° in the rocks and from 10 to 24° in the pegmatites; $2V$ varies from 50 to 90° (usually 75-85° in the rock arfvedsonite and 60-65° in the pegmatitic variety).

Refractive indices: $Ng = 1·668—1·701$, $Np = 1·658—1·683$, $Ng-Np = 0·016—0·018$. Pronounced pleochroism is characteristic: Ng—yellowish-green, greenish-yellow, sometimes the same colours but with a blue tint; Nm—bluish-green with violet tint; Np—greenish-blue and blue-green. Sometimes anomalous interference colours can be observed. The absorption is $Np > Nm > Ng$.

In some rock varieties zonal crystals of arfvedsonite are present. The central part of such crystals is made up of another variety of alkaline amphibole, pleochroic in yellow tones, with an extinction angle $c : Np = 28-35°$, which is in all probability kataphorite.

In the pegmatites arfvedsonite sometimes forms simple and polysynthetic twins. Its crystals often have a zonal structure, the outer parts being more strongly coloured.

Arfvedsonite is not soluble in acids. Recalculation of the chemical analyses (Table 52) shows that its composition can be given by the theoretical formula $Na_3(Fe^{2+}, Mg)_4 (Fe^{3+}, Al) [Si_4O_{11}]_2 (OH, F)_2$.

V. M. Senderova determined 1·91 per cent of fluorine and 0·03 per cent of vanadium oxide by chemical assay in arfvedsonite from Kedykvyrpakhk pegmatites. Strontium, barium, lanthanum, lithium, chromium, gallium, niobium, zinc, beryllium, lead, tin, copper and molybdenum were detected by the spectrographic method in thirteen analyses of arfvedsonite from various parts of the massif, lead and molybdenum being characteristic of the rock arfvedsonite and niobium and rare earths only of the pegmatitic arfvedsonite from the differentiated complex of Flora. The other elements are present in both rock and pegmatitic arfvedsonite.

Arfvedsonite is contained in large amounts only in the hornblende-lujavrites (Table 53); in the other rocks it is a secondary mineral.

TABLE 52 Chemical compositions of arfvedsonite

Constituent	From Kuamdespakhk hornblende-lujavrite %	From Ninchurt urtite %	Atomic proportions	Calculation of atomic ratios	Kedykvyrpakhk %	Atomic proportions	First Eastern stream on Alluaiv %	Calculation of atomic ratios
SiO₂	50·86	49·66	0·8268		53·70	0·894	50·00	0·833
TiO₂	1·65	1·33	0·0206	0·8832 8·03 −8	1·68	0·021	2·40	0·030
ZrO₂	—	—	—		0·09	0·002	—	—
Al₂O₃	3·29	3·36	< 0·0358 / 0·0300	0·1182 1·07 −1	5·80	0·114	2·87	0·056
Fe₂O₃	8·61	7·04	0·0882		5·01	0·062	8·59	0·108
FeO	10·85	13·82	0·1923		13·01	0·181	13·34	0·186
MnO	1·26	1·65	0·0232		0·75	0·011	1·70	0·024
MgO	9·32	8·35	0·2071	0·4475 4·07 −4	6·98	0·173	9·35	0·231
CaO	1·40	1·02	0·0249		2·08	0·037	1·75	0·031
Na₂O	8·08	9·60	0·3096		8·28	0·268	6·92	0·224
K₂O	3·08	1·88	0·0398	0·3494 3·17 −3	2·35	0·050	1·98	0·042
H₂O	1·40	1·01	0·1122		nil	—	0·54	0·058
Cl	0·08	0·41	0·0115	0·2411 2·17 −2	nil	—	—	—
F	0·42	2·23	0·1174		—	—	—	—
P₂O₅	—	—	—		—	—	0·12	0·002
			O = 2·4274	2·4274 22·07 −22				
Total	100·30	101·36			99·73		99·56	
−O = (F, Cl)₂	−0·18	−1·11						
—	100·12	100·25						
Specific gravity	—		—		—		3·25	
Analyst		Moleva			Vorob'eva		Kazakova	
Investigator		Vorob'eva			Gerasimovskii		Tikhonenkov	

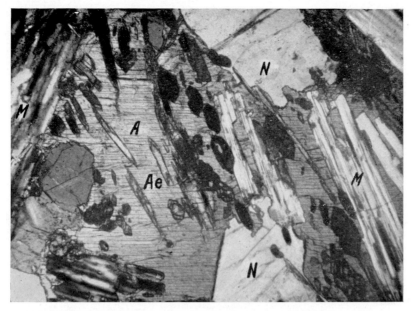

Fig. 139. Arfvedsonite (A), filling interstices between aegirine (Ae), nepheline (N) and microcline (M) crystals. ×46. Crossed nicols

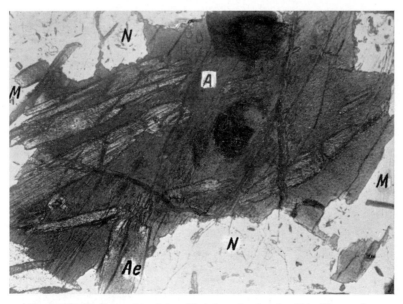

Fig. 140. Relicts of aegirine (Ae) in arfvedsonite (A); N—nepheline; M—microcline; black—loparite. ×46. Without analyser

In the hornblende-lujavrites of the top part of the differentiated complex the largest amounts of arfvedsonite are found in the central parts of the horizons, the content decreasing more sharply towards the roofs than towards the floors. In the middle part of the complex the largest concentrations of this mineral occur in the floors of the hornblende-lujavrite horizons at their contact with the foyaites. From the floor to the roof the arfvedsonite content gradually diminishes and the aegirine content gradually increases.

The arfvedsonite content in the other rocks of the massif increases from the leucocratic rocks (urtites and foyaites) to the melanocratic (aegirine-lujavrites, eudialytic lujavrites and porphyritic lujavrites); the aegirine-lujavrites contain more arfvedsonite in the undifferentiated than in the differentiated parts of the massif.

In the aegirine-lujavrites there is a certain increase in the arfvedsonite amount with depth.

In the pegmatites arfvedsonite occurs mainly as a secondary mineral in the peripheral equigranular and porphyritic zones or, more rarely, crystals of it form phenocrysts, along with microcline, in the fine-grained mass of vein bodies. Occasionally large arfvedsonite crystals are present in the central natrolite zones.

As regards its time of separation, rock arfvedsonite is later than aegirine II, nepheline and microcline, and fills up the interstices between these (Fig. 139). It is often found to have replaced aegirine II, irregularly-shaped relicts of which remain in the arfvedsonite (Fig. 140).

In the pegmatites arfvedsonite crystallized before aegirine II, in which it forms phenocrysts, together with aegirine I, of prismatic crystals and radiate-fibrous accumulations. It is xenomorphic in relation to aegirine I but has a characteristic clear-cut idiomorphism in relation to ramsayite and eudialyte. Phenocrysts of it are contained in eudialyte, ramsayite, nepheline and microcline. The interstices between the arfvedsonite crystals are usually filled with aegirine II, ramsayite, neptunite and natrolite. In some of the pegmatitic bodies late arfvedsonite has been observed along with the earlier variety, filling up the interstices between segregations of microcline, eudialyte and other high-temperature minerals, and replacing second-generation poikilitic aegirine.

Early arfvedsonite began to crystallize from a pegmatitic melt solution some-

TABLE 53 Arfvedsonite content in Lovozero rocks

Differentiated complex	Content, per cent	Eudialytic lujavrite complex	Content, per cent	Poikilitic syenite complex	Content, per cent
Foyaites	0-1·6	Eudialytic		Poikilitic-sodalite	
Urtites	0-0·5	lujavrites	1·3-5·5	syenites	0·7-1·8
Aegirine-		Porphyritic		Poikilitic nephe-	
lujavrites	0·3-6·5	lujavrites	0·5-1·6	line- and	
Hornblende-		Porphyritic		hydrosodalitic	
lujavrites	13·45-42·3	juvites	0·2-0·3	syenites	0·2-1·5
Malignites	0·2-0·4	Porphyritic			
		foyaites	0·4-0·5		

what later than aegirine I and then separated simultaneously with the latter. In the pegmatites richer in potassium (Lepkhe-Nel'm), arfvedsonite crystallized after the precipitation of the main mass of potassium feldspar, roughly at the end of its crystallization period but earlier than the high-temperature rare-metal minerals eudialyte, ramsayite and murmanite, as is evident from its idiomorphism in relation to those minerals. Late arfvedsonite seems to have crystallized after the high-temperature rare-metal minerals and after aegirine II, from which it develops.

During the later processes of pegmatite formation arfvedsonite suffered hardly any alteration at all; there is only one recorded case of its replacement by chlorite.

CHAPTER TWO

RARE-METAL MINERALS

THE Lovozero massif is known to contain more than 60 rare-metal minerals, including twenty-seven minerals of titanium and niobium, more than eleven of the rare earths and thorium, ten of zirconium, five of lithium and eight of beryllium. The commonest are the zirconium-, titanium- and niobium-bearing groups.

I. ZIRCONIUM MINERALS

Seven minerals of this group have so far been found in the non-pegmatitic rocks of the massif: eudialyte, eucolite, mesodialyte, lovozerite, catapleiite, zirfesite and zircon. In addition, elpidite, titan-låvenite and seidozerite occur in the pegmatites. In the eudialytic-lujavrites and eudialytites and in most of the pegmatites the commonest of these minerals—those of the eudialyte-eucolite group—are often the main rock-forming minerals. The rest occur in small amounts and, except for zircon, are secondary, formed during the replacement of eudialyte-eucolite minerals. Zircon is not characteristic of the massif and occurs only in the contaminated rocks, hybrid pegmatites and contact zones.

12. Minerals of the eudialyte-eucolite group
(Na, Ca)$_5$ZrSi$_6$O$_{17}$; hex.; sp.gr. 2·78—2·95; H. 5—5·5

These minerals are, of course, zirconium metasilicates, forming an isomorphous series in which eudialyte is the more sodic member and eucolite the more calcic. In 1929 Kostyleva (1929, 1937) distinguished an intermediate member of the group, mesodialyte. The end-members of this isomorphous series (purely sodic or calcic) have not yet been found.

Both in the rocks and in the pegmatites eudialyte and mesodialyte are the most widely distributed, eudialyte being the more extensively developed of the two. Eucolite occurs very rarely and mainly as a secondary mineral from eudialyte or, more often, mesodialyte. It is found only locally, in the contaminated poikilitic hydrosodalite-syenites of the Lovozero complex and in the pegmatites associated with them.

In the non-pegmatitic rocks the minerals of the eudialyte-eucolite group usually form irregularly shaped segregations or, more rarely, euhedral crystals. Eudialyte crystals are found only in eudialytic lujavrites and the eudialytites. They vary in size from microscopic dimensions to $0.5 \times 0.3 \times 0.3$ cm, those in the eudialytites being larger than those in the eudialytic lujavrites. In other rocks the size of the segregations varies with the grain size of the rock: they are never larger than $0.2 \times 0.1 \times 0.1$ cm in the urtites, juvites and malignites or $0.5 \times 0.3 \times 0.3$ cm in the foyaites and lujavrites.

In the pegmatites the minerals of this group form rounded or hexagonal (in cross-section) segregations, from 2-3 mm in the peripheral zones to $10 \times 10 \times 15$ cm in the block zones. In pegmatites very rich in zirconium eudialyte forms large,

type 5

type 4

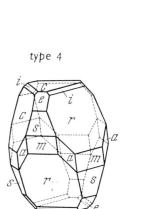
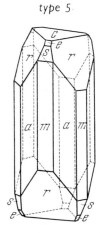
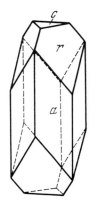

FIG. 141. Eudialyte and mesodialyte crystal types 4 and 5 from eudialytic lujavrites (after Kostyleva)

FIG. 142. Type 6 eudia-lyte crystal from Vavnbed eudialytites

almost monomineralic fine-grained segregations, sometimes as much as 3-4 m long and 1 m wide.

Study of the crystal forms has shown that the minerals in this group correspond to Kostyleva's fourth and fifth crystal types (1937). The fifth type, the commoner, is characterized by crystals greatly elongated along the vertical axis (Fig. 141) with a poorly developed basal pinacoid face c (0001) and well-developed faces of the principal rhombohedron r (10$\bar{1}$1) and prisms m (10$\bar{1}$0) and a (11$\bar{2}$0). In addition, faces t (21$\bar{3}$1), z (10$\bar{1}$4), e (01$\bar{1}$2) and s (02$\bar{2}$1) occur. The $a : c$ ratio is 1 : 2.1292. The fourth type of eudialyte crystal is short-columnar (see Fig. 141). The characteristic feature of this type is the presence of a poorly-developed basal pinacoid face c (0001), poorly-developed faces of the principal rhombohedron r (10$\bar{1}$1) and well-developed faces of the prisms m (10$\bar{1}$0) and a (11$\bar{2}$0). In addition, the z (10$\bar{1}$4), e (01$\bar{1}$2) and h (01$\bar{1}$5) faces are present. The presence of a scaleno-hedron t (21$\bar{3}$1) in the form of narrow faces is characteristic (Kostyleva, 1937). The $a : c$ ratio is 1 : 2.1230.

Khalezova detected a hitherto unknown sixth type of eudialyte crystal in the eudialytites (Fig. 142). Like Kostyleva's fifth type this is represented by long-prismatic fine crystals but is distinguished by the small number of faces. The basal pinacoid is poorly developed; the rhombohedral (10$\bar{1}$1) and prismatic (11$\bar{2}$0)

TABLE 54 Specific gravity and refractive indices of minerals in the eudialyte-eucolite group

Rock	Specific gravity	Ne	No	Ne-No	Predominant mineral	Investigator
Differentiated complex:						
Foyaite	2·758-2·90	1·598-1·606	1·593-1·601	0·005	Eudialyte	Present authors
Urtite	2·86 -2·92	1·603-1·609	—	—	Mesodialyte	,,
Aegirine-lujavrite	2·76 -2·90	1·600-1·608	1·598-1·605	0·003	,,	,,
Hornblende-lujavrite	2·825	1·601-1·603	—	—	,,	,,
Pegmatites:						
Flora	—	1·598-1·613	1·591-1·610	0·003-0·010	Eudialyte	Borodin
,,	—	1·600-1·604	—	—	Mesodialyte	,,
Upper reaches of Kitkuai	—	1·608	1·613	0·005	Eucolite	Semenov
Kitkn'yun	—	1·605	—	—	Mesodialyte	,,
Alluaiv	—	1·616	1·611	0·005	Eudialyte	Tikhonenkov
Pegmatite horizon	—	1·606	1·603	0·003	,,	,,
Eudialytic lujavrite complex:						
Eudialytic lujavrite	2·788-2·855	1·601-1·605	1·600-1·603	0·001-0·002	Mesodialyte	Present authors
Eudialytite	2·883-2·893	1·603	1·594	0·006	Eudialyte	,,
Pegmatites:						
Tyul'bn'yunuai valley	—	1·611-1·613	1·609-1·610	0·001-0·003	,,	Slepnev
Kedykvyrpakhk	—	1·604	1·599	0·005	,,	,,
Mannepakhk cirque	—	1·596-1·598	1·593-1·595	0·003	,,	Semenov
Poikilitic syenite complex:						
Poikilitic sodalite-syenites	2·857-2·910	1·604-1·608	1·600-1·604	0·004	Eudialyte	Present authors
Poikilitic nepheline-syenites	2·873	1·601	1·605	—	Mesodialyte	,,
Poikilitic hydrosodalite-syenites	2·854-2·945	1·604-1·612	1·602-1·617	0·002-0·005	Mesodialyte, eucolite	,,
Pegmatites:						
Malyi Punkaruaiv	—	1·602-1·611	1·596-1·607	0·004-0·006	Eudialyte	Borodin
Chinglusuai valley	—	1·603	1·601	0·002	,,	Gerasimovskii
Lenkhe-Nel'm	—	1·617	—	—	Mesodialyte	Semenov

faces are well developed but the remaining faces are lacking. The $(02\bar{2}1)$ and $(01\bar{1}2)$ faces were observed in some of the crystals but were very poorly developed.

The minerals of this group are of various shades of pinkish- and cherry-red, brownish-red, brown, yellowish-brown, light-yellow and pink. The brownish-red colour is peculiar rather to the rock eudialyte, the pinkish- or cherry-red to the mesodialyte and the various shades of pink to the eucolite. The lustre is vitreous. Cleavage is not macroscopically observable. Fracture small-conchoidal. Opaque to transparent in thin fragments. Specific gravity usually variable in different parts of a single grain, because of the zonal structure of the minerals.

The minerals of this group are optically uniaxial. Sometimes anomalous biaxial character is observed. The eudialyte is optically positive, the mesodialyte isotropic, the eucolite negative. Pleochroism is poorly shown in the eudialyte and mesodialyte but distinct in the eucolite. The following pleochroic schemes occur: in eudialyte, Ne—bright-yellow to yellow, No—light-yellow to colourless, $Ne>No$; in mesodialyte, Ne yellowish-pink to pink, No light-yellow; in eucolite, Ne pale pink to colourless, No yellowish-pink to bright-pink, $Ne<No$. Refractive indices vary widely (Table 54), as do the specific gravities, rising from eudialyte, through mesodialyte to eucolite; this is due to the change in chemical composition.

The minerals show a characteristic zonality, zones of different composition and interference colour alternating with one another. This is most apparent where the minerals occur in eudialytic lujavrites or eudialytites. Usually eudialyte forms the inner part of the crystals and grains, and mesodialyte the margin. Where there are several zones eudialyte is sometimes found in the centre of the grain, followed by mesodialyte, with eudialyte again on the outside. In other cases the central part is of mesodialyte, giving way to eudialyte, and the outer zone of mesodialyte again (Fig. 143). In certain eudialyte grains the zonality produces an hourglass effect (Fig. 144). Concentric zoning does not occur in xenomorphic segregations of the minerals in this group. Isotropic and anisotropic parts, of irregular form, or parallel-striped zoning can usually be distinguished in them.

TABLE 55 Interplanar spacings of eudialyte and eucolite

Line no.	Eudialyte		Eucolite		Line no.	Eudialyte		Eucolite	
	I	d	I	d		I	d	I	d
1	m	4·21	w	4·50	13	vw	2·12	w	2·12
2	w	3·96	,,	4·08	14	—	—	,,	1·97
3	,,	3·63	,,	3·73	15	—	—	,,	1·93
4	w	3·44	—	—	16	vw	1·803	,,	1·83
5	,,	3·31	—	—	17	—	—	,,	1·78
6	m	3·11	m	3·11	18	w	1·741	,,	1·72
7	w	2·91	,,	2·95	19	—	—	vw	1·647
8	—	—	,,	2·82	20	vw	1·580	w	1·586
9	m	2·66	w	2·68	21	—	—	w(b)	1·482
10	w	2·63	—	—	22	vw	1·356	w	1·366
11	,,	2·53	vw	2·56	23	—	—	,,	1·345
12	vw	2·366	w	2·36					

Note. m = medium, b = broad line, w = weak, vw = very weak

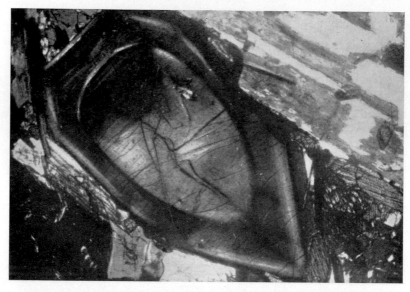

FIG. 143. Zoned grain of eudialyte; light: eudialyte; dark: meso-dialyte. ×46. Crossed nicols

FIG. 144. Zoned eudialyte with hour-glass structure, from Vavn-bed eudialytites. ×46. Crossed nicols

According to E. E. Kostyleva cleavage can be observed in the minerals of this group, under the microscope, in several directions: c (0001)—distinct; m (10$\bar{1}$0) and a (11$\bar{2}$0)—imperfect; z (10$\bar{1}$4); r (10$\bar{1}$1) and h (01$\bar{1}$3)—indistinct.

X-ray study of the eudialyte and eucolite, according to Semenov (Table 55), showed that the two minerals are similar in structure.

The minerals of this group are readily soluble in cold concentrated HCl and on heating in concentrated HNO_3 and H_2SO_4. Comparison of chemical analyses (Table 56) shows that they differ in chemical composition, mainly in calcium and sodium content, the one being inversely proportional in amount to the other.

The more calcium-rich varieties are characteristic of the aegirine-lujavrites, the eudialytic lujavrites and the poikilitic syenites with hydrosodalite, whereas the more sodium-rich minerals are characteristic of the pegmatites, eudialytites, poikilitic sodalite-syenites and foyaites. The highest content in volatile substances (Cl, OH) is characteristic of the minerals in this group from foyaites, eudialytites and pegmatites.

A higher zirconium content (14·16-14·37 per cent ZrO_2) is found in minerals of this group from the eudialytites and poikilitic sodalite-syenites, while the rare-earth content is higher in the eudialyte and mesodialyte from rocks of the differentiated complex (2·38-2·43 per cent $R.E._2O_3$), from the eudialytites (2·92 per cent $R.E._2O_3$) and from the pegmatites (2·12 per cent $R.E._2O_3$). The largest amount of niobium is found in eudialyte-group minerals from rocks of the differentiated complex, the eudialytites and the poikilitic sodalite-syenites (1·05-1·16 per cent Nb_2O_5); the Nb_2O_5 content (0·54-0·93 per cent) in the eudialyte and mesodialyte from the eudialytic lujavrites and pegmatites is slightly lower. The titanium content in the minerals of this group from rocks of the differentiated complex, poikilitic syenites and pegmatites varies little (from 0·34-0·57 per cent TiO_2). In the meso-dialyte from the eudialytic lujavrites and eudialytites the titanium content is higher (0·9 per cent TiO_2).

Recalculation of the chemical analysis of eudialyte showed that its composition is expressed by the formula $(Na, Ca)_5ZrSi_6O_{16}(OH, Cl)_2$, which is distinguished from the formula $Na_4Ca_2ZrSi_6O_{18}(Cl, OH)$, suggested for eudialyte by Zachariasen and Kunitz (Borneman, 1947) by the small number of cations in group A, the low oxygen content and the larger number of chlorine atoms and hydroxyl groups in the anionic part. Our own researches and those of Borneman (1947), Borodin and Nazarenko (1957) show that the formula for minerals of the eudialyte group is variable, the ratio of Si atoms to other cations varying from 6 : 6 to 6 : 7, and the number of atoms in the anionic part from 17 to 18.

Unlike most of the rare-earth minerals in the massif, the minerals of the eudialyte-eucolite group have a high tenor of the yttrium subgroup of rare earths, particularly yttrium itself. Barinskii gives the following proportions (R.E. = 100): La_{11}; Ce_{28}; $Pr_{4·3}$; $Nd_{13·5}$; $Sm_{4·5}$; $Eu_{1·1}$; $Gd_{4·5}$; $Tb_{0·6}$; $Dy_{3·6}$; $Ho_{0·6}$; $Er_{2·6}$; $Tu_{0·5}$; $Yb_{1·8}$; $Lu_{0·3}$; $Y_{23·1}$. The ratio between the elements in the yttrium and cerium subgroups in the eudialyte is 1 : 1·66.

In 21 specimens of minerals belonging to this group, taken from various parts of the massif, spectrographic analysis revealed beryllium, lead, tin, copper and gallium. Tungsten was detected in the eudialyte from the pegmatitic horizon and the pegmatites of the Kitkuai valley.

The minerals of the eudialyte-eucolite group are widely distributed in the rocks (Table 57) and in the pegmatites of the Lovozero massif other than those of the hybrid pegmatites. They are most abundant in the rocks of the eudialytic and porphyritic lujavrite complex. A number of recurrent patterns can be observed in their distribution in the differentiated complex and in the eudialytic lujavrites (see Part One Chapter Five).

All members of the eudialyte-eucolite group are present in the poikilitic syenite complex. Eudialyte is more characteristic of the sodalitic (hackmanitic) variety, in which mesodialyte occurs in negligible amounts. In the nepheline-bearing variety mesodialyte predominates over eudialyte, but in the hydrosodalitic variety

TABLE 56 Chemical compositions of

Constituent	Eudialyte from foyaite					Mesodialyte		
	per cent	Atomic proportions	Calculation of atomic ratios			From Karnasurt aegirine-lujavrite, per cent	Crimson, from Ninchurt lujavrite, per cent	From eudialytic lujavrite, per cent
SiO$_2$	49·65	0·8252	0.8252	5·89	− 6	48·58	50·90	49·95
Al$_2$O$_3$	trace	—	—			trace	2·10	not det.
TiO$_2$	0·35	0·0043	⎱			0·34	0·50	0·90
ZrO$_2$	13·73	0·1114				13·57	11·00	13·15
Nb$_2$O$_5$	1·15	0·0086	0·1477	1·05	− 1	0·97	1·10	0·93
Ta$_2$O$_3$	not det.	—				not det.	not det.	not det.
Fe$_2$O$_3$	1·88	0·0234	⎰			1·07	2·80	0·90
FeO	1·98	0.0275	⎱			3·13	0·70	2·78
MnO	2·33	0·0328				1·91	2·25	1·75
MgO	0·09	0·0022				0·33	0·24	0·22
CaO	8·79	0·1567				10·24	10·34	11·60
SrO	trace	—	0·6852	4·89	− 5	not det.	not det.	0·13
BaO	not det.	—				,, ,,	,, ,,	0·65
ΣRE$_2$O$_3$	2·38	0·0146				2·43	2·30	0·81
Na$_2$O	13·58	0·4380				14·07	11·52	12·33
K$_2$O	0·64	0·0134	⎰			1·15	0·74	0·84
H$_2$O$^+$	2·05	0·2274	⎱			1·71	2·04	1·44
H$_2$O$^-$	0·32	—	0·2793	1·99	− 2	not det.	not det.	0·16
Cl	1·84	0·0519				1·29	1·28	1·43
S	not det.	—	⎰			not det.	not det.	not det.
		O = 2·2656	2·2656	16·18	− 16			
Total	100·76		—			100·79	99·81	99·97
− O = Cl$_2$	− 0·41		—			− 0·29	− 0·29	− 0·32
—	100·35		—			100·50	99·52	99·65
Analyst	Kazakova, 1952						Moleva	Kazakova, 1952

it is the commonest mineral, and eucolite sometimes develops from it. The poikilitic syenites vary greatly in their content of minerals of this group, which in some parts are absent or occur in negligible amounts (up to 0·5 per cent), whereas other parts are rich in them (up to 3-5 per cent and sometimes even 15-25 per cent on Ninchurt, Punkaruaiv and elsewhere).

In the pegmatites the minerals of the eudialyte-eucolite group are usually concentrated in the outer fine-grained and block feldspar-aegirine zones, where they sometimes account for 20-30 per cent of the rock. They are developed in all the pegmatitic bodies except the hybrid pegmatites, in which zirconium minerals are represented mainly by zircon. In the small undifferentiated pegmatitic bodies eudialyte is distributed throughout their mass though its concentration towards the margin of the bodies has been noted. In certain pegmatitic bodies the eudialyte makes up large regions or entire zones, where it accounts for 60-90 per cent of

minerals in the eudialyte-eucolite group

Eudialyte from Vavnbed eudialytite		Eudialyte from Karnasurt poikilitic sodalite-syenite, per cent	Mesodialyte from Ninchurt poikilitic hydro-sodalite-syenite, per cent	Eudialyte	
Brownish red, per cent	Cherry brown, per cent			From Ang-vundaschorr pegmatite,* per cent	From Mannepakhk pegmatite,† per cent
49·77	49·16	48·69	47·45	50·09	51·23
not determined	not determined	not determined	not determined	not determined	not determined
0·48	0·72	0·50	0·57	0·39	0·56
14·16	14·17	14·37	13·07	12·82	13·98
1·08	not determined	1·16	not determined	0·54	not determined
not determined	,, ,,	not determined	,, ,,	0·06	,, ,,
,, ,,	0·78	1·04	,, ,,	0·60	0·67
4·23	3·57	3·07	..	1·79	3·39
1·80	1·64	2·38	,, ,,	2·31	2·50
not determined	trace	0·24	0·49	trace	0·27
8·59	7·01	7·45	10·65	8·96	9·62
not determined	1·42	0·85	not determined	not determined	trace
,, ,,	not determined	not determined	,, ,,	,, ,,	not determined
1·78	2·29	1·82	,, ,,	2·12	1·68
14·67	15·82	13·84	12·63	15·55	11·16
not determined	0·43	1·19	0·84	0·62	0·69
1·16	1·26	1·54	not determined	3·06	2·88
not determined	not determined	0·13	,, ,,	not determined	not determined
1·63	2·19	1·16	,, ,,	0·74	1·26
not determined	nil	not determined	,, ,,	not determined	not determined
99·35	100·46	99·43	—	99·65	99·89
−0·36	−0·49	−0·23	—	−0·15	−0·27
98·99	99·97	99·20	—	99·50	99·62
Khalezova, 1949	Vladimirova	Kasakova		Vlodavets	Egorova

* † Gerasimovskii's data

TABLE 57 Content of minerals of the eudialyte-eucolite group in Lovozero rocks

Differentiated complex	Content, per cent	Eudialytic lujavrite complex	Content, per cent	Poikilitic syenite complex	Content, per cent
Upper:		Eudialytic lujavrites:		Poikilitic sodalite-syenites	0-7-8·3
Foyaites	1-4·8	Melanocratic	10·8-25·1	Poikilitic nepheline-syenites	0·5-3·5
Urtites	0-6·2	Mesocratic	7·3-12·5	Poikilitic hydrosodalite-syenites	0·1-2·5
Aegirine-lujavrites	0-4-5·3	Leucocratic	3·8-8·2		
Hornblende-lujavrites	0·2-1·3	Porphyritic lujavrites	6·9-11·8		
Malignites	0-3·2	Porphyritic juvites	7·3-9·1		
Middle:		Porphyritic foyaites	0-6-2·5		
Foyaites	0·6-3·9				
Urtites	0-3·6				
Aegirine-lujavrites	0·7-4·7				
Hornblende-lujavrites	0·7-1·5				
Lower:					
Foyaites	0·4-1·8				
Urtites	0·2-0·8				
Aegirine-lujavrites	0·3-1·2				

the rock (see the description of the ussingitic pegmatite body on Malyi Punkaruaiv).

Both in the rocks and in the pegmatites the eudialyte-eucolite minerals, which are relatively sodium-rich in composition, are found in paragenetic association with the more sodic rare-metal minerals, lomonosovite, murmanite, lamprophyllite and others and, conversely, the more calcium-rich members of the group are found in close association with the rare-metal calcium minerals, loparite, apatite, sphene and others.

As regards time of crystallization, the minerals of this group are comparatively early, having in many cases crystallized in the eudialytites and eudialytic lujavrites

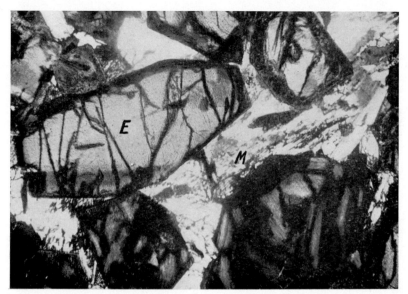

Fig. 145. Interrelationship between eudialyte (E) and microcline (M). × 10. Crossed nicols

before the potassium feldspars, nepheline and aegirine. In the eudialytites they form euhedral crystals, the spaces between which are filled with microcline, arfvedsonite, aegirine, murmanite, lamprophyllite and natrolite (Fig. 145). In the eudialytic lujavrites they sometimes form small, well-formed hexagonal crystals, chiefly in the margins of the nepheline and microcline crystals, but most of them occur in the form of idiomorphic segregations in the spaces between these minerals. Accumulations of aegirine II as a rule surround crystals of mesodialyte and, very rarely, thin needles of it are included in the margins of eudialyte. The minerals of this group occasionally fill the interstices between crystals of aegirine II.

The main bulk of the minerals we are describing thus separated, in these rocks, at the end of the nepheline and potassium feldspar crystallization but before aegirine II began to crystallize, and only a negligible amount of mesodialyte formed after aegirine II.

In the rocks of the differentiated and the poikilitic syenite complexes the

FIG. 146. Interrelationship of eudialyte (E) with microcline (M) and nepheline (N). ×46. Crossed nicols

FIG. 147. Interrelationship of eudialyte (E) with ramsayite (R) and microcline (M); N—nepheline. ×46. Crossed nicols

eudialyte-eucolite minerals fill up interstices of irregular, often bizarre, shape between the rock-forming minerals (Fig. 146). Eudialyte-eucolite minerals enclose such minerals as loparite, apatite, and more rarely lamprophyllite and ramsayite. All other minerals in the rocks of these complexes have accommodated themselves to the shapes of the eudialyte segregations, as it were cementing them.

In the pegmatites the minerals of this group crystallized mainly during the formation of outer fine-grained and feldspar-aegirine zones, roughly at the same time as ramsayite, slightly earlier than murmanite and at the end of the period of early potassium feldspar crystallization. They are xenomorphic in relation to nepheline, aegirine I and arfvedsonite. In relation to microcline, eudialyte is sometimes idiomorphic (Karnasurt and Kedykvyrpakhk pegmatites; Fig. 147), but is often concentrated in the interstices between microcline crystals. It is idiomorphic to aegirine II and aenigmatite, which fill interstices between its segregations.

In the contaminated rocks and pegmatites of the central part of the massif and Flora, and more rarely in the pure pegmatites, replacement of eudialyte and mesodialyte by eucolite is observed, the eucolite sometimes forming complete

TABLE 58 Chemical compositions of eudialyte and its alteration products (per cent)

Constituent	Eudialyte from foyaite	Altered eudialyte		
		Creamy pink, from foyaite	Black, from eudialytic lujavrite	From Karnasurt pegmatite
SiO_2	49·65	42·52	48·38	25·80
Al_2O_3	trace	0·53	1·42	2·52
TiO_2	0·35	2·50	2·99	1·42
ZrO_2	13·73	18·39	14·60	28·36
Nb_2O_5	1·15	1·32	0·33	1·68
ΣRE_2O_3	2·38	2·66	0·57	2·64
Fe_2O_3	1·88	1·32	2·32	4·48
FeO	1·98	not determined	not determined	not determined
MnO	2·33	1·07	,, ,,	8·16
MnO_2	not determined	not determined	7·86	not determined
MgO	0·09	0·12	0·07	0·24
CaO	8·79	5·30	3·30	3·52
SrO	trace	not determined	not determined	not determined
Na_2O	13·58	5·82	4·58	1·10
K_2O	0·64	4·28	3·19	1·16
Cl	1·84	not determined	not determined	not determined
H_2O^+	2·05	7·54	5·47	18·62
H_2O^-	0·32	4·44	5·23	not determined
Other	not determined	1·08*	not determined	,, ,,
P_2O_5	,, ,,	not determined	0·32	,, ,,
Total	100·76	98·89	100·63	99·70
$-O = Cl_2$	$-0·41$			
—	100·35			
Analyst		Kazakova, 1951		Burova, 1951

* CO_2 present

pseudomorphs after them. The replacement of mesodialyte by eucolite usually begins along the cleavages.

Minerals of the eudialyte-eucolite group are replaced by catapleiite, elpidite, lovozerite and zirfesite in the late hydrothermal and hypergene stages. Replacement by zirfesite is the most widely developed.

The action of hydrothermal solutions and surface waters at first converted the eudialyte-eucolite minerals into a porous mass of cream, brown, brownish-black or black colour showing aggregate polarization and occupying an intermediate position in chemical composition between eudialyte and zirfesite. This alteration process first affected the peripheral parts of the eudialyte segregations, then the solutions penetrated along the cracks, often converting an entire grain. Zirfesite is an end-product of eudialyte alteration under hypergene conditions.

The process of alteration in this group of minerals is most evident in the large pegmatitic bodies, where they never occur fresh (Karnasurt) and also in the rocks of the upper part of the differentiated complex. In the urtites these minerals are usually completely altered, while in the foyaites and lujavrites decomposed eudialyte predominates over the unaltered minerals. A direct relationship between the natrolite content in the rocks and the degree of decomposition of the eudialyte-eucolite minerals is apparent. In the differentiated complex the amount of alteration distinctly lessens with depth; in the eudialytic lujavrites and the rocks of the poikilitic syenite complex their alteration is less advanced.

Comparing the chemical analyses of eudialyte and the products of its progressive alteration (Table 58 and 63) we find that its decomposition is associated with loss of sodium and chlorine and accession of water. With more profound alteration silica is also lost and there is a concentration of manganese in black decomposed eudialyte and in zirfesite. The zirconium content rises steadily from fresh eudialyte to zirfesite.

13. Lovozerite

$(Na,Ca)_2(Zr,Ti)Si_6O_{13}(OH)_6 . 3H_2O$; hex.; sp.gr. 2·3—2·7; H. 5

Lovozerite was discovered by Gerasimovskii (1940[4]) in the porphyritic lujavrites of the Lovozero massif and his data have been taken into account in the following description. The mineral is widely distributed in the rocks but rarely and in minute amounts in the pegmatites.

Two varieties are distinguished, differing in the character of their segregations: (1) a primary variety, filling up interstices between various minerals and (2) a secondary variety, formed by replacement of eudialyte and mesodialyte. Primary lovozerite occurs as large, irregularly-shaped segregations, measuring 0·1 × 0·1 to 2 × 1 cm and forming single optically continuous individuals, which often exhibit a simple twinned structure. It contains a large number of inclusions of microcline, nepheline, aegirine, lamprophyllite and other minerals (Fig. 148). Secondary lovozerite develops from the periphery of the grains of minerals of the eudialyte-eucolite group, forming rims round them (Fig. 149), and often complete pseudomorphs.

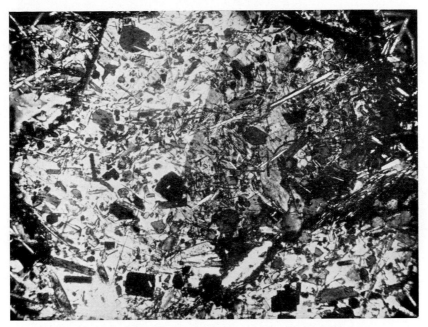

Fig. 148. Nepheline, aegirine, and potassium feldspar inclusions in primary lovozerite (light). ×46. Crossed nicols

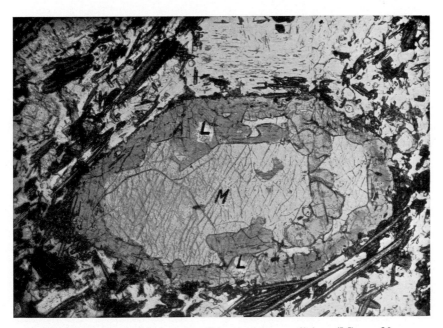

Fig. 149. Rim of lovozerite (L) around mesodialyte (M). ×20. Without analyser

Lovozerite is yellowish-pink; where the decomposition process is far advanced the colour is black or dark-brown. Opaque. Streak brown. Pitch-like lustre. Fracture uneven, conchoidal. Specific gravity: rock lovozerite 2·384 (Gerasimovskii, 1940$_4$); pegmatitic lovozerite 2·708 (Semenov).

In thin sections lovozerite is yellowish-pink. Decomposed parts have a brown or dark-brown, almost black colour. The mineral is uniaxial and negative. Slightly pleochroic in yellowish-pink shades. Absorption system $Ne>No$. In thin sec-

FIG. 150. Twinned lovozerite (L). ×46. Crossed nicols

tions there is a poor but perceptible cleavage in two directions. Fedorov universal-stage measurements show that one of these contains No while the pole of the other makes an angle of 60° with Ne and an angle of 33° with the pole of the twin-composition plane (Gerasimovskii, 1940$_4$).

Twins, often polysynthetic (Fig. 150), are characteristic of lovozerite. In twins the Ne of one growth makes an angle of 73-74° with the Ne of the other. The refractive indices are $No=1·561$; $Ne=1·549$; $No-Ne=0·012$. The interplanar spacings of pegmatitic lovozerite as calculated by Berkhin are shown in Table 59.

TABLE 59 Interplanar spacings of Lovozerite

Line no.	I	d	Line no.	I	d
1	w	5·22	5	w	3·46
2	m	4·36	6	vw	2·79
3	s	3·90	7	w	2·536
4	w	3·60	8	,,	2·403

Lovozerite is insoluble in acids. Recalculation of the chemical analysis (Table 60) shows that its composition is expressed by the formula $(Na, Ca, Mn)_2 ZrSi_6O_{16} \cdot 6H_2O$.

Small amounts of lead, tin, copper, barium, beryllium and hafnium have been detected spectroscopically in lovozerite. Quantitative X-ray chemical analysis performed by Borovskii showed a hafnium content of 0·1 per cent. Krutetskaya, using the chemical method, determined the U_3O_8 content as 0·042 per cent. Dehydration experiments showed that the water content (9 per cent) was gradually eliminated at temperatures of 100-500°; this indicates that the water is of zeolitic character.

In the differentiated complex only secondary lovozerite occurs, chiefly in rocks in which zeolitization has been comparatively slight. Such conditions occur in the middle and lower parts of the complex, where lovozerite is present in the foyaites, aegirine-lujavrites and, more rarely, in the urtites. The lovozerite concentration here does not exceed 0·5-1 per cent. In the rocks of the upper part of the differentiated complex, where hypergene processes are strongly developed and there is free circulation of the surface waters, there is usually no lovozerite. Under these conditions, products of the more profound alteration of zirconium minerals, all the way to zirfesite, develop on the minerals of the eudialyte-eucolite group. Unaltered lovozerite is observed in the upper part of the complex only in

TABLE 60 Chemical composition of Lovozerite from porphyritic lujavrite in the upper reaches of the river El'maraik

Constituent	Analysis 1			Analysis 2
	per cent	Atomic proportions	Calculation of atomic ratios	
SiO_2	52·12	0·8678	} 0·8756 6·16 — 6	not determined
Al_2O_3	0·40	0·0078		0·86
Fe_2O_3	0·72	0·0090		
TiO_2	1·02	0·0128	} 0·1560 1·09 — 1	not determined
ZrO_2	16·54	0·1342		15·55
RE_2O_3	0·56	0·0034		not determined
FeO	not determined	—		,, ,,
MnO	3·46	0·0487		,, ,,
MgO	0·76	0·0188	} 0·2980 2·09 — 2	,, ,,
CaO	3·34	0·0595		,, ,,
SrO	0·06	0·0006		,, ,,
Na_2O	3·74	0·1266		,, ,,
K_2O	1·90	0·0404		,, ,,
H_2O^+	8·62	0·9576	} 1·6698 11·76 —12	,, ,,
H_2O^-	6·41	0·7122		
		$O = 3·1059$	3·1059 21·89 —22	
Total	99·65	—	—	—
Analyst	Burova			Kazakova
Reference	Gerasimovskii (1940₄)			From Semenov's data

the foyaites bedded at considerable depth below the surface, where its content does not exceed 0·2-0·5 per cent.

It is mainly secondary lovozerite that is developed in the eudialytic lujavrites, where it does not usually account for more than 1-2 per cent of the rock. In the porphyritic lujavrites both varieties of lovozerite are represented and the total amount sometimes increases slightly. Lovozerite is particularly widely developed in the porphyritic lujavrites of the northern, central and western parts of the massif.

In the rocks of the poikilitic syenite complex only secondary lovozerite occurs, in amounts varying between 0·1 and 3 per cent; in the sodalitic and hackmanitic varieties, however, it is not present at all, or only in extremely small amounts. The nepheline and hydrosodalite varieties of the poikilitic syenites are richest in lovozerite, containing as much as 1-3 per cent of it in places.

Lovozerite formed after eudialyte, which it replaces, and after lamprophyllite, murmanite, ramsayite and other minerals, segregations of which are, as it were, cemented by primary lovozerite.

Under surface conditions lovozerite is unstable and is converted into a brown and black ochreous mass consisting of the oxide and hydroxides of manganese, iron, zirconium, silicon and other elements.

14. Catapleiite

$Na_2Zr [Si_3O_9] . 2H_2O$; hex. and mon. (?); sp.gr. 2·65—2·76; H. 5—6

Small amounts of catapleiite are found in the rocks and pegmatites of the massif, in the form of thin tabular segregations up to 5 cm long and 1 mm wide, and also as thin streaks in minerals of the eudialyte-eucolite group, of which it sometimes forms complete pseudomorphs, in close association with zirfesite. The catapleiite segregations usually have a finely flaky (to cryptocrystalline) structure. The individual flakes are sometimes gathered into radial aggregates.

The colour is pale cinnamon-brown, in some cases with a pinkish tint. Streak white. Lustre vitreous. Opaque. Perfect cleavage along (0001). Fracture uneven. Specific gravity, according to Vladimirova's data, 2·65.

In thin sections catapleiite is colourless, sometimes yellow or brownish-yellow. Slightly pleochroic in shades of yellow. Optically uniaxial, positive. Semenov reports that a biaxial, negative catapleiite, with optical properties resembling catapleiite from Norway and Greenland, sometimes occurs.

Refractive indices: $Ne = 1·624$, $No = 1·596$, $Ne - No = 0·028$ (Gerasimovskii). Uniaxial and biaxial catapleiite are very similar but not identical in structure (Table 61).

Catapeliite is readily soluble in strong acids without heating. The chemical composition of uniaxial catapleiite (Table 62) is in general expressed by the theoretical formula $Na_2Zr [Si_3O_9] . 2H_2O$ but an alkali deficiency is observable balanced by an excess of water; this is probably due to some leaching of the catapleiite.

Biaxial catapleiite differs from uniaxial in having a lower zirconium and a higher calcium content. It forms, apparently, in the process of replacement of the

TABLE 61 Interplanar spacings of catapleiite

Line no.	uniaxial I	uniaxial d	biaxial I	biaxial d	Line no.	uniaxial I	uniaxial d	biaxial I	biaxial d
1	3	6·36	vw	6·387	21	7	1·492	m	1·488
2	3	5·41	w	5·326	22	5	1·459	vw	1·455
3	8	3·96	s	3·954	23	6	1·420	m	1·408
4	1	3·72	vw	3·920	24	7	1·357	,,	1·345
5	8	3·06	s	3·045	25	3	1·325	vw	1·313
6	9	2·98	,,	2·967	26	4	1·261	,,	1·254
7	8	2·70	,,	2·702	27	3	1·240	,,	1·230
8	2	2·51	vw	2·498	28	2	1·225	,,	1·219
9	8	2·43	,,	2·418	29	4	1·184	,,	1·175
10	1	2·30	—	—	30	2	1·162	,,	1·156
11	4	2·19	w	2·176	31	4	1·148	,,	1·142
12	1	2·08	—	—	32	3	1·121	—	—
13	10	1·976	s	1·968	33	4	1·109	vw	1·103
14	1	1·937	—	—	34	1	1·095	—	—
15	8	1·859	m	1·852	35	3	1·075	—	—
16	1	1·785	—	—	36	1	1·057	—	—
17	9	1·752	s	1·736	37	4	1·050	—	—
18	4	1·656	w	1·674	38	4	1·042	—	—
19	3	1·629	vw	1·620	39	1	1·029	—	—
20	6	1·533	m	1·525					

TABLE 62 Chemical composition of catapleiite

Consti-tuent	Uniaxial catapleiite, Suoluai valley* per cent	Atomic pro-portions	Calculation of atomic ratios			Biaxial catapleiite, Kitkn'yun† per cent	Atomic pro-portions	Calculation of atomic ratios		
SiO_2	44·73	0·745	⎫			46·50	0·776	⎫		
P_2O_5	—	—	⎬0·761	3·04	—3	1·18	0·016	⎬0·828	3·06	—3
Al_2O_3	0·80	0·016	⎭			1·80	0·036	⎭		
ZrO_2	31·24	0·254	⎫			23·91	0·194	⎫		
TiO_2	0·16	0·002	⎪			1·42	0·018	⎪		
Nb_2O_5	—	—	⎬0·264	1·05	—1	0·95	0·008	⎬0·246	0·91	—1
Fe_2O_3	0·48	0·006	⎪			1·87	0·024	⎪		
RE_2O_3	0·24	0·002	⎭			0·39	0·002	⎭		
MgO	0·04	—		—		—	—		—	
MnO	nil	—		—		—	—		—	
CaO	2·06	0·037	⎫			6·44	0·115	⎫		
Na_2O	9·28	0·298	⎬0·495	1·98	—2	4·35	0·140	⎬0·509	1·88	—2
K_2O	0·80	0·018	⎭			2·57	0·054	⎭		
H_2O^+	10·28	<0·142 ⎰1·000				7·52	<0·200 ⎰0·634			
H_2O^-	0·22	0·024	⎬1·024	4·09	—4	1·18	0·130	⎬0·764	2·83	—3
		O =2·816	2·816	11·2	—11		O =2·823	2·823	10·45	—10·5
Total	100·33	—		—		100·08	—		—	
Analyst	Vladimirova					Starostina, 1951				

* Gerasimovskii's data † Semenov's data (1953)

more calcic minerals of the eudialyte-eucolite group (mesodialyte and eucolite). An alkali deficiency is observable in biaxial catapleiite too; when this is compensated for by water the formula for catapleiite takes the form $Na_2Zr [Si_3O_9]$. 1·5 H_2O.

X-ray chemical analysis of catapleiite from the Kitkn'yun pegmatites showed about 0·3 per cent of hafnium, 0·5 per cent of strontium and 0·2 per cent of manganese. Of the rare-earth elements, yttrium, cerium, neodymium and samarium were found. A beryllium oxide content of 0·15 per cent was determined by

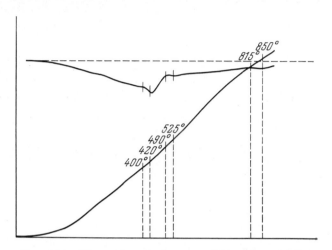

Fig. 151. Thermal analysis curve of biaxial catapleiite

quantitative spectrographic analysis (Semenov). A high aluminium and phosphorus content in biaxial catapleiite seems to be connected with impurities.

Thermal analysis of biaxial catapleiite (Fig. 151) from Kitkn'yun pegmatites (Semenov, 1956₁) gives a curve with one endothermic effect in the 400-420° range, apparently connected with the loss of water.

Catapleiite occurs mainly in the foyaites of the differentiated complex and in the poikilitic sodalite-syenites in places where the zeolitization process has been weak. In the zeolitized parts catapleiite, like lovozerite, is converted, under the influence of zeolitizing solutions, into further alteration products of eudialyte, connected with a still greater loss of alkalis. In the above-mentioned rocks its content does not exceed 0·1 per cent.

In the pegmatites the process of replacement of eudialyte by catapleiite has developed more widely. It is most intensive in the complex replacement pegmatites. Catapleiite is usually closely associated with other secondary products of eudialyte alteration (zirfesite and manganese hydroxides).

15. Zirfesite

$mZrO_2$. nFe_2O_3 . $pSiO_2$. qH_2O; amorph.; sp.gr. 2·70, H. 1

Zirfesite, first discovered and studied by Kostyleva (1945), is one of the commonest alteration products of the Lovozero eudialyte-eucolite minerals. It

FIG. 152. Replacement of eudialyte by zirfesite (dark) along
fissures. ×46. Crossed nicols

usually forms crusts up to 0·5 cm thick on eudialyte and mesodialyte or replaces
them along the cleavages (Fig. 152). Pseudomorphs of zirfesite after these minerals
are found.

Zirfesite is a light-yellow powdery mineral. Its segregations are usually made

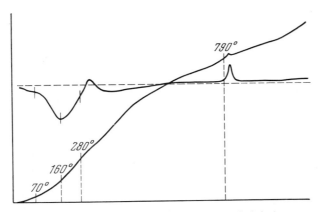

FIG. 153. Thermal analysis curve of zirfesite

up of small flakes (up to 1 mm) with a pearly lustre. The mineral is structureless
to X-ray analysis and optically isotropic. The refractive index varies between
1·60 and 1·65 (Semenov). Zirfesite is readily soluble on heating and gelatinizes
in diluted HCl. A 5 per cent solution of sodium carbonate extracts appreciable
amounts of zirconium and iron from zirfesite; this behaviour, together with the

character of the thermal analysis curve, indicates that zirfesite is one of the amorphous minerals of the allophane group (Kostyleva, 1945).

Comparison of the chemical composition of zirfesite (Table 63) with that of unaltered eudialyte (Table 56) shows that leaching of sodium, calcium, silicon, addition of water and concentration of zirconium, iron and niobium occurs in the process of conversion of eudialyte into zirfesite. As zirfesite is structureless and its chemical composition varies its formula should be written in the oxide form. Recalculation of the chemical analyses shows that its composition is expressed by the formula $2ZrO_2 . Fe_2O_3 . 3SiO_2 . 12H_2O$.

Beryllium, zinc, barium and strontium have been detected by the spectrographic method in pegmatitic zirfesite from various parts of the massif. X-ray chemical analysis performed by Muravitskaya and Voronova showed about 0·3 per cent of hafnium, 0·3 per cent of yttrium, 0·1 per cent of lanthanum, 0·1 per cent of cerium, 0·05 per cent of praseodymium, 0·1 per cent of neodymium and 0·2 per cent of strontium.

A pronounced endothermic effect can be observed on the thermal analysis curve for zirfesite (Fig. 153) in the 70-160° interval, owing to the removal of water, and exothermic effects at 280 and 790°. Experiments in dehydrating zirfesite, performed by Kostyleva, showed that on heating to 135°, 20·96 per cent of the water is lost; at 300° the water loss ceases.

Zirfesite occurs in the rocks of all the complexes, exclusively in surface outcrops, the greatest amounts being found in the eudialytic lujavrites. In the peg-

TABLE 63 Chemical composition of zirfesite

Constituent	Angvundaschorr			Vavnbed
	per cent	Atomic proportions	Calculation of atomic ratios	per cent
SiO_2	21·27	0·3534	⎱0·3654 3·04 —3	22·06
TiO_2	0·96	0·0120		1·33
ZrO_2	30·47	0·2473	⎱0·2563 2·13 —2	30·33
$(Nb, Ta)_2O_5$	2·40	0·0090		—
Fe_2O_3	14·27	0·0893		21·44*
Al_2O_3	1·63	0·0160		—
ΣRE_2O_3	2·12	0·0094		—
MnO	0·24	0·0034	0·1347 1·12 —1	—
CaO	0·14	0·0025		1·30
MgO	0·57	0·0141		trace
Na_2O	—	—	—	—
K_2O	0·21	0·0022	—	—
H_2O^+	9·66	⎱1·4337	1·4337 11·97 —12	23·44
H_2O^-	16·17			
Total	100·11	—	—	99·90
Analyst	Tumilovich			Kazakova
Reference	Kostyleva (1945)			Semenov (1953)

* Nb_2O_5, RE_2O_3, etc. are included with Fe_2O_3, as the analysis was performed on a very small sample.

matites it has been detected on Vavnbed, Flora, Kedykvyrpakhk, Alluaiv, Lepkhe-Nel'm, Mannepakhk, Kitkn'yun and other mountains. Large segregations of this mineral have been noted in pegmatites containing segregations of eudialyte and mesodialyte of various sizes.

The fact that the zirfesite is restricted to surface outcrops, together with its structureless condition and its close association with the secondary alteration products of zirconium minerals up to and including iron and manganese oxide, justify the assumption that the replacement of minerals of the eudialyte-eucolite group by zirfesite occurs under hypergene conditions.

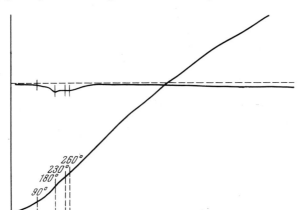

FIG. 154. Thermal analysis curve of elpidite

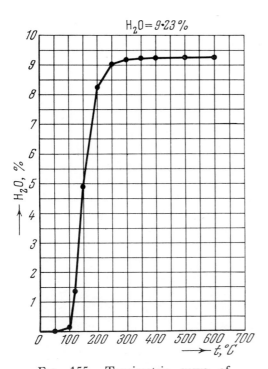

FIG. 155. Tensimetric curve of elpidite dehydration

TABLE 64

Interplanar spacings of elpidite

Line no.	Narsarsuk		Lovozero	
	I	d	I	d
1	3	6·94	6	6·95
2	3	6·55	3	6·457
3	2	5·13	6	5·11
4	4	4·82	3	4·81
5	3	4·14	5	4·11
6	2	3·60	5	3·55
7	10	3·26	10	3·25
8	7	3·12	8	3·10
9	5	2·93	8	2·94
10	4	2·65	6	2·66
11	5	2·52	8	2·54
12	5	2·39	7	2·39
13	1	2·16	2	2·17
14	3	2·09	4	2·09
15	4	2·00	5	2·01
16	7	1·945	8	1·943
17	5	1·827	5	1·825
18	7	1·759	8	1·757
19	2	1·727	4	1·720
20	1	1·685	3	1·684
21	7	1·590	8	1·590
22	2	1·560	3	1·500
23	6	1·492	7	1·484
24	5	1·466	6	1·467
25	6	1·435	7	1·435
26	7	1·352	8	1·352
27	2	1·328	3	1·328
28	3	1·193	4	1·185
29	2	1·174	3	1·186
30	5	1·129	7	1·122
31	2	1·115	5	1·114
32	5	4·089	5	1·088
33	4	1·075	4	1·075

16. Elpidite

$Na_2ZrSi_6O_{15}$. $3H_2O$; orthorhomb.; sp.gr. 2·62, H. 7

Elpidite was first found [at Lovozero] by Semenov and Tikhonenkov in a pegmatitic vein on Kuftn'yun and later in the Alluaiv pegmatites. The description given here is based on the data given by these investigators (Tikhonenkov et al., 1957).

Elpidite occurs in the form of finely acicular and elongate-prismatic crystals measuring up to 1×0.2 cm and also as radiate-fibrous growths and spherulites up to 1·5 cm in diameter (see Fig. 50). The colour is white, sometimes brownish. Lustre vitreous. Cleavage distinct on (110). Specific gravity 2·615.

In thin sections elpidite is colourless, with high relief. The interference colour is second-order blue. Biaxial, positive. Extinction straight. Elongation negative; $2V = 72\text{-}84°$; $Ng = 1·575$; $Nm = 1·566$; $Np = 1·561$; $Ng - Np = 0·014$.

The X-ray powder patterns of the Alluaiv pegmatitic elpidite and of standard elpidite from the alkaline pegmatites of Narsarsuk (Greenland) are similar (Table 64).

The chemical composition of these elpidites (Table 65) is also similar. Recalculation of the chemical analyses shows that the composition of the Lovozero elpidite is in general expressed by the conventional formula $NaZrSi_6O_{15}$. $3H_2O$. Some excess of water is probably due to leaching of the material analysed. Beryllium, copper, barium, strontium, magnesium, manganese, aluminium, yttrium and hafnium have been detected spectroscopically in elpidite.

TABLE 65 Chemical composition of elpidite

Constituent	Lovozero				Narsarsuk			
	per cent	Atomic pro-portions	Calculation of atomic ratios			per cent	Atomic pro-portions	Calculation of atomic ratios	
SiO_2	57·13	0·9507	0·9507	5·86	—6	59·44	0·9891	0·9891 5·99	—6
ZrO_2	20·33	0·1650				20·48	0·1662		
TiO_2	0·05	0·0006				trace	—		
Nb_2O_5	1·43	0·0106	0·1778	1·09	—1	—	—	0·1680 1·02	—1
Fe_2O_3	0·14	0·0016				0·14	0·0018		
CaO	0·43	0·0076				0·17	0·0030		
Na_2O	9·89	0·3190	0·3306	2·04	—2	10·41	0·3036	0·3094 1·87	—2
K_2O	0·19	0·0040				0·13	0·0028		
H_2O	9·94	1·1034	1·1034	6·81	—7	9·61	1·0668	1·0668 6·46	—6
F	0·12	0·0063	—			—	—	—	
Cl	0·18	0·0050	—			0·15	0·0042	—	
		O = 2·9767	2·9767	18·34	—18			O = 3·0026 18·2	—18
Total	99·83	—	—			100·53	—	—	
− O = (F, Cl)$_2$	−0·09	—	—			−0·04	—	—	
—	99·74	—	—			100·49	—	—	
Analyst	Kazakova, 1952					Lindstrom			
Reference	Tikhonenkov et al. (1957)								

The thermal analysis curve (Fig. 154) shows a pronounced endothermic effect in the 90-260° interval, because of the elimination of water. Experiments in the dehydration of elpidite (Fig. 155) performed by Karpova have shown that when the mineral is heated to 200° it loses up to 8 per cent of its water and that at 300° water loss ceases. This indicates the zeolitic character of the water.

As to the nature of their formation primary and secondary elpidite differ, the latter being more extensively developed. Elpidite is closely associated with catapleiite, more rarely with zirfesite, and develops during the replacement of eudialyte-eucolite minerals. Primary elpidite is associated with albite. In the pegmatitic vein on Kuftn'yun it occasionally occurs in the central albititic zone, where it forms druses in the albite cavities.

17. Titan-lavenite

$(Na,Ca,Mn)_3(Zr,Ti) [SiO_4]_2 (O,F_2)$; mon.; sp.gr. 3·41—3·55; H. 5—6

This variety of låvenite was first discovered by Kutukova in 1936 in aplite streaks in the middle part of the Koklukhtiuai valley. These streaks consist of microcline (87·4 per cent) and titan-låvenite (10·4 per cent) unevenly dispersed

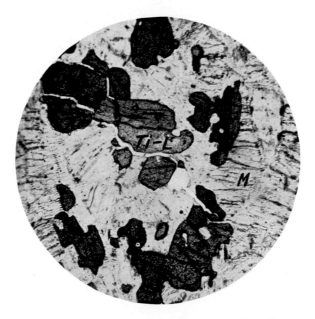

FIG. 156. Titan-låvenite (Ti-L) in microcline
(M). ×42. Without analyser

in the microcline mass (Fig. 156). Sphene, hornblende, pyrrhotine, mangan-ilmenite and, in one instance, sphalerite occur as accessory minerals. Titan-låvenite, unlike låvenite, contains 11·3 per cent of titanium oxide, which gives it its name. This mineral was later found by Semenov in the poikilitic hydrosodalite-syenites and their associated pegmatites (river Muruai valley). In the poikilitic hydrosodalite-syenites and pegmatites titan-låvenite is closely associated with

TABLE 66 Interplanar spacings of titan-låvenite and låvenite
(Analyst Sludskaya. Exposure 18 hours, Fe-radiation, $D = 57\cdot9$ mm, $d = 0\cdot6$ mm)

Line no.	Titan-låvenite		Låvenite		Line no.	Titan-låvenite		Låvenite		Line no.	Titan-låvenite		Låvenite	
	I	d	I	d		I	d	I	d		I	d	I	d
1	4	7·12–5·98	—	—	10	3	2·42	—	—	19	2	1·692	1	1·696
2	5	3·97	1	3·95	11	2	2·38	2	2·34	20	4	1·649	3	1·655
3	2	3·59	1	3·57	12	1	2·29	—	—	21	3	1·579	1	1·592
4	1	3·32	—	—	13	3	2·20	2	2·21	22	1	1·560	—	—
5	7	3·21	4	3·21	14	5	2·00	3	2·01	23	1	1·540	1	1·543
6	1	3·09	—	—	15	5	1·792	2	1·802	24	2	1·523	2	1·527
7	10	2·89	7	2·91	16	2	1·773	1	1·778	25	2	1·497	1	1·509
8	9	2·82	6	2·82	17	3	1·745	3	1·754	26	1	1·396	2	1·402
9	2	2·48	—	—	18	1	1·718	2	1·729	27	1	1·241	—	—

sphene, magnetite, calcite, fluorite and seidozerite. The mineral is described from data given by Kutukova (1940) and Semenov (Semenov *et al.*, 1958).

Titan-låvenite is represented by xenomorphic grains up to 1-2 cm in size. The colour is brownish-red. Streak yellow. Lustre vitreous. Fracture uneven. Opaque to semi-transparent. Brittle. Melts readily before the blow-pipe into a light-brown glass. In thin sections well-marked cleavage in one direction is

TABLE 67 Chemical composition of titan-låvenite

Constituent	Kokluktiuai valley				Muruai valley	Låvenite from Langesundfjord Norway
	per cent	Atomic proportions	Calculation of atomic ratios		per cent	per cent
SiO_2	30·92	0·514	0·514	2·00 —2	30·94	29·63
TiO_2	11·30	0·141			5·28	2·35
ZrO_2	16·72	0·137	0·302	1·17 —1	23·20	28·79
$(Nb, Ta)_2O_5$	3·01	0·022			2·97	5·20
Fe_2O_3	0·12	0·002			2·29	4·73
FeO	4·89	0·068			3·73	—
MnO	10·34	0·145			6·00	5·59
CaO	10·92	0·194	0·751	2·93 —3	13·61	9·70
K_2O	trace	—			0·11	—
Na_2O	10·70	0·344			9·74	10·77
H_2O^-	—	—	—		0·96	2·24
F	1·55	0·082	0·232	0·9 —1	2·41	—
		$O = \begin{cases} 0·150 \\ 2·031 \end{cases}$	2·031	7·9 —8		
Total	100·47				101·24	99·00
$-O = F_2$	−0·65	—	—		−1·00	—
—	99·82	—	—		100·24	—
Analyst	Burova, 1940				Kazakova, 1954	Kleve, 1890
Reference	Kutukova (1940)				Semenov *et al.* (1958)	

visible. Twins often form parallel with the cleavage. Fedorov universal stage measurements: BNg=21°30′; BNm=84°30′; BNp=70°30′; B coincides with the pole of the composition plane and with the pole of the cleavage. Refractive indices: Ng 1·760; Nm 1·746; Np 1·720; $Ng-Np$ 0·040; $2V$=73-80°. Optically negative. Distinct pleochroism: Ng orange-yellow, Nm slightly greenish-yellow, Np pale-yellow with greenish tint; absorption system $Ng>Nm>Np$. The sign of the principal zone is negative. The X-ray powder pattern of Lovozero titan-låvenite is similar to that of the låvenite from South Norway (Table 66).

Titan-låvenite does not dissolve in HNO_3 and H_2SO_4 but partially dissolves in HCl on heating. The chemical analyses (Table 67) show that Lovozero titan-låvenite differs from Norwegian låvenite in having a smaller zirconium oxide content and a considerably higher titanium and manganese oxide content. The relative ZrO_2 deficiency is offset by a high TiO_2 content, owing to the isomorphous substitution of zirconium by titanium. The high manganese content in Lovozero titan-låvenite accords with data given by Brögger (1890), who notes that the darkest varieties of this mineral contain most manganese and iron.

Recalculation of the chemical analyses shows that the composition of titan-låvenite is well expressed by the conventional chemical formula for låvenite: (Na, Ca, Mn)$_3$ (Zr, Ti) [SiO$_4$]$_2$(O, F$_2$).

Tin, aluminium, beryllium, magnesium, chromium and lead have been detected in titan-låvenite by the spectrographic method. Shevalevskii determined the presence of 0·3 per cent HfO_2 in titan-lavenite in the Muruai valley pegmatites by spectrographic analysis.

Titan-låvenite is one of the earliest minerals. It formed before microcline, hornblende and biotite and almost at the same time as sphene, though grains of it are sometimes included in the latter.

18. Seidozerite

Na$_8$Mn$_2$Zr$_3$ [SiO$_4$] $_4$F$_4$; mon.; sp.gr. 3·472; H. 4—5

Seidozerite was discovered by Semenov (Semenov et al., 1958) and the description given here is based on his data. It occurs in the alkalic pegmatites in the form of spheroidal growths of elongated reddish-yellow to brown-red crystals measuring 5×1 cm. Semi-transparent. Lustre vitreous. Brittle. Cleavage

TABLE 68 Interplanar spacings of seidozerite
(Analyst Sludskaya. Exposure 18 hours, Fe-radiation D=57·9 mm, d=0·6 mm)

Line no.	I	d	Line no.	I	d	Line no.	I	d
1	2	3·29	10	3	1·761	19	2	1·459
2	1	3·15	11	1	1·714	20	2	1·426
3	10	2·97	12	2	1·677	21	3	1·386
4	7	2·87	13	4	1·633	22	2	1·367
5	4	2·58	14	1	1·612	23	2	1·276
6	3	2·43	15	1	1·572	24	2	1·216
7	3	2·25	16	3	1·527	25	1	1·200
8	1	2·14	17	1	1·509			
9	7	1·830	18	2	1·481			

perfect along (001). Parameters of unit cell: $a_0 = 5.53 \pm 0.03$ A; $b_0 = 7.10 \pm 0.04$ A; $c_0 = 18.30 \pm 0.10$ A; $\beta = 102°43'$; $a : b : c$ ratio $0.779 : 1 : 2.58$. Crystals elongated along y-axis (Fig. 157).

The most commonly developed crystallographic forms are $c(001)$, $a(100)$, $n(203)$, $m(011)$ and $p(111)$. Seidozerite has no powder pattern analogues (Table 68).

The mineral is biaxial, positive. Refractive indices: Ng 1.830; Nm 1.758; Np 1.725; $Ng - Np$ 0.105; $2V = 68°$. Orientation of optical indicatrix: $Ng = a$,

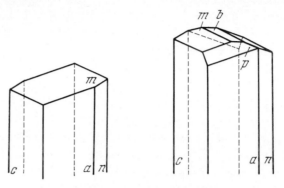

Fig. 157. Seidozerite crystals

$Nm: c = 13°$, $Np = b$. Strong pleochroism: Ng—light-yellow, Nm—red, Np—dark-red.

In chemical composition seidozerite (Table 69) belongs to the minerals of the wöhlerite group and is nearest to titan-låvenite (see Table 67).

By quantitative X-ray spectrographic analysis Shevalevskii established 0.4 per

TABLE 69 Chemical composition of seidozerite

Constituent	Content, per cent	Atomic proportions
SiO_2	31.40	0.523
ZrO_2	23.14	0.188
TiO_2	13.16	0.164
Nb_2O_5	0.60	0.004
Al_2O_3	1.38	0.027
Fe_2O_3	2.85	0.036
FeO	1.06	0.015
MnO	4.22	0.060
MgO	1.79	0.045
CaO	2.80	0.050
Na_2O	14.55	0.469
K_2O	nil	—
H_2O	0.60	0.067
F	3.56	0.187
Total	101.11	
$-O = F_2$	-1.49	—
—	99.62	—
Analyst	Kazakova, 1954-1956	

cent HfO_2 in seidozerite. In addition, tin, lead, chromium, beryllium and gallium were detected by spectrographic analysis.

Compared with titan-låvenite, seidozerite is characterized by a higher titanium and sodium content and a lower calcium content.

The mineral occurs in the poikilitic nepheline-syenite pegmatites in the upper reaches of the rivers Muruai and Uel'kuai, in close association with microcline and aegirine. Under the influence of hydrothermal solutions it is replaced by a mineral of the catapleiite type.

19. Zircon

$ZrSiO_4$; tetr.; sp.gr. 4·55—4·67; H. 7·5

Zircon is a characteristic mineral of the contaminated rocks and hybrid pegmatites and also of metasomatic zones developed at the contact of the massif. It occurs in the foyaites and lujavrites at the top of the differentiated complex and in the eudialytic lujavrites of the central part of the massif, in places where assimilation of the roof has resulted in heavy alteration. Near xenoliths in the foyaites

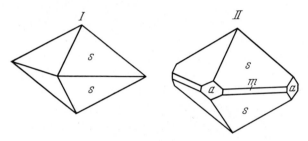

FIG. 158. Habits of zircon crystals (I, II)

and lujavrites the zircon content varies from 0·2 to 3-5 per cent, rises even higher in the contaminated eudialytic lujavrites, but gradually decreases with distance from the xenoliths and completely disappears 1-3 m from the contacts; in the hybrid pegmatites it sometimes makes up as much as 15-20 per cent. The mineral is most widely developed in the rocks and pegmatites of Malyi Punkaruaiv, in the Koklukhtiuai valley, in the upper reaches of the Suoluaiv valley, on Kuivchorr, on the north-eastern slope of Flora and in other regions.

In the rocks zircon occurs in the form of xenomorphic segregations measuring up to 0·5 × 0·4 × 0·3 cm, or, more rarely, in the form of small dipyramidal crystals. In the pegmatites and metasomatic zones it forms dipyramidal crystals measuring 1 × 1 × 1 mm to 2 cm in diameter. Two types of dipyramidal crystals are found (Fig. 158), the fundamental form of which is a tetragonal dipyramid s(111); in the second type of crystal, apart from the dipyramid s(111) the forms m(110) and a(100) are slightly developed.

Zircon is light and dark cinnamon-brown in colour. Cleavage imperfect. Lustre vitreous to brilliant. Fracture uneven. Semi-transparent to opaque. Specific gravity 4·555 for zircon from contaminated foyaites and 4·60—4·7 for zircon from the Flora-Vavnbed hybrid pegmatites.

In thin sections zircon is greyish-brown. No pleochroism. Optically uniaxial, positive. Characteristic high relief and very strong birefringence. Refractive indices: Ne 1·98; No 1·91, $Ne - No$ 0·07 (for rock zircon) and Ne 2·04, No 1·96 (for pegmatitic zircon). In thin sections the crystals sometimes show a zonal structure.

Recalculation of the chemical analyses (Table 70) shows that the composition of zircon is expressed by the theoretical formula $ZrSiO_4$. The rock and pegmatitic varieties are of similar chemical composition. A hafnium content of about 3 per cent and an yttrium content of about 2 per cent have been established by X-ray spectrographic analysis (K. I. Narbutt).

Rare earths separated by chemical means from zircon found in the contact zones of Vavnbed were subjected to X-ray spectrographic analysis by R. L. Barinskii with the following results expressed as percentages of the total rare-earth ($R.E._2O_3$) content: La_2O_3—0·5; Ce_2O_3—1·1; Pr_2O_3—0·4; Nd_2O_3—1·4; Sm_2O_3—2·3; Eu_2O_3—0·6; Gd_2O_3—6; Tb_2O_3—1·3; Dy_2O_3—13; Ho_2O_3—3·3; Er_2O_3—11; Tu_2O_3—1·7; Yb_2O_3—11; Lu_2O_3—2 and Y_2O_3—40. The rare earths in zircon are thus represented mainly by elements of the yttrium subgroup; cerium and lanthanum are found in minute quantities. Apart from the above-mentioned elements, manganese, beryllium, niobium and copper have been detected spectroscopically.

Both in the pegmatites and in the rocks zircon is closely associated with ilmenite, sphene, apatite and biotite. It fills up interstices between crystals of potassium feldspar and contains inclusions of aegirine, apatite, sphene and ilmenite. Biotite, natrolite, aegirine II, analcite and hydrargillite usually accom-

TABLE 70   Chemical composition of zircon

Constituent	From contaminated foyaite, Koklukhtiuai			From hybrid pegmatite, Flora		
	per cent	Atomic proportions	Calculated atomic ratios	per cent	Atomic proportions	Calculated atomic ratios
SiO_2	32·60	0·5426	} 0·5578 1·01 —1	34·16	0·5688	0·5688 1·00 —1
Al_2O_3	0·78	0·0152		—	—	—
TiO_2	0·16	0·0020		—	—	
ZrO_2	65·08	0·5281		61·42	0·4985	
ThO_2	not det.	—		0·05	0·0002	
RE_2O_3	not found	—	} 0·5500 1·00 —1	1·65	0·0100	} 0·5803 1·02 —1
Fe_2O_3	0·80	0·0100		0·38	0·0048	
MgO	0·12	0·0028		—	—	
CaO	0·40	0·0071		2·50	0·0046	
H_2O	not det.	—		0·20	0·0222	
		$O = 2·1931$	2·1931 3·98 —4	—	$O = 2·2464$	2·2464 3·95 —4
Total	99·94	—	—	100·36	—	—
Specific gravity	4·554			4·60		
Analyst	Burova, 1952			Kazakova		

modate themselves to the shapes of its segregations. In the metasomatic zone on the eastern slope of Vavnbed, which conforms with the contact between the Lovozero massif and the enclosing granite-gneisses, zircon is usually associated with albite, forming regular crystals in its miarolitic cavities.

In the pegmatites of the central part of the massif zircon inclusions can be seen in late fibrous aegirine and in the albite and analcite of the central replacement zones. Zircon is sharply idiomorphic in relation to natrolite.

On the basis of the mineral paragenesis characteristic of zircon we may conclude that, as a result of the assimilation of augite-porphyrites rich in Fe, Mn, Mg, Ti and Ca and of silicon-rich granite-gneisses, the ratio of the main chemical elements (Si, Al, Na, K, Ca and others) in the alkali magma has changed and that this has led to the formation of minerals (zircon, ilmenite, biotite etc.) not common in the main line of descent of Lovozero rocks.

Zircon does not form in normal alkali rocks because of the high alkali content and low silica content in the magma. When an alkali magma is enriched in silicon during the reworking of granite-gneisses zirconium plays the part of a cation and forms a zirconium silicate, zircon.

II. Niobium and Titanium Minerals

In the Lovozero massif niobium and titanium as a rule enter into the same minerals. Some thirty niobium and titanium minerals have been counted in the massif (see Table 28), only ten of them (loparite, metaloparite, lomonosovite, murmanite, ramsayite, lamprophyllite, sphene, neptunite, chinglusuite and manganilmenite) being characteristic of the non-pegmatitic rocks. The commonest are loparite, lomonosovite, murmanite, ramsayite and lamprophyllite. The rest occur only rarely.

20. Loparite

$(Ce,Na,Ca)_2(Ti,Nb)_2O_6$; cub.; sp.gr. 4·64—4·89; H. 6

Loparite was first detected in the Lovozero massif by Ramsay and Hackman and described by them (1889-1894) as mineral No. 1. It was later studied by workers from the USSR Academy of Sciences and named loparite. In the rocks of the massif loparite forms three types of crystallization: (1) penetration twins on the Fluorite law, (2) monocrystals in the form of cubes and octahedra and (3) xeno-morphic segregations.

The most widespread are the loparite twins, of which the fundamental forms are the cube and the octahedron. The octahedral faces are not always present and the degree of their development varies. In some twins they are barely perceptible, in others they have developed equally with the faces of a cube, in yet others they are more strongly developed. According to V. P. Dubinina's data loparite twins from the Lovozero rocks are identical in the number and character of their forms with loparite twins from the Khibiny tundras (Fig. 159). According to Kuznetsov

(1925) and Chirva (1937), the outward shape of the loparite crystals is defined by a cube face $c(100)$ and an octahedral face $p(111)$, which in some cases are modified by faces $a(190)$, $\beta(180)$, $\tau(170)$, 'c'(160), $f(140)$, $g(250)$, $e(120)$, $h(350)$, $b(230)$, $i(340)$, $d(110)$, $k(141)$, $m(131)$, $q(121)$, $t(343)$ etc.

The diameter of loparite twins varies from $0 \cdot 1$ mm to 1 cm and depends on the grain size of the rock-forming minerals. The smallest loparite crystals are characteristic of the urtites ($0 \cdot 1$-$0 \cdot 5$ mm); those in the urtites of the upper horizons in the differentiated complex are bigger than those in the urtites of the lower

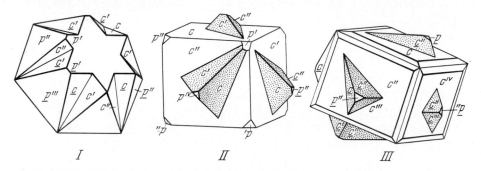

$$I \qquad\qquad II \qquad\qquad III$$

FIG. 159. Habits of loparite crystals from the Khibiny massif (Bonshtedt, 1937)

I—Loparite twin with equal development of cube and octahedron in both parts; II—loparite twin with predominance of cube in both parts; III—loparite twin with different developments in the two parts

horizons. In each urtite horizon the loparite grains are biggest in those parts that are richest in the mineral.

The biggest loparite crystals are characteristic of the poikilitic syenites and are usually $0 \cdot 2$-$0 \cdot 4$ cm in diameter but not infrequently $0 \cdot 5$-1 cm. The biggest crystals occur in the pegmatoid varieties of these rocks.

Loparite in the form of monocrystals—cubes and octahedra—is extremely rare in the Lovozero massif. Monocrystals were found by Gerasimovskii in the eudialytic lujavrites at the top of Kedykvyrpakhk.

Xenomorphic grains of loparite measuring $0 \cdot 8 \times 0 \cdot 3$ mm are present in very small amounts in all the rock varieties. Such loparite is most widespread in the foyaites of the differentiated complex and in some varieties of the poikilitic syenites.

Colour black. Streak cinnamon-brownish to brown. Lustre metallic. Cleavage lacking. Fracture uneven. Opaque. Specific gravity of loparite in the rocks of the differentiated complex increases with depth. According to Gaertner the structure is of perovskite type, the pseudocubic unit cell edge $a = 3 \cdot 54 \pm 0 \cdot 018$ A. Co-ordinates: Ti(Nb)—1/2 1/2 1/2; Ga(Ce, Na)—000; O—1/2 1/2 0; 1/2 0 1/2; 0 1/2 1/2.

In thin sections well-shaped twinned loparite crystals can often be observed (Fig. 160) and, more rarely, xenomorphic grains (Fig. 161). In transmitted light it has a black tint and in thin sections a dark-brown tint. Crystals with zonal coloration occur, the central parts being more intensely coloured than the margins. The mineral is isotropic. Anisotropic patches can sometimes be detected in very

FIG. 160. Loparite crystals (black) in rocks of the Lovozero massif; N—nepheline; Ae—aegirine. ×20. Without analyser

FIG. 161. Xenomorphic segregations of loparite (black) in poikilitic nepheline-syenite. ×20. Without analyser

thin sections. In reflected light loparite is light-grey or white with a creamy tinge (Fig. 162). Brownish-red internal reflections are characteristic, coinciding with cracks in the crystal. Under oblique light the powder is brown. The refractive index varies from 2·26 to 2·38; according to Dubinina it increases to 2·44 after ignition.

Loparite is decomposed by anhydrous hydrofluoric acid but is less soluble in H_2SO_4.

As can be seen from Table 71, the chemical composition of the twinned loparite from the rocks of the differentiated complex follows a regular pattern of

FIG. 162. Loparite twins in reflected light. × 20

change in the vertical direction. Loparite from the rocks of the lower horizons usually contains more rare earths and less niobium than that from the top horizons (Bykova, 1941). According to Gerasimovskii there is in loparite a definite relationship between the content of niobium and titanium, niobium and rare earths, rare earths and strontium. A higher niobium content leads to a lower titanium content and, conversely, a lower niobium content leads to a higher TiO_2 and $R.E._2O_3$ content. The tenor of rare earths varies inversely with the strontium content. These conclusions of Bykova and Gerasimovskii have been confirmed by Tumilovich's investigations.

According to these workers' data, in the loparite from the rocks of the differentiated complex the following changes in the proportions of the principal components are observed:

(a) the niobium pentoxide content decreases downwards from 10·28 to 7·09 per cent, the amount of tantalum pentoxide remaining roughly constant;

TABLE 71 Chemical compositions of loparites from rocks of the differentiated complex (per cent)

Constituent	From lujavrites			From upper horizon urtite		From malignites		From lower horizon urtite		
	Vavnbed		Ninchurt	Ninchurt	Vavnbed	Vavnbed	Engpor	Engpor	Suoluaiv	Kuftn'yun
	analysis 1	analysis 2	analysis 3	analysis 4	analysis 5	analysis 6	analysis 7	analysis 8	analysis 9	analysis 10
SiO_2	0·38	not det.	not det.	0·44	0·46	0·30	not det.	0·40	not det.	not det.
TiO_2	39·65	,, ,,	,, ,,	39·88	not det.	40·20	,, ,,	40·70	,, ,,	40·62
ZrO_2	nil	,, ,,	,, ,,	nil	,, ,,	nil	,, ,,	nil	,, ,,	not det.
P_2O_5	not det.	,, ,,	,, ,,	not det.	,, ,,	not det.	,, ,,	0·08	,, ,,	,, ,,
Nb_2O_5	9·74 } 10·49	10·08	10·06	9·38 } 10·10	10·28	8·87 } 9·52	9·46	8·04 } 8·66	8·44	8·82
Ta_2O_5	0·75			0·72		0·65		0·62		
ThO_2	0·76			0·74		0·64		0·62		
Ce_2O_3	16·04 } 31·56	32·28 [1]	not det.	16·26 } 31·92	32·34 [2]	16·37 } 32·21	not det.	17·50 } 34·12	35·06 [3]	34·71 [4]
ΣCe_2O_3	14·76			14·92		15·20		16·00		
ΣY_2O_3	nil	not det.	,, ,,	nil	nil	nil	,, ,,	nil	not det.	not det.
Al_2O_3	0·20	,, ,,	,, ,,	0·14	not det.	0·20	,, ,,	0·20	,, ,,	,, ,,
Fe_2O_3	0·36	,, ,,	,, ,,	0·40	,, ,,	0·36	,, ,,	0·56	,, ,,	,, ,,
FeO	nil			nil	,, ,,	nil	,, ,,	nil		
MnO	nil	,, ,,	,, ,,	nil	,, ,,	nil	,, ,,	nil	,, ,,	,, ,,
CaO	5·00	4·92	,, ,,	5·08	5·00	5·30	,, ,,	4·86	4·82	5·10
SrO	3·42	3·20	,, ,,	3·30	3·20	3·14	,, ,,	2·10	2·00	2·20
MgO	nil	not det.	,, ,,	nil	not det.	nil	,, ,,	nil	not det.	not det.
K_2O	0·13	,, ,,	,, ,,	0·17	,, ,,	0·28	,, ,,	0·20	,, ,,	,, ,,
Na_2O	8·32	,, ,,	,, ,,	8·50	,, ,,	8·10	,, ,,	8·20	,, ,,	,, ,,
F	not det.	,, ,,	,, ,,	0·03	,, ,,	not det.	,, ,,	not det.	,, ,,	,, ,,
Other	0·57	,, ,,	,, ,,	0·20	,, ,,	0·64	,, ,,	0·48	,, ,,	,, ,,
Total	100·08	—	—	100·16	—	100·25	—	100·56	—	—
Specific gravity[5]	—	4·77	—	4·79	4·87	4·77	—	4·60	4·82	4·82
Analyst										

Bykova, 1941

[1-4] This amount includes ΣY_2O_3.
[5] The specific gravity of loparite in analyses 2, 5, 6, 9, 10 was determined by Yakovleva (Kola base of the USSR Academy of Sciences); in analysis 4 by Gerasimovskii.

(b) in the same direction there is a regular increase in the total rare-earth content, from 30·00 to 35·29 per cent;

(c) the calcium and strontium contents diminish with depth: CaO from 5·6 to 3·7 per cent, SrO from 3·42 to 1·76 per cent.

In addition, Tumilovich has established that the chemical composition of the loparite from various parts of the same horizon, or from different rocks in any particular three-component stratal group, is very similar. This once again confirms that the rocks of each stratal group are genetically closely related.

The chemical composition of the pegmatitic loparite resembles that of the rock loparite (Table 72).

In monocrystalline loparite (Table 73), as compared with the twinned loparite (see Tables 71 and 72) there is a high niobium pentoxide content (roughly 3 per cent more Nb_2O_5) and a correspondingly lower titanium oxide content. No inference, however, should be drawn from this fact, since the loparites taken for analysis were from various rocks. It should be noted that in the loparite forming xenomorphic segregations in the foyaites of the differentiated complex (Table 73)

TABLE 72 Chemical composition of loparite from pegmatites (per cent)

Constituent	Ninchurt, from pegmatite	Flora		Lepkhe-nel'm, from pegmatite
		From pegmatite	From mesocratic lujavrite	
SiO_2	0·27	1·52	1·56	0·39
TiO_2	39·24	38·54	39·12	41·45
ZrO_2	not determined	not determined	not determined	not determined
Nb_2O_5	10·82 }11·48	11·34	10·08	8·00
Ta_2O_5	0·66			
ThO_2	0·67	0·87	0·00	0·39
Ce_2O_3	16·29			—
ΣCe_2O_3	15·55 }32·97	30·65	32·62	33·85
ΣY_2O_3	0·46			
Al_2O_3	nil	0·10	0·42	0·99
Fe_2O_3	} 0·06	0·15	0·48	
FeO		not determined	not determined	1·14
MnO	not determined	trace	0·30	not determined
MgO	,, ,,	not determined	not determined	,, ,,
CaO	5·26	3·48	3·67	5·46
SrO	0·62	4·38	3·92	not determined
K_2O	0·76	trace	trace	1·50
Na_2O	9·06	8·22	7·84	6·96
F	not determined	not determined	not determined	not determined
Cl	,, ,,	,, ,,	,, ,,	,, ,,
H_2O	,, ,,	,, ,,	,, ,,	,, ,,
Insoluble residue	,, ,,	1·03	0·24	,, ,,
Total	99·72	100·28	100·25	100·13
Specific gravity	4·77			
Analyst	Burova	Tumilovich		Burova
Investigator	Gerasimovskii	Borodin	—	Semenov

more niobium pentoxide and tantalum was detected (10·5 per cent) than in the twinned loparite from the urtites of the same horizon.

Gaertner (1930), on the basis of X-ray structural investigation, suggested the formula $(Ti, Nb)_2(Na, Ce, Ca)_2O_6$. Borneman (1947) later derived a general formula for this mineral in the form $A_2B_2O_6$, where $A = Na$, Ca, R.E., $B = Ti$, Nb and so forth. She regards loparite as an isomorphous compound of the components $NaCeTi_2O_6$, $Na_2Nb_2O_6$ and $Ca_2Ti_2O_6$.

Barinskii's X-ray spectrographic analysis showed that the rare earths were represented in loparite mainly by the cerium group (Semenov, Barinskii, 1958): La_{25} $Ce_{53·25}$ Pr_6 Md_{14} $Sm_{0·9}$ $Ev_{0·08}$ $Gd_{0·56}$ $Tb_{0·037}$ $Dy_{0·12}$ $Ho_{0·008}$ $Er_{0·016}$ $Tu_{0·003}$ $Yb_{0·008}$ $Lu_{0·002}$ $Y_{0·008}$ where the total $R.E._2O_3$ is taken as 100.

In the loparite from the rocks and pegmatites of various parts of the massif (Lepkhe-Nel'm, Alluaiv, Flora, Kuftn'yun, the Chinglusuai valley and elsewhere), manganese, vanadium, copper, beryllium, lead, zirconium and tin have been detected spectroscopically.

Loparite is a characteristic mineral of the rocks in the differentiated complex

TABLE 73 Chemical composition of loparite from monocrystals and xenomorphic grains (per cent)

Constituent	From eudialytic lujavrite of Kedykvyrpakhk*				From foyaite of lower part of massif
	Cubes			Octahedra	Xenomorphic grains
SiO_2	0·40	not determined	not determined	0·41	0·33
TiO_2	38·31	,, ,,	,, ,,	38·50	41·00
Ta_2O_5	0·62 }13·43	}13·20	13·06	0·77 }13·40	10·50
Nb_2O_5	12·81			12·63	
ThO_2	0·57			0·46	not determined
Ce_2O_3	15·59 }31·24	not determined	not determined	15·35 }31·53	18·18
La_2O_3	15·08			15·72	15·92
Al_2O_3	not determined	,, ,,	,, ,,	not determined	not determined
Fe_2O_3	}0·20	,, ,,	,, ,,	0·56	1·65
FeO		,, ,,	,, ,,		not determined
MnO	not determined	,, ,,	,, ,,	not determined	,, ,,
MgO	0·42	,, ,,	,, ,,	0·16	trace
CaO	3·74	,, ,,	6·32	3·18	3·00
SrO	2·71	,, ,,	not determined	3·14	not determined
Na_2O	8·78	,, ,,	,, ,,	8·71	7·96
K_2O	0·27	,, ,,	,, ,,	0·45	0·92
H_2O	0·20	,, ,,	,, ,,	0·20	0·00
F	not determined	,, ,,	,, ,,	not determined	not determined
Cl	,, ,,	,, ,,	,, ,,	,, ,,	,, ,,
P_2O_5	,, ,,	,, ,,	,, ,,	,, ,,	,, ,,
Total	99·70	—	—	100·24	99·46
Specific gravity	4·74	4·69	—	4·64	4·70
Analyst	Borneman				Kazakova, 1951

* Gerasimovskii's data

and, to a lesser extent, in those of the eudialytic lujavrite complex. In the nepheline-rich rocks (urtites, porphyritic juvites) and in the melanocratic varieties (malignites, aegirine-lujavrites) the loparite content is high. In other rocks of these complexes, as well as in the poikilitic syenite complex, loparite is present in very small amounts. The highest concentration is found in parts of the rocks where differentiation is greatest. In each three-component stratal group of the differentiated complex the loparite content is highest at the contact between the urtitic horizons and the underlying lujavrites and lowest in the foyaites. The peak loparite content in the urtitic horizons occurs in their floors; towards the roof it gradually diminishes. As the urtites give way to underlying juvites, and then to foyaites, the loparite content in the stratal group falls to a minimum. Aegirine-lujavrites are usually rich in loparite at their contacts with underlying urtites. As a rule, the loparite content in the lujavrites diminishes from the roofs of the horizons to the floors—in other words, towards the leucocratic varieties of these rocks. In the foyaites the amount of loparite is smallest in the central parts of the horizons and increases in the direction of the aegirine-lujavrites and urtites.

The mean loparite content in the poorly-differentiated middle part of the complex is equal to, or even slightly higher than in the well-differentiated upper part. The difference is that in the upper part the loparite is more distinctly and completely concentrated in the floors of the urtitic horizons. In parts of the middle of the differentiated complex, where incomplete three-component stratal groups occur, the loparite distribution obeys the same rules as in the rocks of the top part, but the pattern is less clear.

In the rocks of the eudialytic lujavrite complex, except for the juvites, loparite is present in very small quantities and only in certain parts does it amount to 0·1-0·2 per cent of the rock. This might well be due to the extensive development of eudialyte in these rocks, since eudialyte is an early rock-forming mineral and contains, though in minute quantities, all the elements that go to make up loparite.

In the poikilitic syenites the mean loparite content is higher than in the differentiated complex, but no large concentrations are observed. Only in certain parts is it present in quantities up to 1 per cent—rarely more.

Loparite is not characteristic of the pegmatites. It has been found in pegmatitic bodies on the western slope of Alluaiv, in the Chinglusuai and Tyul'bn'yunuai valleys, on the northern slope of Lepkhe-Nel'm, on Kuftn'yun and Kitkn'yun, on the first eastern stream of Karnasurt and on Flora. In the pegmatites loparite is usually concentrated in the peripheral fine-grained zones, where it is closely associated with nepheline, microcline, aegirine I and eudialyte.

In time of crystallization loparite is one one of the earliest rare-metal minerals in the Lovozero rocks and pegmatites. Its crystals are usually included in aegirine, arfvedsonite, all secondary and rare-metal minerals (see Fig. 160) and, more rarely, in the peripheral parts of microcline and nepheline crystals. Xenomorphic, apparently later, grains of loparite occur mainly in rocks containing little of this mineral.

Under the influence of natrolitizing solutions loparite changes into metaloparite.

21. Metaloparite

CaCe$_2$(Ti, Nb)$_6$O$_{16}$. 2H$_2$O; sp.gr. 4·41—4·58; H. 5

Metaloparite was discovered by Gerasimovskii (1941). In 1947 Dubinina discovered a somewhat different variety of metaloparite, which appeared in the literature as metaloparite II. The data provided by both authors has been taken into account in the following description.

Both varieties of metaloparite are represented by irregularly-shaped segregations formed in the process of loparite-crystal replacement. These often grow round the loparite grain in the form of borders or fill up cracks in it. Entire pseudomorphs of metaloparite after loparite are quite often found, the form of the loparite crystal and its twins being preserved.

Metaloparite I has a cinnamon-brownish-yellow and brownish-yellow colour. Metaloparite II is grey with a bluish-green tint. Streak pale greenish-yellow. Lustre brilliant. Cleavage lacking. Fracture uneven. Brittle. Opaque. The hardness, difficult to determine because of the small number of individual growths, is roughly 5. Metaloparite II has the higher specific gravity.

In transmitted light metaloparite I is dark-brown with a greenish, or, more rarely, a yellowish-green tint. Metaloparite II is coloured in greenish-yellow shades. Segregations of both varieties are represented by an aggregate of very small growths, difficult to distinguish even when highly magnified. If a Lazo lens is used metaloparite is more readily distinguishable among the unaltered parts of loparite.

The refractive index of metaloparite I, according to Gerasimovskii, is roughly 2·24; that of metaloparite II, according to Dubinina's data, varies between 2·185

TABLE 74 Chemical composition of metaloparite

Constituent	Content, per cent	Atomic proportions	Calculated atomic ratios	
SiO$_2$	1·27	0·0211		
TiO$_2$	44·01	0·5508		
Nb$_2$O$_3$	10·78	0·0804	0·6552	—4
Ta$_2$O$_5$	0·66	0·0029		
ThO$_2$				
Ce$_2$O$_3$				
ΣLa$_2$O$_3$	34·20	0·2098		
Y$_2$O$_3$				
Al$_2$O$_3$	not determined	—	0·3108	—2
Fe$_2$O$_3$ + FeO	,, ,,	—		
CaO	5·25	0·0936		
SrO				
K$_2$O	0·23	0·0074		
Na$_2$O				
H$_2$O	3·49	0·3874	0·3874	—2
		O = 1·9580	1·9580	—12
Total	99·89	—	—	
Analyst	Borneman			
Reference	Gerasimovskii (1941)			

and 2·265, the average being 2·21. In physical properties metaloparite II is intermediate between loparite and metaloparite I. Under the blow-pipe metaloparite blackens but does not melt. It decomposes in H_2SO_4. Its chemical composition (Table 74) corresponds to the formula $(Ce, Ca)_2 (Ti, Nb)_4O_{11} . H_2O$.

Comparison of the analyses of loparite (see Table 71) and metaloparite shows that their composition is similar. Unlike loparite, metaloparite contains up to 3·49 per cent H_2O and hardly any alkalis. The conversion of loparite into metaloparite is consequently accompanied by loss of alkalis and addition of water, with the result that the relative amount of titanium, niobium and rare earths increases. Manganese and beryllium have been detected in metaloparite I by spectrographic analysis.

Metaloparite occurs only in the urtites, aegirine-lujavrites and malignites of the differentiated complex. It is most abundant in the upper rocks of the complex, the amount of metaloparite gradually decreasing with depth until it practically disappears in the lower part. In the upper part metaloparite I is concentrated mainly at the boundary between the urtite, and lujavrite horizons and between the urtite and malignite horizons, at a distance of 1 to 3 m in either direction from the contact. It is in this interval that zeolitization processes have developed most intensively. In the middle part of the complex the largest amount of metaloparite is found in the apatitic urtite of horizon V at its contact with lujavrite. In the underlying urtite horizons metaloparite occurs hardly at all. Metaloparite II, which does not occur in the upper part of the complex, has developed extensively along with metaloparite I in the apatitic urtite of horizon V. Metaloparite II seems to be an intermediate alteration product of loparite when late hydrothermal solutions have been somewhat deficient.

22. Pyrochlore

$(Na,Ca)_2(Nb,T_i)_2O_6(F,OH)$; cub.; sp.gr. 4·2—4·36 H. 5—5·5

Pyrochlore was first discovered in the Lovozero massif by Borodin in the contaminated pegmatites of the differentiated complex in the Koklukhtiuai valley in the central part of the massif. It was later found by Semenov in the pegmatites of the upper reaches of the Kitkuai valley on Mannepakhk. It rarely occurs in the non-pegmatitic rocks and then only in very small amounts. The following description is based on Borodin's data.

Pyrochlore occurs in the form of small grains, 0·5-1 mm in diameter, of reddish and cinnamon-brown colour, or in the form of cinnamon-brownish crystals of octahedral or cubic habit, up to 2 mm in diameter. A combination of cube and octahedron is also found. In thin sections pyrochlore is brownish to cinnamon-brown, with a high relief. Optically isotropic; $N=1·8$.

Table 75 shows a partial chemical analysis of pyrochlore from the Koklukhtiuai valley pegmatites. Muravitskaya and Voronova, using X-ray spectroscopy, determined 4-5 per cent of strontium, 1-2 per cent of tantalum, 1 per cent of potassium, 5 per cent of manganese, 0·5 per cent of lanthanum, 2 per cent of chlorine, 0·3 per cent of praseodymium and 1 per cent of neodymium. Silicon,

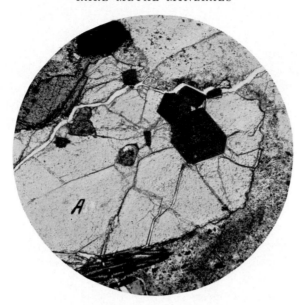

FIG. 163. Pyrochlore (dark) in apatite (A). ×46.
Without analyser

aluminium, barium, beryllium, lead, copper and zinc have also been determined
spectroscopically.

In the contaminated pegmatites pyrochlore is localized either in the border
zones, in the form of separate crystals included in other minerals, or in the central
zones (Koklukhtiuai valley pegmatites), where it forms accumulations in late
apatite (Fig. 163).

TABLE 75 Chemical composition of pyrochlore

Constituent	Content, per cent	Atomic proportions
TiO_2	8·04	0·1006
ZrO_2	0·99	0·0080
$(Nb, Ta)_2O_5$	52·09	0·3928
ΣRE_2O_3	3·38	0·0204
UO_2	0·97	0·0035
Fe_2O_3	3·28	0·0410
MgO	0·26	0·0064
CaO	13·45	0·2398
$(Na, K)_2O$	3·30	0·1064
H_2O^+	5·81	0·6448
H_2O^-	1·90	0·1108
F	3·70	0·1947
Total	—	—
Analyst	Kazakova, 1949	

23. Sphene

CaTi [SiO$_4$] O; mon.; sp.gr. 3·5; H. 5

In the non-pegmatitic rocks sphene forms fine or short-prismatic crystals of a golden-yellow colour, measuring $0.5 \times 0.1 \times 0.05$ cm. Such crystals sometimes make up segregations of irregular shape measuring $10 \times 5 \times 2$ cm. In the pegmatoid varieties of the poikilitic syenites sphene occurs in the form of long-prismatic, poorly-shaped crystals, golden-yellow and light-cinnamon-brown, measuring up to $1 \times 0.2 \times 0.2$ cm, on which only the vertical prism and pinacoid faces (110) and (100) can be detected.

In the pegmatites sphene is represented by yellow finely-fibrous, sometimes radiate-fibrous segregations up to 3 cm in diameter. In the orthoclase-natrolitic pegmatite of the northern slope of Lepkhe-Nel'm, Semenov observed spherulites of sphene, up to 0·4 cm in diameter, white, often with ramsayite crystals in the centre. In the upper part of the pegmatitic body on Kuivchorr and in the central zone of the tainiolitic pegmatite on Lepkhe-Nel'm Semenov found a previously unknown blue sphene that forms spherulites up to 1 cm in diameter, whose margins are usually more intensely coloured.

A strong vitreous lustre is characteristic of sphene. Fracture conchoidal or uneven. Semi-transparent to opaque. Cleavage not macroscopically observable. Specific gravity 3·505. Optically biaxial, positive. According to Gerasimovskii, Ng varies between 2·05 and 2·11, Np is roughly 1·92 and $2V = 22$-$25°$. Clearly marked pleochroism: Ng—cinnamon and brownish-cinnamon; Nm—light-cinnamon and cinnamon-brown; Np—light-greyish-cinnamon- and light-cinnamon-brown. Blue sphene is pleochroic from dark blue on Ng to almost colourless on Np.

Interplanar spacings of white silky and blue sphene from pegmatites of the central part of the Lovozero massif (determined by N. N. Sludskaya) are shown in Table 76. The similarity of the white silky, the blue and the ordinary cinnamon-brown sphene is established by comparison of their powder patterns.

TABLE 76 Interplanar spacings of sphene
(Analyst Sludskaya)

Line no.	White silky		Blue		Line no.	White silky		Blue	
	I	d	I	d		I	d	I	d
1	1	4·85	—	—	14	3	1·535	4	1·532
2	9	3·21	8	3·23	15	8	1·498	8	1·507
3	7	2·97	8	2·97	16	7	1·414	5	1·417
4	1	2·84	—	—	17	5	1·349	5	1·349
5	10	2·59	10	2·58	18	5	1·307	4	1·308
6	6	2·27	7	2·27	19	5	1·277	3	1·278
7	6	2·06	7	2·06	20	3	1·231	2	1·188
8	1	1·943	1	1·952	21	—	—	1	1·158
9	5	1·805	5	1·805	22	7	1·135	5	1·138
10	3	1·750	3	1·757	23	7	1·110	5	1·110
11	5	1·707	3	1·707	24	7	1·080	1	1·081
12	8	1·647	8	1·649	25	2	1·061	1	1·046
13	6	1·558	5	1·558					

Sphene dissolves completely in concentrated H_2SO_4 and partially, only on boiling, in HCl. Table 77 shows the chemical analysis data for yellowish-brown prismatic sphene (analysis 1) and the white radiate-fibrous variety (analysis 2) from the pegmatites of the upper reaches of the Suoluai valley and Lepkhe-Nel'm.

X-ray chemical analysis by Borovskii showed a Nb_2O_5 content of 1·5 per cent in coppery-yellow sphene and of 7-10 per cent in blue sphene—considerably higher than in ordinary sphene. Zinc, tin, germanium, vanadium, phosphorus, beryllium and gallium ($n \times 10^{-4}$) have been detected spectroscopically in sphene.

The sphene content in the rocks varies from 0·1 to 2 per cent. The largest amounts are characteristic of the contaminated rocks in the central part of the massif. In the rocks of the eudialytic lujavrite complex sphene occurs in amounts of up to 0·2 per cent in the melanocratic and mesocratic eudialytic lujavrites. In the differentiated complex it has developed most extensively in the aegirine- and hornblende-lujavrites (up to 0·1-0·6 per cent), the content increasing with depth. The mineral rarely occurs in foyaites and urtites. In the poikilitic syenite complex sphene is mostly found in the hydrosodalitic varieties, where in some parts it amounts to 2 per cent (Lepkhe-Nel'm, Mannepakhk, Ninchurt and elsewhere).

Sphene is usually closely associated with manganilmenite apatite, zircon and other minerals characteristic of the contaminated rocks of the massif and the hybrid pegmatites (see description of the Koklukhtiuai, Flora and other pegma-

TABLE 77 Chemical composition of sphene (per cent)

Constituent	Analysis 1*	Analysis 2
SiO_2	29·26	30·46
ZrO_2	0·52	0·20
TiO_2	40·50	38·06
Al_2O_3	0·64	nil
Nb_2O_5	—	—
Ta_2O_5	—	0·23
FeO	0·42	2·27
Fe_2O_3	1·77	0·40
MnO	0·09	—
MgO	0·00	0·12
CaO	25·10	23·97
RE_2O_3	—	0·74
SrO	—	1·04
Na_2O	0·87	1·75
K_2O	0·25	nil
F	—	0·33
H_2O^+	—	0·36
H_2O^-	0·10	0·41
Cl	0·26	—
Other	0·35	—
Total	100·13	100·34
$- O = (Cl, F)_2$	− 0·06	− 0·14
—	100·07	100·20
Analyst	Senderova	Zabavnikova, 1957

* Gerasimovskii's data

tites). It separated comparatively early. In the rocks, sphene fills up interstices between the main rock-forming minerals. Inclusions of it are more rarely found in aegirine II, arfvedsonite, eudialyte and lamprophyllite. In the pegmatites it is usually localized in the marginal, even-grained zones, along with nepheline, aegirine I, eudialyte and microcline, and fills up the spaces between the main minerals. It is rarely present in the zeolites of the central replacement zones (blue sphene).

24. Lomonosovite

$Na_2Ti_2Si_2O_9 . Na_3PO_4$; mon. or tric.; sp.gr. 3·13—3·15; H. 3—4

This mineral was first discovered in the Lovozero massif in 1936 by Gerasimovskii (1950), in the Chinglusuai valley pegmatites genetically connected with the poikilitic sodalitic syenites.

Lomonosovite is the phosphorus-bearing end-member of the minerals forming the lomonosovite-murmanite group, containing up to 14·62 per cent P_2O_5. It contains no water, whereas murmanite contains 10·2-20·34 per cent water and no phosphorus.

In this series of minerals the transitions from one member to another are gradual and it is difficult to draw boundaries between them. We shall therefore first describe lomonosovite with the intermediate varieties and then murmanite.

Recent research has established that the minerals of this series are more widely developed in the rocks of the massif than in the pegmatites and are found in almost all varieties of the nepheline-syenites. The intermediate varieties are the more common. Murmanite occurs more rarely, chiefly in surface outcrops, and lomonosovite only at depth.

In the rocks lomonosovite and the intermediate varieties form finely lamellar often flaky segregations measuring from 0·1 × 0·2 to 2·5 × 1·5 cm. The largest segregations occur in the coarse-grained foyaites and poikilitic sodalite-syenites, the smallest in the fine-grained rocks (urtites, ijolitic urtites, malignites and others). In the pegmatites lomonosovite is represented by tabular-lamellar segregations measuring 7 × 5 × 0·6 cm.

The colour is dark-cinnamon to black; the transitional varieties are cinnamon-yellow, yellow and violet-pink. Streak pale, pinkish-cinnamon. Lustre vitreous on cleavage surfaces, greasy perpendicular to cleavage. Fracture uneven. The minerals are very brittle. Hardness varies from 2 to 4, the intermediate varieties being the less hard. Specific gravity varies from 2·81 to 3·15; a high specific gravity is characteristic of lomonosovite, and it gradually falls with transition to murmanite. Highly perfect cleavage along (100) is characteristic of the segregations of lomonosovite and the intermediate varieties. In the trachytoid rocks of the massif plates of these minerals are usually orientated parallel with the trachytoidal plane. In the non-trachytoid rocks they have a random orientation.

In transmitted light lomonosovite is dark-cinnamon, the intermediate varieties being yellow and pink. Very pronounced pleochroism is characteristic: dark cinnamon and dark-brown to cinnamon on Ng, cinnamon-yellow and orange-

FIG. 164. Replacement of yellow variety of a
mineral of lomonosovite-murmanite series (2)
by the pink variety (3); 1. microcline; 4. natrolite. ×46. Crossed nicols

TABLE 78 Interplanar spacings of minerals of the lomonosovite-murmanite group
(Analyst Sludskaya)

Line no.	From rocks Lomonosovite		Intermediate yellow variety				Intermediate violet-pink variety			
			From foyaite		From lujavrite		From foyaite		From lujavrite	
	I	d	I	d	I	d	I	d	I	d
1	1	4·07	—	—	—	—	—	—	—	—
2	1	3·51	—	—	—	—	—	—	—	—
3	7	2·83	1	2·89	1	2·88	1	2·89	1	2·88
4	3 broad lines	{ 2·77	—	—	—	—	—	—	—	—
		2·59	—	—	—	—	—	—	—	—
5	1	2·52	—	—	—	—	—	—	—	—
6	1	2·41	—	—	—	—	—	—	—	—
7	1	2·34	—	—	—	—	—	—	—	—
8	3	2·07	—	—	1	2·14	—	—	—	—
9	3	1·845	—	—	—	—	—	—	—	—
10	5	1·777	1	1·771	1	1·775	1	1·764	1	1·768
11	3	1·675	—	—	—	—	—	—	—	—
12	3	1·614	—	—	—	—	—	—	—	—
13	3	1·605	1	1·599	1	1·608	1	1·599	1	1·608
14	3	1·481	—	—	—	—	—	—	—	—
15	1	1·340	—	—	—	—	—	—	—	—
16	2	1·328	—	—	—	—	—	—	—	—
17	1	1·260	—	—	—	—	—	—	—	—
18	1	1·209	—	—	—	—	—	—·	—	—

yellow along Nm, yellow and pale yellow along Np. In the transitional varieties the pleochroism is less marked. In the yellow transitional varieties, for example, pleochroism is in shades of yellow: Ng—cinnamon-yellow, Nm—brownish-yellow, Np—straw-yellow; while in the violet-pink varieties the pleochroism is in yellow and pink shades: Ng—brownish-yellow, Nm—pale yellow, Np—pink, pale pink. Absorption system: $Ng>Nm>Np$.

The minerals are biaxial, optically negative. Elongation positive. $2V = 56\text{-}64°$. Extinction oblique to cleavage. Refractive indices (rock lomonosovite): Ng 1·764, Nm 1·736, Np 1·654, $Ng - Np$ 0·110 and (pegmatitic lomonosovite, Gerasimovskii, 1950) Ng 1·778, Nm 1·750, Np 1·670, $Ng - Np$ 0·108. In the intermediate varieties the refractive indices vary widely, increasing as the phosphorus content diminishes.

The co-ordinates of the pole to the (100) cleavage in rock lomonosovite are $PNg = 59°00'$, $PNm = 70°00'$; $PNp = 38°00'$. In sections parallel to the cleavage simple and polysynthetic twins can be seen. The composition plane of the simple

TABLE 79 Chemical compositions of

Constituent	From rocks							
	Lomonosovite				Transitional variety			
	From foyaite of Karnasurt differentiated complex				From foyaite		From lujavrite	
	per cent	Atomic pro-portions	Calculated atomic ratios		Yellow	Violet-rose	Yellow	Violet-rose
SiO$_2$	24·48	0·4075	}0·4149	2·18 —2	32·46	30·62	29·71	31·89
Al$_2$O$_3$	0·38	0·0074			0·15	0·25	not det.	not det.
(Nb, Ta)$_2$O$_5$	6·34	0·0476			5·50	7·59	6·82	8·47
TiO$_2$	19·73	0·2471			25·40	25·63	not det.	24·30
ZrO$_2$	2·55	0·0207			1·40	2·88	1·20	1·08
Fe$_2$O$_3$	1·59	0·0198	}0·3820	2·01 —2	2·24	3·26	2·87	4·31
FeO	1·43	0·0199			—	—	not det.	not det.
MgO	0·13	0·0032			0·93	0·31	0·40	0·28
MnO	1·68	0·0237			1·97	1·97	not det.	1·23
CaO	1·25	0·0223			3·61	3·03	3·44	5·08
BaO	0·09	0·0006			nil	0·15	not det.	not det.
Na$_2$O	24·72	0·7974	}0·9166	4·82 —5	10·18	11·18	13·34	9·93
K$_2$O	0·98	0·0208			1·68	1·03	1·54	1·88
H$_2$O$^+$	0·58	0·0644			4·46	5·43	4·00	5·48
H$_2$O$^-$	0·10	0·0111			5·60	3·83	5·33	4·49
P$_2$O$_5$	14·62	0·2058	0·2058	1·08 —1	4·57	2·70	3·11	1·47
Cl	not det.	—	—		not det.	not det.	not det.	not det.
S	„ „	—	—		„ „	„ „	„ „	„ „
		O = 2·5414	2·5414	13·35 —13				
Total	100·65	—	—		100·15	99·86	—	--
Specific gravity	3·15				—	—	—	—
Analyst	Kazakova, 1950-1952							
Reference	—							

twins coincides with the cleavage plane. The co-ordinates of the composition plane in polysynthetic twins are $PNg = 18°00'$, $PNm = 72°00'$, $PNp = 89°00'$.

There are gradual colour transitions between lomonosovite and the intermediate varieties, but lomonosovite relics can be observed in the intermediate varieties and relics of the yellow intermediate variety in the pink (Fig. 164).

The powder patterns of the intermediate varieties are very indistinct, but a number of lines common to both lomonosovite and the intermediate varieties can be established (Table 78), indicating a structural similarity.

It is clear from a comparison of the chemical analyses of rock and pegmatitic lomonosovites (Table 79) that the rock lomonosovite contains more phosphorus (14·62 per cent P_2O_5) and less alkali (25·60 per cent $Na_2O + K_2O$). Recalculation of the chemical analyses shows that the composition of lomonosovite and the intermediate varieties is expressed by the formula suggested by Borneman (1946-1947): $nA_2B_2Si_2O_9 \cdot (n - x) Na_3PO_4$, where $A = Na$, K, Ca and partly Mn, that is,

lomonosovite and transitional varieties

			From Chinglusuai valley pegmatite				
Lomonosovite			Transitional variety				
per cent	Atomic proportions	Calculated atomic ratios	Brown	Pinkish-violet		Pale yellow	
24·07	0·4011	} 0·4011 2·01 —2	24·20	26·17	30·85	29·88	32·11
—	—		0·38	—	—	—	0·10
3·00	0·0226		1·72	5·66	6·82	3·96	5·74
24·43	0·3051		25·53	26·79	25·32	29·77	29·44
2·10	0·0170		2·50	0·91	1·31	1·98	2·31
2·39	0·0300	} 0·4338 2·17 —2	2·40	2·27	2·78	2·88	2·85
—	—		—	—	—	—	—
0·58	0·0144		0·65	0·60	0·60	0·60	0·35
3·17	0·0447		3·80	1·20	1·00	1·70	1·45
0·80	0·0143		1·08	1·60	1·94	1·69	2·80
—	—		—	—	—	—	—
26·09	0·8416	} 0·8847 4·42 —5	23·78	20·31	15·72	15·25	10·28
—	—		—	—	trace	trace	0·83
0·26	0·0288		2·20	2·24	2·52	2·53	4·17
—	—		—	3·96	5·28	5·68	6·03
12·84	0·1808	0·1808 0·90 —1	11·95	8·20	5·94	4·36	0·60
trace	—	—	0·10	—	—	—	—
not det.	—	—	0·16	—	—	—	—
99·73	—	—	100·45	99·91	100·08	100·28	99·06
3·13			—	2·957	2·946	2·906	2·883
Burova			Kaza-kova	Borneman			

Gerasimovskii (1950)

elements in which the ionic radius is close to or slightly greater than 1 Å; B = Ti, Nb, Zr, Fe^{3+}, Fe^{2+}, Mg, Mn—elements in which the ionic radius varies between 0·52 and 0·87 Å. When $x = n$ there will be a phosphorus-free member of the group (murmanite) $Na_2Ti_2Si_2O_9 . nH_2O$ and when $x = 0$ a phosphoric member (lomonosovite)—$Na_2Ti_2Si_2O_9 . Na_3PO_4$.

It has been established by Borneman that the sodium phosphate in lomonosovite and the transitional varieties is readily leached by water not only on heating but also in the cold. The water extract from lomonosovite has an alkaline reaction and contains Na_2O and P_2O_5 in the molecular ratio 3 : 1. In Borneman's opinion the capacity of sodium phosphate to be leached by water indicates an absence of close chemical bonding between the phosphoric and silicate parts in lomonosovite. Borneman (1947) regards lomonosovite as a solid solution, where very small domains of sodium phosphate have been lodged in the lattice cavities of sodium niobotitanosilicate. Table 80 shows the ratio of the silicate to phosphate parts in rock and pegmatitic lomonosovite.

As Table 79 shows, the intermediate varieties contain phosphorus and sodium in smaller amounts than does lomonosovite. The phosphorus pentoxide content, for example, falls from 14·62 to 0·60 per cent in the transition from lomonosovite to murmanite. The alkali content also varies in the same direction (25·70 per cent in lomonosovite, falling to 11 per cent in the intermediate varieties). The water content rises sharply in the intermediate varieties. The silicate parts of the lomonosovite and of the intermediate varieties are identical. Some enrichment of the intermediate varieties in silica, titanium oxide and certain other elements can be observed. The violet-pink intermediate variety in the rocks is more altered. The pink colour is apparently due to the presence of high-valency manganese.

Apart from the elements determined by chemical methods, strontium, zinc, beryllium, gallium, lead, tin, copper and tantalum have been detected spectroscopically in minerals of the lomonosovite-murmanite group. A very distinct endothermic effect at a temperature of about 900° is characteristic of the thermal analysis curve for lomonosovite obtained by Shmakova. Borneman (1946, 1947) explains this is due to the melting of the sodium phosphate (Fig. 165). The dehydration curves for the yellow and violet-pink intermediate varieties, whether from the same rock or from different rocks are similar (Figs. 166 and 167).

The minerals of the lomonosovite-murmanite group are the characteristic rare-metal minerals of the foyaites in the upper and lower parts of the differentiated complex and the aegirine-lujavrites in its middle part (Table 81).

The largest concentrations and largest segregations of these minerals are found in the central parts of the foyaitic horizons and, more rarely, in their roofs. Usually,

TABLE 80   Ratio of silicate to phosphate in lomonosovite

Lomonosovite	$A_2B_2Si_2O_9$	$(Na, H)_3PO_4$
From pegmatite	52·6	47·4
From rock	50·19	49·81

TABLE 81 Content of minerals of the lomonosovite-murmanite group in Lovozero rocks

Differentiated complex	Content, per cent	Eudialytic lujavrite complex	Content, per cent	Poikilitic syenite complex	Content, per cent
Upper division:		Eudialytic lujavrites:		Poikilitic sodalite-syenites	0-1·5
Foyaites	0·25-5·1	Melanocratic	0-0·08	Poikilitic nepheline-syenites	0-3·5
Urtites	0·1-1·4	Mesocratic	0·1-0·2	Poikilitic hydrosodalite-syenites	0-0·3
Aegirine-lujavrites	0-1·5	Leucocratic	0·2-0·3		
Hornblende-lujavrites	0-0·3	Porphyritic lujavrites	—		
Malignites	0-0·9	Porphyritic juvites	0·03-0·1		
Middle division:		Porphyritic foyaites	0·1-2·2		
Foyaites	0·1-2·5				
Urtites	0-0·3				
Aegirine-lujavrites	0·4-3				
Hornblende-lujavrites	0-0·1				
Lower division:					
Foyaites	0·3-1·5				
Urtites	0-0·2				
Aegirine-lujavrites	0-0·3				

the thicker the foyaitic horizon and the more distinctly it is defined, the more lomonosovite it contains. The amount of these minerals gradually declines and the size of the segregations gradually diminishes with transition from the foyaites to the underlying urtites. In the urtitic horizons the largest amounts of the minerals in the lomonosovite group are usually found in the roofs. Towards the lower surfaces the amount gradually diminishes and the lomonosovite minerals are gradually replaced by loparite. In the lujavrites of the three-component stratal groups in these parts of the complex, minerals of the lomonosovite-murmanite group are as a rule absent. Small quantities of them are found in the transition zones between the foyaites and the

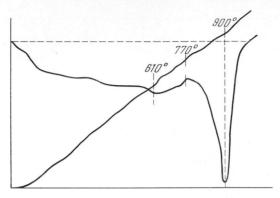

FIG. 165. Thermal analysis curve for lomonosovite

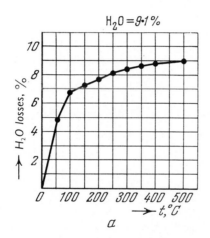

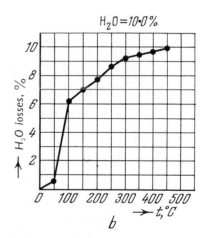

FIG. 166. Dehydration curves for intermediate mineral varieties in the lomonosovite-murmanite group from foyaite in the upper division of the differentiated complex

a—yellow variety; b—violet-pink variety

lujavrites. As the amount of dark-coloured minerals (aegirine, hornblende) in the lujavrites increases the amount of lomonosovite-murmanite minerals decreases.

In the aegirine-lujavrites of the middle part of the complex the minerals of this group are more widespread and occur jointly with loparite.

Minerals of the group are not characteristic of the eudialytic lujavrite complex. The amount increases from the melanocratic eudialytic lujavrites to the leucocratic. In the differentiated parts of the complex these minerals accumulate in the foyaites as well, while the urtites and lujavrites are enriched in eudialyte.

Sometimes, however, murmanitic varieties of the porphyritic lujavrites occur, containing both murmanite and eudialyte.

In the poikilitic syenites the largest quantities of the lomonosovite-murmanite minerals are found in the sodalitic varieties, characteristically distributed in pockets.

In the pegmatites lomonosovites occur only in the deep part of the massif and in the small schlieren-like pegmatites of the Chinglusuai valley, in which the hydrothermal stages are not in evidence.

From the above we may conclude that the leucocratic, feldspathic rocks of the massif are those that contain the largest amount of minerals belonging to this

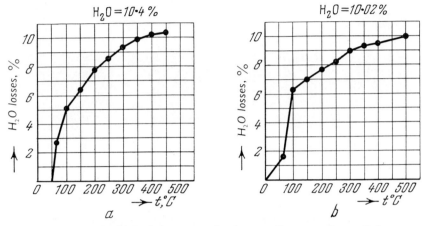

FIG. 167. Dehydration curves for intermediate members of the lomonosovite-murmanite group from aegirine-lujavrite in the middle division of the differentiated complex

a—yellow variety; b—violet-pink variety

group, which are the predominant rare-metal minerals in them. The pegmatitic veins genetically connected with the leucocratic nepheline-syenites, poikilitic syenites and foyaites also contain more of these minerals than the pegmatites of the melanocratic rocks.

Parageneses involving anhydrous minerals and, in the first place, the absence of natrolite are characteristic of lomonosovite. The presence of villiaumite is a prospecting sign indicating lomonosovite, since both these minerals remain unaltered only under anhydrous conditions and invariably occur together.

Lomonosovite is a primary magmatic mineral. Minerals of the lomonosovite-murmanite group fill up interstices of irregular shape between nepheline, microcline, orthoclase and aegirine, accommodating themselves to the shapes of the crystals of these minerals. Owing to the large amount of nepheline and early sodalite inclusions that they contain they sometimes have a 'skeletal' form (Fig. 168). They usually contain inclusions of loparite, apatite, sphene and ramsayite as well. In rocks where these minerals become the main rock-forming minerals they are found in intergrowth with microcline (Fig. 169).

The interrelationship between minerals of the lomonosovite-murmanite group and arfvedsonite is twofold. In most cases the lomonosovite-murmanite minerals

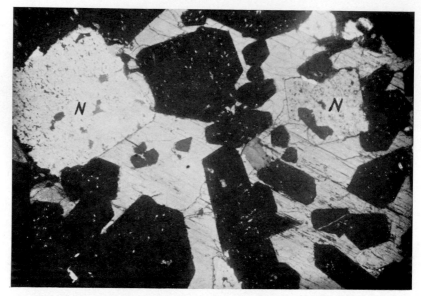

FIG. 168. Nepheline inclusions (N) and early sodalite (black) in lomonosovite from poikilitic syenite.   × 46. Crossed nicols

FIG. 169. Intergrowth of minerals of the lomonosovite-murmanite group (Mr) with albitized microcline (M).   × 90. Crossed nicols

fill up interstices between arfvedsonite segregations, often attacking them and replacing them from the margin (Fig. 170). More rarely there is a peculiar intergrowth of these minerals with arfvedsonite in the border parts; this may be an indication of simultaneous growth.

Lomonosovite is converted by late hydrothermal solutions and surface waters into the yellow variety and then into the violet-pink variety and murmanite. In the vertical section of the massif murmanite is widespread in the surface outcrops

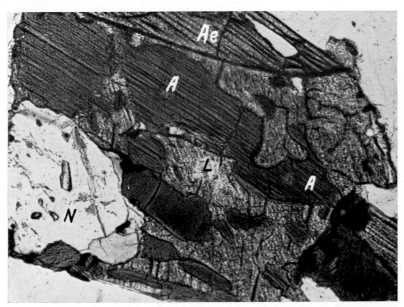

FIG. 170. Interrelationship of lomonosovite (L), arfvedsonite (A), aegirine (Ae) and nepheline (N). ×46. Without analyser

of the rocks, giving way, with depth, to the violet-pink and then to the yellow intermediate varieties, which are widespread at depths of 100 to 200 m. Below this is a zone containing the yellow variety and lomonosovite and still lower down only lomonosovite is present.

25. Murmanite

$Na_2(Ti,Nb)_2Si_2O_9 . nH_2O$; mon; sp.gr. 2·4—2·85; H. 2—3

Murmanite is widespread in the rocks and pegmatites of the Lovozero massif. It was first discovered by Ramsay in 1890 and described as mineral No. 3. In 1923, in the records of Fersman's expedition, it was called 'violophyllite' but was later, after more detailed study by N. N. Gutkova (1930), named murmanite after the locality.

In the rocks of the massif murmanite forms flaky segregations of microscopic size, up to $0.5 \times 1.5 \times 2.5$ cm. In the pegmatites it is represented by lamellar segregations measuring $5 \times 3 \times 1$ mm to $8 \times 8 \times 3$ cm, or it forms radial growths (bundles) of crystals. In some fine-grained parts of the pegmatites murmanite forms almost monomineralic accumulations more than 10 cm in diameter.

Well-formed crystals are seldom found. Some investigators have succeeded in measuring a few faces. Ramsay, for example, notes two faces on murmanite crystals, intersecting at an angle of 40°, one of them wide and lamellar, which he took to be the front pinacoid (100), the other narrow, which he took as the basal pinacoid (001). Gutkova, using applied goniometry, measured a fragment of murmanite crystal in which, in addition to the (100) and (001) faces, she detected the faces (101), (201), (144) and (342). (*Minerals of the Khibiny and Lovozero tundras*, 1937).

The colour of murmanite is lilac-pink or bright pink or, in the altered varieties, yellow, brown, cinnamon-brown to black. Perfect cleavage along (100), along which it can be readily split into thin flakes, is very characteristic. Lustre vitreous on cleavage surfaces, greasy on the fracture. Opaque. Fracture uneven. Brittle. Specific gravity of murmanite from Chinglusuai valley and Malyi Punkaruaiv pegmatites, according to Borneman (1946) and Gerasimovskii (1936_3) 2·76-2·84 for fresh varieties and 2·47-2·64 for altered varieties. In thin sections pale pink or brownish. Distinct pleochroism, pinkish-cinnamon along Ng, light-brown along Nm, pinkish-grey and pale pink along Np. Absorption scheme $Ng > Nm > Np$.

Optically biaxial, negative. Refractive indices (Gerasimovskii) Ng 1·807; Nm 1·770; Np 1·682; $Ng - Np$ 0·125. The refractive indices diminish when the

TABLE 82 Chemical composition of murmanite (per cent)

Constituent	Unaltered murmanite			Much-decomposed murmanite		
	Chinglusuai	Sengischorr	Punkaruaiv	Punkaruaiv		Karnasurt
SiO_2	30·06	31·24	30·93	28·86	24·52	30·60
ZrO_2	2·08	1·62	1·40	1·50	1·18	2·36
TiO_2		30·40	29·51	29·42	31·36	22·92
Nb_2O_5	38·24	6·56	7·71	8·32	10·00	7·47
Ta_2O_5		0·56	0·50		0·56	
Al_2O_3	—	—	—	—	0·24	3·79
Fe_2O_3	2·33	2·96	3·34	3·08	3·04	2·34
FeO	0·30	—	—	—	—	—
MgO	0·35	0·64	0·27	0·21	0·38	0·54
MnO	2·30	2·38	2·42	2·84	2·26	4·88
CaO	2·56	3·16	2·74	3·44	3·76	2·19
SrO	—	trace	trace	trace	trace	—
BaO	—	—	—	—	—	5·18
Na_2O	10·38	8·64	7·44	3·04	2·34	1·72
K_2O	0·83	0·62	0·56	0·78	0·70	4·88
H_2O^+	4·17	5·37	6·46	9·30	9·35	7·92
H_2O^-	6·03	6·13	6·06	9·52	10·69	3·74
F	—	—	0·19	—	—	—
P_2O_5	—	—	—	—	—	nil
Total	99·63	100·28	99·53	100·31	100·38	100·53
Specific gravity	2·84	2·763	2·769	2·472-2·475		—
Analyst	Borneman, 1937	Burova, 1937				Burova 1951
Reference		Gerasimovskii's data				—

mineral is altered. $2V = 57\text{-}64°$. Dispersion distinct: $r > v$; $2V_{Li} = 61°$; $2V_{Na} = 59°$; $2V_{Te} = 57.5°$. Optic axial plane parallel to (001). In sections parallel to (001), according to Gutkova's data, cleavage is observable, roughly definable as $PNg = 90°$, $PNm = 80\text{-}82°$, $PNp = 8\text{-}10°$.

Murmanite is the hydrous phosphorus-free end-member of the lomonosovite-murmanite group. It is readily soluble, without heating, in HCl and poorly soluble on heating in HNO_3 and H_2SO_4.

Comparison of the chemical analysis data (Table 82) shows that in murmanite at the first stages of alteration there is loss of sodium and, in part, silicon and addition of water. In subsequent stages the mineral is completely broken down and turns into a finely-aggregated brown material with almost no sodium but

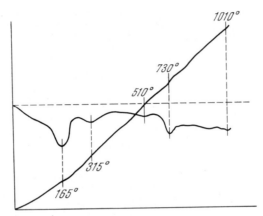

FIG. 171. Thermal analysis curve for murmanite

with a slightly higher potassium and barium content. This is apparently due to sorption of potassium and barium from late solutions. Phosphorus, yttrium, lanthanum, strontium, beryllium, barium, copper, zinc and lead have been spectro-scopically detected in murmanite from the rocks and pegmatites in different parts of the massif (Flora, southern slope of Kuftn'yun, Tyul'bn'yuai valley, Sengischorr cirque, Kedykvyrpakhk and elsewhere). It should be noted that in the greatly decomposed varieties of this mineral (the light-yellow and silver-white varieties) from the pegmatites, the presence of rare earths (lanthanum and yttrium) has been noted (Kuftn'yun, Tyul'bn'yuai valley, Kedykvyrpakhk). Phosphorus is normally present in most of the murmanite specimens from the rocks and as a rule lacking in the fresh murmanite from pegmatites.

The thermal analysis curve produced by V. G. Shmakova (Institute of Geo-logical Sciences, USSR Academy of Sciences) shows three endothermic effects at temperatures of 165°, 315° and 730° (Fig. 171). In Borneman's opinion the endo-thermic effects at 165° and 315° reflect the elimination of low-temperature water and of the hydrogen present in the murmanite molecules in place of alkalis.

The distribution pattern of the minerals in this group (see description of lomonosovite), the conversion of lomonosovite into murmanite when the phosphate part is leached, the replacement of lomonosovite by murmanite and the presence of phosphorus in rock murmanite give grounds for supposing that the matrix of this mineral in the rocks formed from lomonosovite under the action of aqueous solutions of deep or surface origin.

In the pegmatites murmanite is localized in small schlieren-like bodies and in the outer fine-grained feldspathic aegirine zones of fully-differentiated bodies; it is more rarely found in the natrolite of the central zones. In the poorly-differentiated pegmatitic bodies it is usually found in the central parts, which are rich

FIG. 172. Interrelationship of murmanite (Mr) with nepheline (N), microcline (M) and aegirine (Ae). ×46. Without analyser

in aegirine II. In the pegmatites murmanite is usually xenomorphic towards aegirine I, nepheline, eudialyte, ramsayite, lamprophyllite and microcline (Fig. 172), but when it is abundant in the fine-grained zones it forms intergrowths with microcline and even idiomorphic inclusions in it. Murmanite is always idiomorphic to aegirine II. Separation apparently began at the end of the period of early microcline crystallization and finished after it, before the crystallization of aegirine II.

The absence of phosphorus, as well as of lomonosovite relicts, from pegmatitic murmanite gives reason to suppose that in this case murmanite is of primary magmatic origin. The abundance of volatile substances, including water, in the molten solution probably made for the formation of murmanite instead of lomonosovite. Apart from the primary magmatic murmanite, secondary murmanite, formed after lomonosovite, is occasionally found in small pegmatitic bodies in which hydrothermal processes are not in evidence (Chinglusuai valley pegmatites).

In the process of alteration murmanite turns into belyankinite and various ochreous products of hypergene origin. These are poorly-individualized powdery and micaceous masses, structureless under X-rays, with refractive indices lower than those of murmanite. According to Semenov (1957₄) they consist mainly of hydroxides of titanium (leucoxene) and niobium, while manganese, iron, zirconium and barium also sometimes accumulate; sodium and silicon are lost (see Table 82).

26. Nenadkevichite

$(Na,Ca)(Nb,Ti) [Si_2O_7] . 2H_2O$; orthorhomb.; sp.gr. 2·82—2·88; H. 5

Nenadkevichite was first detected by Kuz'menko (1955) in a natrolite-albitite pegmatitic vein on the north-eastern slope of Karnasurt, genetically connected with poikilitic hackmanite-syenites (see pegmatite descriptions). It forms lamellar segregations ranging from a few millimetres in length to $4 \times 2·5 \times 0·4$ cm (Fig. 173). It does not occur as well-formed crystals. In some crystal fragments, apart from

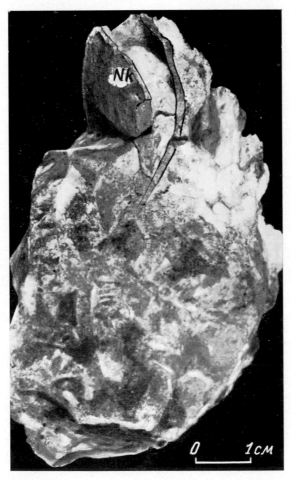

FIG. 173. Plate-like nenadkevichite segregations (Nk) in pegmatite

the well-developed face taken as (100), two narrow faces can be seen which, according to rough measurements made by Kupletskaya, truncate (100) at angles of 41·5 and 46·5°.

The colour is dark-brown, brown, pinkish-brown to pink, sometimes brownish-pink. The brownish tinge in the pink variety seems to be due to contamination

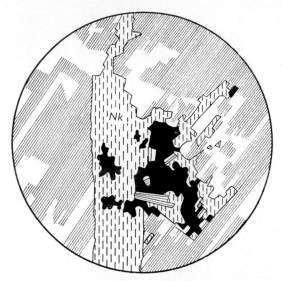

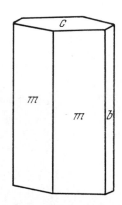

FIG. 174. Nenadkevichite (Nk) in microcline; black—Mn hydroxides. × 46. Crossed nicols

FIG. 175. Labuntsovite crystal (after Semenov)

by manganese hydroxides. These often form dendritic black films on the faces of lamellar segregations of the mineral. Streak pale pink, almost white. Lustre dull to vitreous. Opaque to semi-transparent in very thin slivers. Fracture uneven.

Lamellar segregations of nenadkevichite are made up of a very fine-grained aggregate which is often not resolvable by visual examination. Aggregate polarization between crossed nicols. Grain size not greater than 0·15 mm in diameter. Form rectangular, nearly square. Cleavage distinct parallel to (100) and (001). Extinction straight. Optically biaxial, positive. Refractive indices: Ng 1·785; Nm 1·686; Np 1·659; $Ng - Np$ 0·126; $2V = 46°$. Pleochroism weak: Ng—pale pink, Nm—pale

TABLE 83 Interplanar spacings of nenadkevichite

Line no.	I	d	Line no.	I	d	Line no.	I	d
1	1	7·43	10	2	2·02	18	2	1·462
2	7	6·82	11	3	1·919	19	10	1·427
3	2	4·85	12	2	1·874	20	9	1·289
4	10	3·20	13	3	1·809	21	2	1·255
5	10	3·10	14	6	1·733	22	1	1·144
6	3	2·90	15	7	1·705	23	2	1·132
7	7	2·58	16	6	1·567	24	2	1·103
8	8	2·49	17	5	1·526	25	2	1·050
9	6	2·44						

yellow, Np—colourless; $Ng-y$, $Nm=z$, $Np-x$. Optic axial plane parallel to (001).

The nenadkevichite powder pattern is unlike that of any other known mineral (Table 83).

Nenadkevichite readily decomposes in sulphuric acid and with more difficulty in HNO_3 and HCl. Recalculation of the results of chemical analysis (Table 84) shows that its composition is expressed by the formula: $AB[Si_2O_7] \cdot 2H_2O$, where A = Na, K, Ca, R.E., Mn, Ba, Mg; and B = Nb, Ti, Fe^{3+}.

In chemical composition nenadkevichite is similar to murmanite but differs from it in having a marked predominance of niobium over titanium and a lower alkali content. The mineral is not so readily decomposed by acids.

Beryllium, zinc, copper, tantalum, lead and silver have been detected in nenadkevichite by the spectrographic method.

The mineral occurs in large quantities, not only in the natrolite-albite pegmatitic vein mentioned above, but also in certain other pegmatitic bodies on the northern slope of Karnasurt and the north-western slope of Flora. In the natrolite-albite vein it is usually localized in interstices between microcline crystals in the outer fine-grained and medium-grained zones. Small nenadkevichite crystals occur as well, included in microcline and forming irregular intergrowths with it (Fig. 174). It appears to have crystallized at the end of the period of microcline separation.

TABLE 84 Chemical composition of nenadkevichite

Constituent	Brown variety				Pink variety	
	per cent	Atomic proportions	Calculation of atomic ratios		per cent	Atomic proportions
SiO_2	37·72	0·6280	0·6402 2·06 —2		37·15	0·6185
Al_2O_3	0·62	0·0122			1·15	0·0226
TiO_2	9·69	0·1213			12·12	0·1517
ZrO_2	nil	—			nil	—
Nb_2O_5	24·05	0·1810	0·3199 1·03 —1		24·61	0·1850
Fe_2O_3	1·40	0·0176			0·80	0·0100
ΣRE_2O_3	0·25	0·0016			0·30	0·0018
FeO	nil	—			nil	—
MnO	1·08	0·0152			2·90	0·0409
MgO	0·45	0·0112			0·52	0·0129
BaO	2·75	0·0179	0·2873 0·93 —1		1·39	0·0091
CaO	4·30	0·0768			1·75	0·0312
Na_2O	3·34	0·1078			4·16	0·1342
K_2O	2·68	0·0568			2·24	0·0476
H_2O^+	8·98 ⎫	1·2588	1·2588 4·06 —4		8·84 ⎫	1·2032
H_2O^-	2·36 ⎭				2·00 ⎭	
		O = 2·8310	2·8310 8·96 —9		—	O = 2·8411
Total	99·67	—	—		99·93	—
Specific gravity	2·838				2·885	
Analyst	Kazakova, 1948					

At the hypergene stage nenadkevichite is replaced by waxy-yellow, pale greenish-yellow ochreous minerals of the leucoxene group.

27. Labuntsovite

(Ba,K,Na)(Ti,Nb) [Si_2O_7] . H_2O; orthorhomb.; sp.gr. 2·901; H. 6

Labuntsovite was first detected and studied by Semenov and the description here is based on his data (Semenov and Burova, 1955). It occurs in the form of prismatic crystals measuring $12 \times 3 \times 2$ mm (Fig. 175). In crystallographic properties it resembles elpidite (Table 85), but the faces (100), (120) and (122) are absent, while (111) and (011) are not always present.

TABLE 85 Polar co-ordinates of labuntsovite and elpidite

Face	Labuntsovite		Elpidite	
	ρ	ϕ	ρ	ϕ
c (001)	0°00′	—	0°00′	—
b (010)	90°00′	0°00′	90°00′	0°00′
a (100)	—	—	90°00′	90°00′
m (110)	90°00′	62°56′	90°00′	62°39′
d (011)	44°15′	0°00′	44°20′	0°00′
s (111)	47°03′	62°56′	—	—
n (120)	—	—	90°00′	44°11′
g (102)	—	—	43°48′	90°00′

TABLE 86 Interplanar spacings of labuntsovite, nenadkevichite and elpidite

Line no.	Labuntsovite		Nenadkevichite		Elpidite (Greenland)	
	I	d	I	d	I	d
1	10	3·15	1	7·43	4	4·82
2	8	3·09	7	6·82	10	3·26
3	6	3·02	2	4·85	7	3·12
4	9	2·56	10	3·20	5	2·93
5	7	2·47	10	3·10	4	2·65
6	1	2·34	3	2·90	5	2·52
7	3	2·04	7	2·58	5	2·39
8	2	2·00	8	2·49	4	2·00
9	7	1·780	6	2·44	7	1·945
10	7	1·718	2	2·02	5	1·827
11	8	1·677	3	1·919	7	1·759
12	9	1·543	2	1·874	7	1·590
13	3	1·515	3	1·809	6	1·492
14	4	1·465	6	1·733	5	1·466
15	5	1·438	7	1·705	6	1·435
16	9	1·413	6	1·567	7	1·352
17	3	1·304	5	1·526	5	1·129
18	2	1·277	2	1·462	5	1·089
19	1	1·253	10	1·427	1	1·075
20	5	1·255	9	1·289	—	—
21	—	—	2	1·255	—	—
22	—	—	1	1·144	—	—
23	—	—	2	1·132	—	—
24	—	—	2	1·103	—	—
25	—	—	2	1·050	—	—

The axial ratios are $a : b : c = 0.511 : 1 : 0.489$.

The colour is brownish-yellow or pink. Lustre greasy. In thin fragments semi-transparent, brittle. Cleavage perfect along (100). Pleochroism: Ng— brownish-yellow, Np—light-yellow; absorption $Ng > Nm > Np$. Refractive indices: Ng 1·795, Nm 1·702, Np 1·689, $Ng - Np$ 0·106; $2V = (+)41°$; $Ng = x$, $Nm = z$, $Np = y$. Optic axial plane parallel to (001).

If we compare the interplanar spacings of labuntsovite (as calculated by Sludskaya) and elpidite (Table 86) it is clear that despite the similarity of crystallographic morphology the powder patterns of these two minerals differ greatly, whereas in this respect labuntsovite shows a similarity to nenadkevichite.

Labuntsovite decomposes with difficulty in HCl, HNO_3 and H_2SO_4. The calculation of the chemical analysis (Table 87) shows that its composition is expressed by the formula $AB[Si_2O_7] . H_2O$, where A = K, Na, Ca and B = Ti, Nb, Fe, Mg, Mn. Comparison of the chemical composition of labuntsovite and nenadkevichite (see Table 84) shows that these minerals belong to a single isomorphous series in which labuntsovite is the extreme titaniferous and nenadkevichite the extreme niobian member.

Rubidium (0·3 per cent), strontium, yttrium, cerium and thorium have been detected in labuntsovite by X-ray chemical analysis and beryllium, lead, zinc, copper, tin and vanadium by spectrographic analysis. Thermal investigations of labuntsovite performed by Karpova showed that water is gradually eliminated from it between 200 and 400°.

Labuntsovite is usually closely associated with minerals of the replacement complex and forms druses of small crystals in the cavities between growths of albite (Fig. 176) or natrolite which fill up the central parts of the pegmatitic bodies

TABLE 87 Chemical composition of labuntsovite

Constituent	Content, per cent	Atomic proportions	Calculation of atomic ratios		
SiO_2	39·59	0·660	} 0·685	1·96	—2
Al_2O_3	1·30	0·025			
Fe_2O_3	1·56	0·020			
Nb_2O_5	1·45	0·011			
TiO_2	25·49	0·319	} 0·383	1·09	—1
ZrO_2	trace	—			
MgO	0·42	0·010			
MnO	2·34	0·033			
RE_2O_3	—	—			
CaO	1·19	0·021			
BaO	8·61	0·056	} 0·414	1·18	—1
K_2O	7·23	0·154			
Na_2O	3·18	0·103			
H_2O	7·91	0·080			
		0·800	0·800	2·28	—2
		O = 2·740	2·740	7·83	—8
Total	100·27	—	—		
Analyst		Burova, 1953			

(Kuftn'yun, Kitkn'yun and elsewhere). In many pegmatites it is associated with hydrothermal alteration products of murmanite, forming pseudomorphs after the latter. Labuntsovite crystals are sometimes covered with a thin film of anatase leucoxene, which has probably developed in the process of late-hydrothermal alteration.

FIG. 176. Labuntsovite crystals in cavity in albite. Natural size

28. Ramsayite

$Na_2Ti_2Si_2O_9$; orthorhomb.; sp.gr. 3·437, H. 6

In the rocks ramsayite forms lamellar segregations measuring $0.5 \times 0.1 \times 0.2$ to $3 \times 0.8 \times 0.8$ cm. The largest segregations are characteristic of the rocks in the poikilitic syenite complex and the smallest of rocks of the eudialytic lujavrite complex. In the pegmatites ramsayite segregations occur in four different forms: (1) crystals, (2) fine-grained, (3) lamellar and (4) fibrous; the bulk of the mineral consists of the lamellar variety.

The idiomorphic ramsayite crystals vary in size from $1 \times 1 \times 2$ mm to $1.5 \times 2 \times 3$ cm (Fig. 177), but sometimes reach sizes of $6 \times 5 \times 3.5$ cm. According to Kostyleva (1925) and Rimskaya-Korsakova (1939), they are usually elongated along the z-axis (Fig. 178). The general habit is defined by the forms $s(111)$, $m(210)$ and $a(100)$, and sometimes by the form (211). In addition, the following forms are found: $l(110)$, $n(320)$, $f(410)$, $d(011)$, $u(311)$, $v(411)$, $l(126)$, $\epsilon(221)$, $\psi(421)$ and $z(131)$. The axial ratio $a : b : c$ is $1.64983 : 1 : 0.605227$. Fine-grained ramsayite forms irregularly-shaped segregations measuring $4 \times 3 \times 2$ cm. Examination under the microscope shows that these segregations are accumulations of very small idiomorphic ramsayite crystals. The lamellar ramsayite is found in the

Fig. 177. Ramsayite crystals in aegirine-albite rock. Natural size

form of monocrystalline segregations measuring 1×1.5 cm in cross-section to $7 \times 6 \times 4$ cm, or monomineralic aggregates, measuring up to $20 \times 10 \times 10$ cm, of flattened crystals with a well-developed pinacoid and poorly-developed prism faces or pyramids. The fibrous ramsayite forms segregations of irregular shape, measuring $1 \times 1 \times 0.5$ cm, of fibrous or felted structure (Fig. 179). It has been found in only two pegmatitic bodies on Alluaiv, in close association with aegirine II and manganilmenite, on which it develops.

The colour ranges from dark-brown to yellowish-brown in secondary ramsayite. The lustre on the crystal faces and cleavage planes varies from vitreous to sub-metallic or, more rarely, dull; on the fracture the lustre is greasy. Cleavage perfect along (100) and less perfect along (210). The dark varieties are opaque, the lighter ones vary from semi-transparent to transparent. The specific gravity of ramsayite from the foyaites of the differentiated complex is 3·42, somewhat lower than that of the pegmatitic ramsayite (3·437). Fracture uneven.

In thin sections ramsayite is characterized by a high relief and shagreen surface. Pleochroism is barely perceptible: Ng—yellowish-brown to light-brown, Nm—light yellowish-brown and Np—brownish to dark-brown. Extinction straight or nearly so. Elongation negative. The mineral is optically biaxial, negative. Orientation of optic indicatrix: $Np=x$, $Nm=y$, $Ng=z$; $2V$ varies from 37° to 41°. The refractive indices of rock ramsayite vary within the following limits: $Ng=2.02$—2.06; $Nm=2.01$—2.04; $Np=1.93$—1.95; $Ng-Np=0.10$—0.11. According to Gerasimovskii's data, pegmatitic ramsayite has the following refractive indices: $Ng=2.06$; $Np=1.93$; $Ng-Np=0.13$.

Ramsayite does not dissolve in concentrated HNO_3 or H_2SO_4. In chemical composition it is sodium titanosilicate and has the formula $Na_2Ti_2Si_2O_9$. The crystal structure has been analysed by Academician N. V. Belov, who has demonstrated the presence of the pyroxene radical (SiO_3) and has suggested that the formula for ramsayite should be written $Na_2Ti_2[Si_2O_6]O_3$ (Belov, Belyaev, 1949).

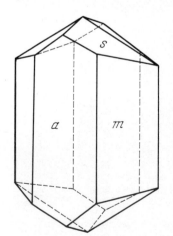

The chemical analyses of rock and pegmatitic ramsayites are very similar (Table 88). An unusually high niobium content (3·07 per cent Nb_2O_5) is found in ramsayite from the foyaites of the differentiated

FIG. 178. Ramsayite crystal (after Kostyleva)

complex. Burova determined the $(Nb, Ta)_2O_5$ content in ramsayite from the pegmatites of the Sengischorr cirque as 1·63 per cent. Borovskii determined the Nb_2O_5 content in ramsayite from the Tyul'bn'yunuai valley pegmatites as 2·8 per cent, using X-ray chemical analysis.

TABLE 88 Chemical composition of ramsayite

| Constituent | From foyaite of Karnasurt differentiated complex | | | From pegmatite | | | | Tyul'bn'yunua valley |
| | per cent | Atomic proportions | Calculation of atomic ratios | Upper reaches of Tavaiok | | Angvundaschorr | | |
				per cent	Atomic proportions	per cent	Atomic proportions	per cent
SiO_2	33·94	0·5651	0·5709 2·00 —2	34·06	0·5671	34·07	0·5676	34·25
Al_2O_3	0·30	0·0058		0·90	0·0176	—	—	0·24
TiO_2	42·05	0·5263		46·26	0·5789	47·00	0·5755	44·21
ZrO_2	0·40	0·0032		not determined	—	—	—	0·09
Nb_2O_5	3·07	0·0224	0·5774 2·02 —2	,,	—	—	—	0·59*
Fe_2O_3	0·47	0·0058		1·03	0·143	—	—	0·44
FeO	1·19	0·0166		0·02	0·0002	1·71	0·0237	0·40
MnO	0·07	0·0009		trace	—	—	—	0·02
MgO	0·09	0·0022		0·35	0·0062	—	—	0·06
CaO	0·25	0·0045		0·32	0·0018	0·09	0·0016	0·05
RE_2O_3	not determined	—		—	—	—	—	—
Na_2O	16·61	0·5358	0·6011 2·10 —2	16·20	0·5226	16·88	0·5436	17·29
K_2O	0·94	0·0198		0·28	0·0058	0·12	0·0042	0·58
H_2O^+	0·37	0·0410		0·33	0·0366	—	—	0·66
H_2O^-	0·10	—		—	—	—	—	0·20
P_2O_5	nil	O = 2·5851	2·5851 9·05 —9	—	—	—	—	—
Total	99·85	—	—	99·75	—	99·87	—	99·08
Specific gravity	3·42			3·43		—		—
Analyst	Kazakova			Beloglazov		Kurbatov		Fioletova
Reference				Minerals of the Khibiny and Lovozero tundras (1937)				Gerasimovskii's data

* 0·09 per cent of this is Ta_2O_5

Strontium, nickel, beryllium, phosphorus, tin, copper, zinc, lead and gallium have been spectroscopically detected in rock and pegmatite ramsayite (18 analyses).

In the rocks ramsayite is an accessory mineral. In the differentiated complex it is present in the aegirine- and hornblende-lujavrites, more rarely in the foyaites, in amounts varying from 0·1 to 0·5 per cent. It does not occur in the urtites, ijolitic urtites or malignites. In these rocks the ramsayite content is inversely

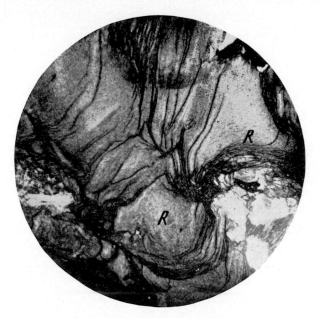

Fig. 179. Fibrous ramsayite (R).   ×20. Without analyser

proportional to the amounts of other titaniferous minerals. In the rocks enriched in these minerals ramsayite occurs in very small amounts or is absent. The amounts of murmanite and lamprophyllite decrease with depth, particularly in the lower part of the complex, while the ramsayite content increases.

In the eudialytic lujavrites ramsayite is present in amounts varying from 0·1 to 0·5 per cent or, rarely, more; the ramsayite content is found to increase from the leucocratic to the melanocratic varieties. Ramsayite occurs extremely rarely in the porphyritic rocks of this complex.

The ramsayite distribution in the rocks of the poikilitic syenite complex is uneven. In the sodalitic and hackmanitic varieties, in which lomonosovite, murmanite and lamprophyllite have developed extensively, it is either absent or occurs in very small amounts. The largest quantities are found in the nepheline and hydrosodalitic poikilitic syenites, where the ramsayite content amounts to 1 per cent, rising in some parts to 3 per cent.

Ramsayite is commoner in the pegmatites than in the rocks. In the pegmatites of the differentiated complex emplaced in the lujavrites and in the pegmatites of the eudialytic lujavrite complex it appears as one of the main minerals. It is usually localized in the feldspathic-aegirine zones of the large differentiated pegmatite bodies or in the central parts of undifferentiated pegmatites; it rarely occurs in the fine-grained border zones.

In the rocks ramsayite fills up interstices between nepheline, microcline, aegirine and hornblende (Fig. 180) and contains inclusions of apatite, sphene, loparite and ilmenite. In the eudialytic lujavrites eudialyite is observed to be idiomorphic in relation to ramsayite (Fig. 181), whereas in the rocks of the other complex ramsayite separated before eudialyte. Lamprophyllite and the minerals of the lomonosovite-murmanite group usually fill up interstices between ramsayite segregations, often replacing them from the periphery. The groundmass ramsayite in the pegmatites is concentrated in the interstices between large microcline crystals, but is sometimes found to be idiomorphic in relation to microcline (Fig. 182). Lamellar ramsayite seems to have crystallized at the end of the period of microcline formation. In degree of idiomorphism ramsayite yields place to arfvedsonite and often contains inclusions of the latter. It usually fills up, together with eudialyte and aegirine II, interstices between microcline and arfvedsonite. Ramsayite grains are often included in an aegirine II aggregate; moreover, late aegirine penetrates the ramsayite crystals along cracks. Pegmatite ramsayite is a later mineral than eudialyte, since it often contains inclusions of eudialyte and usually occupies spaces between crystals of the latter. More rarely (in the fine-grained pegmatite zones) ramsayite is idiomorphic to eudialyte or forms inclusions in eudialyte and sodalite.

Lamellar ramsayite crystallized after lamprophyllite, inclusions of which are found in it, but earlier than murmanite, which fills up interstices between its crystals.

Well crystallized ramsayite and the finely-crystalline variety are extensively developed in the pegmatites of the differentiated complex on Flora, where the albitization process is very apparent. Albite forms poikilitic growths with ramsayite (Fig. 183) or attacks its crystals, producing typical corrosion structures. In all probability this ramsayite is connected with the albitization stage and the bulk of it crystallized before albite.

Ramsayite is sometimes replaced by neptunite and leucoxene.

29. Lamprophyllite

$Na_4Sr_2Fe_2Ti_4Si_6O_{25}F_2$; mon.; sp.gr. 3·38—3·46; H. 2—3

Lamprophyllite is present in all the Lovozero rock types and in most of the pegmatites. In the rocks it occurs most frequently in the form of long tabular crystals or crystal aggregates. Individual crystals attain a length of 0·5-1 cm and a width of 0·2-0·3 cm. The crystal aggregates measure $1·5 \times 1 \times 0·3$ cm. In the foyaites of the differentiated complex, the poikilitic syenites and the porphyritic lujavrites stellate clusters of aciculate lamprophyllite crystals measuring up to 0·5-1 cm in diameter are sometimes to be found and, more rarely, irregularly-

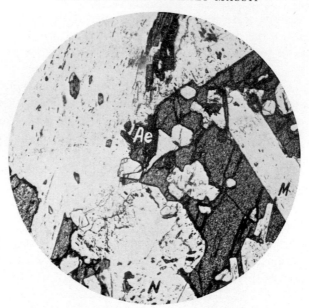

FIG. 180. Interrelationship between ramsayite (dark) and microcline (M), nepheline (N) and aegirine (Ae). ×46. Without analyser

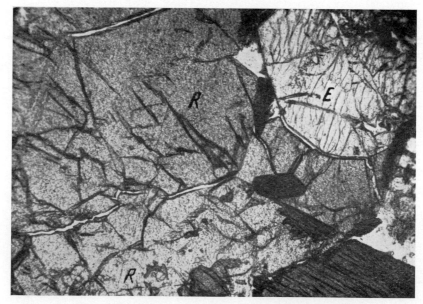

FIG. 181. Interrelationship between ramsayite (R) and eudialyte (E). Dark patches: arfvedsonite. ×46. Without analyser

FIG. 182. Interrelationship between ramsayite (R) and microcline (M). ×10. Crossed nicols

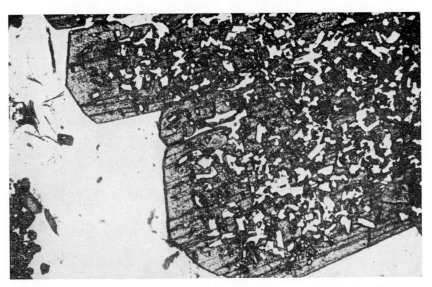

FIG. 183. Poikilitic inclusions of albite (light) in ramsayite (dark). ×46. Without analyser

shaped segregations of finely acicular and felted fabric measuring up to 0·5 × 0·3 × 0·2 cm.

In the pegmatites lamprophyllite occurs most widely in the form of long prismatic platy crystals, measuring up to 3 × 0·6 × 0·4 cm, in finely granular zones and in the form of sheaf-like aggregates of platy crystals up to 20 cm long in block feldspathic-aegirine zones. Radiate-fibrous aggregates of platy lamprophyllite crystals, up to 10 cm in diameter, occur in the large pegmatitic bodies of the differentiated complex and the eudialytic lujavrite complex. More rarely, finely acicular and fibrous segregations are found in close association with aegirine II; such lamprophyllite, together with aegirine II, sometimes forms coronas round aenigmatite ('coronites'). Lamprophyllite crystals are usually elongated along

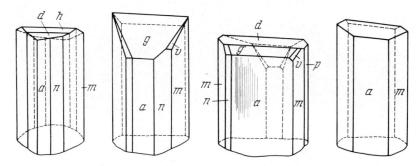

FIG. 184. Lamprophyllite crystals (after Bonshtedt)

the z-axis; terminal faces are seldom found (Fig. 184). Bonshtedt (1930) made a crystallographic study of lamprophyllite and established that it belonged to the monoclinic system. She gives the axial ratios as $a : b : c = 0·9231 : 1 : 0·6052$; $\beta = 102°43'$. Eleven forms were established for lamprophyllite: $a(100)$, $r(230)$, $n(530)$, $m(110)$, $p(130)$, $h(304)$, $e(101)$, $g(301)$, $t(551)$, $s(111)$ and $v(851)$.

The colour is dark-brown, brownish-yellow and straw yellow, sometimes reddish-brown with a golden tint. The finely acicular and fibrous varieties are the lightest in colour. Streak pale yellow, sometimes with orange tint. Opaque, translucent in thin sections. Brittle. Fracture uneven. Cleavage highly perfect along (100), so that the mineral readily divides into thin plates. Lustre on cleavage planes submetallic. Specific gravity varies between 3·388 and 3·461 and is lower in the lamprophyllite from the eudialytic lujavrites and in the finely fibrous and stellate segregations than in the long prismatic crystals.

In thin sections all varieties of lamprophyllite are yellow. Pleochroism clearly marked: Ng—orange-yellow, Nm—straw-yellow, Np—yellow, pale yellow. Absorption scheme: $Ng > Nm \geqslant Np$. Optically biaxial, positive. Elongation positive; $2V$ varies from 21° to 41°. Optic axial plane ⊥ (010); $Np = y$. Twinning usually on (100), more rarely polysynthetic. Extinction angle $c : Ng$ varies from 3° to 8°. Refractive indices: $Ng = 1·775$-$1·781$; $Np = 1·745$—$1·749$; $Ng - Np = 0·030$—$0·032$.

Lamprophyllite is readily soluble in concentrated HCl and HNO_3 and very

TABLE 89 Chemical composition of lamprophyllite (per cent)

Constituent	From foyaite of differentiated complex (Karnasurt) per cent	Atomic proportions	Calculation of atomic ratios	From eudialytic lujavrite	Sengischorr	From pegmatite — Chinglusuai valley	From pegmatite — Chinglusuai valley
SiO_2	30·93	0·5150	0·5260 6·00 —6	29·60	30·80	31·76	31·75
Al_2O_3	0·56	0·0110		0·66	—	—	—
TiO_2	27·14	0·3522	0·3534 4·03 —4	29·78	31·26	30·33	25·26
ZrO_2	—	—		—	0·05	—	—
$(Nb,Ta)_2O_5$	0·16	0·0012		0·62	not determined	—	0·29
Fe_2O_3	1·36	0·0170		0·78	0·37	2·79	5·21
FeO	2·31	0·0321	0·1077 1·73 —2	2·95	3·16	2·92	3·29
MnO	3·46	0·0487		2·61	3·21	0·18	0·26
MgO	0·40	0·0099		0·30	0·53	4·85	1·72
CaO	2·48	0·0442		1·83	1·20	7·46	16·76
SrO	14·12	0·1362	0·2031 2·32 —2	13·43	14·49	1·44	0·56
BaO	3·49	0·0227		1·47	1·09	12·15	10·83
Na_2O	10·64	0·3432	0·3699 4·21 —4	11·84	12·70	0·73	1·50
K_2O	1·26	0·0267	0·1754 2·00 —2	1·16	—	other 0·75	0·36
H_2O^+	0·56	0·0622		0·62	0·39		1·83
F	1·10	0·0578		1·34	1·65	—	—
H_2O^-	0·16	—		0·26	—	—	—
Cl	—	—	2·2402 24·79 —25	0·08	0·27	—	0·62
		O = 2·2402					
Total	100·13	—	—	99·33	101·17	—	100·24
$-O = (F,Cl)_2$	−0·46			−0·60	−0·76		−0·91
	99·67	—	—	98·73	100·41	—	99·33
Analyst	Kazakova, 1949–1951			Vlodavets, 1929		Beloglazov, 1924	Borneman, 1929
Reference	—					Bonshtedt (1930)	

poorly soluble in H_2SO_4. Comparative chemical analyses of the lamprophyllite from different rocks (Table 89) shows that there is less F, H_2O, FeO, Al_2O_3 and Nb_2O_5 and more MnO, CaO, BaO, Fe_2O_3 and MgO in the foyaite lamprophyllite than in the eudialytic lujavrite variety. The fluorine and iron content of pegmatitic lamprophyllite is higher.

All the chemical analyses of lamprophyllite can be well expressed by the formula $Na_4Sr_2Fe_2Ti_4Si_6O_{25}F_2$ suggested by Borneman (1947). She believes that the isomorphism in titanosilicates is not atomic but molecular and suggests that lamprophyllite should be regarded as a solid solution of the fluorine-strontium compound $Sr_2Fe_2Si_2O_7F_2$ and ramsayite $2Na_2Ti_2Si_2O_9$.

On this basis we can represent the formula for lamprophyllite as $2Na_2Ti_2Si_2O_9 + Sr_2Fe_2Si_2O_7F_2$. Between 67 per cent and 74 per cent of the $Na_2Ti_2Si_2O_9$ molecule and between 26 per cent and 33 per cent of the $Sr_2Fe_2Si_2O_7F_2$ molecule enters into the composition of the pegmatitic lamprophyllite. The Lovozero rock lamprophyllites examined by us contained 66·72-73·16 per cent of the $Na_2Ti_2Si_2O_9$ molecule and 26-32·65 per cent of the $Sr_2Fe_2Si_2O_7F_2$ molecule (Table 90).

Beryllium, lead, copper, vanadium and cerium were detected in lamprophyllite spectroscopically.

This mineral is most characteristic of the leucocratic rocks (foyaites, porphyritic foyaites and poikilitic sodalite-syenites), which have a high fluorine and strontium content (Table 91).

In the rocks of the differentiated complex, which are richest in lamprophyllite, the highest lamprophyllite content occurs in the roofs and the central parts of the foyaitic horizons (up to 2·7 per cent). As the foyaites gradually give way to juvites and urtites the lamprophyllite content falls to 0·5 per cent. In the lujavritic horizons of each three-component stratal group the lamprophyllite content reaches 1 per cent, gradually increasing from the roofs to the underlying foyaites in proportion to the increase in feldspar content in the lujavrites.

In the poorly differentiated middle part of the complex the lamprophyllite content in the aegirine-lujavrites rises to 2·5 per cent and increases slightly in the leucocratic varieties of these rocks. The aegirine-lujavrites of the undifferentiated parts of the complex always contain more lamprophyllite than the lujavrites of the differentiated parts. The lamprophyllite content in the lower part of the complex is far lower than in the middle and upper parts.

The mineral is present in all rock types in the eudialytic lujavrite complex, the content increasing from the melanocratic to the leucocratic varieties as the amount of eudialyte decreases. In the porphyritic rocks the lamprophyllite

TABLE 90 $Na_2Ti_2Si_2O_9$ and $Sr_2Fe^{2+}_2Si_2O_7F_2$ content in lamprophyllite

Constituent	Analysis		
	1	2	3
$Na_2Ti_2Si_2O_9$	66·72	73·16	73·62
$Sr_2Fe''_2·Si_2O_7F_2$	32·65	26·11	26·38

FIG. 185. Interrelationship of lamprophyllite (grey) with microcline (M) and nepheline (N). ×46. Without analyser

FIG. 186. Arfvedsonite relict (A) in lamprophyllite. ×46. Without analyser

TABLE 91 Lamprophyllite content in rocks

Differentiated complex	Content, per cent	Eudialytic lujavrite complex	Content, per cent	Poikilitic syenite complex	Content, per cent
Upper division of complex:		Eudialytic lujavrites:		Poikilitic sodalite-syenites	0·1-1·3
Foyaites	0·3-2·7	Melanocratic	0·3-1·0	Poikilitic nepheline-syenites	0-0·9
Urtites	0-0·5	Mesocratic	0·5-1·4	Poikilitic hydrosodalite-syenites	0-0·3
Aegirine-lujavrites	0-1·0	Leucocratic	0·4-2·3		
Hornblende-lujavrites	0·1-0·3	Porphyritic lujavrites	0·05-0·8		
Malignites	0-0·15	Porphyritic juvites	0·3-1·0		
Middle divison of complex:		Porphyritic foyaites	2·2		
Foyaites	0·5-1·8				
Urtites	0-0·1				
Aegirine-lujavrites	0·3-2·5				
Hornblende-lujavrites	0-0·3				
Lower division of complex:					
Foyaites	0·5-1·2				
Urtites	0-0·05				
Aegirine-lujavrites	0·2-0·5				

content is found to rise as the porphyritic lujavrites give way to porphyritic juvites and foyaites. In the porphyritic lujavrites and juvites there is less lamprophyllite in regions with a high loparite content.

Lamprophyllite occurs rarely and in small amounts in the rocks of the poikilitic syenite complex (see Table 91). The nepheline and hydrosodalitic poikilitic syenites invariably contain less lamprophyllite than the sodalitic and hackmanitic varieties.

In the pegmatites lamprophyllite occurs in all the complexes but is most widespread in the eudialytic lujavrite pegmatites. It is usually localized in the

FIG. 187. Lamprophyllite inclusions (L) in microcline. ×46. Crossed nicols

marginal fine-grained or block zones of the large differentiated pegmatitic bodies or in the central parts of the undifferentiated pegmatites, which are rich in aegirine II, where it is closely associated with ramsayite, eudialyte, nepheline and aegirine II.

In the rocks and in the pegmatites lamprophyllite is usually associated with sodic rare-metal and accessory minerals. It is characteristically associated with lomonosovite, murmanite, ramsayite, eudialyte and villiaumite.

In the rocks lamprophyllite fills up spaces between nepheline (Fig. 185) and microcline, often lodging in the marginal parts of microcline crystals. Its relationship to aegirine II is ambiguous: in most cases it cements the latter, but sometimes lamprophyllite inclusions can be found in aegirine II. Arfvedsonite sometimes contains small lamprophyllite crystals in its margins; more commonly, however, it is replaced by lamprophyllite (Fig. 186). Loparite, apatite, sphene and ramsayite fairly often form inclusions in lamprophyllite. All the remaining rare-metal minerals in the rocks—lomonosovite, murmanite, eudialyte and others—fill up

LAM 2B

spaces between lamprophyllite segregations. In the rocks of the eudialytic lujavrite complex eudialyte is earlier than lamprophyllite.

In the pegmatites lamprophyllite is one of the early minerals. It is usually more idiomorphic than ramsayite and eudialyte, and is often included in the marginal parts of microcline crystals (Fig. 187). In relation to nepheline it is xenomorphic. The bulk of the lamprophyllite, along with ramsayite and eudialyte, occurs in interstices between microcline crystals. Inclusions of idiomorphic lamprophyllite crystals are sometimes to be found in arfvedsonite.

The acicular and fibrous varieties seem to have separated at the same time as aegirine II, with which they form felted mineral mixtures.

In the pegmatites lamprophyllite is replaced by leucoxene during the process of alteration; in the rocks it is usually unaltered.

30. Astrophyllite

$(K,Na)_2(Fe,Mn)_4Ti [Si_2O_7]_2(OH,F)_2$; mon.; sp.gr. 3·3; H. 3

The Lovozero astrophyllite was first described by Gerasimovskii. It occurs very rarely and in negligible amounts, in the form of tabular segregations ranging in size from a few mm to $3·5 \times 8$ cm. Colour dark golden-brown. Streak brownish-yellow. Transparent in thin flakes. Cleavage perfect in one direction. Lustre brilliant, on cleavage planes pearly. Brittle. Fracture uneven. Yellow in thin sections. Optically biaxial, positive. Extinction angle $c : Ng = 3$-$8°$, elongation positive. Refractive indices: $Ng = 1·738$, $Nm = 1·707$ (Gerasimovskii's data). Clearly-marked pleochroism: Ng—greenish-yellow; Nm—orange-yellow; Np—bright orange; absorption scheme: $Np > Nm > Ng$.

Astrophyllite is readily soluble in HCl, poorly in HNO_3 and very poorly in H_2SO_4. No chemical analysis was made. Apart from the principal constituents, magnesium, aluminium, zirconium, strontium, barium, niobium, copper, beryllium and zinc were detected by spectrographic analysis in the pegmatitic astrophyllite of Malyi Punkaruaiv and Alluaiv.

In the pegmatites astrophyllite is known as a secondary mineral. Gerasimovskii found it on Malyi Punkaruaiv in two pegmatitic bodies emplaced in the foyaites of the differentiated complex, as a secondary mineral on aenigmatite. In these bodies it occurs in association with nepheline, microcline, aegirine, eudialyte, sodalite, ramsayite and aenigmatite.

In 1950 Tikhonenkov succeeded in finding astrophyllite in the pegmatite of the First Western stream on Alluaiv, in close association with secondary ramsayite, and also in the form of a single xenomorphic segregation between nepheline grains.

31. Kupletskite

$K_2Mn_4Ti [Si_2O_7]_2(OH,F)_2$; mon.; sp.gr. 3·201; H. 3

Kupletskite was first detected in the Lovozero alkali massif and studied by Semenov (1956). This mineral belongs to the astrophyllite group, from which it is distinguished by its physical properties and chemical composition. It is the manganese-bearing end-member of the isomorphous series astrophyllite—kupletskite.

Kupletskite forms tabular finely-scaly segregations measuring up to $5 \times 3 \times 1$ cm. The colour is dark-brown to black; streak brown. Lustre on cleavage planes high, vitreous. Optically biaxial, negative. Refractive indices: $Ng = 1.731$; $Nm = 1.699$; Np (calculated) $= 1.656$; $2V = (-)79°$. Dispersion of optic axes strong: $r > v$. Pleochroic from cinnamon-brown (Ng) to orange-yellow (Np). Absorption system: $Ng > Np$. Elongation positive. Powder pattern similar to that of astrophyllite (Table 92).

Recalculation of the chemical analyses (Table 93) by Semenov showed that its composition was expressed by the conventional formula for minerals of the astrophyllite group: $(K, Na)_2(Fe, Mn)_4(Ti, Zr)[Si_2O_7]_2(OH,F)_2$.

A tenor of about 1 per cent strontium, 0·2 per cent rubidium, 0·1 per cent cerium and 0·1 per cent neodymium was established by the X-ray chemical method. Beryllium, zinc, gallium and tantalum were detected spectroscopically.

Isomorphism of potassium with sodium, calcium, barium and rubidium, of titanium with niobium and of iron with manganese is a common phenomenon in minerals of the astrophyllite group, including kupletskite (see Table 93). Kupletskite contains the largest amounts of manganese, niobium (2·48-4·35 per cent) calcium and barium of any mineral in the astrophyllite group. The total content of iron and manganese together in the astrophyllite minerals is always constant, an increase in the amount of iron entailing a decrease in the amount of manganese. The amount of the oxides of these elements contained in the minerals of this group varies widely: FeO from 34 to 5 per cent, MnO from 28 to 1 per cent. Semenov was thus able to establish a continuous isomorphous series of minerals from astrophyllite to kupletskite, in which astrophyllite $K_2Fe_4Ti[Si_2O_7]_2(OH)_2$ is the iron-rich end-member and kupletskite $K_2Mn_4Ti[Si_2O_7]_2(OH)_2$ the manganese-rich end member, minerals in which the Mn : Fe ratio is greater than unity being referred to as kupletskite, as distinct from astrophyllite, in which the Mn : Fe ratio is less than unity.

TABLE 92 Interplanar spacings of kupletskite and astrophyllite
(Analyst Sludskaya)

Kupletskite		Astrophyllite		Kupletskite		Astrophyllite	
l	d, Å	l	d, Å	l	d, Å	l	d, Å
8	3·505	10	3·49	—	—	1	2·03
1	3·249	1	3·23	—	—	4	1·757
1	2·998	1	3·03	3	1·732	3	1·729
1	2·764	1	2·76	1	1·665	2	1·651
8	2·642	10	2·63	1	1·590	2	1·594
4	2·573	3	2·59	—	—	2	1·576
1	2·423	1	2·47	1	1·553	1	1·552
—	—	1	2·38	1	1·438	2	1·435
1	2·294	1	2·29	1	1·408	1	1·407
1	2·212	1	2·22	—	—	1	1·314
3	2·099	4	2·10				

TABLE 93 Chemical compositions of minerals of the astrophyllite-kupletskite group

Constituent	Kupletskite				Astrophyllite					
	Kuivchorr		Lepkhe-Nel'm		Langesund-fjord (Norway)	Lake Los (Africa)	Khibiny (USSR)	Keivy (USSR)	Colorado (USA)	Greenland
	per cent	Atomic proportions	per cent	Atomic proportions						
SiO_2	32·60	0·543	33·54	0·559	33·81	34·22	34·78	not det.	34·68	34·1
TiO_2	12·04	0·150	10·64	0·133	8·02	8·96	11·86	10·36	13·58	12·2
ZrO_2	1·19	0·010	nil	—	5·34	3·89	0·57	not det.	2·20	0·8
Nb_2O_5	0·66	0·005	2·48	0·019	—	not det.	not det.	„ „	0·80	—
Al_2O_3	1·68	0·032	1·00	0·020	1·72	1·31	0·60	„ „	0·70	1·2
Fe_2O_3	5·44	0·068	7·80	0·098	4·36	3·98	2·76 ⎱	„ „ ⎱	6·56	3·9
FeO			5·35	0·074	16·58	20·18	26·71 ⎰	34·23 ⎰	26·10	29·8
MnO	27·65	0·389	23·60	0·331	15·18	12·97	6·65	1·38	3·48	2·8
MgO	2·98	0·074	1·63	0·040	0·63	1·07	1·54	—	0·30	0·9
CaO	3·60	0·064	1·45	0·026	1·16	0·72	1·66	2·12	0·42	1·2
BaO	—	—	0·32	0·002	not det.	—	0·15	—	—	not det.
K_2O	4·38	0·093	5·63	0·120	6·12	5·85	5·90	3·50	5·61	6·7
Na_2O	2·14	0·069	2·14	0·068	3·18	2·96	3·00	2·16	2·54	2·2
$H_2O^{+110°}$	3·83	0·426	3·90	0·434	3·43	3·62	2·98	—	3·54	3·3
$H_2O^{-110°}$	1·08	0·112	0·80	0·090	not det.	—	0·11	not det.	not det.	not det.
F	1·22	0·064	—	—	0·70	not det.	1·21	„ „	„ „	„ „
Total $-O=F_2$	100·49 −0·51	—	100·28	—	100·23 −0·30	99·73	100·48 0·44	—	100·51	99·1
	99·98	—	—	—	100·23	—	100·04	—	—	—
Analyst	Burova		Moleva		Reindl'	Kunits	Vlodavets	Tishenk	Kenig	Kunits
Reference	Semenov (1956)				B. Gossner (1935)	A. Lacroix (1911)	Minerals of the Khibiny and Lovozero tundras (1937)	Semenov (1956)		O. Böggild (1905)

Kupletskitc occurs in the pegmatites of the central part of the massif (Lepkhe-Nel'm and Kuivchorr), both in the fine-grained contact and in the central zones. In the former it forms idiomorphic ingrowths in microcline and eudialyte or replaces ramsayite and eudialyte from the margin inwards. In the central zeolitic zones it occurs in the form of finely-scaly segregations in close association with schizolite, neptunite and other manganese minerals.

Kupletskite separated later than lamprophyllite and zircon.

The appearance of manganese minerals of the astrophyllite group in the Lovozero massif is connected with the general increase in manganese content in the pegmatites, where manganese varieties of other minerals also occur (mangan-ilmenite and mangan-neptunite).

32. Mangan-neptunite

$(Na,K)_2(Mn,Fe)TiSi_4O_{12}$; mon.; sp.gr. 3·19; H. 5—6

This mineral is widespread in the Lovozero alkali massif and occurs in almost all the rock types and most of the pegmatites. In the non-pegmatitic rocks it takes the form of xenomorphic grains measuring $0·2 \times 0·1 \times 0·1$ cm in the sodalitized and natrolitized sectors. In addition it forms thin borders round altered segregations of lamprophyllite, murmanite and lomonosovite and also fills up veinlets in these minerals. In the pegmatites it occurs as segregations of various shapes, usually forming earthy crusts and blooms on aegirine II and other minerals, more rarely taking the form of crystals measuring $6 \times 3 \times 2$ cm, sometimes grouped into monomineralic aggregates measuring up to $30 \times 5 \times 5$ cm. It can also be seen in the form of irregularly-shaped segregations measuring up to $3 \times 2 \times 1$ cm, small crystals up to 1·5 mm in diameter in leaching cavities on microcline faces, druses and rosettes up to 1-2 cm in diameter consisting of a large number of small crystals measuring up to 1-2 mm along the long axis, in the cavities of aegirine II and natrolite.

Mangan-neptunite crystals have a prismatic habit and are somewhat elongated along the z axis. According to Kravchenko (1936) the following forms occur: c (001), a (100), b (010), m (110), s ($\bar{1}11$), o (111), ρ ($\bar{3}11$), i ($\bar{1}12$), r ($\bar{2}21$) and k ($\bar{3}21$)

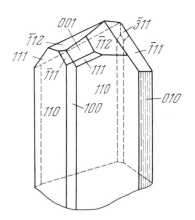

(Fig. 188). The mineral is dark-red to black in small crystals. In thin fragments it is translucent cherry-red, and in powder and fine-grained aggregates brown. Streak brick-red. Lustre vitreous. Fracture uneven. Opaque. Brittle. In thin sections mangan-neptunite is light-yellow, orange and orange-red. The middle of the grain is often tinted yellow while the peripheral part has an orange or orange-red tint. Cleavage distinct in two directions, intersecting at an angle of about

FIG. 188. Neptunite crystal (after Kravchenko)

[Face-symbols as in Russian original. Eds.]

80°. Optically biaxial, positive. Pleochroism distinctly shown: Ng—orange-red; Nm—orange or orange-yellow; Np—light yellow. Absorption scheme: $Ng > Nm > Np$. Extinction angle $c : Ng = 15\text{-}17°$. Refractive indices vary: $Ng = 1\cdot713$—$1\cdot728$; $Nm = 1\cdot696$—$1\cdot698$; $Np = 1\cdot694$—$1\cdot696$; $Ng - Np = 0\cdot020$—$0\cdot032$; $2V = 31\text{-}34°$. Axial dispersion very strong; $v > r$. Optic axial plane parallel to (010).

Mangan-neptunite is not soluble in HCl, HNO_3 or H_2SO_4. Recalculation of the chemical analysis (Table 94) shows that the composition of the Lovozero mangan-neptunites is on the whole expressed by the conventional chemical formula for this mineral $(Na, K)_2(Mn, Fe)TiSi_4 O_{12}$. The high lithium oxide content is an interesting peculiarity of this mineral (up to $1\cdot08$ per cent Li_2O).

Niobium, strontium, beryllium, zirconium, barium, lead, copper, gallium and lanthanum have been detected spectroscopically (5 analyses) in the mangan-neptunite from different parts of the massif, the highest beryllium content having been found in the mangan-neptunite from the pegmatites in the Karnasurt poikilitic (hackmanitic) syenite complex and the highest niobium content in the mangan-neptunite from the pegmatites of the eudialytic lujavrite complex in the upper part of the Tyul'bn'yunuai Valley.

All the neptunite varieties known at present can be distinguished from one another by their content of iron and manganese. The Lovozero mangan-neptunite is the manganese-bearing end-member of the neptunite mineral series. Differences in the chemical composition of minerals in this group produce modification of

TABLE 94   Chemical composition of mangan-neptunite

| Constituent | Karnasurt | | | Tyul'bn'unuai Valley* |
	per cent	Atomic proportions	Calculation of atomic ratios	
SiO_2	52·65	0·8766	0·8766 3·94 —4	53·58
TiO_2	17·38	0·2175	0·2175 0·98 —1	15·07
Al_2O_3	0·99	0·0194		—
Fe_2O_3	1·07	0·0134		1·70
FeO	5·54	0·0771	0·2387 1·07 —1	2·68
MnO	8·87	0·1251		12·94
MgO	0·15	0·0037		nil
CaO	0·37	0·0066		0·40
Na_2O	5·12	0·1652	0·3778 1·70 —2	8·78
K_2O	6·30	0·1338		5·36
Li_2O	1·08	0·0722		not determined
MnO	nil	—	—	,, ,,
RE_2O_3	,,	—	—	,, ,,
H_2O^+	0·06	—	—	0·04
H_2O^-	0·10	—	—	0·08
		O = 2·6355	2·6355 11·86 —12	—
Total	99·68	—	—	100·63
Specific gravity	3·17	—	—	—
Analyst	Kazakova			Nesterova

* Gerasimovskii's data (1936_2)

the optical properties (Table 95): as the manganese tenor increases and iron decreases the refractive indices, the birefringence and the optic axial angle decrease.

Mangan-neptunite is present in amounts up to 0·1 per cent in the non-pegmatitic Lovozero rocks. The highest content has been found in the poikilitic sodalite-syenites and foyaites of the differentiated complex. In the lujavrites (aegirine-, hornblende- and eudialytic) it occurs rarely, and it is completely absent from the urtites and ijolite-urtites.

In time of segregation this is again one of the late Lovozero minerals. It fills up interstices between murmanite, lomonosovite, lamprophyllite, eudialyte, mesodialyte, pectolite and villiaumite and appears in the form of inclusions in large segregations of replacement sodalite. Such mangan-neptunite seems to have crystallized directly from the melt at late stages of the rock formation. In addition, secondary mangan-neptunite, forming fringes and segregations of irregular shape on murmanite, lomonosovite, minerals of the eudialyte-eucolite group and others, occurs in the rocks and fills up cracks in them, in close association with natrolite.

Mangan-neptunite is more widespread in the pegmatites than in the rocks and often occurs in considerable quantities in them. It is usually found in the central parts of the bodies where it forms large crystals in natrolite or ussingite, or in the zeolitized parts of outer fine-grained zones, or else in feldspathic aegirine zones, where it appears in the form of earthy crusts and blooms on aegirine II, or sometimes as large irregular aggregates of fine grains in replacement zones, cemented by black manganese hydroxides.

Both in the pegmatites and in the non-pegmatitic rocks a distinction should be made between early and late mangan-neptunite. The former occurs as large crystals and irregular aggregations in natrolite (Fig. 189) and ussingite in the central pegmatite zones (Lepkhe-Nel'm, Malyi Punkaruaiv and elsewhere) and seems to be earlier than these minerals. The fine-grained mangan-neptunite represented in the Karnasurt pegmatites, which forms crusts on rods of aegirine II in replacement zones and fills up cavities in aegirine II, is later. It crystallized after the bulk of the prismatic natrolite precipitated, from late hydrothermal solutions enriched in manganese, iron and titanium in the process of replacement

TABLE 95 Comparison of some properties of neptunite from different deposits
(Gerasimovskii's data)

Property	California	Greenland	Khibiny tundra	Lovozero tundra
Content, per cent:				
Fe_2O_3	—	—	—	1·70
FeO	11·23-11·69	10·23-10·91	5·16	2·68- 5·54
MnO	0·85-1·78	4·97-5·22	9·95	8·87-12·94
***				
Ng	—	1·736	1·722	1·713-1·728
Nm	—	1·700	1·695	1·696-1·698
Np	1·700	1·690	1·693	1·694-1·696
$Ng-Np$	—	0·046	0·029	0·020-0·032
$2V$	48°	49°	—	31·34°

of eudialyte, schizolite, murmanite and other early minerals. Secondary neptunite formed in the process of alteration of ramsayite, lamprophyllite and other titanium minerals should also be classified as late mangan-neptunite.

FIG. 189. Interrelationship between neptunite (N), natrolite (Na) and late aegirine (Ae); A: arfvedsonite. ×46. Crossed nicols

33. Aenigmatite

$Na_2(Fe,Mn)_6Ti [Si_2O_7]_3$; tric.; sp.gr. 3·73; H. 5·5—6

Aenigmatite is present in the Lovozero alkali massif mainly in the pegmatites of the differentiated complex. In particular, it has been found in large amounts in the pegmatites of Flora, Karnasurt, Punkaruaiv, Kitkn'yun and other mountains, in the form of irregularly-shaped segregations measuring up to 10×5 cm and also as poorly-developed crystals from 1 cm long to $8 \times 2 \times 2$ cm. The colour is velvet-black. Streak dark brown with reddish tinge. Lustre greasy to semi-metallic. Opaque. Fracture uneven. In thin sections aenigmatite is reddish-brown to black. Pleochroism distinctly shown: Ng—black; Nm—reddish-brown; Np—light-brown. Absorption scheme: $Ng>Nm>Np$. Cleavage distinct in one direction. Optically biaxial, positive. Refractive indices: Ng—1·89; Np—1·79-1·8. Extinction angle $c : Ng$ 40-44° (Gerasimovskii, 1936_2).

Aenigmatite is poorly soluble in concentrated acids. Its chemical composition (Table 96) is given by the formula $Na_2(Fe, Mn)_6TiSi_6O_{21}$, suggested by Borneman, but some iron and manganese deficiency has been observed (*Minerals of the Khibiny and Lovozero tundras*, 1937). A content of about 10^{-3} per cent of strontium, zinc, beryllium, vanadium, copper and gallium and also of lead was shown by spectroscopic analysis.

Aenigmatite is usually closely associated with aegirine II, eudialyte and microcline. It is later than the last two, for it fills up cracks between them along with aegirine II; it is earlier than aegirine II itself. Aegirine II fills up spaces between aenigmatite segregations and jointly with lamprophyllite or astrophyllite forms radiate-fibrous outgrowths round aenigmatite, replacing it.

TABLE 96   Chemical composition of aenigmatite
(Gerasimovskii's data)

Constituent	Content, per cent	Atomic proportions	Calculation of atomic ratios		
SiO_2	40·86	0·6803	0·6803	5·94	—6
TiO_2	8·16	0·1146	0·1146	0·9	—1
Al_2O_3	1·87	0·0366			
Fe_2O_3	6·28	0·0786			
FeO	31·50	0·4384	0·6201	5·41	—6
MnO	2·42	0·0341			
MgO	1·31	0·0324			
CaO	0·48	0·0085			
Na_2O	6·58	0·2122	0·2337	2·04	—2
K_2O	0·62	0·0130			
H_2O^+	0·21	0·0334		—	
H_2O^-	0·04	—		—	
F	—	—		—	
Cl	trace	—		—	
S	0·14	—		—	
		O = 2·4003	2·4003	20·95	—21
Total	100·47	—		—	
Analyst		Vladimirova			

34. Narsarsukite

$Na_2(Ti,Fe)Si_4O_{10}(OH,F)$; tetrag.; sp.gr. 2·75; H. 7—7·5

Narsarsukite was first discovered and studied in the Lovozero alkali massif by Gerasimovskii, who found it in the albitized contact zone between the nepheline-syenites and a xenolith of Devonian rocks on the north-west slope of Flora. In other parts of the massif it has either not been found or is present in very small amounts (Vavnbed and Strashempakhk). Our description is based on Gerasimov-skii's data.

Narsarsukite has developed in the form of separate lath-like crystals measuring up to 1×0.3 cm or of continuous fine-grained segregations included in a mass of saccharoidal albite. Colour yellow; in altered varieties, light-yellow or yellowish-brown. Reliable determinations of specific gravity, hardness, fracture, lustre and other properties have proved impossible, because of the large number of albite inclusions (up to 50 per cent of the total volume). These albite inclusions are orientated in various directions.

In thin sections narsarsukite is colourless or slightly yellowish-tinted. Inter-ference colours bright, of the 1st and 2nd order. Optically uniaxial, positive.

Refractive indices: $Ne=1\cdot623$ and $No=1\cdot607$. Elongation negative. Cleavage perfect perpendicular to the crystal elongation. Poorly-shown pleochroism: Ne—pale yellow, sometimes with greenish tinge; No colourless.

Acid-insoluble. Table 97 shows the results of chemical analysis of Flora narsarsukite. The material analysed contained a large number of albite inclusions that could not be separated. The Table also shows the same analysis recalculated to 100 after subtraction of the oxides of elements forming part of the albite; for comparison, the results of chemical analyses of this mineral from Greenland and Montana are also given.

Zirconium, copper, niobium, gallium, vanadium, strontium and beryllium were detected spectroscopically in the Flora narsarsukite.

Recalculation of the chemical analysis results showed that the composition of Greenland narsarsukite was expressed by the formula $Na_2(Ti,Fe)Si_4O_{10}(O,OH,F)$, whereas a silicon and alkali deficiency is observed in Lovozero narsarsukite.

Apart from the albitized zone on the north-western slope of Flora, where the narsarsukite content in certain places reaches 90 per cent, this mineral has also been found in an albitized pegmatitic body. In addition, narsarsukite was detected by Gerasimovskii on the northern slope of Vavnbed in albitite débris situated at the contact with a pegmatitic body and also on the south-western slope of Strashempakhk, where rare segregations of it are observed along the contact between the alkali rocks and the country rock.

TABLE 97 Chemical composition of narsarsukite
(Gerasimovskii's data)

Consti-tuent	Lovozero massif			Greenland			Montana
	per cent	Recalculation to 100 per cent after deduction of albite	Atomic proportions	per cent	Atomic proportions	Calculation of atomic ratios	per cent
SiO_2	62·51	52·59	0·8752	61·63	1·0255	1·0255 3·94 —4	62·30
TiO_2	7·19	19·25	0·2409	14·00	0·1752 ⎫	—	16·80
Al_2O_3	12·12	—	—	0·28	0·0054 ⎬		0·32
Fe_2O_3	3·61	9·67	0·1214 ⎫	6·30	0·0688 ⎬	0·2619 1·01 —1 ⎫	3·46
FeO	0·13	0·35	0·0049 ⎭			⎬	
MgO	0·37	0·99	0·0245	0·24	0·0059		0·46
MnO	0·04	0·10	0·0014	0·47	0·0066 ⎭	⎭	—
CaO	0·34	0·91	0·0162	—	—	—	0·18
Na_2O	11·83	11·91	0·3842	16·12	0·5204	0·5204 2·00 —2	15·31
K_2O	0·37	0·99	0·0210	—	—	—	0·41
H_2O^+	0·47	1·26 ⎫	0·3596 ⎫	0·29	0·0322 ⎫		not det.
H_2O^-	0·74	1·98 ⎭	⎭		⎬	0·0695 0·27 ⎫	—
Cl	nil	—	—	—	⎭	⎬ 11	—
F	,,	—	—	0·71	0·0373 ⎭	2·7981 10·76 ⎭	—
					$O=2\cdot7981$		
Total	99·72	100·00	—	100·04	—	—	99·24
Analyst	Nesterova						Ellestad

In time of separation narsarsukite is a late mineral, though probably slightly earlier than albite. Albite forms inclusions in it and at the same time fills up interstices between its segregations, corroding them peripherally (Fig. 190).

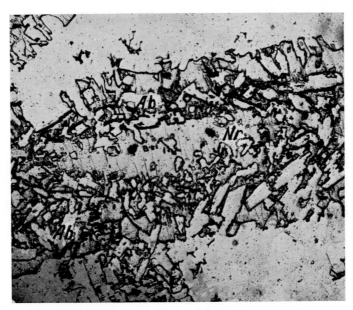

FIG. 190. Narsarsukite (Nr) with albite inclusion (Ab).
× 20. Without analyser

35. Vinogradovite

$Na_5Ti_4AlSi_6O_{24} . 3H_2O$; mon.; sp.gr. 2·878; H. 4

Vinogradovite was first detected and studied by Semenov and others (1956). It forms small prismatic crystals, elongated along the z axis and tabular along the y axis (Fig. 191). It is sometimes found in the form of finely fibrous segregations of irregular shape, measuring up to 5 cm, radiate-fibrous outgrowths and spherulites up to 1 cm in diameter. The crystallographic axial ratio is $a : b : c = 1·18 : 1 : 0·76$.

The mineral is colourless, transparent, with vitreous lustre. In aggregates it is white. Brittle. Fracture uneven. Cleavage perfect along (010).

Optically biaxial, negative. Refractive indices: $Ng = 1·775$; $Nm = 1·770$; $Np = 1·745 \pm 0·004$; $Ng - Np = 0·03$. Elongation positive. Extinction angle $c : Ng = 7°$. Optic axial plane $\perp$ (010). Poorly pleochroic from brown along Ng to colourless along Np. Absorption scheme $Ng > Np$. Dispersion of optic axes $r > v$. Twinning sometimes observed on (010). Interplanar spacings as calculated by Sludskaya are given in Table 98.

Vinogradovite is readily acid-soluble on heating. Recalculation of the chemical analysis (Table 99) shows that the composition of the Lovozero vinogradovite is not represented by the formula $Na_5Ti_4Al[SiO_4]_6 . 3H_2O$ derived by Semenov for this mineral. The reason is probably that this vinogradovite is in an advanced state of alteration and that the sodium has been leached out.

Up to 3·5 per cent Nb_2O_5 was found in vinogradovite by X-ray chemical analysis. Quantitative spectrographic analysis by Dudykin showed 0·08 per cent of beryllium. The spectrographic analysis revealed the presence of iron, manganese, strontium, gallium and zirconium.

From thermal investigations performed by Skripkina it was established that water is eliminated in the range 200-500° and probably has a zeolitic character.

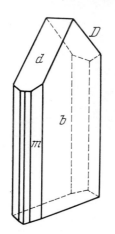

Vinogradovite was found in the Lepkhe-Nel'm, Kuftn'yun, Kitkn'yun, Karnasurt and Mannepakhk pegmatites. It is closely associated with minerals of the hydrothermal stage of the pegmatite-forming process and usually localized in cavities in natrolite or analcite in the central parts of pegmatitic bodies. It is sometimes found in the form of pseudomorphs after ramsayite and lamprophyllite or in the form of fibrous outgrowths round those minerals. Under surface conditions leucoxene develops after vinogradovite.

FIG. 191. Crystal of vinogradovite (after Bonshtedt)

36. Chinglusuite

$Na_2O.MnO_2.TiO_2.4SiO_2.8H_2O$; amorph.; sp.gr. 2·151; h. 2—3

Chinglusuite occurs in the Lovozero massif only in the poikilitic sodalite-syenites of the Chinglusuai valley, in amounts up to 1·5 per cent, and in the pegmatites of that complex. The mineral was first discovered by Gerasimovskii (1938).

In the non-pegmatitic rocks chinglusuite forms irregularly-shaped grains measuring $0·2 \times 0·2 \times 0·1$ cm, against $1·5 \times 1 \times 0·8$ cm in the pegmatoid parts (Fig. 192), where the chinglusuite content is sometimes 5-10 per cent.

Colour black and brownish-black, more rarely yellow and brown, the latter coloration being characteristic of the fresh grains, which are very rarely observed in unaltered rocks, in association with villiaumite inside large poikilitic syenite blocks. Lustre greasy in fresh specimens and submetallic in the altered examples. Opaque. Fracture uneven. Specific gravity of altered chinglusuite 2·151 (Gerasimovskii); of unaltered varieties 2·78.

TABLE 98   Interplanar spacings of vinogradovite
(Lepkhe-Nel'm)

Line no.	I	d	Line no.	I	d	Line no.	I	d
1	4	5·83	9	3	2·42	17	1	1·667
2	2	4·45	10	1	2·25	18	8	1·618
3	1	3·51	11	2	2·13	19	6	1·562
4	10	3·20	12	2	2·07	20	6	1·494
5	10	3·05	13	2	2·00	21	6	1·438
6	7	2·71	14	2	1·946	22	1	1·384
7	6	2·58	15	4	1·734	23	1	1·337
8	7	2·47	16	1	1·705	24	2	1·287

In thin sections unaltered chinglusuite is pale yellow; in altered sections it is black. Isotropic. Refractive index 1·582 (Gerasimovskii). Amorphous to X-rays.

The mineral is readily soluble in HCl, first losing its colour. In concentrated HNO_3 it dissolves only on heating; in concentrated H_2SO_4 it dissolves with difficulty even on heating. In both the latter acids it partially loses colour.

Chemical analysis of fresh chinglusuite was impossible owing to lack of sufficient material. Black altered chinglusuite has been twice analysed (Table 100).

FIG. 192. Chinglusuite (dark) filling spaces between grains of sodalite (light)

Kazakova established that manganese occurred in chinglusuite not in the divalent form (II) but in the tetravalent form (I).

Recalculation of the chemical analysis leads to the empirical formula $Na_2O . MnO_2 . TiO_2 . 4SiO_2 . 8H_2O$. The oxidized form of manganese, the high hygroscopic water content and the excess of water due to alkali deficiency indicate

TABLE 99 Chemical composition of vinogradovite from Lepkhe-Nel'm pegmatite

Constituent	Content, per cent	Atomic proportions	Calculation of atomic ratios		
SiO_2	40·83	0·6700 0·0195	0·6795	6·17	—6
Al_2O_3	4·88	0·0956	0·1151	1·08	—1
TiO_2	35·86	0·4488	0·4488	4·19	—4
MgO	0·42	0·0104			
CaO	0·66	0·0118	0·4020	3·76	—4
Na_2O	10·39	0·3352			
K_2O	2·10	0·0446			
H_2O^+ H_2O^-	5·50	0·6106	0·6106	5·71	—6
		O =2·895	2·895	27·06	—27
Total	100·64	—		—	
Analyst		Moleva			

an advanced state of decomposition and make it impossible to deduce the atomic formula.

In 1949 Krutetskaya established the presence of 0·46 per cent U_3O_8 in chinglusuite. This explained the unusually high radioactivity of this mineral, which does not correspond to the thorium content previously determined (0·06 per cent ThO_2). The following ratio of rare-earth elements in chinglusuite was established by quantitative X-ray chemical analysis: Ce : La : Nd : Pr = 1 : 0·2 : 1·35 : 0·2. Of the other rare-earth elements, Sm, Gd, Dy, Tb, Er, and Yb are present, along with a considerable amount of Y. In addition, beryllium, aluminium, strontium and tin have been detected by spectrographic analysis.

Gerasimovskii believes that chinglusuite is a metamict mineral. Semenov, who studied the black decomposed variety, believes it to be colloidal.

Thermal investigations of chinglusuite performed in the EelM Laboratory of the USSR Academy of Sciences showed that all water was eliminated at low temperatures (Fig. 193).

Under surface conditions chinglusuite often proves unstable. During its alteration black films of manganese hydroxides form, filling in cracks in the mineral

TABLE 100   Chemical composition of chinglusuite

Constituent	I			II*
	per cent	Molecular proportions	Calculation of molecular ratios	per cent
SiO_2	37·24	0·6200	0·6200 3·91 —4	39·50
TiO_2	9·56	0·1196		9·62
ZrO_2	2·80	0·0227		3·02
RE_2O_3	0·94	0·0028	0·1759 1·11 —1	1·18
ThO_2	not determined	—		0·06
Al_2O_3	trace	—		not determined
Fe_2O_3	4·92	0·0308		2·84
FeO	nil	—	—	—
MgO	trace	—	—	nil
MnO	nil	—	—	14·53
MnO_2	13·54	0·1557	0·1557 0·98 —1	—
CaO	1·90	0·0338		1·75
SrO	—	—	0·1201 0·76 —1	nil
Na_2O	5·02	0·0809		5·52
K_2O	0·51	0·0054		0·41
H_2O^+	6·78	0·3763	1·3177 8·30 —8	7·92
H_2O^-	16·96	0·9414		13·92
Cl	not determined	—	—	0·12
F	—	—	—	nil
P_2O_5	—	—	—	trace
Total	100·17	—	—	100·39
$-O = Cl_2$				−0·02
—	—	—	—	100·37
Analyst	Kazakova, 1952			Burova

* Gerasimovskii's data

or replacing it from the periphery. In the Chinglusuai valley the fresh varieties of chinglusuite occur in close association with minerals containing no water or (OH) in their composition. It is usually associated with villiaumite, lomonosovite and sodalite. It is extremely unevenly distributed in the rock. It fills up spaces between sodalite, aegirine, eudialyte, lomonosovite and murmanite.

In the pegmatites and pegmatoid parts of the rocks in this region the altered variety of chinglusuite is mainly represented, in close association with sodalite, ussingite, lomonosovite, nordite, schizolite, neptunite, molybdenite, sphalerite and other minerals.

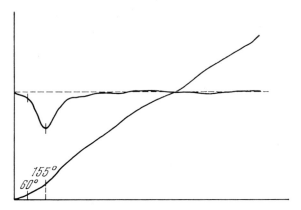

FIG. 193. Thermal analysis curve for chinglusuite

37. Manganilmenite

$(Mn,Fe)TiO_3$; trig.; sp.gr. 4·62—4·72; H. 5—6

Manganilmenite was first discovered in the massif by Gerasimovskii (1940_2) in the pegmatites and in certain of the rocks. In the latter it occurs in the form of platy and thin-tabular segregations measuring 0·2 to 5 cm along the long axis, the platelets being up to 0·3 cm thick and often measuring $1 \times 0·3 \times 0·05$ cm.

The largest segregations are characteristic of the pegmatoid parts of the massif. The mineral is not found in well-formed crystals.

In the pegmatites manganilmenite forms fine-platy crystals measuring up to $2 \times 2 \times 0·1$ cm, or more rarely thick platy crystals measuring up to 12×8 cm in area and 2 to 3 cm in thickness (Fig. 194). Goniometric measurements of thick platy crystals from the pegmatoid parts of the Vavnbed metasomatic zone by Khalezova showed the following forms c (0001); r ($10\bar{1}1$); n ($22\bar{4}3$) (Fig. 195). In another type of manganilmenite crystal, apart from the forms indicated above, there are ϵ ($20\bar{2}5$) and π ($11\bar{2}3$) faces. Sometimes manganilmenite occurs in the form of irregularly-shaped crystals up to 1·5 cm long filling up spaces between crystals of aegirine I or included in natrolite.

Colour green-black. Streak black. Lustre metallic. Opaque. Cleavage absent. Fracture conchoidal to uneven. Under reflected light the mineral is creamy white, sometimes with a pinkish tint. Anisotropic. Specific gravity varies from

4·62 to 4·723, depending on the iron and manganese content (the more manganese, the lower the specific gravity).

The X-ray powder patterns of Lovozero manganilmenite and of the ilmenite from the zircon vein on Kukisvumchorr in the Khibiny tundras are similar to the standards (Barth and Posnjak, 1934).

Manganilmenite is not soluble in concentrated HNO_3 or H_2SO_4 and is poorly soluble in HCl, colouring the solution bright yellow. As can be seen from Table 101 the Lovozero manganilmenite differs from the Khibiny ilmenite in having a high manganese content and a lower iron content. The chemical composition of the manganilmenites from the pegmatites and from the nonpegmatitic rocks is very

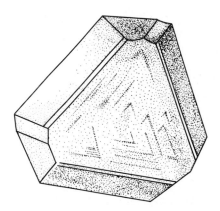

FIG. 194. Crystal of manganilmenite. Natural size

FIG. 195. Crystal of manganilmenite (after Khalezova)

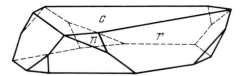

similar. Some difference is observed in the titanium, iron and manganese contents a higher manganese tenor being characteristic of the pegmatitic variety. A comparatively high niobium content (1·44 per cent Nb_2O_5) was found in the manganilmenite from the Flora hybrid pegmatites.

The chemical composition of the mineral corresponds to the formula (Mn, Fe)TiO_3. Table 102 shows the ratio of ilmenite and pyrophanite molecules in the mineral.

Copper, beryllium, zinc, cobalt, lanthanum and zirconium have been detected in manganilmenite spectroscopically (6 assays).

Manganilmenite in association with zircon, sphene and apatite is present in the contaminated rock varieties of all the complexes in amounts up to 3 per cent, the maximum being found near the Devonian xenoliths. The amount of this mineral diminishes with distance from the contact and at 2-3 m it has completely disappeared. The rocks richest in manganilmenite are the contaminated poikilitic syenites and the foyaites and lujavrites of the differentiated complex.

Manganilmenite has developed in the hybrid pegmatites and in the pegmatites of the differentiated complex which are genetically connected with the contaminated rocks. It is usually localized in the selvedges of pegmatite veins. The largest number of pegmatitic bodies containing manganilmenite is found in the southeastern (Ninchurt, Mannepakhk, Ankisuai canyon etc.) and central (Koklukhtiuai valley, Kuivchorr) parts of the massif, where most of them are emplaced in nephe-

FIG. 196. Crystals of manganilmenite (I) in albite (Ab). Natural size

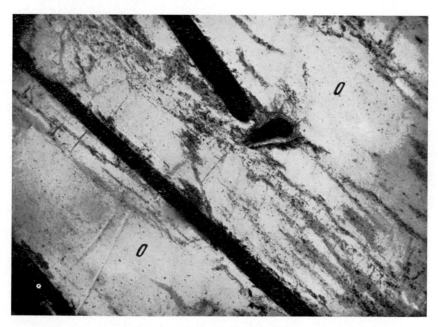

FIG. 197. Manganilmenite inclusions (dark) in orthoclase (O). × 10. Without analyser

line and hydrosodalitic poikilitic syenites, or more rarely in equigranular and porphyritic syenites. So far this mineral has been found in more than 50 pegmatitic bodies, mostly in very small amounts, reaching 10-20 per cent in only a few cases (Flora, Ninchurt, Alluaiv and elsewhere). In the rocks and pegmatites it is characteristically associated with orthoclase, zircon, sphene, apatite, biotite and, more rarely, albite (Fig. 196).

This is one of the earliest pegmatite minerals. In thin sections regular fine-platy crystals of it are found included in orthoclase and nepheline and also in eudialyte, zircon and apatite (Fig. 197). It is later than aegirine I, since it fills up spaces between crystals of the latter.

According to I. P. Tikhonenkov, ramsayite and astrophyllite are sometimes

TABLE 101   Chemical compositions of manganilmenite and ilmenite

Constituent	Manganilmenite					Ilmenite
	From Koklukhtiuai valley contaminated foyaite			From Koklukhtiuai valley pegmatite	From Flora hybrid pegmatite	From Khibiny tundra
	per cent	Atomic pro- portions	Calculation of atomic ratios	per cent	per cent	per cent
SiO_2	0·19	0·0031	⎫	0·11	1·24	not determined
TiO_2	51·22	0·6410	⎬ 0·6595 —1	51·35	49·98	52·54
$(Nb, Ta)_2O_5$	0·26	0·0018	⎪	not determined	1·44	not determined
Al_2O_3	0·70	0·0136	⎭	,, ,,	0·35	,, ,,
Fe_2O_4	3·95	0·0494	⎫	4·67	5·14	12·18
FeO	31·26	0·4211	⎬ 0·6537 —1	28·46	25·76	35·45
MnO	13·00	0·1832	⎭	14·73	16·05	0·08
MgO	nil	—	—	0·56	—	0·12
CaO	,,	—	—	0·20	0·24	not determined
H_2O	,,	O =1·9915	1·9915 —3	—	0·30	,, ,,
Total	100·58	—	—	100·08	100·50	100·37
Specific gravity	4·685	—		4·679	4·62	—
Analyst	Burova, 1953			Vladimirova	Kazakova, 1949	Iskyul'
Reference	—			Gerasimovskii (1940₂)	—	Minerals of the Khibiny and Lovozero tundras (1937)

TABLE 102   Content of $FeTiO_3$ and $MnTiO_3$ molecules in manganilmenite (per cent)

Manganilmenite	$FeTiO_3$	$MnTiO_3$
From Koklukhtiuai valley contaminated pegmatite	71·97	28·03
From Koklukhtiuai valley pegmatite	66·76	33·24
From Flora hybrid pegmatite	65·58	34·42

found replacing manganilmenite in the pegmatites connected with contaminated rocks; in ramsayite this process may extend to the formation of pseudomorphs.

38. Brookite (arkansite)

TiO_2; orthorhomb.; sp.gr. 4·05; H. 6

Semenov (1957₄) established that minerals consisting of various modifications of titanium dioxide (rutile, anatase, brookite) were fairly widespread in the alkali pegmatites of the Lovozero tundras.

Brookite is represented in the Lovozero massif by its pseudo-hexagonal variety arkansite, which is found in small amounts in the pegmatite vein on Kuivchorr. Arkansite forms equant crystals measuring up to 0·4 cm or irregularly-shaped

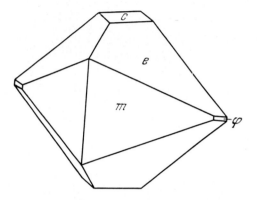

Fig. 198. Crystal of brookite (after Semenov)

segregations up to 1·5 cm in diameter. Colour black. Streak greyish. Lustre adamantine. Fracture conchoidal. Arkansite crystals were measured by Semenov with a two-circle Goldschmidt goniometer. They have a pseudohexagonal habit (Fig. 198), because of the equal development of the *m* prism faces (120) and the dipyramid *e* (111). Apart from these forms a pinacoid *c* (001) is also found and, very indistinctly, faces of a second rhombic prism, roughly identified as *φ* (110).

Table 103 shows the interplanar spacings calculated from the powder patterns obtained by Krutetskaya for arkansite.

Under the microscope arkansite is poorly translucent and has a greenish-brown colour. It is intensely pleochroic in green and yellow shades. The interference colours are bright and of the higher orders. Refractive indices very high ($N>2$). Biaxial, with small optic axial angle. A zonal crystal structure can sometimes be

TABLE 103 Interplanar spacings of arkansite

Line no.	I	d	Line no.	I	d	Line no.	I	d
1	10	3·50	7	8	1·894	13	4	1·501
2	10	2·90	8	2	1·830	14	3	1·467
3	4	2·47	9	7	1·688	15	3	1·451
4	1	2·25	10	7	1·659	16	2	1·423
5	1	2·12	11	4	1·616	17	8	1·124
6	8	1·973	12	2	1·543			

TABLE 104 Chemical composition of arkansite (per cent)

Constituents	Lovozero, Kuivchorr	Arkansas, Magnet Bay
TiO_2	86·89	98·78
$(Nb + Ta)_2O_5$	3·44	—
$Fe_2O_3 + FeO$	3·31	1·43
MnO	0·12	—
MgO	1·00	—
SiO_2	1·45	—
Al_2O_3	1·30	—
CaO	0·66	—
Other	1·80	—
Total	99·97	100·21
Analyst	Kazakova, 1950	Pfeil
Reference	Semenov (1957[4])	

detected, a yellowish-brown zone being found in the centre of the crystal and a green zone round the edges. The chemical analysis (Table 104) indicates that Lovozero arkansite has an unusually high tenor of silicon and aluminium, apparently due to contamination of the material analysed. Lovozero arkansite is characterized by a high niobium and iron content (Table 104).

X-ray spectrographic analysis shows 0·1 per cent of lead, 0·5 per cent of zirconium and 0·2 per cent of strontium in arkansite and the presence of vanadium and tungsten was established spectroscopically.

Arkansite is closely associated with lamprophyllite and, in all probability, forms in the process of lamprophyllite alteration. In the pegmatite vein on Kuivchorr it is found in the form of druses in leaching cavities of nepheline among zeolites.

TABLE 105 Interplanar spacings of anatase

Line no.	Synthetic anatase (after Kitaigorodskii)		Blue anatase, Kuivchorr		Niobian anatase, Sengischorr	
	I	d	I	d	I	d
1	10	3·52	7	3·48	7	3·54
2	2·4	2·37	1	2·36	3	2·38
3	4	1·88	5	1·888	5	1·917
4	2·8	1·70	3	1·696	3	1·716
5	2·4	1·66	3	1·659	—	—
6	2·4	1·480	2	1·478	2	1·509
7	0·8	1·362	1	1·362	—	—
8	0·8	1·335	1	1·333	—	—
9	1·1	1·262	2	1·260	—	—
10	0·6	1·164	1	1·161	—	—
11	0·3	1·045	—	—	—	—

39. Anatase

TiO_2; tetr.; sp.gr. 3·9; H. 5—6

Anatase leucoxene is widely distributed in the Lovozero pegmatites. According to Semenov (1957[4]) its formation accompanies the hypergene alteration of titanium minerals (murmanite, lamprophyllite etc.); in such cases it is a yellow ochreous aggregate replacing those minerals round the margin or forming complete pseudomorphs after them (anatase leucoxene). It is more rarely found in the form of tetragonal dipyramidal crystals in zeolite cavities in the central parts of pegmatite bodies (the pegmatite vein on Kuivchorr) in close association with arkansite; in such cases its origin is probably hydrothermal.

Colour bluish-grey. Optically uniaxial, negative. Pleochroic in blue tones, from dark-blue to colourless. Refracted index $N \gg 2$. X-ray powder pattern similar to the standard powder pattern for synthetic anatase (Table 105).

Semenov found a white floury anatase in the Kukisvumchorr pegmatites, with a Nb : Ti ratio of 0·42. The powder pattern of this anatase was near to that of the standard (see Table 105).

The presence of 2·1 per cent Nb_2O_5 in anatase was established by chemical analysis and titanium (strong lines), iron (medium lines), together with barium, vanadium, zirconium and manganese, by spectrographic analysis.

FIG. 199. Belyankinite (light) in aegirine II (Ae)

40. Rutile

TiO_2; tetr.; sp.gr. 4·2—4·3

Rutile is found in the central zone of the pegmatite vein on Kuivchorr as a secondary mineral after manganilmenite, platelets of which are entirely replaced by an orange-yellow ochreous rutile leucoxene.

Under the microscope rutile has a brownish colour with very high interference colours and relief. Relicts of manganilmenite and limonite, which is also a product of ilmenite alteration, are sometimes found among segregations of rutile.

Spectrographic analysis has revealed titanium (very strong lines), iron (strong lines), niobium, calcium, aluminium, manganese, silicon (medium to strong lines) and also magnesium, tin, zirconium, vanadium and beryllium in rutile leucoxene. V. G. Starostina established by chemical analysis 3 per cent Nb_2O_5 and 2·26 per cent Fe_2O_3 in leucoxene from Ninchurt.

In Semenov's opinion (1957[4]) replacement of manganilmenite by leucoxene results from the action of low-temperature hydrothermal solutions, since this process is observed only in the central part of the pegmatite, where the replacement stage has developed.

41. Belyankinite

$Ti(OH)_4$ (?); orthorhomb.; sp.gr. 2·32—2·40; H. 2—3

Belyankinite was first discovered by Gerasimovskii and described by him jointly with Kazakova (1950). It has more recently been studied by Semenov (1957[4]). The following description is based on the data given by these investigators*.

Belyankinite forms platy segregations measuring $1 \times 0.5 \times 0.1$ to $20 \times 15 \times 0.5$ cm (Fig. 199). It has not been found in the form of crystals. Colour white, yellowish-white (ivory), sometimes with a brown tint; in the manganese variety, black. Lustre on cleavage planes nacreous, on the fracture vitreous to greasy. Cleavage perfect in one direction, parallel to the broad faces of the plates. Fracture uneven. Brittle. Opaque. High specific gravity is characteristic of mangan-belyankinite (2·54).

The mineral is optically biaxial, negative. Elongation positive, Ng near to Nm. Refractive indices: $Nm = 1.775$—1.780; $Np = 1.740$; $Ng - Nm = 0.002$—0.003; $2V = 21$-$25°$. Clearly-marked pleochroism: Ng—light cinnamon or light brownish-cinnamon, Nm—light-brown, sometimes yellowish-brown, Np—cinnamon to dark cinnamon. Extinction straight in relation to cleavage. Optical orientation (Semenov, 1957[4]): $Ng = y$, $Nm = x$, $Np = z$. Optic axial plane $\perp$ (001).

The X-ray powder pattern is indistinct, only two lines being distinguishable: (1) $I = 4$, $d = 3.70$; (2) $I = 5$, $d = 1.89$. Organova, using a Laue photograph, measured the following interplanar spacings in belyankinite:

Line No.	I	d	Line No.	I	d
1	5	1·96—1·66	3	3	0·782
2	7	1·365	4	2	0·617

* The manganese variety of belyankinite was discovered and studied by the authors of the present work.

According to Semenov's data (1957₄) the powder pattern of belyankinite heated above the exothermic temperature effect (900°C) is exactly similar to that of rutile. The refractive indices of ignited belyankinite are a good deal higher (>2·05) and seem to approach those of rutile.

Belyankinite is readily soluble, on heating, in hydrochloric, nitric and sulphuric acids.

Mangan-belyankinite differs from ordinary belyankinite in having a higher content of alkalis, manganese and iron and a higher specific gravity (Table 106). Burova determined 0·93 per cent Ta_2O_5 in belyankinite from the Mannepakhk pegmatites. According to the spectrographic analysis hafnium, lead and copper occur in minute amounts in this mineral. The thermal analysis curve (Fig. 200) shows that the water in belyankinite is liberated at low temperatures, as is indicated by the clearly-marked endothermic effect in the 70-360° interval. The exothermic effect at 720° seems to be due to phase changes.

The conversion of belyankinite after ignition into a mineral similar to rutile, as well as the sharp predominance of titanium over other cations, gave Semenov grounds for supposing that belyankinite was a titanium hydroxide in which part of the titanium was isomorphously replaced by zirconium, niobium and manganese in the following proportions: $Ti_{0.7}Zr_{0.06}Nb_{0.07}Fe_{0.03}Ca_{0.13}(OH)_{3.78}$.

Belyankinite differs from murmanite in having a higher titanium, calcium and

TABLE 106 Chemical compositions of belyankinite and mangan-belyankinite (per cent)

Constituents	Belyankinite				Manganbelyankinite	
	1	2	3	4	5	6
SiO_2	3·96	2·80	3·22	3·11	3·34	1·51
TiO_2	48·76	48·19	49·26	49·32	44·32	44·30
Nb_2O_5	} 7·16	7·51	7·80	7·00	7·86	7·42
Ta_2O_5						
ZrO_2	6·64	6·56	5·58	6·50	3·06	—
Al_2O_3	0·46	0·24	0·76	0·90	0·60	—
Fe_2O_3	not determined	1·85	1·66	1·40	4·12	3·77
MnO	nil	0·04	0·14	not determined	not determined	—
MnO_2	—	—	—	—	6·45	14·03
MgO	nil	0·14	0·08	0·10	1·10	—
CaO	6·72	6·40	5·80	6·80	6·00	5·77
Na_2O	0·55	0·23	—	—	—	—
K_2O	trace	0·20	—	—	0·90	—
H_2O^+	8·35	7·20	19·55	not determined	9·09	} 22·36
H_2O^-	17·21	18·50	5·58	6·50	13·61	
P_2O_5	—	—	—	—	0·23	—
Total	99·81	99·86	99·43	—	100·68	99·16
Specific gravity	—	—	2·39	2·35	2·54	—
Analyst	Burova	Kazakova, 1950			Kazakova, 1951	Kapitonov
Reference	Gerasimovskii, Kazakova (1950)				—	Semenov (1957₄)

water content and almost no silicon or alkalis. Like murmanite it is usually localized in the outer fine-grained and feldspathic-aegirine zones of pegmatites (see description of the Koklukhtiuai valley, 'Bear's Den' and Flora pegmatites). The presence of murmanite relicts in belyankinite and mangan-belyankinite is evidence that they were formed in the process of replacement. According to Semenov, however, belyankinite occurs also as an independent mineral and is not always connected with murmanite. Under surface conditions it is converted into an ochreous aggregate of secondary products (leucoxene).

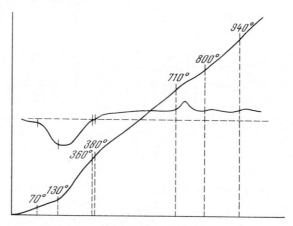

FIG. 200. Thermal analysis curve for belyankinite

42. Gerasimovskite

$NbTi(OH)_9$; sp.gr. 2·52—2·58; H. 2

Gerasimovskite is the niobium member of the isomorphous series belyankinite-gerasimovskite. It was first found by Gerasimovskii and later studied in detail by Semenov (1957_4) and is named after its discoverer.

Gerasimovskite forms platy segregations measuring $1·5 \times 1 \times 0·3$ cm, of a cinnamon brown to grey (and light-grey) colour. Lustre nacreous. X-ray powder pattern amorphous. After ignition to 900°C it gives a clear Debye powder pattern similar to that of rutile and belyankinite (Table 107) and identical to that of the high-temperature H-modification of Nb_2O_5 (according to Bauer). Optically biaxial, negative. Refractive indices: $Ng \approx Nm \approx 1·81$; $Np \approx 1·74$; $2V = -18°$. Extinction straight. Elongation positive. Cleavage perfect in one direction.

TABLE 107 Interplanar spacings of gerasimovskite
(Fe-radiation); $D = 57·3$ mm; $d = 0·6$ mm

Line no.	Gerasimovskite		Belyankinite		Line no.	Gerasimovskite		Belyankinite	
	I	d	I	d		I	d	I	d
1	4	3·70	3	3·70	4	5	1·89	5	1·89
2	3	3·18	—	—	5	1	1·64	—	—
3	2	2·10	—	—					

Chemical analysis of gerasimovskite (Table 108) shows that it is a hydroxide of titanium in which half the titanium has been replaced by niobium. Its formula can be written in the form: $(Nb_{0.84}Ti_{0.84}Mn_{0.28}Ca_{0.06})$ $[OH_{5.66}O_{1.52}]$.

The thermal dehydration curves (Fig. 201) are similar to those of belyankinite.

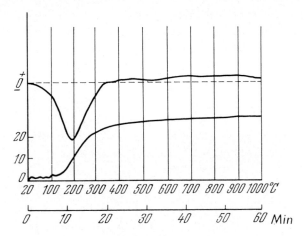

FIG. 201.   Thermal analysis and weight loss curves for gerasimovskite

Gerasimovskite occurs in the Strashempakhk, Lepkhe-Nel'm and Alluaiv pegmatites. It probably forms at the hydrothermal stage in the process of alteration of niobium-rich minerals of the lomonosovite and murmanite group (epistolite and others). In the [continuing] process of alteration it is replaced by leucoxene.

TABLE 108   Chemical composition of gerasimovskite

Constituents	Analysis 1	Analysis 2	
	per cent	per cent	Atomic proportions
Nb_2O_5	43·91	44·90	0·338
Ta_2O_5	0·38	0·50	0·002
TiO_2	24·37	23·44	0·293
SiO_2	1·83	2·30	0·038
Fe_2O_3	trace	0·21	0·003
Al_2O_3	—	0·65	0·013
MnO	7·85	2·65	0·037
CaO	1·37	1·95	0·035
MgO	—	0·30	0·007
Na_2O	—	0·10	0·003
K_2O	—	0·21	0·005
CO_2	—	0·20	0·004
H_2O^+	3·85	7·73	⎫ 2·503
H_2O^-	16·55	14·77	⎭
Total	100·11	99·91	
Analyst	Burova	Kazakova	
Reference		Semenov (1957₄)	

III. Rare Earth and Thorium Minerals

The rare-earths and thorium minerals (see Table 28) in the Lovozero rocks and pegmatites are less widely distributed than the zirconium, titanium and niobium minerals. Only four of them are present in the non-pegmatitic rocks (rare-earth apatite, rinkolite, lovchorrite and nordite) but all the minerals of this group are found in the pegmatites (steenstrupine, manganosteenstrupine, hydrocerite, thorite, erikite, belovite, karnasurtite and others). The largest amounts of rare-earth and thorium minerals are found in pegmatites genetically associated with the poikilitic nepheline-sodalite-syenites.

43. Rare-earth apatites

$Ca_{10} [PO_4]_6 (F,OH)_2$; hex.; sp.gr. 3·12—3·43; H. 5

The commonest of the apatite minerals in the Lovozero massif is rare-earth fluorapatite.

It occurs in the rocks in the form of small prismatic colourless or light-green crystals, measuring from a fraction of a millimetre to 1 cm along the long axis, often grouped in irregularly-shaped segregations measuring $3·5 \times 2·5 \times 1·5$ cm.

FIG. 202. Prismatic crystal of green apatite (Ap) in natrolite (Na)

The largest segregations are found in the poikilitic syenites, the smallest in the urtites of the differentiated complex. The rare-earth apatite in the rocks had not been studied before we made our investigations.

In the pegmatites fluorapatite forms predominantly short-columnar hexagonal prismatic light-green crystals, measuring from a fraction of a centimetre to $3 \times 3 \times 10$ cm (Fig. 202) or large monomineralic segregations of irregular shape (up to $50 \times 50 \times 30$ cm). In one of the pegmatitic bodies in the Koklukhtiuai valley, genetically associated with contaminated rocks, a fine-grained aggregate of green apatite fills up almost the entire central zone. Sometimes it is found in the form of spherulites and platy segregations. The spherulites are radiate-fibrous outgrowths diverging from one centre, of long-prismatic stepped crystals up to 8 mm long, which thicken from the centre to the edges of the spherulites. Sometimes the spherulites are micaceous, and then the apatite crystals acquire a platy shape. Segregations of platy apatites sometimes reach sizes of $5 \times 5 \times 3$ cm.

More rarely, apatite fills up cavities in natrolite druses in the form of small (up to $1 \times 0.3 \times 0.3$ cm) poorly-formed brown crystals, which sometimes form dendritic networks, resembling corals, with cavities between the individual crystals. In some cases a fine-grained aggregate of brown apatite forms, jointly with tainiolite, natrolite and limonite, paramorphs on large crystals of higher-temperature (possibly green) apatite. These paramorphs sometimes reach dimensions of $6 \times 6 \times 10$ cm.

Apatite is also occasionally found in the form of acicular, spheroidal, fibrous and granular segregations in natrolite cavities. The colour of such apatite varies in azure, dark-blue, violet and yellowish-grey shades.

In the rocks of the differentiated complex apatite is transparent; in those of other complexes and in the pegmatites it is semi-transparent. Lustre vitreous.

TABLE 109 Specific gravities and refractive indices of rare-earth apatites

Rare-earth apatite	Specific gravity	Refractive indices			Investigator	
		No	Ne	$No-Ne$		
From Karnasurt malignite	3·43	1·645	1·639	0·006	Present authors	
From Karnasurt ijolite-urtite	3·4055	1·643	1·638	0·005	,,	,,
From Kuftn'yun apatite urtite (horizon V)	3·3480	1·635	1·631	0·004	,,	,,
From Karnasurt urtite, lower division of [differentiated] complex	3·3605	1·637	1·632	0·005	,,	,,
From Karnasurt eudialytic lujavrite	3·292	1·630	1·628	0·002	,,	,,
From Koklukhtiuai valley contaminated foyaite	3·281	1·633	1·630	0·003	,,	,,
From Koklukhtiuai valley pegmatite:						
Light green prismatic	3·276	1·633	1·630	0·003	Gerasimovskii	
White saccharoidal	—	1·632	1·629	0·003	Borodin	
From Lepkhe-Nel'm pegmatite:						
Green prismatic	3·366	1·639	1·635	0·004	Semenov	
Green spherulitic	—	1·644	1·635	0·009	,,	
Light brown fine-crystalline	3·125	1·626	1·622	0·004	,,	
Azure short-columnar	—	1·636	1·633	0·003	,,	

TABLE 110 Chemical compositions of rare-earth apatites (per cent)

Constituent	From Karnasurt malignite	From Karnasurt ijolite urtite	From Kuftn'yun apatitic urtite	From Karnasurt urtite, lower division of differentiated complex	From Karnasurt eudialytic lujavrite	From Koklukhtiuai contaminated foyaite	From Koklukhtiuai pegmatite per cent	Atomic proportions	Calculation of atomic ratios
P_2O_5	37·47	38·63	38·40	39·00	39·66	41·26	39·80	0·5606	0·5606 5·93 —6
SiO_2	0·39	0·12	0·12	0·11	0·09	0·10	trace	not det.	—
Al_2O_3	not det.	0·45	0·20	0·32	0·40	not det.	0·70	0·0136	
Fe_2O_3	0·93	0·11	trace	0·06	0·35	0·13	0·15	0·0020	
RE_2O_3	7·71	7·10	6·78	7·44	2·00	2·32	3·20	0·0196	0·9881 10·45 —10
CaO	43·81	47·28	46·56	48·18	48·50	51·93	48·80	0·8702	
MgO	—	—	—	not det.	0·09	—	0·30	0·0074	
SrO	6·14	3·19	5·39	2·31	6·25	2·43	5·50	0·0531	
Na_2O	0·50	0·52	0·74	0·56	not det.	not det.	0·69	0·0222	
H_2O^+	0·52	0·36	0·36	0·38	—	—	nil	—	
H_2O^-		0·44	0·40	1·27	3·38	0·29	2·14	0·1126	—
F	3·49	3·00	3·15	1·70	0·30	2·69			0·1835 1·94 —2
SO_3	—	—	—	—	—	—	—	—	
Cl	—	—	—	—	—	—	0·04	0·0011	
Insoluble residue	0·53	—	—	—	—	—	—	0·0698	
								$O = 2·2700$	2·2700 24·02 —24
Total	101·49	101·20	102·10	101·33	101·02	101·15	101·32	—	—
$-O = F_2$	−1·47	−1·25	−1·33	−0·70	−1·42	−1·13	−0·90		
	100·02	99·95	100·77	100·63	99·60	100·02	100·42	—	—
Analyst	Borneman, 1952		Burova, 1952			Borneman, 1952	Yashchenko		

Fracture uneven to conchoidal. The specific gravity and refractive indices increase in proportion to the amount of rare earths in the mineral (Table 109).

In thin sections all varieties of apatite are transparent. The coloured varieties are weakly pleochroic. The mineral is optically uniaxial, negative. Elongation negative. Refractive indices vary: $No = 1.626$—1.645; $Ne = 1.622$—1.639; $No - Ne = 0.002$—0.009 (see Table 109). Apatite is poorly soluble in concentrated HCl, HNO_3 and H_2SO_4.

The Lovozero apatites are characterized by a high strontium and rare-earth content. The maximum rare-earth tenor is found in apatites from the malignites and urtites in the differentiated complex (Table 110). In the eudialytic lujavrites, contaminated foyaites and pegmatites, the rare-earth content of the apatite is considerably lower.

As is well known, minerals of the apatite group have a chemical formula of the type $A_{10}(XO_4)_6Z_2$, where $A = Ca$, Sr, R.E. etc.; $X = P$, Si, S etc.; $Z = F$, Cl, OH, O, CO_3 (Belov, 1939). The chemical composition of rare-earth apatite is given by the formula $(Ca, Sr, R.E., Na)_{10}P_6O_{24}(F, OH)_2$. Some excess of group A cations is observed in most analyses, probably because it is difficult to separate calcium and strontium, with the result that the molecular proportion of CaO is increased. Also, an excess of fluorine and water has been observed in some apatites. According to R. L. Barinskii the rare earths in the apatite from rocks of the differentiated complex are represented mainly by the cerium group, their ratios in the apatites of the various horizons being roughly the same: $La_{22}Ce_{51}Pr_6Nd_{17}Sm_{1.8}Eu_{0.2}Gd_{1.6}Tb_{0.6}Dy_{0.3}$. In the azure short-columnar apatite from the Lepkhe-Nel'm pegmatites, according to Kazakova, the manganese oxide tenor is 1·31 per cent. This would seem to account for the blue colour.

Spectroscopic study (12 analyses) showed that the Lovozero apatite contains, in addition to the elements identified by chemical methods, barium, zirconium, titanium, vanadium, manganese, copper, silver, niobium, beryllium, zinc, lead and thallium. We note that the pegmatitic apatite contains more trace elements, such as manganese, beryllium, niobium, vanadium, silver, zinc, lead and others, than the rock apatite.

Rare-earth apatite is present in the rocks of all the complexes, reaching its largest amounts in the urtites of the differentiated complex (Table 111). It is absent from the urtites of horizons I, III and IV. The underlying urtite horizons invariably contain apatite; the lower their position and the thicker and more nearly monomineralic they are, the greater the amount of apatite in them. In each horizon the maximum amounts of apatite are concentrated at the base, to the extent that monomineralic apatitic interlayers form in the ijolite-urtites and the urtites of the lower part of the complex.

In the foyaites of the well-formed three-component stratal groups apatite, as a rule, is not observed or is present in very small amounts near the urtite contacts. In the poorly-developed three-component groups (middle part of the complex), in which the urtitic horizon is either lacking or is poorly developed, the apatite content in individual parts of the foyaites increases to 3·2 per cent.

TABLE 111 Content of rare-earth apatite in Lovozero rocks

Differentiated complex	Content, per cent	Eudialytic lujavrite complex	Content, per cent	Poikilitic syenite complex	Content, per cent
Upper division of complex:		Eudialytic lujavrites		Poikilitic sodalite-syenites	nil
Foyaites	0–0·3	Melanocratic	0·05–0·2	Poikilitic nepheline-syenites	0–0·3
Urtites	0–2·6	Mesocratic	0–0·1	Poikilitic hydrosodalite-syenites	0·2–0·7
Aegirine-lujavrites	nil	Leucocratic	—		
Hornblende-lujavrites	0–0·6				
Malignites	0–0·7	Porphyritic lujavrites	nil		
Middle division of complex:		Porphyritic juvites	,,		
Foyaites	0–3·2	Porphyritic foyaites	,,		
Urtites	0–25·4				
Aegirine-lujavrites	0–1·3				
Hornblende-lujavrites	0·2–2·5				
Lower division of complex:					
Foyaites	0–1·8				
Urtites	0–2·8				
Aegirine-lujavrites	0–0·2				

In the aegirine-lujavrites of the upper part of the complex apatite is absent. The maximum amounts (up to 1·3 per cent) are observed in the lujavrites of the middle part of the complex, but only in those horizons bedded below the urtites, even if these are poorly developed. Apatite has been noted in a bed 0·5-1 m thick, which gradually diminishes until it completely disappears. It has been observed that in the aegirine-lujavrites the apatite tenor decreases as the degree of differentiation of the rocks increases.

In the hornblende-lujavrites apatite is commoner in the middle part of the complex (0·2-2·5 per cent). In each horizon of these rocks the largest quantities are found in the central parts and the apatite tenor decreases towards the roof and floor. In the malignites it is most widespread in the roof, in direct contact with the overlying urtites. Below this enriched zone apatite occurs in very small quantities or not at all. It has been noted that the amount of apatite in the floor of this zone increases and the amount in the underlying malignites decreases as the urtite horizon above the malignites becomes thicker and more nearly monomineralic.

In the rocks of the eudialytic lujavrite complex apatite occurs rarely, mainly in the upper part, its tenor increasing from the mesocratic and leucocratic (from 0·1 per cent) to the melanocratic (up to 0·2 per cent) varieties. In the porphyritic lujavrites, juvites and foyaites apatite is not found.

In the poikilitic syenites apatite is observed only in the nepheline (0-0·3 per cent) and hydrosodalitic (0·2-0·7 per cent) varieties. In the contaminated poikilitic syenites large segregations of it, measuring up to 10 × 3 cm, sometimes occur with hydrosodalite, or veinlets of it from 1 to 5 cm thick.

In the pegmatites there are considerable amounts of apatite in the central part of the massif on Lepkhe-Nel'm, Kuivchorr, Ninchurt and in the Koklukhtiuai and Strashempakhk valleys, where the influence of assimilation appears to a greater or less degree. The green variety is more widespread than the others. The largest amounts of this apatite are found in the contaminated pegmatites of the differentiated complex in the Koklukhtiuai valley, where it makes up, in the form of a monomineralic aggregation, the central part of one of the pegmatite bodies and is present in considerable quantities in all the others. It is present in large amounts also in the orthoclase-natrolite pegmatite body on Lepkhe-Nel'm, in the form of large prismatic crystals and monomineralic segregations. The dark-blue and violet varieties are mineralogical rarities and have been found only as isolated occurrences. The brown, white and yellowish-grey varieties occur mainly in major, fully differentiated pegmatite bodies that have passed through a late hydrothermal replacement stage.

In the non-pegmatitic rocks apatite is one of the early minerals. It is found in the urtites in the form of individual, well-formed crystals and accumulations of crystals set along the junctions between nepheline grains (Fig. 203); the apatite crystals are often included in nepheline. The interrelationship between apatite and loparite has a twofold character. In most cases the loparite crystals are included in the apatite (Fig. 204). More rarely, irregularly-shaped grains and

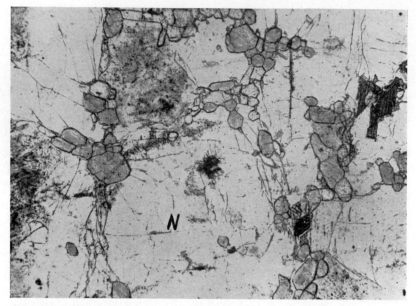

FIG. 203. Small chains of apatite grains at the boundaries of nepheline grains (N). ×46. Without analyser

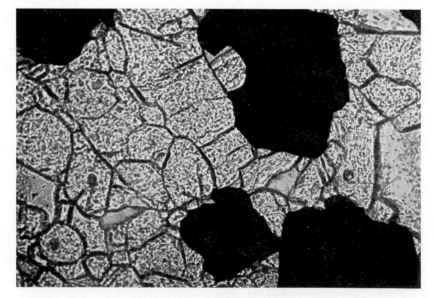

FIG. 204. Loparite crystals (black) in apatite. ×90. Without analyser

well-formed crystals of apatite are included in the loparite. Occasionally one finds a single apatite crystal dividing a loparite monocrystal into two parts (Fig. 205). All this indicates that the two minerals formed almost contemporaneously.

All the remaining urtite minerals contain apatite inclusions. In almost mono-mineralic accumulations apatite is the earliest mineral; nepheline, microcline, aegirine and other minerals fill up spaces between its crystals.

The other rocks of the differentiated, the eudialytic lujavrite and the poikilitic syenite complexes contain apatite in two forms: (1) short-columnar crystals and (2) irregularly-shaped grains. The former are usually present in very small amounts in the form of inclusions in microcline, orthoclase (Fig. 206), aegirine and arfved-sonite, as well as in other, later minerals. The other form (irregularly-shaped individuals), is usually found in spaces between aegirine and arfvedsonite crystals but is idiomorphic in relation to eudialyte, lamprophyllite, ramsayite and other minerals.

Apatite is later in the pegmatites than in the rocks. Green prismatic apatite is usually localized in the central parts of the pegmatite bodies and forms inclusions of regular idiomorphic crystals in prismatic natrolite. It must therefore have separated earlier than the latter, but later than nepheline, microcline, aegirine I, arfvedsonite, eudialyte and the other minerals making up the outer zones of the pegmatite bodies.

Fine-grained segregations of light-green, green, white, brown, azure and yellow apatite are of low-temperature origin as compared with the green variety. They usually fill up cracks and cavities in prismatic natrolite, in close association with tainiolite, limonite, staffelite [francolite] and other minerals of the replace-ment complex.

44. Belovite

$(Sr,Ce)_{10} [PO_4]_6 (O,OH)_2$; hex.; sp.gr. 4·19; H. 5

This mineral was first found by L. S. Borodin in 1950 in an ussingitic pegma-tite body on the south-eastern slope of Malyi Punkaruaiv. The following descrip-tion is based on his data (Borodin, 1954[1]).

Belovite occurs in ussingite in the form of hexagonal prismatic crystals up to 2 cm long. Crystallographically it resembles apatite and is usually characterized by the development of the prism and pinacoid faces $(10\bar{1}0)$ and (0001), dipyramidal faces sometimes being found in thin sections. Cleavage imperfect parallel to the prism. Fracture uneven. Brittle. Colour copper-yellow. Lustre vitreous, on the fracture greasy. Optically uniaxial, negative. Refractive indices, $No=1·660$; $Ne=1·640$; $No-Ne=0·020$. Colourless or yellowish in thin sections. X-ray structural study by Sludskaya and Organova has shown that belovite belongs to the apatite group.

Table 112 shows the interplanar spacings as measured from the Debye powder pattern. The following dimensions are characteristic of the unit cell: $a=9·62$ A, $c=7·12$ A; axial ratio $c:a=0·74$.

Belovite is readily soluble in dilute nitric, hydrochloric and, with slightly more

LAM 2D

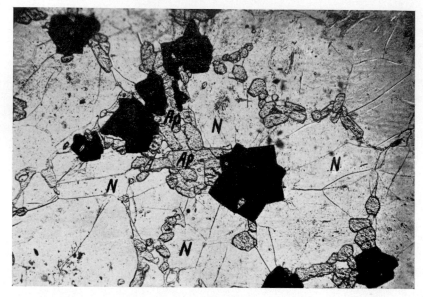

FIG. 205. Interrelationship between apatite (Ap) loparite (dark) and nepheline (N). ×46. Without analyser

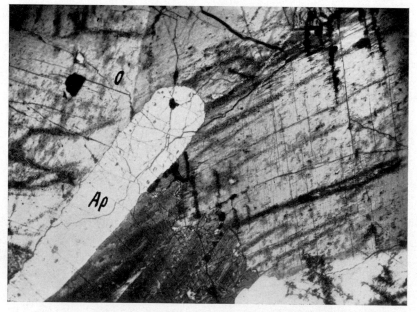

FIG. 206. Apatite crystal (Ap) included in orthoclase (O). ×46. Without analyser

difficulty, sulphuric acids. The results of chemical analysis are shown in Table 113.

Recalculation of the chemical analysis shows that the composition is expressed by the general formula for minerals of the apatite group $A_{10}X_6O_{24}Z_2$, where A represents cations with an ionic radius of about 1 A; X, cations with a radius of 0·3—0·4 A; Z, additional anions. Sr^{2+}, Ce^{3+}, Ca^{2+} and Na^+ belong to the A group in belovite. Fe^{3+}, Mg^{2+}, Ba^{2+} and K^+ are also present in very small quantity. P^{5+}, S^{6+} and S^{4+} belong to the X group. The Z group is represented by the hydroxyl. Belovite is thus a member of the apatite group in which nearly all the

TABLE 112 Interplanar spacings of belovite (Fe-radiation; $2R=57·3$; $d=0·6$)

Line no.	I	d_{meas}	hkl_{hex}	d_{calc}	Size of unit cell	Indices from apatite
1	3	3·56	201	3·60	—	—
			002	3·56	$c=7·12$	002
2	5	3·28	102	3·28	—	102
3	6	3·15	210	3·15	$a=9·61$	120
4	10	2·87	211	2·88	—	121
5	7	2·78	300	2·77	$a=9·63$	300
6	3	2·31	310	2·31	$a=9·62$	130
7	1	2·19	311	2·20	—	131
8	3	2·14	113	2·13	—	113
9	8	1·998	222	1·990	—	222
10	7	1·943	312	1·937	—	132
11	8	1·900	213	1·897	—	123
12	7	1·843	321	1·844	—	231
13	7 broad	1·830	410	1·820	$a=9·69$	140
			303	1·802	—	—
			402	1·797	—	402
		1·787	004	1·779	$c=7·15$	004
14	2	1·560	403	1·564	—	—
			124	1·570	—	—
15	4	1·509	502	1·509	—	502
16	4	1·494	510	1·497	$a=9·60$	—
			323	1·495	—	233
17	2	1·467	511	1·463	—	151
			332	1·460	—	332
18	5 double	1·316	423	1·314	—	—
		1·306	521	1·310	—	—
			324	1·300	—	not indexed further
19	6	1·275	432	1·278	—	
			414	1·272	—	
20	6	1·252	611	1·250	—	
			522	1·248	—	
21	3 broad	1·209	504	2·214	—	
			334	1·189	—	
		1·184	441; 433	1·182	$c=7·10$	
22	1	1·166	523	1·160	—	
23	3	1·158	721	1·158	—	
24	4	1·148	116; 514	1·150; 1·143	—	
25	4	1·132	702	1·128	—	
26	3	1·105	216	1·109	—	
27	6	1·070	443; 524	1·070; 1·068	—	
28	3	1·064	533; 335; 226	1·062	—	
29	8	1·037	631; 623; 107	1·036; 1·009	—	
30	4	1·010	632; 326	1·005	—	

calcium has been isomorphously replaced by strontium and rare earths ($CaO = 5.23$ per cent; $Sr = 33.6$ per cent; $R.E._2O_3 = 24$ per cent). Belovite can be represented as an isomorphous mixture of several chemical compounds, its formula taking the following form: $mSr_{10}P_6O_{24}(OH)_2 + nCe_5Na_5P_6O_{24} + pCe_2Ca_8P_6O_{26}$, where $m : n : p = 5 : 3 : 2$.

Voronova established the following rare-earth ratios in belovite by X-ray chemical analysis: $Ce : La : Nd : Pr = 1 : 0.6 : 0.5 : 0.2$.

Belovite is closely associated with ussingite which crystallized in the hydro-thermal stage of the pegmatitic process. Its presence shows that the replacement of calcium by strontium and rare earths can occur on a larger scale than had until recently been thought.

TABLE 113   Chemical composition of belovite

Constituent	Content, per cent	Atomic proportions	Calculation of atomic ratios		
Na_2O	3.60	0.1162			
K_2O	0.20	0.0042			
MgO	0.16	0.0039			
CaO	5.23	0.0932	0.7017	9.98	—10
SrO	33.60	0.3242			
BaO	0.96	0.0062			
ΣLa_2O_3	24.00	0.1464			
Fe_2O_3	0.60	0.0074			
P_2O_5	28.88	0.4068	0.4228	6.01	—6
SiO_2	0.20	0.0033			
SO_3	1.12	0.0127			
H_2O	0.89	0.0988	0.0988	1.26	—1
—	—	$O = 0.8291$	1.8291	26.02	—26
Total	99.44	—	—		
Analyst		Kazakova, 1952			
Reference		Borodin (1954₁)			

45. Rinkolite and lovchorrite

$Na_2Ca_4(Ce,La)(Ti,Nb) (Si_2O_7)_2(F,OH)_4$; mon.; sp.gr. 3.2—3.4; H. 5

Rinkolite occurs rarely in the Lovozero alkali massif, chiefly in the non-pegmatitic rocks. It forms irregularly-shaped individuals, measuring up to $0.5 \times 0.3 \times 0.1$ cm, or platy segregations up to 5 cm long.

Colour light-yellow, greenish-yellow or light-brown. Parts consisting of lovchorrite, measuring up to $0.2 \times 0.3 \times 0.4$ cm and varying in colour from dark-yellow to brownish-yellow tones, are sometimes found inside the rinkolite individuals. Gradual transitions between rinkolite and lovchorrite are observed.

In thin sections it can be seen that the rinkolite segregations are either individual columnar crystals (Fig. 207) or finely acicular aggregates. Sometimes large segregations have a zonal structure, the central parts being isotropic and the marginal parts having birefringence up to 0·010. Optically biaxial, positive. Elongation negative. Extinction almost straight; $c : Np = 0\text{-}3°$. Pleochroism poorly expressed: Ng – light-yellow; Np – colourless; absorption $Ng > Np$. Refractive indices: $Ng = 1\text{·}667$; $Nm = 1\text{·}660$; $Np = 1\text{·}655$; $Ng - Np = 0\text{·}012$; $2V = 68\text{-}72°$. Lovchorrite is optically isotropic. Its refractive index is similar to the rinkolite $Ng: N = 1\text{·}665\text{—}1\text{·}670$. Recalculation of the chemical analysis data for Lovozero rinkolite (Table 114) shows that its composition is expressed by the formula: $A_7B(Si_2O_7)_2[F, OH, O]_4$, where group A contains chemical elements with an

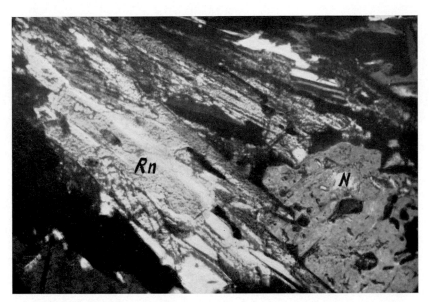

FIG. 207. Elongated rinkolite crystals (Rn); N—nepheline. $\times 90$. Crossed nicols

ionic radius near to or greater than 1 A (Na, K, Ca, Sr, Mg, R.E.), and group B elements with an ionic radius varying from 0·64—0·87A (Ti, Nb, Fe²⁺). The expanded formula for rinkolite will have the following form: $Na_2Ca_4(Ce, La)$ $(Ti, Nb) (Si_2O_7)_2(F, OH, O)_4$.

Comparison of the chemical analyses of Lovozero and Khibiny tundra rinkolites (see Table 114) shows that in the main their composition is similar. The difference is that the Lovozero rinkolite is richer in rare earths and contains less fluorine and yttrium. According to the quantitative X-ray spectrographic analysis data (analysts L. A. Voronova and G. N. Muravitskaya) the rare-earth ratio in rinkolite is as follows: $La_{28.4}Ce_{44.4}Pr_{5.7}Nd_{16.8}Sm_{2.3}Gd_{1.1}Dy_{0.6}Y_{0.7}$ (per cent). In addition, manganese, tantalum, beryllium, gallium and lead were detected spectroscopically in rinkolite.

Rinkolite occurs mainly in the rocks of the differentiated complex, more rarely in the poikilitic syenites. In the rocks of the differentiated complex it is distributed extremely unevenly. In the upper part of the complex it is present only in the malignites, urtites and juvites, in amounts varying from 0·05 to 0·2 per cent; it is not present in the other rocks. The maximum content is found in urtites bedded above malignites and in the malignites themselves (tenths of 1 per cent), the quantity diminishing from the floor to the roof of the urtite horizon. Rinkolite is present in urtites of the 1st, 2nd and 4th horizons in considerably smaller amounts (0·03-0·05 per cent).

In the middle part of the differentiated complex rinkolite occurs mainly in the aegirine-lujavrites, more rarely in the hornblende-lujavrites and foyaites. It is present in the urtites in minute amounts. Its tenor in the aegirine-lujavrites varies from 0·1 to 2 per cent, reaching 3-5 per cent in particular parts. The rocks richest in rinkolite are the melanocratic lujavrites. The amount of rinkolite diminishes as the feldspar content of the rocks increases, until it completely disappears in the leucocratic lujavrites and foyaites. The largest amounts are found in the lujavrites, in parts where the lomonosovite-murmanite group minerals are absent or present in only extremely small quantity. As a rule the rinkolite tenor in the lujavrites of the middle part of the complex increases with depth.

In the lower part of the complex rinkolite is present in much smaller quantity than in the middle part, and mainly in the aegirine-lujavrites, where its tenor does

TABLE 114 Chemical composition of rinkolite

Constituent	Lovozero (aegirine-lujavrite)			Khibiny (Takhtarvumchorr pegmatite)*	
	per cent	Atomic proportions	Calculation of atomic ratios	per cent	Atomic proportions
SiO_2	28·38	0·4725	} 0·4957 4·00 —4	29·44	0·4902
Al_2O_3	1·18	0·0232		1·52	0·0298
TiO_2	8·27	0·1035	}	8·43	0·1055
ZrO_2	trace	—	} 0·1263 1·02 —1	0·16	0·0013
Nb_2O_5	2·58	0·0194		2·57	0·0194
Fe_2O_3	0·27	0·0034		0·06	0·0008
ThO_2	0·63	0·0024	}	0·46	0·0017
Y_2O_3	0·14	0·0012	} 0·1162 0·95 —1	1·80	0·0158
Ce_2O_3	8·84	0·0538		7·02	0·0428
La_2O_3	9·57	0·0588	}	6·69	0·0410
FeO	—	—	—	—	—
MnO	—	—	—	0·12	0·0017
MgO	0·24	0·0059	}	—	—
CaO	26·68	0·4758	} 0·4856 3·92 —4	26·38	0·4704
SrO	0·40	0·0039	}	1·62	0·0156
Na_2O	7·83	0·2526	} 0·2602 2·09 —2	6·52	0·2104
K_2O	0·36	0·0076		0·42	0·0090
F	4·40	0·2315	} 0·4115 3·32 —3	5·98	0·3147
H_2O	1·62	0·1800		1·78	0·1978
	—	O =1·8259	1·8259 14·75 —15	—	—
Total	101·39	—	—	100·97	—
$-O = F_2$	− 1·85			− 2·52	
—	99·54	—	—	98·45	—
Analyst	Kazakova (1952)			Burova, 1934	

* Figures taken from *Minerals of the Khibiny and Lovozero tundras* (1937)

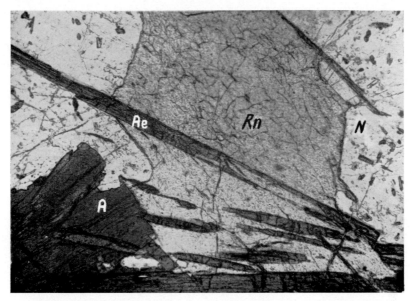

FIG. 208. Interrelationship of rinkolite (Rn) with nepheline (N),
aegirine (Ae) and arfvedsonite (A). ×46. Without analyser

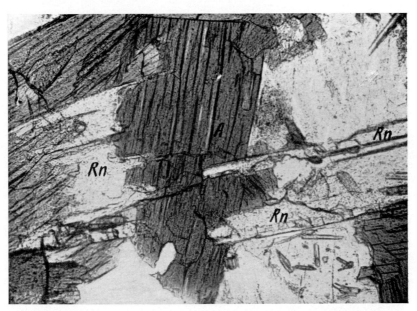

FIG. 209. Interrelationship of arfvedsonite (A) with rinkolite (Rn).
×46. Without analyser

not exceed 0·05-0·01 per cent. In the poikilitic syenites it has been found in isolated cases on Karnasurt and in the Chinglusuai valley.

In the pegmatites this mineral is very rare. Gerasimovskii found it in contaminated pegmatites of the Suoluaiv valley in close association with apatite and sphene. In addition, heavily altered rinkolite has been observed in the pegmatites on the northern slope of Lepkhe-Nel'm, in the form of inclusions in orthoclase.

In time of separation the rock rinkolite is later than aegirine II, with which it is closely associated. Rinkolite fills up spaces between lath-like microcline and nepheline (Fig. 208). Very often it cements aegirine II and arfvedsonite, more rarely replacing them (Fig. 209). It contains inclusions of loparite, apatite, lomonosovite and lamprophyllite, and is itself present in the form of inclusions in pectolite, sodalite and natrolite. In association with pectolite and sodalite, rinkolite is usually unaltered, but in association with natrolite it is partially converted into vudyavrite. In the pegmatites it is as a rule extensively replaced by vudyavrite.

46. Nordite

$Na_3(Sr,Ca)(Mn,Mg,Fe)(Ce,La)(SiO_3)_6$; orthorhomb.; sp.gr. 3·43; H. 5—6

Nordite is extremely rare in the Lovozero alkali massif. It was first detected there by Gerasimovskii in 1935 and the following description takes his data into account.

In the poikilitic syenites nordite forms platy segregations measuring up to

Fig. 210. Interrelationship of nordite (Nd) with sodalite (S) and aegirine (dark). ×90. Crossed nicols

$0·3 \times 0·2 \times 0·05$ cm, which often have a fanlike shape (Fig. 210). More rarely it is present in the form of radiate-fibrous rosettes up to 0·4 cm in diameter. In the schlieren-like pegmatites the platy segregations of nordite are sometimes as big as $1 \times 0·5 \times 0·1$ cm. Occasionally poorly-formed crystals of the mineral are found, with the following crystallographic forms (Gerasimovskii, 1941₂) *a* (100), *b* (010), *m* (110), *n* (120), *y* (212) and *r* (101). The large crystal face, which determines the platy habit, is taken as (100). The other faces are poorly developed in the form of narrow bands. Figure 211 shows the general appearance of a nordite crystal; the (212) and (010) faces are exaggerated in width to make them stand out more clearly. Axial ratio $a : b : c = 0.730 : 1 : 0.527$.

The colour of nordite is light brown. Cleavage distinct along (100). Lustre vitreous. Semitransparent. Brittle. Fracture uneven to conchoidal. Specific gravity 3·428 (rock) and 3·430 (pegmatite). In thin sections nordite is colourless or light-grey. Optically biaxial, negative. Refractive indices $Ng = 1.642$—1.644; $Nm = 1.630$—1.640; $Np = 1.619$—1.620; $Ng - Np = 0.023$—0.024. $2V = 27$-$30°$. Orientation of optical indicatrix: $x = Np$, $y = Nm$, $z = Ng$. Pole to the cleavage coincides with Np axis.

As can be seen from Table 115, the physical and optical properties of nordite from the poikilitic syenites and pegmatites are identical.

Recalculation of the chemical analysis (Table 116) shows that the composition of nordite is expressed by the formula $Na_3(Sr, Ca)(Mn, Mg, Fe)(Ce, La)(SiO_3)_6$. Titanium and gallium (1×10^{-4}) were detected spectroscopically. Borovskii obtained the following results from an X-ray chemical study of the rare-earth content: La_2O_3—8·55 per cent, Ce_2O_3—8·1 per cent, Pr_2O_3—1·6 per cent, Nd_2O_3 —1·85 per cent, Ce : La : Pr : Nd = 1 : 1·05 : 0·20 : 0·23.

Nordite has been found in the poikilitic sodalite-syenites of the Chinglusuai valley in amounts varying from 0·1 to 0·2 per cent (rarely up to 0·5 per cent) and also in the associated pegmatites. Its segregations coincide with the sodalitic parts, in which it fills up interstices between grains of primary sodalite, microcline, nepheline and aegirine and is cemented, as it were, by replacement sodalite. Close association with lomonosovite, chinglusuite, neptunite, sphalerite and other minerals is characteristic of it. Nordite is idiomorphic to chinglusuite. Gerasimovskii found it in very small amounts in the Malyi Punkeruaiv pegmatites, in close association with ussingite.

47. Steenstrupine

$(Ce, La, Th, Ca, Na)_2(Mn, Fe)[SiO_3]_4 \cdot 5H_2O$; amorph.; sp.gr. 3·1, H. 4—5

Gerasimovskii (1936₂) was the first to discover and study steenstrupine in the Lovozero massif, where he found it in large quantity in the Malyi Punkaruaiv ussingitic pegmatites. Subsequently, minerals similar to steenstrupine were found in the pegmatites of the north-eastern slope of Karnasurt, the northern slope of Lepkhe-

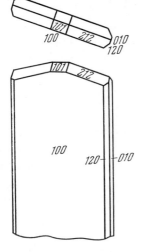

FIG. 211. Nordite crystal (after Gerasimovskii)

Nel'm and the upper reaches of the Kitkuai river. The following brief description
is based mainly on Gerasimovskii's data.

Steenstrupine is found in the form of irregularly-shaped segregations or idiomorphic individuals (up to 1·5 cm in diameter) in ussingite and ussingitized
sodalite. Colour dark-brown or black. Streak brown. Lustre resinous. Fracture
conchoidal. Two determinations of specific gravity gave 3·080 and 3·106. In
thin sections the mineral is light-yellow in the fresh varieties and brown in shades
varying all the way to black in altered parts. Optically isotropic. Refractive index

TABLE 115 Physical and optical properties of nordite

| Property | Nordite | |
	From poikilitic syenite	From pegmatite (Gerasimovskii, 1941₂)
Specific gravity	2·428	2·43
Optic axial angle $2V$	27–29°	~30°00′
Orientation of cleavage pole:		
PNg	89°30′	90°00′
PNm	89°00′	89°00′
PNp	0°30′	1°00′
Refractive index:		
Ng	1·644	1·642
Nm	1·635	1·630–1·640
Np	1·620	1·619
Ng-Np	0·024	0·023

TABLE 116 Chemical composition of nordite from Chinglusuai pegmatites*

Constituent	Content, per cent	Atomic proportions	Calculation of atomic ratios		
SiO_2	45·53	0·7581	0·7581	6·00	—6
TiO_2	nil	—	—		
Nb_2O_5	,,	—	—		
Ta_2O_5	,,	—	—		
Ce_2O_3	8·77	0·0534			
La_2O_3	10·48	0·0644	}0·1262	1·00	—1
Y_2O_3	0·95	0·0084			
Fe_2O_3	1·84	0·0230			
MnO	6·04	0·0851	}0·1577	1·25	—1
MgO	2·00	0·0496			
CaO	4·46	0·0795	}0·1509	1·19	—1
SrO	7·40	0·0714			
Na_2O	11·70	0·3774	}0·3792	3·00	—3
K_2O	0·08	0·0018			
F	nil	—	—		
Cl	trace	—	—		
Other	nil	—	—		
—	—	O = 2·2152	2·2152	17·55	—18
Total	99·25	—			
Analyst	Burova				

* Gerasimovskii's figures (1941₂)

varies from 1·695 in the fresh varieties to 1·653 in the altered ones. Amorphous to X-rays. After ignition to 900° the mineral gives a powder pattern which is analysed in Table 117.

Steenstrupine is readily soluble in concentrated HCl without heating and in HNO_3 on heating, but is poorly soluble even with heating in concentrated H_2SO_4.

It should be noted that the name steenstrupine covers a whole group of minerals, differing greatly in chemical composition (Table 118). The tenor of the chief components in these minerals varies within wide limits (expressed as percentages): SiO_2 20·6-32·1; P_2O_5 3·74-8·19; ThO_2 2·13-10·23; $(Ce, La)_2O_3$ 25-35; MnO 5-9; Na_2O 2·09-11·23; H_2O 3·45-12·74. Recalculation of the chemical analyses of minerals in this group shows that they can all be reduced to a formula of the type $(A_2B[SiO_3]_m(OH, F)_n pH_2O)$, where A = Ce, La, Th, Ca, Na, B = Mn, Fe, Nb, Al, the coefficients in the anionic parts varying, depending on the ratios of the principal cations in the A and B groups; $m = 2$—4; $n = 0$—3; $p = 0$—5. In conformity with this type of formula the expanded formulae for the steenstrupine minerals analysed will be:

1. $(Ce, La, Th, Ca, Na)_2(Mn, Fe, Nb)[SiO_3]_4 . 5H_2O$
2. $(Ce, La, Th, Ca, Na)_2(Mn, Fe)[SiO_3]_2(OH)_3 . 2H_2O$
3. $(Na, Ce, La, Th, Ca)_2(Mn, Fe)[SiO_3]_2(OH, F)_2$

Gerasimovskii is inclined to explain the difference in chemical composition indicated above as due to different degrees of alteration of the steenstrupine. On the other hand, the alteration process of Lovozero minerals entails in the first place loss of sodium and phosphorus, accession of water and, in advanced decomposition, loss of silicon. By contrast the Lovozero steenstrupine that contains the largest amount of water and seems to have been the most altered contains the largest amount of silica found in this mineral. Moreover, the Lovozero steenstrupine differs from the Greenland steenstrupine in having a higher thorium and manganese content and a lower calcium, iron, phosphorus and sodium content.

The presence of similar minerals with even higher tenor of manganese (17·98 per cent MnO—see description of manganosteenstrupine) indicates that we are here dealing with a group of complex minerals that have as yet been insufficiently studied.

Strontium, barium, beryllium, lead, zinc and nickel, have been detected spectroscopically in steenstrupine. Steenstrupine is a characteristic mineral of the pegmatites in the poikilitic syenite complex; in the pegmatites of the other complexes it is either lacking or present only in very small quantity. Voronova's

TABLE 117 Interplanar spacings of steenstrupine

Line no.	I	d	Line no.	I	d	Line no.	I	d
1	8	3·13	6	3	1·877	11	2	1·372
2	4	2·85	7	4	1·696	12	1	1·337
3	6	2·74	8	7	1·651	13	5	1·258
4	2	2·13	9	2	1·583	14	1	1·216
5	8	1·934	10	2	1·449	15	4	1·115

reports of isolated occurrences in the poikilitic syenites are the only indications that it occurs in the non-pegmatite rocks of the massif. Usually steenstrupine is associated with ussingite, sodalite, natrolite, schizolite and erikite, and is localized either in the central zeolitic zones of the fully differentiated pegmatite bodies or in the zeolitized parts of outer equigranular zones. It forms inclusions in ussingite and in ussingitized sodalite and is consequently earlier than ussingite.

In the pegmatites of the poikilitic syenite complex a number of hydrous silicates of thorium, manganese and rare earths resembling steenstrupine have been mistaken for it in field work. One such mineral is described below, under the provisional name of manganosteenstrupine.

TABLE 118   Chemical composition of steenstrupine

Consti-tuent	Lovozero, Punkaruaiv			Greenland, Kangerdluarsuk			
	per cent	Atomic pro-portions	Calculations of atomic ratios	per cent	Atomic pro-portions	per cent	Atomic pro-portions
SiO_2	32·10	0·5344	} 0·5860 4·00 —4	20·60	0·3428	26·72	0·4446
P_2O_5	3·74	0·0526		4·53	0·0638	8·19	0·1154
Ta_2O_5	} 2·13	0·0160		1·28	0·0096	—	—
Nb_2O_5						4·37	0·0952
Fe_2O_3	1·81	0·0227		5·18	0·0650	2·67	0·0334
Al_2O_3	0·34	0·0066	} 0·1742 1·20 —1	0·40	0·0078	—	—
Mn_2O_3	—	—		5·79	0·0734	—	—
MnO	9·06	0·1277		—	—	6·60	0·0930
MgO	0·05	0·0012		—	—	0·31	0·0076
BeO	—	—		1·22	0·0488	—	—
ThO_2	10·23	0·0386		3·84	0·0145	2·13	0·0081
CeO_2	—	—		17·85	0·1037	} 29·60	0·1816
Ce_2O_3	10·45	0·0636		—	—		
La_2O_3	—	—		15·52	0·0952		
ΣCe_2O_3	13·56	0·0826	} 0·2913 2·00 —2	—	—		
ΣY_2O_3	0·77	0·0062		2·19	0·0194	0·36	0·0030
CaO	1·85	0·0329		4·22	0·0752	2·33	0·0415
PbO	—	—		1·02	0·0046	—	—
Na_2O	2·09	0·0674		2·53	0·0816	11·23	0·3884
$H_2O\pm$	12·74	1·4142	1·4142 9·75 —10	12·73	1·4132	3·45	0·3830
F	—	—	—	—	—	1·24	0·0653
		$O = 2·4925$	2·4925 17·18 —17	—	2·3717	—	—
Total	100·92	—	—	98·90	—	99·20	—
$-O = F_2$						−0·52	
						98·68	
Specific gravity	3·080-3·106			3·1901		3·5122	—
Analyst	Borneman			Blomstrand		Christensen	
Reference	Gerasimovskii (1936₂)			Böggild (1905)			

48. Manganosteenstrupine

$(Ce,La,Th)(Mn,Fe) [SiO_3] (OH)_2 . 2H_2O$; amorphous; sp.gr. 3·288; H. 5·5—6

Manganosteenstrupine is found in the pegmatites of the north-eastern slope of Karnasurt, genetically connected with poikilitic sodalite- (hackmanite-)syenites (see description of Karnasurt albite-natrolite vein). It forms irregularly-shaped segregations measuring 0·5 mm to 3 cm in cross-section (Fig. 212), or almost monomineralic accumulations of irregular shape, up to 10 cm in diameter. Colour

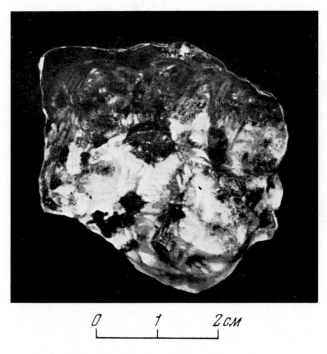

$0 \qquad 1 \qquad 2 \; CM$

FIG. 212. Manganosteenstrupine segregations (dark) in natrolite (light)

black. Opaque. In thin splinters it is translucent, brownish-red. Lustre resinous. Streak dark-brown. Fracture conchoidal. Cleavage absent. Heavily fractured. Brittle. In thin sections the colour varies from pale yellow, almost colourless, to black, translucent with red. Optically isotropic. Refractive index $N > 1·80$.

Comparing the chemical analyses of manganosteenstrupine (Table 119) and steenstrupine we can see that the former differs appreciably from the latter in having a high tenor of manganese and calcium, a lower content of silica and an almost total absence of phosphorus and alkalis. Recalculation of the chemical analysis shows that the composition of manganosteenstrupine is represented by the formula: $(Ce, La, Th, Ca, Na) (Mn, Fe) SiO_3 (OH)_2 2H_2O$, as distinct from steenstrupine, for which the formula has the form: $(Ce, La, Th, Ca, Na)_2 (Mn, Fe) [SiO_3]_m (OH)_n . pH_2O$.

X-ray spectrographic analysis of the rare earths by R. L. Barinskii gave the following percentages: $La_{4.1}$ $Ce_{23.8}$ $Pr_{8.6}$ $Nd_{16.3}$ $Sm_{0.77}$ $Gd_{0.14}$ $Dy_{0.24}$. Strontium, barium, and beryllium were detected spectroscopically.

Endothermic effects in the 90-200 and 350-390° intervals and an exothermic effect at 850° are observed on the thermal analysis curve.

Manganosteenstrupine, as has already been noted, occurs in the pegmatites of the poikilitic syenite complex. It has not been found in the non-pegmatitic rocks of the massif. It is usually localized in outer fine-grained zones of pegmatite bodies, where it is closely associated with microcline, aegirine, hackmanite, nenadkevichite, schizolite and other minerals. It is sometimes associated with monocrystalline hackmanite and natrolite.

In time of separation manganosteenstrupine is a comparatively early mineral. It fills up interstices between crystals of early microcline and is also found in the form of segregations of idiomorphic crystals of square or pentagonal shape and segregations of irregular shape in prismatic natrolite and hackmanite (Fig. 213). In all probability manganosteenstrupine crystallized after early microcline during the period of hackmanite formation.

At late stages in the pegmatite formation manganosteenstrupine is replaced by

TABLE 119 Chemical composition of manganosteenstrupine

Constituent	Content, per cent	Atomic proportions	Calculation of atomic ratios		
SiO_2	21·36	0·3556	⎫ 0·3648	1·21	—1
P_2O_5	0·65	0·0092	⎭		
Al_2O_3	0·91	0·0178	⎫		
TiO_2	1·49	0·0186			
Ta_2O_5	—	—			
Nb_2O_5	—	—			
ZrO_2	1·08	0·0087	⎬ 0·3409	1·13	—1
Fe_2O_3	1·99	0·0250			
Mn_2O_3	—	—			
MnO	17·98	0·2535			
MgO	0·70	0·0173	⎭		
ThO_2	11·28	0·0427	⎫		
UO_2	0·20	0·0007			
PbO	0·10	0·0004			
Ce_2O_3	9·79	0·0596			
ΣCe_2O_3	—	—			
ΣLa_2O_3	10·27	0·0630	⎬ 0·2711	0·90	—1
ΣY_2O_3	0·13	0·0012			
CeO_2	—	—			
CaO	4·66	0·0831			
Na_2O	0·48	0·0154			
K_2O	0·24	0·0050	⎭		
H_2O^+	12·86 ⎱	1·8250	1·8250	6·08	—6
H_2O^-	3·58 ⎰				
F	—	—	—	—	
		$O = 2·0469$	2·0469	6·82	—7
Total	99·75	—	—		
Specific gravity	3·288	—	—		
Analyst	Kazakova, 1948				

an ochreous aggregate of brown and orange, optically isotropic, secondary, hydrous rare-earth silicates of variable composition, containing phosphorus. The refractive index of these aggregates varies between 1·580 and 1·690, being lower in the lighter varieties. As the colour becomes more intense the refractive index also rises. The end-product of manganosteenstrupine alteration is hydrocerite.

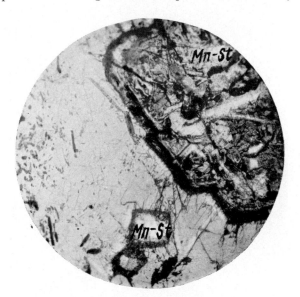

FIG. 213. Manganosteenstrupine (Mn-St) in natrolite. ×46. Without analyser

49. Karnasurtite

(Ce,La,Th)(Ti, Nb)(Al,Fe)(Si,P)$_2$O$_7$(OH)$_4$. 3H$_2$O; hex. (?); sp.gr. 2·89—2·95; H. 2

Karnasurtite was first discovered in 1947 by Kozhanov and Kuz'menko (1959) in a natrolitic hackmanite pegmatitic stock on Karnasurt, and named after that mountain.

It occurs in the form of hexagonal segregations up to 1 cm in diameter or accumulations of platy crystals measuring less than a centimetre to 10 × 6 × 2 cm (Fig. 214). The colour varies from copper-yellow in the fresher varieties to light yellow in the altered varieties. Streak yellow. Lustre greasy. Hardness 2. Brittle. Light-yellow in thin sections. Relief high. Cleavage perfect in one direction and imperfect in another. No appreciable pleochroism. Interference colour reaching second-order blue. Optically uniaxial, negative. Slightly anomalously biaxial. Extinction straight. Elongation positive. Refractive indices $No = 1·617$; $Ne = 1·595$; $No - Ne = 0·022$.

The mineral is amorphous to X-rays. On heating to 900° it gives a powder pattern similar to that of monazite (Table 120). Recalculation of the chemical analysis (Table 121) leads to the following formula: (Ce, La, Th) (Ti, Nb) (Al, Fe) (Si, P)$_2$O$_7$(OH)$_4$. 3H$_2$O.

In chemical composition the mineral most resembling karnasurtite is britholite,

Fig. 214. Karnasurtite (K) in polylithionite

TABLE 120 Interplanar spacings of products of heating karnasurtite and monazite
(Fe-radiation; $2R = 57 \cdot 9$; $d = 0 \cdot 6$)

Line no.	Karnasurtite		Monazite		Line no.	Karnasurtite		Monazite	
	I	d	I	d		I	d	I	d
1	5	3·49	4	3·53	16	—	—	2	1·857
2	6	3·29	6	3·29	17	1	1·807	2	1·810
3	7	3·10	8	3·09	18	3	1·764	2	1·784
4	3	2·97	3	2·98	19	5	1·723	4	1·749
5	7	2·88	7	2·89	20	2	1·712	2	1·692
6	—	—	3	2·65	21	4	1·647	2	1·646
7	—	—	3	2·48	22	1	1·598	3	1·603
8	4	2·44	1	2·44	23	2	1·540	3	1·550
9	4	2·14	4	2·19	24	—	—	1	1·486
10	—	—	2	2·156	25	1	1·438	2	1·45
11	1	2·07	3	2·110	26	2	1·377	—	—
12	2	1·970	—	—	27	1	1·339	—	—
13	2	1·943	—	—	28	3	1·199	—	—
14	3	1·908	—	—	29	1	1·164	—	—
15	4	1·883	3	1·893					

a complex silicate and phosphate of rare earths and calcium from the alkali pegmatites of Greenland. Britholite, however, is distinguished by having higher refractive indices, a biaxial optical character, a higher specific gravity (4·4) and greater hardness (5·5). Moreover, britholite contains less titanium and niobium.

Strontium, zinc, arsenic, copper and gallium have also been detected spectroscopically in karnasurtite. The dehydration curve obtained by Karpova by the tensimetric method (Fig. 215), shows that the mineral loses half its weight up to 100° and the rest in the interval 100-650°.

Karnasurtite occurs in small quantity in the replacement zones of the pegmatites in the poikilitic syenite complex on Karnasurt and Punkaruaiv, in close association with polylithionite, natrolite and ussingite, and can therefore be regarded as a late mineral. It is early in comparison with polylithionite, which corrodes and fills cracks in it. More rarely, karnasurtite segregations occur in coarse-prismatic natrolite (Fig. 216).

TABLE 121 Chemical composition of karnasurtite

| Constituent | Karnasurt | | | | | Punkaruaiv* |
	per cent	per cent	Atomic proportions	Calculation of atomic ratios	per cent	per cent
SiO$_2$	22·33	20·47	0·3406	} 0·3870 1·9 —2	30·27	24·91
P$_2$O$_5$	5·55	3·29	0·0464		2·42	6·81
BeO	0·35	—	—		—	—
Al$_2$O$_3$	6·40	7·46	0·1464	} 0·1828 0·9 —1	8·43	5·52
Fe$_2$O$_3$	3·50	1·10	0·0138		0·75	1·07
MgO	0·45	0·91	0·0226		3·41	0·60
TiO$_2$	10·73	12·14	0·1519	} 0·2135 1·07 —1	6·65	12·33
ZrO$_2$	0·00	—	—		—	1·20
Nb$_2$O$_5$	6·25	8·20	0·0616		5·00	2·20
ThO$_2$	5·40	6·22	0·0235		2·82	6·04
Ce$_2$O$_3$	6·55	17·58	0·1080		5·15	8·11
ΣLa$_2$O$_3$	9·82	—	—		10·63	8·55
CaO	2·23	1·66	0·0286	} 0·2101 1·05 —1	1·73	3·20
BaO	—	0·68	0·0044		—	—
Na$_2$O	0·50	0·91	0·0294		0·97	—
K$_2$O	1·57	0·76	0·0162		1·05	—
H$_2$O$^+$ } H$_2$O$^-$	17·90	7·22 } 10·84	2·0048	2·0048 10·02 —10	8·68 10·67	7·29 12·29
F	—	0·91	0·0479 O =2·7851	} 2·8090 14·04 —14	—	—
Total	99·53	100·35			98·63	100·12
− O =F$_2$		− 0·38		—		
		99·97				
Specific gravity		2·89			—	—
Analyst	Kazakova, 1951	Sokova, 1951			Kazakova	Kazakova

* Semenov's data

50. Erikite

(La,Ce)PO$_4$. H$_2$O; orthorhomb. (?); sp.gr. 3·77—3·79; H. 2—3

Erikite occurs, rarely and in very small amounts, only in the pegmatites. It was first discovered by Gerasimovskii (1937$_2$) in the Malyi Punkaruaiv pegmatites and the following description is based on his data.

In the Malyi Punkaruaiv pegmatites erikite occurs in crystals and grains measuring 0·2 to 0·7 cm or, rarely, up to 1·5 cm in diameter. The crystals are usually imperfect, prismatic, not infrequently doubly-terminated and uniformly developed along all three axes. Sometimes crystals are found to be flattened in the direction taken as the z axis (Fig. 217). In measuring crystal fragments Gerasimovskii detected the following forms (the setting of the crystal was according to Böggild's system): a (100), b (010), c (001), m (110), o (130), g (021), r (101), s (201), t (111), v (132), w (211), x (221) and y (212). Of these the habit of the crystals is determined by (100), (010), (001), (110), (021), (111) and (101).

In the Karnasurt pegmatites erikite forms irregularly-shaped segregations measuring up to $5 \times 3 \times 2$ cm, filling up leaching cavities between microcline crystals in the coarse-grained zone.

Colour pale yellowish-green or greenish-yellow. Lustre on crystal faces

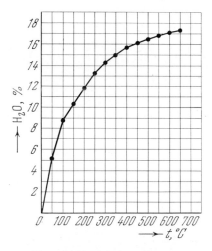

FIG. 215. Tensimetric curve for karnasurtite

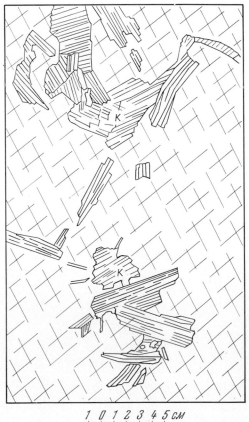

FIG. 216. Karnasurtite (K) in prismatic natrolite

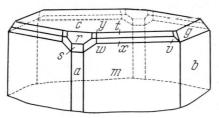

Fig. 217. Erikite crystal (after Gerasimovskii)

weak, pearly. Opaque. Hardness 2—3. Fracture uneven, earthy. Under the microscope erikite can be seen to have a very finely scaly structure, as a result of which it is very difficult to determine its optical character. The scales are hexagonal, size 0·01-0·1 mm. Under the microscope the colour is brownish-grey. Gerasimovskii suggests that the Lovozero erikite is uniaxial, positive; refractive indices: $Ne=1·730$ and $No=1·700$.

TABLE 122 Chemical composition of erikite

Constituent	Karnasurt			Punkaruaiv	Greenland
	per cent	Atomic proportions	Calculation of atomic ratios	per cent	per cent
SiO_2	10·82	0·1801	⎫	3·42	15·12
BeO	0·50	0·0200	⎬ 0·4827 1·12 —1	—	—
P_2O_5	20·06	0·2826	⎭	24·31	17·78
TiO_2	0·25	0·0031	⎫	—	—
ZrO_2	0·43	0·0035		—	—
Nb_2O_5	0·00	—		0·90	—
Fe_2O_3	1·80	0·0226		0·30	—
Al_2O_3	0·66	0·0130		0·23	9·28
FeO	—	—		—	—
MnO	0·50	0·0070		0·12	—
MgO	0·20	0·0050	⎬ 0·4689 1·09 —1	0·98	—
ThO_2	1·15	0·0044		0·32	3·26
Ce_2O_3	21·06	0·1284		55·96	40·51
ΣLa_2O_3	29·24	0·1794		—	—
CaO	1·90	0·0399		1·57	1·81
BaO	0·76	0·0050		—	—
SrO	0·60	0·0058		0·90	—
Na_2O	1·36	0·0438		1·05	5·63
K_2O	0·38	0·0080	⎭	—	—
CO_2	not determined	—	—	1·16	—
H_2O^+	4·70	⎫ 0·8236	0·8236 1·91 —2	7·39	6·28
H_2O^-	2·72	⎭			
—	—	O = 2·1182	2·1182 4·93 —5	—	—
Total	99·09		—	98·61	99·67
Specific gravity		—		3·774-3·793	3·493
Analyst	Kazakova, 1951			Borneman	—
Reference	—			Gerasimovskii (1937₂)	Böggild (1903)

Erikite is readily soluble in concentrated HCl and HNO_3 and in dilute HNO_3 and H_2SO_4 without heating. In concentrated H_2SO_4 and dilute HCl it dissolves with difficulty and only on heating.

Recalculation of the chemical analysis of Karnasurt erikite (Table 122) shows that its composition is expressed by the chemical formula (La, Ce) (P, Si)O_4 . H_2O. The phosphorus-silicon ratio in the anionic part varies from 1 : 1 in the Greenland erikite to 1 : 6 in the Punkaruaiv erikite, though the sum of these elements remains roughly constant. The two elements apparently replace each other isomorphously, and erikite should be regarded as a rare-earth silicophosphate. The ratio between the sum of the alkalis and the calcium, the sum of the rare earths and the sum of the phosphorus and silicon is the same in all erikites: 1 : 6 : 7.

Lead, copper and gallium have been detected spectroscopically in pegmatitic erikite.

Erikite occurs only in the pegmatites of the poikilitic syenite complex. Association with sodalite, schizolite, murmanite, steenstrupine, ussingite, mangano-steenstrupine, belovite, karnasurtite, neptunite and natrolite is characteristic of erikite. Segregations of this mineral are usually included in ussingite and aegirine III. Its formation is apparently due to the leaching of early rare-earth phosphates and silicophosphates, without redeposition, that is, with the formation of pseudo-morphs, or with redeposition in leaching cavities at the replacement stage.

51. Hydrocerite

$(La,Ce,Th)_2(Si,P)_2O_7 . 5H_2O$; cub. (?)

Hydrocerite was first discovered in the Karnasurt natrolite-albite pegmatitic vein (see description of vein) by Kuz'menko in 1947, in the form of pseudomorphs after manganosteenstrupine. It had previously been mistaken for erikite.

The colour is yellow to coppery-yellow. Lustre vitreous. Brittle. Texture fine-grained, recalling that of ochreous aggregates. Transparent and pale yellow in thin sections. Isotropic. Refractive index $N = 1.580$. Amorphous to X-rays.

TABLE 123 Interplanar spacings of heated hydrocerite and cerite
(Cu-radiation; $2R = 57.3$; $d = 0.6$; exposure 20 – 19 hours)

Line no.	Hydrocerite		Cerite		Line no.	Hydrocerite		Cerite	
	I	d	I	d		I	d	I	d
1	4	4·27	—	—	14	2	1·69	3	1·64
2	—	—	3	3·42	15	—	—	4	1·57
3	4	3·33	3	3·36	16	—	—	3	1·424
4	10	3·13	—	—	17	—	—	3	1·395
5	10	2·91	10	2·88	18	4	1·370	1	1·369
6	2	2·62	4	2·62	19	—	—	2	1·345
7	—	—	3	2·52	20	5	1·335	2	1·328
8	5	2·20	—	—	21	5	1·275	—	—
9	5	2·16	4	2·17	22	5	1·235	3	1·233
10	5	1·97	7	1·94	23	—	—	3	1·199
11	8	1·87	8	1·91	24	—	—	1	1·160
12	—	—	4	1·83	25	—	—	4	1·132
13	5	1·75	5	⎰ 1·73 ⎱ 1·72	26	—	—	1	1·074

The mineral seems to occur in the metamict state. The products of heating to 900° give a Debye powder pattern similar to that of cerite (Table 123).

From recalculation of the chemical analysis (Table 124) it can be seen that the composition of hydrocerite is represented by the chemical formula (La, Ce, Th)$_2$(Si, P)$_2$O$_7$. 5H$_2$O, which is distinguished from the formula for cerite by the higher water content. Zinc, arsenic, manganese, lead and copper have also been detected in hydrocerite spectroscopically.

Comparison of the analyses of hydrocerite and manganosteenstrupine (see Table 119) shows that hydrocerite formation is accompanied by loss of manganese and calcium, concentration of iron and titanium and addition of phosphorus and extra water to the crystal lattice.

Like manganosteenstrupine, hydrocerite is present exclusively in pegmatites genetically connected with the hackmanitic varieties of poikilitic syenites and is characteristic only of major pegmatite bodies in which hydrothermal replacement processes are strongly developed. Hydrocerite paragenesis with manganosteen-strupine, neptunite, natrolite and other later minerals has been observed.

As well as karnasurtite, hydrocerite and erikite, the Lovozero pegmatites contain a number of hydrous rare-earth silicophosphates of variable composition, sometimes with thorium, titanium and niobium, which have not yet been con-clusively studied. All these minerals are intimately associated with minerals of the late hydrothermal replacement complexes.

TABLE 124 Chemical composition of hydrocerite

Constituent	Content, per cent	Atomic proportions	Calculation of atomic ratios		
SiO	22·30	0·3713	0·4525	2·04	—2
P$_2$O$_5$	5·76	0·0812			
BeO	0·30	0·0120			
Al$_2$O$_3$	3·66	0·0718			
TiO$_2$	3·33	0·0417			
ZrO$_2$	0·49	0·0040			
Nb$_2$O$_5$	2·00	0·0150			
Fe$_2$O$_3$	6·15	0·0770			
FeO	—	—	0·4378	1·97	—2
MnO	—	—			
MgO	0·14	0·0035			
CaO	2·83	0·0505			
Ce$_2$O$_3$	4·83	0·0294			
ΣLa$_2$O$_3$	12·33	0·0756			
ThO$_2$	15·14	0·0573			
UO$_2$	not determined	—		—	
PbO	,, ,,	—		—	
Na$_2$O	,, ,,	—		—	
K$_2$O	,, ,,	—		—	
H$_2$O+	5·65	2·1970	2·1970	9·80	—10
H$_2$O−	14·14				
—	—	O = 2·7343	2·7343	12·30	—12
Total	99·05				
Analyst		Kazakova			

IV. Lithium Minerals

Lithium minerals are represented in the Lovozero alkali massif mainly by tainiolite, hydrotainiolite, ferrotainiolite, polylithionite and hydropolylithionite. These minerals are found only in the largest of the fully differentiated pegmatite bodies genetically connected with the poikilitic syenite complex.

52. Tainiolite
$KLiMg_2 [Si_4O_{10}] (F,OH)_2$; mon.; sp.gr. 2·82; H. 3

Tainiolite is one of the commonest lithium micas in the alkali pegmatites. It was first discovered by Gerasimovskii (1936_2) in very small amounts in one of the Punkaruaiv pegmatites. In recent years it has been found by Semenov (1957_2) in

FIG. 218. Coarsely crystalline zonal tainiolite in fine-grained polylithionite. ×46. Crossed nicols

the Lepkhe-Nel'm, Kuivchorr and Mannepakhk pegmatites, and the description given here is based mainly on Semenov's data.

Tainiolite forms pseudohexagonal platy crystals measuring up to 3 × 3 × 0·5 cm, of various hues. The large crystals are usually zonal, the central parts being brown and the peripheral parts colourless (Fig. 218). The differently coloured zones have different optical properties and a different chemical composition, the brown zones approximating to tainiolite and the colourless zones to polylithionite. In certain cases there are several thin intermediate zones of tainiolite between the inner and outer zones, alternating with polylithionite zones. These zones, 1-3 mm thick, have hexagonal outlines and are arranged concentrically.

In thin sections tainiolite is light-yellow. Optically biaxial, negative. Under the conoscope and on the Fedorov stage it usually behaves like a uniaxial mineral, except that a slight divergence of the isogyres corresponding to an optic axial angle of about 3-5° can sometimes be observed. Interpenetrating trillings sometimes form on the mica law. In sections parallel to the optic axial plane slight pleochroism from yellowish along Ng to colourless along Np is observed. Refractive indices: $Nm=1.662$; $Np=1.632$ (Gerasimovskii). The light-coloured zones have refractive indices similar to those of polylithionite: $Ng=Nm=1.570$; $Np=1.540$.

Table 125 shows the interplanar spacings calculated from the Debye powder pattern obtained by Sludskaya.

Compared with Greenland tainiolite, the composition of which is fairly ac-

TABLE 125 Interplanar spacings of tainiolite

Line no.	I	d	Line no.	I	d	Line no.	I	d
1	5	9·81	8	7	2·595	15	8	1·501
2	5	5·01	9	4	2·37	16	1	1·433
3	5	4·50	10	1	2·25	17	1	1·346
4	5	3·65	11	1	2·20	18	5	1·303
5	4	3·46	12	1	2·14	19	3	1·245
6	8	3·33	13	10	1·99	20	1	1·203
7	4	2·88	14	5	1·65			

TABLE 126 Chemical composition of tainiolite

Constituent	Lepkhe-Nel'm					Punkaruaiv	Narsarsuk, Greenland
	per cent	Atomic pro-portions	Calculation of atomic ratios				
SiO_2	52·88	0·8804	0·9054	3·98	—4	53·40	52·2
TiO_2	2·00	0·0250				—	—
Al_2O_3	trace	—	—			—	2·7
Fe_2O_3	—	—	—			3·20	—
FeO	1·89	0·0263				—	0·6
MnO	1·38	0·0194	0·4781	2·10	—2	—	19·1
MgO	17·42	0·4324				19·26	
Li_2O	2·44	0·1632	0·2026	0·89	—1	3·21	2·8
Na_2O	1·22	0·0394				2·01	1·8
K_2O	11·38	0·2416	0·2416	10·06	—1	11·07	11·5
H_2O^+	4·24	0·6926	0·6926	3·04	—3	—	8·7*
H_2O^-	2·00						
F	5·36	0·2821	0·2821	1·24	—1	—	—
		$O=2.8573$	2·8573	13·01	—13	—	—
Total	102·21						99·4
$-O=F_2$	-2.25		—			—	
—	99·96		—			—	—
Analyst	Moleva, 1953					Shumilo	Mausebius
Reference	Semenov (1958)					Gerasimovskii (1936₂)	G. Flink (1901)

* Loss on ignition

curately represented by the formula $KLiMg_2[Si_4O_{10}]F_2$, Lovozero tainiolite (Table 126) has a higher tenor of fluorine and water (11·6 per cent $F + H_2O$).

Recalculation of the chemical analysis shows that the composition of tainiolite is expressed by the formula $KLiMg_2[Si_4O_{10}](OH, F)_2 . H_2O$. This may be due to some variability (hydration capacity) of the mineral analysed (transition to hydro-tainiolite).

Also, the presence of calcium, beryllium, niobium, gallium and strontium in

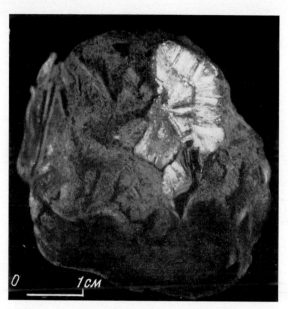

FIG. 219. Tainiolite (light) in fine-grained mass of apatite

tainiolite has been established spectroscopically; 0·3 per cent of rubidium has been detected by X-ray spectrographic analysis.

Darkbrown tainiolite from the Lepkhe-Nel'm pegmatiten costsain 5·03 per-cent FeO and is characterized by more intense pleochroism and higher refractive indices. Semenov (1957₂) distinguishes this variety of tainiolite by the name ferrotainiolite.

An exothermic effect at 850° and an endothermic effect in the 890-920° interval is observed on the thermal analysis curve.

Tainiolite is a characteristic mineral of the complex replacement pegmatites in the poikilitic syenite complex. It is not found in the pegmatites of other com-plexes or in the non-pegmatitic rocks of the massif. It is present in large amounts in the Lepkhe-Nel'm pegmatites, where together with polylithionite it fills cavities and cracks in prismatic natrolite and is one of the typical minerals of the replace-ment complexes. Tainiolite seems to have formed during the late hydrothermal replacement stage, as is shown by its close association with other minerals of the replacement zones, but it is earlier than polylithionite and fine-grained apatite. Large crystals of tainiolite are usually included in fine-grained apatite (Fig. 219) and polylithionite. It may be that the zonal structure of the tainiolite crystals is the result of tainiolite replacement by polylithionite.

In the replacement process tainiolite is converted into hydrotainiolite and with more intensive alteration into minerals of the montmorillonite group.

53. Polylithionite

$KLi_2Al [Si_4O_{10}] (F,OH)_2$; pseudohex.; sp.gr. 2·62—2·82; H. 2—2·5

Polylithionite was first found in the Lovozero massif by Kuz'menko in 1948, in a hackmanite-natrolite pegmatitic stock on the north-eastern slope of Karnasurt. It was later found by Semenov in pegmatites on Lepkhe-Nel'm and in other parts of the massif.

Polylithionite forms irregularly-shaped segregations up to 20 cm in diameter and veinlets in prismatic natrolite, from 0·5 mm to 5 cm thick (Fig. 220). The structure of the polylithionite aggregates is usually finely scaly to cryptocrystalline (Fig. 221). The size of the individual scales varies from 0·001-0·1 mm (Karnasurt) to 2-3 mm, more rarely 5 mm in diameter (Lepkhe-Nel'm). Colour bright pink, pink, pale pink to white, cream to brownish-grey or light-cream to white. Lustre in cryptocrystalline varieties waxy, in crystallized varieties micaceous. Fracture in cryptocrystalline varieties conchoidal. Hardness about 2-2·5 in fresh specimens, about 1 in decomposed specimens. Specific gravity of pink polylithionite 2·76-2·82; of cream polylithionite 2·62.

In thin sections polylithionite is colourless, transparent. The cryptocrystalline varieties have wavy or streaky extinction. Optically biaxial, negative. Optic axial

TABLE 127 Interplanar spacings of lithium micas

Line no.	Pink poly-lithionite, Lovozero		Cream poly-lithionite, Lovozero		Lepi-dolite, Altai		Line no.	Pink poly-lithionite, Lovozero		Cream poly-lithionite, Lovozero		Lepi-dolite, Altai	
	I	d	I	d	I	d		I	d	I	d	I	d
1	8	4·89	7	4·91	2	4·93	20	9	1·631	9	1·633	10	1·649
2	7	4·43	5	4·43	2	4·64	21	3	1·574	2	1·577	2	1·596
3	8	3·58	8	3·59	5	3·45	22	1	1·539	1	1·541	2	1·553
4	10	3·27	9	3·28	8	3·30	23	—	—	—	—	2	1·514
5	8	3·04	8	3·05	5	3·19	24	10	1·493	10	1·496	9	1·497
6	—	—	—	—	6	2·97	25	—	—	—	—	1	1·452
7	8	2·85	7	2·94	5	2·84	26	1	1·423	—	—	1	1·427
8	1	2·64	1	2·66	5	2·83	27	—	—	—	—	1	1·414
9	10	2·56	9	2·57	10	2·56	28	1	1·371	1	1·373	1	1·374
10	5	2·43	3	2·43	3	2·45	29	6	1·329	6	1·330	1	1·339
11	7	2·36	7	2·37	5	2·38	30	—	—	—	—	2	1·317
12	5	2·24	3	2·25	2	2·25	31	9	1·290	9	1·291	8	1·294
13	3	2·17	—	—	2	2·20	32	1	1·279	—	—	—	—
14	5	2·11	5	2·11	7	2·13	33	1	1·266	—	—	3	1·271
15	—	—	—	—	10	1·985	34	5	1·238	5	1·238	6	1·241
16	10	1·969	10	1·976	1	1·961	35	1	1·218	—	—	4	1·219
17	—	—	—	—	3	1·812	36	7	1·191	5	1·193	5	1·202
18	2	1·797	1	1·802	—	—	37	4	1·100	2	1·102	6	1·113
19	2	1·694	1	1·698	3	1·718							

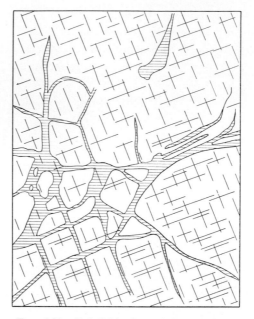

FIG. 220. Polylithionite veinlets in prismatic natrolite

FIG. 221. Fine-scaly structure of polylithionite aggregates. ×290. Crossed nicols

angle varies from 0 to 30°. Refractive indices of pink polylithionite: $Ng=1\cdot551$, $Np=1\cdot538$, $Np-Np=0\cdot013$. The Debye powder patterns of the pink and cream varieties obtained by Sludskaya are similar (Table 127). For comparison this table also shows the calculation of a lepidolite powder pattern. Comparison of the polylithionite and the lepidolite interplanar spacings shows that the structures of these minerals are similar.

Recalculation of the chemical analysis (Table 128) shows that the composition of the bright pink polylithionite is expressed by the theoretical formula KLi_2Al $[Si_4O_{10}](OH, F)_2$. The cream and light varieties are distinguished by containing less silica and alkalis and more aluminium and magnesium. Partial substitution of silicon by aluminium seems to have occurred in the cream varieties, but the valency deficiency is offset either by a reduced tenor of fluorine or by replacement of part of the lithium by magnesium. The cream varieties of polylithionite are similar in chemical composition to irvingite, described by Weidmann (1907); but because

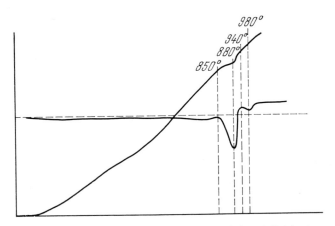

FIG. 222. Thermal analysis curve for pink polylithionite

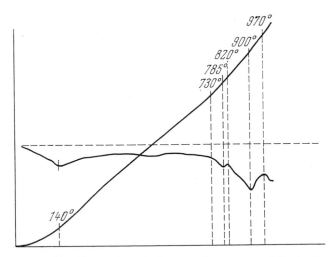

FIG. 223. Thermal analysis curve for cream polylithionite

TABLE 128   Chemical compositions of lithium micas (per cent)

Constituent	Polylithionite								Lepidolite
	Bright pink, Karnasurt			Pink, Karnasurt	Light cream, Karnasurt	White, Lepkhe-Nel'm	Irvingite, Wisconsin	Poly-lithionite, Greenland	
	per cent	Atomic proportions	Calculation of atomic ratios						
SiO_2	60·83	1·0128	1·0128 4·05 —4	60·07	58·44	59·46	57·22	59·25	51·52
TiO_2	trace	—		0·15	0·38	0·20	0·14	—	—
Nb_2O_5	—	—		0·40	0·95	—	—	—	—
Al_2O_3	13·11	0·2572	0·2594 1·04 —1	15·07	14·80	12·25	18·38	12·57	25·96
Fe_2O_3	0·18	0·0022		0·15	0·22	0·95	0·32	0·93	0·31
MnO	0·12	0·0017		0·07	0·09	0·20	trace	—	0·20
MgO	0·24	0·0059		0·36	2·38	2·94	0·09	—	—
Li_2O	6·23	0·4170	0·5040 2·02 —2	5·26	4·21	3·66	4·46	9·04	4·90
CaO	0·73	0·0130		1·17	0·64	0·60	0·20	—	0·18
Na_2O	2·06	0·0664		2·05	1·87	2·60	5·14	7·63	1·06
K_2O	11·13	0·2364	0·2364 0·95 —1	10·95	8·42	12·00	9·12	5·37	11·01
H_2O^+	1·71	OH = 0·2264	0·2264 0·91 —1	1·63	2·72	1·50	1·24	—	0·95
H_2O^-	0·33		0·2264 0·91 —1	0·47	3·08	0·40	0·42	—	—
F	4·50	0·2368	0·2368 0·95 —1	4·2	3·00	5·60	4·58	7·32	5·80
		O = 2·5636	2·5636 10·25 —10						
Total	101·17	—	—	'102·00'	101·20	102·36	101·31	102·11	101·89
$-O = F_2$	-1·89			-1·77	-1·26	-2·35	-1·93		-2·44
—	99·28	—	—	100·23	99·94	100·01	99·38	—	99·45
Analyst	Kazakova, 1949-1952					Moleva, 1953	Lencher		Riggs
Reference	—					Semenov (1957₂)		S. Weidman (1907)	

of their resemblance in composition and properties to polylithionite it seems more suitable to distinguish these varieties as separate minerals.

Lizunov, using quantitative spectrographic analysis, determined 0·020-0·026 per cent of gallium in Lovozero polylithionite. In addition, barium, strontium, beryllium, lead and copper have been spectroscopically determined in pink polylithionite and beryllium, zirconium, strontium, barium, molybdenum, copper, lead and vanadium in the cream variety.

Comparison shows that the thermal analysis curves of pink and cream poly-lithionite are very similar (Figs. 222 and 223). Some excess of water, which separates up to 140°, can be observed in the cream variety. This is due to the high degree of alteration of this variety and its conversion into hydropolylithionite (Semenov, 1957₂). The thermal analysis curves of polylithionite and lepidolite are also similar, the lepidolite curve showing one large endothermic effect at 860°.

Polylithionite occurs in considerable amounts exclusively in the large complex replacement pegmatite bodies of the poikilitic syenite complex, where it is closely associated with minerals of the replacement complexes (see description of the Karnasurt hackmanite-natrolite stock). In time of separation polylithionite is very late. It forms irregular segregations and veinlets in prismatic natrolite and re-places late microcline.

In the course of decomposition polylithionite turns into hydropolylithionite, with a lowering of the specific gravity and refractive indices. Subsequent weather-ing leads to the formation of argillaceous minerals; such minerals, of the mont-morillonite group, develop on polylithionite once all the alkalis have been lost.

Shilin (1953) described Lovozero polylithionite as lithionite, on the basis of the very small differences in the optical properties and chemical composition of some of its varieties as compared with Greenland polylithionite; but we do not think it advisable to distinguish Lovozero polylithionite as a new mineral, because its freshest varieties, which contain the most lithium, are essentially indistinguish-able from Greenland polylithionite.

V. BERYLLIUM MINERALS

Beryllium minerals are comparatively widespread in the Lovozero alkali massif. They are present mainly in the pegmatites genetically connected with the poikilitic syenites, but have been found in isolated cases in the hybrid pegmatites (genthelvite). They have not been found in the non-pegmatitic rocks.

54. Chkalovite
$Na_2(BeSi_2O_6)$; orthorhomb.; sp.gr. 2·662; H. 6

This mineral has been observed only in the pegmatites genetically connected with the rocks of the poikilitic syenite complex. It was discovered by Gerasimovskii (1939) and the following description is based mainly on his data.

Chkalovite has not been found with good crystal form. It forms monocrystalline

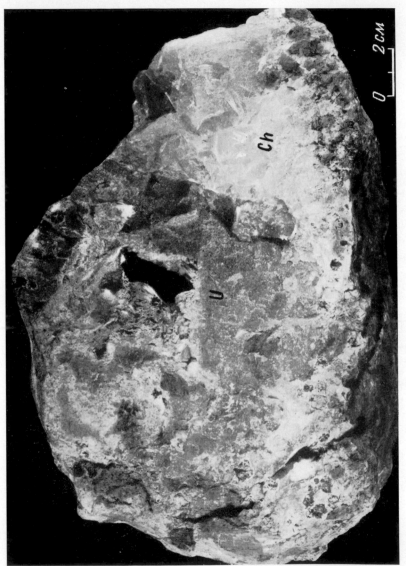

FIG. 224. Chkalovite (Ch) in ussingite (U)

segregations measuring $20 \times 12 \times 10$ cm (Fig. 224). Colour white. Lustre vitreous. Semitransparent. Cleavage imperfect in one direction. In addition, a poorly-expressed cleavage is visible in a second direction. Fracture varies from uneven to conchoidal.

Parameters of unit cell (Pyatenko): $a = 21 \cdot 1 \pm 0 \cdot 01$ A; $b = 21 \cdot 1 \pm 0 \cdot 01$ A; $c = 6 \cdot 87 \pm 0 \cdot 03$ A.

Colourless in thin sections. Optically biaxial, positive. Optic axial angle varies from 62 to 82° in different crystals. Refractive indices: $Ng = 1 \cdot 549$, $Np = 1 \cdot 544$. Plane of optic axes coincides with plane of well-expressed cleavage observable macroscopically, with the following co-ordinates: $PNg = 51°$; $PNm = 54°30'$; $PNp = 60°$. In sections perpendicular to the acute bisectrix a poorly-developed cleavage of different orientation occurs: $PNg = 51°$; $PNm = 89°$; $PNp = 39°$. The angle between the two cleavages usually varies from 68 to 76°, averaging 72°.

Belov, using the Laue method, showed that the mineral belongs to the ortho-rhombic system. The interplanar spacings deduced from his Debye powder patterns are given in Table 129.

Chkalovite dissolves readily and without heating in diluted HCl and HNO_3 to give flocculent silicic acid. It is soluble in H_2SO_4, but very poorly.

Recalculation of the chemical analysis (Table 130) shows that the composition of chkalovite is represented by the structural formula $Na_2[BeSi_2O_6]$ (Pyatenko, 1956). In addition, $0 \cdot 75$ per cent of Al_2O_3 has been determined chemically (Nesterova).

Aluminium, titanium, manganese, magnesium and copper were detected by spectrographic analysis.

In the Lovozero tundras chkalovite is found only on the eastern slope of

TABLE 129 Interplanar spacings of chkalovite

Line no.	I	d	Line no.	I	d
1	m	5·21	20	s	1·40
2	vs	3·97	21	,,	1·38
3	s	3·27	22	m	1·33
4	,,	2·74	23	,,	1·31
5	vs	2·46	24	vw	1·30
6	,,	2·41	25	w	1·28
7	m	2·30	26	,,	1·27
8	,,	2·20	27	vs	1·22
9	,,	2·20	28	m	1·17
10	,,	1·99	29	,,	1·16
11	s	1·79	30	w	1·15
12	w	1·75	31	m	1·12
13	m	1·71	32	s	1·11
14	,,	1·69	33	vs	1·09
15	,,	1·66	34	w	1·08
16	,,	1·60	35	m	1·06
17	,,	1·56	36	,,	1·033
18	,,	1·51	37	,,	1·026
19	s	1·48	38	,,	1·014

Note. m = medium, s = strong, vs = very strong, w = weak, vw = very weak.

Malyi Punkaruaiv in two ussingitic deposits, in association with ussingite, natrolite, schizolite, murmanite, sphalerite, steenstrupine, neptunite and erikite. Chkalovite segregations coincide with the ussingite parts of the pegmatite; none have been detected in eudialyte or microcline. A characteristic feature of chkalovite is the absence of inclusions of other minerals in it, except for rare, isolated cases of schizolite and arfvedsonite inclusions in the marginal parts of large segregations. Chkalovite appears to have crystallized during a replacement stage at the beginning of the period of ussingite crystallization.

TABLE 130 Chemical composition of chkalovite

Constituent	Content per cent	Atomic proportions	Calculation of atomic ratios		
SiO_2	56·81	0·9459 ⎫			
TiO_2	nil	—			
ZrO_2	,,	—	0·9497	1·99	—2
Al_2O_3	,,	—			
Fe_2O_3	0·30	0·0038 ⎭			
FeO	0·12	0·0016			
BeO	12·67	0·5061	0·5061	1·06	—1
BaO	nil	—			
MnO	,,	—			
MgO	,,	—			
CaO	0·37	0·0066 ⎫			
SrO	nil	—			
Na_2O	28·93	0·9332 ⎬	0·9425	1·98	—2
K_2O	0·13	0·0027 ⎭			
H_2O^+	nil	—			
F	,,	—			
Cl	,,	—			
SO_3	0·22	—			
H_2O^-	0·23	—			
		O = 2·8855	2·8855	6·07	—6
Total	99·78	—	—		
Analyst	Pereverzeva				
Reference	Gerasimovskii (1939₂)				

55. Leucophane

CaNa [BeSi₂O₆]; orthorhomb.; sp.gr. 2·96; H. 4

Leucophane was first detected in the Lovozero massif by Semenov (1957₁) in pegmatites paragenetic with rocks of the poikilitic syenite complex. It forms radiate-fibrous segregations (spherulites) in cavities of natrolite druses measuring 1-2 mm to 1 cm in diameter. Colour yellowish-green. Lustre vitreous. Semi-transparent. In thin sections complex twins are often visible. Optically biaxial, negative. Optic axial angle small (about 40°). Refractive indices: $Ng = 1·596$; $Nm = 1·594$; $Np = 1·570$; $Ng - Np = 0·026$.

The Debye powder pattern for Lovozero leucophane obtained by Sludskaya (Table 131) is similar to that of Norwegian leucophane.

In chemical composition leucophane is an alkali silicate of beryllium and calcium (Table 132). Recalculation of the chemical analysis gives the conventional formula: $CaNa[BeSi_2O_6]F$.

In addition to the chemical analysis data, strontium, manganese, yttrium, lanthanum and cerium have been detected in leucophane spectroscopically. In the greenish leucophane, to judge from the spectrographic analysis data, there is more iron and magnesium and less strontium.

Leucophane has been found in the central parts of the orthoclase-natrolite pegmatitic body on Lepkhe-Nel'm, where it fills up cavities between crystals in the natrolite druses. It seems to have crystallized at the late hydrothermal stage of replacement, after natrolite.

TABLE 131 Interplanar spacings of leucophane

Line no.	I	d	Line no.	I	d	Line no.	I	d
1	1	4·93	8	5	2·21	15	3	1·590
2	7	3·59	9	6	1·991	16	3	1·495
3	6	3·29	10	2	1·853	17	2	1·407
4	7	2·97	11	1	1·805	18	1	1·380
5	10	2·75	12	2	1·741	19	2	1·358
6	1	2·62	13	6	1·712	20	4	1·328
7	6	2·32	14	2	1·653			

TABLE 132 Chemical composition of leucophane

Constituent	Content, per cent	Atomic proportions	Calculation of atomic ratios		
SiO_2	45·98	0·767	⎫ 0·812	2·03	—2
Al_2O_3	2·32	0·045	⎬		
FeO	0·22	0·003	⎭ —		
BeO	11·52	0·462	0·462	1·15	—1
MgO	0·30	0·007	⎫ 0·429	1·07	—1
CaO	23·65	0·422	⎬		
Na_2O	10·79	0·348	⎫ 0·363	0·91	—1
K_2O	0·70	0·015	⎬		
H_2O	0·84	0·092	⎫ 0·463	1·16	—1
F	7·04	0·371	⎬		
Total	103·36	—	—		
$-O=F_2$	−2·96				
—	100·40	—	—		
Analyst	Kazakova, 1954				
Reference	Semenov (1957[1])				

56. Minerals of the epididymite group

$NaBeSi_3O_7(OH)$; epididymite—orthorhomb.; eudidymite—mon.; sp.gr. 2·53—2·56; H. 6

Minerals of this group were first found in the Lovozero massif by Semenov and Shilin, in the Karnasurt and Kuivchorr pegmatites (Semenov, Saltykova, 1954; Shilin, Semenov, 1957). Three varieties of minerals in the epididymite group can be distinguished from their outward appearance: (1) finely crystalline to cryptocrystalline, (2) coarsely crystalline to micaceous and (3) spherulitic.

The finely crystalline variety forms irregular segregations measuring up to $15 \times 10 \times 5$ cm and veinlets 3 cm thick in prismatic natrolite (Karnasurt). It is a monomineralic, fine-grained (to cryptocrystalline) aggregate, outwardly resembling porcelain. Crystallized areas, of scaly structure, can sometimes be seen in the

FIG. 225. Radiate segregations of epididymite. × 20. Crossed nicols

dense, cryptocrystalline mass and, more rarely, outgrowths of scaly crystals in the cavities of dense porcelain-like segregations.

The coarsely crystalline micaceous variety forms monomineralic segregations up to 20 cm in diameter (Kuft'yun and Mannepakhk) consisting of outgrowths of platy crystals, sometimes reaching sizes of $2 \times 2 \times 0.5$ cm.

The spherulitic variety is found in the pegmatites of the central part of the massif (Kuivchorr) and also on the western slope of Alluaiv, in the pegmatitic horizon under the ijolite urtites. It is represented by radiate-fibrous segregations measuring up to 1 cm (Fig. 225).

The colour of the minerals in the epididymite group is mainly white, though azure or greyish-blue colours sometimes appear in the finely crystalline varieties. The lustre is pearly on the cleavage planes and vitreous on the fracture.

The finely crystalline varieties are dull, the crystallized varieties transparent. Fracture uneven to conchoidal in the cryptocrystalline varieties.

In thin sections the minerals of the epididymite group are white and transparent. Simple, more rarely polysynthetic twins are characteristic. Cleavage is clearly expressed along (001). Extinction along (001) in the finely crystalline varieties is straight or more rarely oblique; in the coarsely crystalline varieties it is oblique.

According to Aleksandrov's determinations the parameters of the Lovozero epididymite are: $a_0 = 7\cdot28$ Å, $b_0 = 12\cdot54$ Å, $c_0 = 13\cdot43$ Å.

The finely crystalline varieties are optically biaxial, negative; the coarsely crystalline are positive. Refractive indices: $Ng = 1\cdot542$—$1\cdot548$; $Nm = 1\cdot51$—$1\cdot544$; $Np = 1\cdot536$—$1\cdot542$; $Ng - Np = 0\cdot004$. Optic axial angle, $2V = 30\text{-}32°$. Co-ordinates of twinning plane—$PNg = 86°30'$; $PNm = 15°$; $PNp = 75°$. The twinning plane is the cleavage plane (001). The twinning axis lies in the twinning plane. The co-ordinates of the twinning axis are $DNg = 25°30'$; $DNm = 85°$; $DNp = 66°$.

The powder patterns of all the epididymite varieties (Sludskaya) are identical, but differ considerably from those of eudidymite (Table 133).

Epididymite does not dissolve in HCl, HNO_3 or H_3SO_4. It can be seen from Table 134 that all varieties of minerals in the epididymite group are chemically similar to one another and to the Greenland epididymite. Recalculation of the chemical analyses shows that the Lovozero minerals in this group conform to the theoretical formula $NaBeSi_3O_7(OH)$. Danilova determined 0·5 per cent of fluorine in a separate sample of epididymite. In addition titanium, copper, barium, zirconium, zinc, niobium, manganese, strontium, magnesium, gallium and chromium have been detected spectroscopically in minerals of this group.

The dehydration curve obtained by Karpova, using the tensimetric method, shows that almost all the water in epididymite is structural and is eliminated at

TABLE 133 Interplanar spacings of epididymite and eudidymite
(Fe-radiation; $2R = 57\cdot9$ mm, $d = 0\cdot6$ mm)

Line no.	Epididymite		Eudidymite		Line no.	Epididymite		Eudidymite	
	I	d	I	d		I	d	I	d
1	3	6·43	7	6·28	24	8	1·643	—	—
2	2	5·80	1	5·02	25	1	1·590	7	1·576
3	5	4·65	1	4·36	26	8	1·542	7	1·560
4	1	4·07	7	3·70	27	2	1·480	2	1·507
5	7	3·65	8	3·50	28	2	1·451	2	1·461
6	8	3·40	9	3·38	29	7	1·391	2	1·444
7	10	3·10	10	3·16	30	7	1·363	6	1·429
8	10	2·98	9	3·09	31	7	1·328	2	1·411
9	1	2·88	8	3·01	32	1	1·306	4	1·381
10	1	2·75	7	2·85	33	9	1·280	6	1·360
11	6	2·60	3	2·74	34	4	1·251	5	1·307
12	—	—	5	2·59	35	4	1·222	4	1·295
13	7	2·48	3	2·49		3	1·201	2	1·277
14	3	2·41	5	2·40	36 {	broad	1·184	4	1·263
15	5	2·26	3	2·25		line			
16	8	2·13	4	2·13	37	3	1·164	6	1·250
17	1	2·04	8	2·01	38	3	1·147	6	1·219
18	2	1·967	—	—	39	1	1·118	3	1·200
19	1	1·931	2	1·928	40	1	1·109	5	1·188
20	7	1·835	9	1·822	41	1	1·094	6	1·157
21	9	1·797	5	1·764	42	1	1·084	6	1·132
22	4	1·750	7	1·738	43	6	1·075	6	1·110
23	3	1·700	8	1·694	44	6	1·051	—	—

TABLE 134 Chemical compositions of minerals in the epididymite group

Constituent	White porcellanous type, Karnasurt			White fine-crystalline	Azure fine-crystalline	White spherulitic		Narsarsuk, Greenland
	per cent	Atomic proportions	Calculation of atomic ratios	Karnasurt	Karnasurt	Kuivchorr	Alluiav	
SiO_2	71·79	1·1953	1·1953 2·90 —3	72·99	73·31	72·60	72·94	73·74
TiO_2	—			trace	—	—	—	—
Al_2O_3	1·94	0·0380 }	—	1·43	0·51	0·20	0·57	—
Fe_2O_3	0·12	0·0014 }	—	0·17	0·08	0·13	—	—
FeO	trace	—	0·4574 1·14 —1	0·00	—	—	0·29	—
BeO	10·45	0·4180 }		9·66	10·39	10·42	11·20	10·56
MnO	—			—	—	—	—	—
MgO	trace	—		0·06	trace	0·07	—	—
CaO	0·16	0·0028 }	—	0·23	0·23	0·26	0·44	—
Na_2O	11·43	0·3688 }	0·3780 0·95 —1	11·45	11·46	12·63	10·56	12·48
K_2O	0·30	0·0064 }	—	0·63	0·37	0·20	—	—
H_2O^+	4·14	0·4596	0·4596 1·15 —1	2·29	3·86	4·00	4·07	3·73
H_2O^-	0·03	—	—	0·16	0·10	nil	0·35	—
Other	—		3·2879 8·22 —8	1·55	—	—	—	—
		O = 3·2879						
Total	100·36		—	100·62	100·31	100·51	100·42	100·51
Analyst		Kazakova, 1951-1952				Moleva	Bocharova, 1951	G. Flink
Reference						Shilin, Semenov (1957)	After Tikhonenkov	W. Brögger

temperatures between 700 and 800° (Fig. 226). The minerals of this group are present in appreciable amounts only in the large complex replacement pegmatitic bodies of the poikilitic syenite complex, in close association with minerals of the replacement complexes and particularly with late fine-grained albite. The minerals of this group occur rarely and in small quantity in the pegmatites of the differentiated and eudialytic lujavrite complexes.

In the Karnasurt pegmatites finely crystalline varieties of minerals in the epididymite group are usually localized at the contacts with segregations of late fine-grained albite or microcline, corroding prismatic natrolite. In the Kuivchorr, Lepkhe-Nel'm and Alluaiv pegmatites these minerals are also closely associated

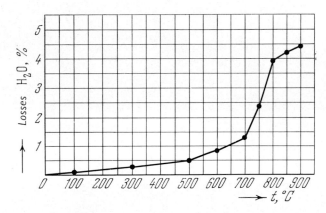

FIG. 226. Tensimetric curve for epididymite

with late albite (Fig. 227), filling up the central parts of pegmatite bodies or replacing earlier potassium feldspars. The epididymite minerals are thus among the latest in time of separation. They fill cracks in prismatic natrolite and albite, partially corroding and replacing these; more rarely, they form rosettes in leaching cavities.

In the course of alteration, sodium is lost from minerals of this group, which become enriched in water, forming beryllite, sphaerobertrandite and gel-bertrandite.

57. Beryllite

$Be_3SiO_4(OH)_2$. H_2O; orthorhomb. or mon.; sp.gr. 2·196; H. 1

Beryllite was first discovered by Kuz'menko (1954). It forms small spherulites 2-3 mm in diameter or incrustations of fibrous structure up to 2 mm thick in epididymite cavities (Fig. 228). Colour white. Lustre silky. Structure of aggregates finely fibrous. Soft. In thin sections white, transparent, radiate-fibrous. Extinction straight. Elongation positive. Optically biaxial, negative. Refractive indices $Ng=1·560$; $Np=1·541$; $Ng-Np=0·019$. Optic axial angle small.

Table 135 shows the interplanar spacings calculated from Debye powder patterns obtained by Sludskaya.

FIG. 227. Eudidymite (Eu) in dark pink albite (Ab)

FIG. 228. Beryllite spherulites (Br) in cavity in epididymite.   ×20

From recalculation of the chemical analysis (Table 136) it is clear that the mineral has the formula $Be_3SiO_4(OH)_2 . H_2O$.

Barium, manganese, phosphorus and copper have also been detected spectroscopically in beryllite.

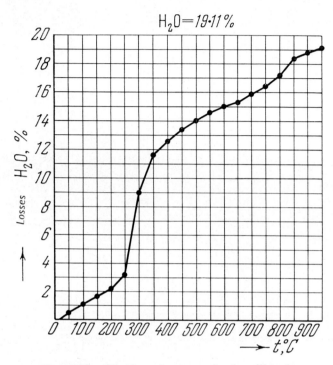

FIG. 229. Tensimetric curve for beryllite dehydration (after Karpova)

The dehydration curve shows that half the water in beryllite is high-temperature [bound water] (Fig. 229).

In the Lovozero massif beryllite occurs in minute amounts, exclusively in the complex replacement pegmatites paragenetic with the poikilitic syenites (Karnasurt, Mannepakhk and elsewhere). It is usually closely associated with minerals

TABLE 135 Interplanar spacings of beryllite

Line no.	I	d	Line no.	I	d	Line no.	I	d
1	5	6·43	12	7	2·03	23	1	1·333
2	10	4·01	13	7	1·937	24	1	1·308
3	9	3·64	14	5	1·807	25	5	1·287
4	7	3·39	15	1	1·754	26	2	1·259
5	7	3·19	16	6	1·703	27	4	1·221
6 }		2·90	17	1	1·649	28	4	1·171
7 }	3	2·66	18	2	1·599	29	5	1·151
8 }		2·50	19	4	1·547	30	3	1·121
9	10	2·34	20	1	1·451	31	2	1·078
10	2	2·20	21	1	1·396	32	1	1·071
11	7	2·12	22	8	1·351			

of the epididymite group, on which it forms, and with albite and argillaceous minerals of the replacement zones. It sometimes fills up small leaching cavities in albite.

TABLE 136 Chemical composition of beryllite

Constituent	Content, per cent	Atomic proportions	Calculation of atomic ratios		
SiO_2	34·10	0·5678 ⎫			
TiO_2	trace	—			
Al_2O_3	1·63	0·0320 ⎬	0·6014	1·08	—1
Fe_2O_3	0·12	0·0016 ⎭			
FeO	not found	—			
MnO	,, ,,	—			
MgO	trace	—			
BeO	40·00	1·6000	1·6000	2·88	—3
CaO	0·50	0·0089			
Na_2O*	2·42	0·0780			
K_2O	not found	—			
H_2O^+	18·95	2·1036	2·1036	3·79	—4
H_2O^-	3·25	—			
		O = 3·8853	3·8853	6·99	—7
Total	100·97	—	—		
Analyst	Kazakova, 1952				

* The role of sodium in beryllite is not clear, since the structure of the mineral has not been studied. It may be that sodium enters to balance the valencies on isomorphous interchange of silicon and beryllium and is situated in the larger cavities of the crystalline structure.

58. Sphaerobertrandite

$Be_5 [Si_2O_7] (OH)_4$; system unknown; sp.gr. about 3; H. 5

Sphaerobertrandite was first found in the Lovozero massif and studied by Semenov (1957₃). The description below is based on his data.

Sphaerobertrandite occurs in the form of spherulites up to 2 mm in diameter in the cavities of epididymite druses. Yellow, sometimes colourless. Optically biaxial, negative; optic axial angle $2V$ about 70°. Refractive indices $Ng = 1·610$; $Np = 1·595$; $Ng - Np = 0·015$. The yellow varieties are pleochroic from yellowish along Np to colourless along Ng. Absorption scheme $Np > Ng$.

It has been established by X-ray investigation that sphaerobertrandite differs substantially from bertrandite and beryllite (Tables 135 and 137).

Table 138 shows that sphaerobertrandite and bertrandite differ in chemical composition, the silicon-beryllium molecular ratio in bertrandite being 1 : 2, compared with 1 : 2·5 in sphaerobertrandite.

Recalculation of the chemical analysis shows that sphaerobertrandite is represented by the formula $Be_5[Si_2O_7](OH)_4$. The dehydration curve shows that water is lost from sphaerobertrandite over the narrow temperature range 600-800° and is probably present as the hydroxyl group (OH).

In the pegmatites of the poikilitic syenite complex sphaerobertrandite is found

in close association with epididymite; Semenov (1957₃) suggests that it is a product
of hydrothermal reworking of the latter. It is sometimes replaced by beryllite.

TABLE 137 Interplanar spacings of sphaerobertrandite and bertrandite

Line no.	Sphaero-bertrandite		Bertrandite (Kounrad)*		Line no.	Sphaero-bertrandite		Bertrandite (Kounrad)*	
	I	d	I	d		I	d	I	d
1	9	4·89	3	4·81	23	1	1·558	8	1·552
2	} 8	4·61	10	4·31	24	7	1·525	—	—
3		4·20	—	—	25	1	1·474	1	1·495
4	8	3·80	7	3·89	26	1	1·454	8	1·467
5	3	3·39	4	3·49	27	5	1·431	7	1·437
6	10	3·15	10	3·14	28	7	1·411	—	—
7	9	2·84	5	2·85	29	1	1·381	1	1·382
8	8	2·73	4	2·78	30	8	1·352	2	1·362
9	9	2·53	10	2·53	31	—	—	3	1·339
10	9	2·39	5	2·42	32	5	1·317	9	1·305
11	10	2·32	9	2·28	33	—	—	4	1·275
12	10	2·17	9	2·20	34	9	1·250	8	1·251
13	—	—	3	2·10	35	2	1·236	8	1·236
14	6	2·04	4	2·03	36	2	1·193	7	1·168
15	7	1·970	8	1·973	37	4	1·156	2	1·150
16	4	1·937	2	1·910	38	8	1·140	—	—
17	} 3	1·807	1	1·812	39	6	1·123	8	1·121
18		1·757	3	1·783	40	1	1·110	—	—
19	4	1·688	7	1·694	41	1	1·103	6	1·105
20	—	—	6	1·649	42	—	—	3	1·089
21	6	1·628	1	1·620	43	1	1·080	3	1·081
22	6	1·587	6	1·580	44	1	1·070	4	1·057
					45	—	—	2	1·050
					46	—	—	4	1·042

* Chukhrov's data

TABLE 138 Chemical compositions of sphaerobertrandite and bertrandite

Constituent	Sphaerobertrandite (Lovozero)					Bertrandite (Altai)
	per cent	Atomic proportions	Calculation of atomic ratios			per cent
SiO₂	41·03	0·684	0·711	2·03	—2	50·12
Al₂O₃	1·40	0·027		—		—
Fe₂O₃	0·07	0·001		—		—
BeO	45·20	1·808	1·808	5·16	—5	40·67
H₂O⁺	11·70	} 1·332	1·332	3·80	—4	8·87
H₂O⁻	0·30					—
		O = 3·883	3·883	11·09	—11	—
Total	99·70	—	—			99·66
Analyst	Kazakova					Pilipenko
Reference	Semenov (1957₃)					

59. Gel-bertrandite

$Be_4 [Si_2O_7] (OH)_2 . nH_2O$; amorph.; sp.gr. 2·176; H. 4

Gel-bertrandite was first found in 1950-1952 and studied by Semenov (1957₃), whose data we have used here. The mineral is a colloidal analogue of bertrandite, differing from it by its low specific gravity, refractive index and higher water content (up to 24 per cent).

Gel-bertrandite segregations measuring up to 3 mm have an irregular shape. Colour light-violet, lustre vitreous. Transparent. Fracture conchoidal. Becomes yellowish-white and opaque when kept for a long time in the light.

Under the microscope gel-bertrandite reveals a cryptocrystalline structure. Under low magnification it seems optically isotropic; under high magnification very small spherulites with a grey interference colour can be seen. Refractive indices vary between 1·511 and 1·530.

The Debye powder pattern is indistinct, probably as a result of the crypto-crystalline structure, and shows great similarity to bertrandite (Tables 137 and 139).

Recalculation of the chemical analysis (Table 140) gives the formula Be_4 $[Si_2O_7](OH)_2 . 3H_2O$. The molecular ratio Be : Si = 2 : 1 as in bertrandite.

The dehydration curve shows that water is gradually lost from gel-bertrandite in the temperature range 40-700°. The property of losing water readily and the fact that its refractive index increases when it is kept for a long time in the air gave Semenov reason to believe that the water content of this mineral was variable

TABLE 139   Interplanar spacings of gel-bertrandite

Line no.	I	d	Line no.	I	d	Line no.	I	d
1	1	4·81	7	4	1·998	12	4	1·310
2	10	4·31	8	2	1·714	13	2	1·261
3	10	3·15	9	2	1·651	14	3	1·224
4	10	2·53	10	4	1·555	15	2	1·171
5	} 8	{ 2·31	11	6	1·454			
6		2·20						

TABLE 140   Chemical composition of gel-bertrandite

Constituent	Content, per cent	Atomic proportions	Calculation of atomic ratios		
SiO_2	38·70	0·645	} 0·668	1·96	—2
Al_2O_3	1·20	0·023			
BeO	34·16	1·366	1·366	4·02	—4
CaO	1·93	0·034	—		
H_2O^+	15·62	} 2·643	2·643	7·77	—8
H_2O^-	8·17				
Total	99·78	—	—		
Analyst	Kazakova				
Reference	Semenov (1957₃)				

and that its formula should be written as: $Be_4[Si_2O_7](OH)_2 . nH_2O$. When dehydrated, gel-bertrandite probably turns into bertrandite. The similarity between this mineral and bertrandite in chemical composition (the difference consists in the presence of large amounts of water), the similarity of their powder patterns and the colloidal structure give reason for regarding this mineral as a hydrous colloidal variety of bertrandite.

Gel-bertrandite has been found in the Karnasurt and Mannepakhk pegmatites in close association with albite, zeolites, epididymite, sphaerobertrandite and beryllite. It usually fills up leaching cavities in epididymite, along with beryllite. Semenov (1957_3) suggests that it forms in the process of epithermal epididymite alteration.

60. Karpinskyite*

$Na_2(Be,Zn,Mg)Al_2Si_6O_{16}(OH)_2 . 1\cdot6H_2O$; trig.; sp.gr. 2·545; H. 1·5—2

Karpinskyite was first found and studied by Shilin (1956) and the present description is based on his data.

The mineral occurs in the form of elongate-prismatic or acicular white crystals, sometimes forming rosettes of radiate-fibrous structure. Colour white to silky white. Lustre vitreous to pearly. Fracture uneven. Size of unit cell: $a=14\cdot24$ Å $c=4\cdot83$ Å.

In thin sections the mineral is colourless. Prismatic cleavage indistinct.

TABLE 141 Interplanar spacings of karpinskyite
(Fe-radiation; $2R=65\cdot8$; $d=0\cdot5$ mm)

Line no.	I	d	Line no.	I	d	Line no.	I	d	Line no.	I	d
1	4	6·274	20	7	2·463	39	3	1·514	58	3	1·199
2	2	5·224	21	6	2·394	40	4	1·494	59	1	1·1786
3	3	5·060	22	1	(2·332)	41	1	1·481	60	1	1·1689
4	2	4·850	23	6	2·218	42	1	1·456	61	2	1·587
5	6	4·709	24	1	2·160	43	4	1·439	62	2	1·1498
6	4	4·551	25	4	2·112	44	1	1·411	63	2 r.	1·1376
7	1	4·245	26	1	2·034	45	2	1·397	64	5	1·1200
8	3	4·147	27	3	1·990	46	4	1·383	65	2	1·1105
9	1	4·030	28	5	1·911	47	1	1·362	66	1	1·1030
10	3	(3·740)	29	2	1·851	48	4	1·345	67	2	1·0930
11	1	3·600	30	2	1·796	49	4	1·319	68	1	1·0700
12	2	3·508	31	1	1·773	50	3	1·291	69	1	1·0614
13	7	3·388	32	7	1·741	51	2	1·278	70	4	1·0544
14	10	3·161	33	3	1·693	52	3	1·262	71	1	1·0474
15	2	3·107	34	1	1·671	53	3	1·250	72	4	1·0417
16	1 r.	2·902	35	2	(1·648)	54	1	1·235	73	3	1·0244
17	2	2·821	36	2	1·627	55	4	1·225	74	3 r.	1·0147
18	3	(2·719)	37	5	1·579	56	1	1·215	75	1	1·0059
19	3	(2·633)	38	3	1·543	57	3	1·207	76	1	0·9978
									77	2	0·9885

* The Russian text reads "Karpinskite" but it is clear that the mineral being described is Karpinskyite (see L. J. Spencer, 1958. Twenty-first list of new mineral names. *Min. Mag.*, XXXI, p. 963.) Eds.

Extinction straight. Elongation positive. Optically uniaxial, positive. Refractive indices: $Ne = 1.518$; $No = 1.511$; $Ne - No = 0.007$.

Table 141 shows the results of X-ray analysis of karpinskyite performed by Denisov.

On ignition in a closed tube karpinskyite readily liberates water and changes colour from silky white to greyish-white. It is not soluble in HCl, HNO_3 or H_2SO_4.

Recalculation of the chemical analysis (Table 142) shows that the composition of karpinskyite is expressed by the chemical formula $Na_2(Be, Zn, Mg)Al_2Si_6O_{16}$ $(OH)_2 \cdot 1.6H_2O$.

In addition, spectrographic analysis performed by Dudykin reveals the presence of gallium ($0.n$ per cent), lead, copper, zirconium, strontium, manganese ($0.0n$ per cent) and niobium (0.01 per cent).

The thermal analysis curve for this mineral shows three poorly-defined endothermic effects at temperatures of 90°, 540° and 900°, of which the first two probably correspond to the liberation of hygroscopic water and bound water and the last to the melting-point of the mineral.

Karpinskyite was found in the Karnasurt pegmatites genetically connected with the poikilitic sodalite-syenites. Close association with albite and natrolite is characteristic, the karpinskyite developing in small cracks in these minerals. According to Shilin's data it is found replacing albite.

TABLE 142   Chemical composition of karpinskyite

Constituent	Content, per cent	Atomic proportions	Calculation of atomic ratios		
SiO_2	56·68	0·9474	0·9474	5·92	—6
TiO_2	trace	—		—	
Al_2O_3	16·40	0·3216	}0·3224	2·01	—2
Fe_2O_3	0·06	0·0008			
BeO	2·58	0·1031			
ZnO	3·26	0·0400	}0·1626	1·02	—1
MgO	0·78	0·0195			
Na_2O	9·18	0·2962	}0·3292	2·06	—2
K_2O	1·55	0·0330			
H_2O^+	5·00	0·5556	}0·8334	5·21	—5·2
H_2O^-	2·50	0·2778			
		O = 3·1069	3·1069	19·42	—19·4
Total	'97·99'	—		—	
Analyst		Moleva			
Reference		Shilin (1956)			

61. Genthelvite

$Zn_8 [BeSiO_4]_6 \cdot S_2$; cub.; sp.gr. 3·55; H. 6—6·5

Genthelvite was first found in the Lovozero massif by Es'kova (1957) in the hybrid pegmatites. It forms irregularly-shaped grains measuring up to $1 \times 0.5 \times 0.3$ cm, but usually smaller (0.2×0.1 cm). Distinct crystals have not been observed.

The colour varies from almost colourless to bluish-green and emerald-green. The colourless varieties are rare. Streak slightly greenish. Lustre vitreous. Fracture uneven. Cleavage absent. Transparent. Brittle.

In thin sections genthelvite is colourless, more rarely slightly yellowish-green. Isotropic. The refractive index of the emerald-green variety is 1·742, that of the colourless varieties slightly higher.

Genthelvite dissolves in acids, liberating hydrogen sulphide. On evaporation of the solution silica is precipitated, forming a gelatinous sediment.

Recalculation of the chemical analysis of Lovozero genthelvite (Table 143) shows that its composition is poorly expressed by the conventional genthelvite formula. This may be because the chemical analysis was based on a small sample and was incomplete, but it was not possible to repeat the analysis because of lack of material.

The main difference between the chemical composition of Lovozero genthelvite and Colorado genthelvite is merely that the former contains more zinc oxide, manganese and iron and less silicon and beryllium oxides.

Magnesium, aluminium, calcium, cobalt, tin and titanium were also detected spectroscopically.

The helvite group of minerals forms an isomorphous series, of which the three end members are helvite, $Mn_8(BeSiO_4)_6 \cdot S_2$, danalite $Fe_8(BeSiO_4)_6 \cdot S_2$ and genthelvite $Zn_8(BeSiO_4)_6 \cdot S_2$. The Lovozero genthelvite is closest in properties to the zincian member of this group.

Genthelvite is found in the Lovozero massif only in the hybrid pegmatites and

TABLE 143 Chemical composition of genthelvite

Constituent	Lovozero			Colorado, U.S.A.		Theoretical composition, %
	%	Atomic proportions	Atomic ratios	%	Atomic proportions	
SiO_2	27·35	0·4554	5·45	30·26	0·5038	30·19
BeO	12·00	0·4796	5·73	12·70	0·5076	12·58
ZnO	40·00	0·4915	⎫	46·20	0·5677	54·54
MnO	10·21	0·1439	⎬ 8·48	1·22	0·0172	—
FeO	6·04	0·0840	⎭	6·81	0·0947	—
S	5·74	0·1792	2·12	5·49	0·1712	5·37
—		O = 1·9306	24·00	—	—	—
Total	101·34			102·68		102·68
− O = S	− 2·87	—	—	2·74	—	2·68
—	98·47	—	—	99·94	—	100·00
Specific gravity	3·55	—	—	3·66	—	3·70
Analyst	Kazakova, 1950					—
Reference	Es'kova (1957)					J. Glass, R. Jahns, R. Stevens (1944)

is closely associated with orthoclase, manganilmenite and zircon. In time of separation it is later than these three minerals and sodalite, filling up spaces between them. It forms instead of such simple beryllium silicates as chkalovite and epididymite, which are characteristic of the pure pegmatites, as a result of assimilation by a pegmatitic melt-solution of iron, manganese, magnesium and calcium from the Devonian augite-porphyrites.

CHAPTER THREE

SECONDARY AND ACCESSORY MINERALS

THE Lovozero secondary and accessory minerals are those found in the rocks and pegmatites in small quantity and containing no rare elements as essential constituents (see Table 28).

62. Pectolite

$Ca_2NaSi_3O_8(OH)$; tric.; sp.gr. 2·74—2·88; H. 5

Pectolite occurs in very small amounts (0-2 per cent) in the rocks of the massif. It forms irregularly-shaped segregations measuring up to 1-2 mm in diameter (Fig. 230) and, more rarely, fine fringes round segregations of minerals belonging to the eudialyte-eucolite group that have been altered to zirfesite.

In thin sections pectolite is colourless. Optically biaxial, positive. Elongation positive. Extinction straight. $2V$ varies from 56 to 62°. Birefringence $Ng - Np = 0·032$—$0·038$.

Pectolite occurs most frequently in rocks with a calcium association of minerals (urtites, ijolite-urtites, malignites and poikilitic nepheline-syenites). A primary and a secondary pectolite are distinguished, differing in the character of their formation: primary pectolite occurs mainly at depth; the secondary variety is found in the upper part of the massif.

In the differentiated complex the amount of pectolite increases from top to bottom, located in the rocks of the undifferentiated parts. In the eudialytic lujavrites mainly the secondary variety has developed, in amounts not exceeding 0·2 per cent. In the poikilitic syenites the pectolite content reaches 0·5 per cent. The mineral is more widely developed in the nepheline-bearing varieties of the poikilitic syenites, with orthoclase, mesodialyte, sphene, apatite and other minerals.

Pectolite is a late mineral. Primary pectolite seems to have crystallized directly from solution at late stages in the formation of the rocks. Segregations of it fill up spaces between the main rock-forming minerals (see Fig. 230) and are included in late sodalite. Secondary pectolite is found in the form of small fringes round minerals of the eudialyte-eucolite group and microcline (Fig. 231). It probably forms in the process of alteration of these minerals by hydrothermal solutions, as is indicated by its close association with natrolite. Under supergene conditions pectolite decomposes and is leached away.

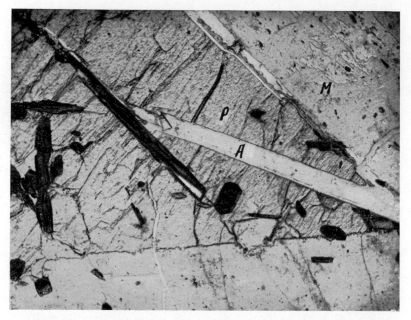

Fig. 230. Pectolite (P) filling spaces between microcline (M), albite (A) and aegirine (dark).   ×46. Without analyser

Fig. 231. Secondary pectolite (P) at the contact between microcline (M) and mesodialyte (dark) segregations.   ×46. Crossed nicols

63. Schizolite

$Na(Ca,Mn)_2Si_3O_8(OH)$; tric.; sp.gr. 2·95—2·97; H. 5—6

Schizolite was first found [at Lovozero] by Gerasimovskii (1936_2) in the Malyi Punkaruaiv pegmatites. We have used his data here.

The mineral forms segregations measuring from 0·5 mm in length to $9 \times 2·5 \times 1$ cm and is of long-prismatic (Fig. 232), sometimes acicular habit. Bonshtedt's

Fig. 232. Schizolite (dark) in natrolite. Natural size

measurements of poorly-formed schizolite crystals (*Minerals of the Khibiny and Lovozero tundras*, 1937) show that they are elongated along the y-axis and bounded mainly by pinaccids $a(100)$ and $c(001)$; the forms $b(010)$, $r(\bar{1}02)$, $n(\bar{1}01)$, $s(\bar{2}01)$, $e(\bar{1}11)$, $v(101)$, $u(102)$ and $g(203)$ have also been observed.

Colour dark-or light-brown, dark-brown to black in the altered varieties. Streak of the same colours. Lustre vitreous, dull in the altered varieties. Cleavage perfect along (001) and fair along (100). Fracture uneven, crumbly in altered schizolite. Hardness 5-5·5; the altered varieties are friable.

In thin sections schizolite is light greyish-brown. Optically biaxial, positive. Extinction angle $c : Ng = 0\text{-}4°$; $2V = 51°$. Refractive indices $Ng = 1·677$; $Nm = 1·641$. Optic axial plane parallel to (100).

Recalculation of the chemical analysis (Table 144) shows that the composition of Lovozero schizolite is in general expressed by the theoretical formula $Na(Ca, Mn)_2Si_3O_8(OH)$.

In the Lovozero schizolite, unlike the Greenland variety, manganese predominates over calcium.

Analyses of the fresh (analysis 1) and altered (analysis 2) varieties of schizolite showed that alteration was accompanied by loss of silicon, calcium and sodium, addition of water and concentration of higher-valency manganese.

Apart from the elements identified by chemical analysis, aluminium and beryllium were spectroscopically detected in schizolite. Schizolite is found in the pegmatites of all the complexes. It has been observed in the Karnasurt, Malyi Punkaruaiv and Kedykvyrpakhk pegmatites and also in the Tyul'bn'yunuai Tavaiok, Uel'kuai, Muruai, Kuftuai and Motchisuai valleys. The greatest quantities of it are found in the large pegmatitic bodies of the poikilitic syenite and eudialytic lujavrite complexes (Karnasurt, Lepkhe-Nel'm, Malyi Punkaruaiv and Kedykvyrpakhk). It is rarely found in the rocks and only in very small amounts, chiefly in the poikilitic sodalite-syenites and foyaites in association with pectolite. It is usually closely associated with hackmanite, ussingite, coarsely prismatic natrolite and aegirine II. In time of separation an early and a late schizolite are distinguished. Early schizolite forms idiomorphic crystals in microcline, sodalite, ussingite, albite, natrolite and aegirine II. It seems to have crystallized earlier

TABLE 144 Chemical composition of schizolite

| Constituent | Lovozero | | | | Greenland | |
| | Analysis 1 | | Analysis 2 | Analysis 3 | Analysis 4 |
	per cent	Atomic proportions			
SiO_2	49·10	0·8225	14·64	51·06	51·06
TiO_2	0·02	0·0002	—	0·68	0·62
Ce_2O_3	} 1·00	0·0061	—	1·47	0·94
Y_2O_3					1·03
Fe_2O_3	0·88	0·0110	—	—	—
FeO	—	—	—	2·79	2·74
MnO	15·92	0·2244	1·88	12·90	9·84
MnO_2	9·35	0·1075	60·69	—	—
CaO	12·72	0·2268	5·52	19·48	22·89
MgO	0·10	0·0025	—	—	—
SrO	0·28	0·0027	—	—	—
BaO	nil	—	—	—	—
Na_2O	7·72	0·2490	4·28	10·71	9·97
K_2O	0·74	0·0158	—	—	—
H_2O^+	1·15	0·1276	11·30	1·36	0·55
		O = 2·5388	—	—	—
Total	98·98	—	—	100·45	99·64
Specific gravity	2·955–2·974		2·677	3·089	2·993
Analyst	Vladimirova		Christensen		
Reference	Minerals of the Khibiny and Lovozero tundras (1937)		O. Böggild (1903)		

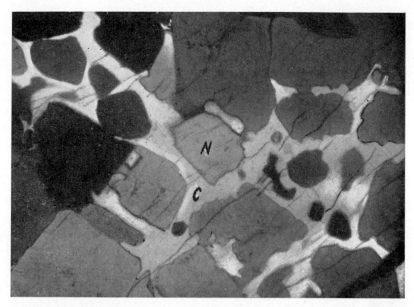

FIG. 233. Replacement of nepheline (N) by cancrinite (C). ×46 Crossed nicols

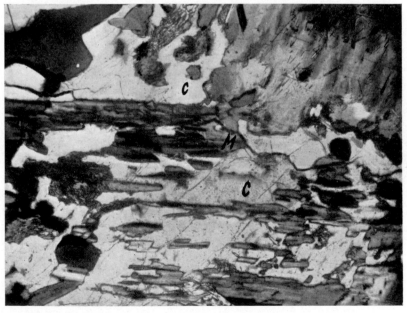

FIG. 234. Replacement of albitized microcline (M) by cancrinite (C). ×46. Crossed nicols

than microcline but later than early aegirine and arfvedsonite. Late schizolite occurs in the form of radial segregations in zeolites and clay minerals of the replacement zones. In the alteration process it is converted into a loose, amorphous, sooty material, dark-brown to black, with a refractive index of about 1·814. In places schizolite has been completely leached, leaving cavities in the shape of its crystals.

64. Cancrinite

$Na_6Ca_2[Al_6Si_6O_{24}]$ $[CO_3,SO_4]$. $3H_2O$; hex.; sp.gr. 2·42—2·5; H. 5—6

Cancrinite has been observed comparatively rarely in the Lovozero alkali massif, mainly in the rocks. It forms irregularly-shaped segregations up to 0·5 cm in diameter. Colour yellow, silky-white, bluish-grey. It fills spaces between rock-forming minerals and contains poikilitic inclusions of almost all the accessory and secondary minerals. It often develops by replacing other minerals (nepheline, albitized microcline, albite and sodalite). The process of nepheline cancrinitization is particularly widely developed in the nepheline-rich rocks of the differentiated complex (Fig. 233). Very rarely, cancrinite is found replacing albitized microcline in these rocks and in those of the poikilitic syenite complex (Fig. 234). This process usually begins at the margin of microcline crystals and sometimes affects the whole crystal, only relicts of which remain. The selective replacement by cancrinite of albitized parts of microcline is noteworthy; the microcline proper remains unreplaced. Still more rarely cancrinite is found replacing late sodalite in rocks of the differentiated and poikilitic syenite complexes.

The highest cancrinite content of the rocks of the poikilitic syenite complex is some tenths of one per cent. In the nepheline-bearing varieties in the south-eastern part of the massif (Ninchurt and Malyi Punkaruaiv) its tenor reaches 15 per cent. In the rocks of the differentiated complex the amount of cancrinite does not exceed 1 per cent, except in certain parts, where it may rise to 5 per cent. Cancrinite is most widespread in the urtites and ijolite-urtites and is rarer in the foyaites. In all the rocks the cancrinite content increases with depth. In the differentiated parts of the complex the greatest amounts of cancrinite are concentrated in the floors of the urtite horizons and in the underlying rocks at the urtite contact (up to 3-5 per cent). In the rocks of the eudialytic lujavrite complex it is found more rarely and in very small amounts (0-0·2 per cent).

Cancrinite separated late, after replacement sodalite, which it sometimes replaces, but before natrolite, by which it is replaced. It is usually absent from the zeolitized parts of the rocks.

65. Biotite

$K(Mg,Fe)_3[Si_3AlO_{10}]$ $(OH,F)_2$; mon.; sp.gr. 2·7—3·1; H. 2·5—3

Biotite has been found in small quantities in the contaminated rocks and pegmatites of the Koklukhtiuai valley and on Ninchurt and Kuivchorr. It forms imperfect pseudohexagonal platy crystals measuring up to $1 \times 1 \times 0·3$ cm or irregular platy segregations up to 2 cm in diameter.

The colour is brown or brownish-black. Lustre on cleavage planes bright pearly. Cleavage along (001) is perfect. Translucent to opaque. In thin sections brown or yellowish-brown. Distinctly expressed pleochroism. Along Ng brown to dark brown, along Np pale, yellowish-brown. Absorption scheme $Ng>Np$. Optically biaxial, negative. The highest refractive index, according to Gerasimovskii's data, varies within the limits $Ng=1.589—1.692$. $2V=25\text{-}26°$.

Recalculation of the chemical analysis of Lovozero biotite (Table 145) shows that its composition is in general represented by the theoretical formula $K(Mg, Fe)_3[Si_3AlO_{10}](OH, F)_2$, though in analysis 2 there is some deficiency of the (OH) group, which may be due to the lack of a fluorine determination.

Apart from the constituents determined chemically, vanadium, nickel, zirconium, gallium (0.005 per cent) and silver have been spectroscopically detected in biotite. Quantitative spectrographic analysis revealed 1.10 per cent Li_2O in the Kuivchorr pegmatite biotite. The lithium in biotite seems to replace magnesium isomorphously.

In the contaminated rocks of the poikilitic syenite complex the biotite content sometimes amounts to 1-2 per cent. In the contaminated pegmatites it is usually

TABLE 145 Chemical composition of biotite*

Constituent	From hornblende-syenite, Koklukhtiuai valley (Analysis 1)		From pegmatite, Ninchurt (Analysis 2)		
	per cent	Atomic proportions	per cent	Atomic proportions	Calculation of atomic ratios
SiO$_2$	42·80	0·7126	39·84	0·6633	
Al$_2$O$_3$	10·36	0·2032	10·45	0·2050	0·8878 3·91 —4
TiO$_2$	2·80	0·0350	1·56	0·0195	
Fe$_2$O$_3$	0·69	0·0086	1·73	0·0216	
FeO	10·55	0·1468	11·03	0·1535	
NiO	—	—	0·20	0·0027	
CaO	—	—	0·04	0·0007	0·6977 3·07 —3
MgO	16·25	0·4030	20·31	0·5037	
BaO	—	—	—	—	
MnO	1·12	0·0158	1·10	0·0155	
K$_2$O	8·76	0·1860	9·17	0·1946	0·2352 1·03 —1
Na$_2$O	2·61	0·0842	1·25	0·0406	
H$_2$O$^+$	} 1·72	0·1910	1·96	} 0·2610	0·2610 1·15 —1
H$_2$O$^-$			0·39		
F	3·84	0·2021	not determined	—	
Cl	—	—	present	—	
CO$_2$	—	—	—	—	
		O = 2·5081	—	O = 2·6297	2·6297 11·57 —12
Total	101·50		99·03		
− O = F$_2$	− 1·62				
	99·88				
Analyst	Vladimirova				

* Data of Vorob'eva and Gerasimovskii

localized in the central natrolitic zones or immediately at the pegmatite contacts with Devonian xenoliths.

Association with orthoclase, manganilmenite, sphene, zircon, apatite and natrolite is characteristic of biotite. Idiomorphic inclusions of apatite are found in its crystals, though the groundmass apatite occurs in spaces between the biotite crystals. Biotite may have begun to crystallize later than apatite and may have finished earlier. In relation to natrolite it is idiomorphic. On alteration of biotite minerals of the chlorite group sometimes form.

66. Hydromuscovite

$KAl_2[AlSi_3O_{10}](OH)_2 . nH_2O$; mon.; sp.gr. 2·80; H. 2—3

Hydromuscovite is found in the rocks and in the pegmatites. Gerasimovskii, who was the first to note its presence in the Lovozero massif, called it sericite, but later research by Semenov (1957_2) showed that low-temperature water, characteristic of hydromicas, was present in the mica. All the constants given in the following description are taken from Semenov.

Hydromuscovite forms pseudomorphs, represented by a finely scaly aggregate, after nepheline and microcline. The flakes are usually gathered into radiate-fibrous segregations or orientated parallel to one side of the nepheline grains or along the cleavage of the microcline. The colour is pale green, sometimes with a greyish or brownish tinge.

In thin sections hydromuscovite is colourless or brownish. Optically biaxial, negative. Extinction straight. Elongation positive. Refractive indices: $Ng = 1·572$; $Np = 1·561$; $Ng - Np = 0·011$. $2V$ about 40°. Specific gravity 2·716.

The Debye powder patterns from the Karnasurt alteration zone are of the normal type for this mineral.

The Lovozero hydromuscovite has not been chemically analysed. Apart from the main constituents (silicon, aluminium, potassium, iron and sodium), magnesium, calcium, barium, strontium, titanium, manganese, beryllium, gallium, copper, zirconium, niobium and phosphorus have been determined spectroscopically.

There is a clearly-marked endothermic effect on the heating curve in the 30°-135° interval, because of the elimination of low-temperature water, characteristic of hydromicas (Fig. 235). A second endothermic effect noticeable in the 575-675° range is apparently due to the loss of hydroxyl water. According to Semenov's data hydromuscovite, unlike muscovite, contains more water and less potassium.

This mineral is commonest in the rocks of the upper part of the differentiated complex and in the Karnasurt fracture zones. The greatest quantities occur in the foyaites of the first, third and fourth horizons in the upper part of the differentiated complex, where it replaces nepheline and microcline to the extent of 50-70 per cent (Fig. 236). It is found regularly localized in the central parts of the foyaite horizons, while in the upper and lower surfaces of these horizons nepheline and microcline are replaced by natrolite; from the borders to the central parts of the horizons, hydromuscovite gradually replaces natrolite. In the middle parts natrolite is present along with hydromuscovite, developing primarily after nephe-

line, whereas the hydromuscovite develops after microcline. Usually hydromuscovite in the foyaites replaces pure non-albitized microcline, leaving albitized
parts in the form of relicts. In the urtites and aegirine-lujavrites hydromuscovite
is rarely found.

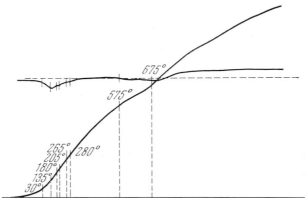

FIG. 235. Thermal analysis curve for hydromuscovite

In the pegmatites this mineral is present exclusively in undifferentiated natrolite
free bodies of small thickness. In particular, it has been detected in considerable
quantity in the lowest pegmatitic body of the pegmatite horizon underlying the
ijolite-urtites in the First Eastern stream on Karnasurt, where all the leucocratic
minerals are almost entirely replaced by hydromuscovite.

FIG. 236. Replacement of nepheline (N) and microcline (M) by
fine-grained hydromuscovite aggregate. × 46. Crossed nicols

TABLE 146 Interplanar spacings of spodiophyllite
(Fe-radiation; $2R = 57.9$ mm; $d = 0.6$ mm)

Line no.	Lovozero		Greenland (Narsarsuk)		Line no.	Lovozero		Greenland (Narsarsuk)	
	I	d	I	d		I	d	I	d
1	—	—	5	11·14	18	8	1·966	4	1·999
2	8	10·09	7	9·94	19	2	1·837	1	1·829
3	1	5·06	4	4·98	20	1	1·740	—	—
4	2	4·59	4	4·52	21	7	1·659	3	1·654
5	—	—	1	4·34	22	1	1·633	—	—
6	—	—	1	3·89	23	1	1·603	—	—
7	7	3·65	5	3·61	24	1	1·576	—	—
8	9	3·32	9	3·33	25	8	1·520	2	1·509
9	4	3·129	5	3·11	26	1	1·424	—	—
10	7	2·882	4	2·89	27	3	1·353	1	1·350
11	—	—	1	2·68	28	2	1·314	1	1·303
12	8	2·603	5	2·57	29	2	1·288	—	—
13	2	2·511	—	—	30	1	1·253	1	1·247
14	7	2·405	5	2·39	31	1	1·211	—	—
15	2	2·279	1	2·25	32	2	1·122	—	—
16	—	—	1	2·21					
17	4	2·14	3	2·14					

TABLE 147 Chemical composition of spodiophyllite

Constituent	Lovozero, Mannepakhk		Greenland, Narsarsuk	
	per cent	Atomic proportions	per cent	Atomic proportions
SiO_2	49·20	0·819	52·30	0·872
TiO_2	1·14	0·014	1·50	0·019
Al_2O_3	4·84	0·095	5·00	0·098
Fe_2O_3	2·35	0·028	2·10	0·026
FeO	3·51	0·049	3·70	0·051
MnO	0·60	0·009	0·13	0·002
MgO	19·04	0·472	14·50	0·360
CaO	0·32	0·005	0·20	0·004
Li_2O	0·47	0·031	1·45	0·194
Na_2O	3·11	0·101	4·50	0·290
K_2O	9·70	0·206	10·20	0·234
H_2O^+	2·06 ⎱ 0·295		—	—
H_2O^-	0·60 ⎰		—	—
F	4·20	0·221	7·90	0·416
Total	101·14		103·48	
$-O = F_2$	−1·77	—	−3·52	—
—	99·37	—	99·96	—
Analyst	Bykova, 1950			
Reference	Semenov (1957₂)			

Hydromuscovite probably forms under hydrothermal conditions where there is a water deficiency; the evidence for this is that it coincides with parts of the rocks and pegmatites where natrolite is absent or poorly developed.

67. Spodiophyllite

K(Mg,Fe)$_3$Si$_4$O$_{10}$(F,OH)$_2$; sp.gr. 2·633; H. 3

Spodiophyllite was first detected in the Lovozero massif by Semenov (1957$_2$) and the following description is based on his data. The mineral occurs very rarely, exclusively in the pegmatites, in the form of hexagonal grey crystals, measuring up to 1 cm. Cleavage is perfect along the pinacoid. Optically uniaxial, negative. Refractive indices: $No = 1·580$; $Ne = 1·550$; $N_0 - Ne = 0·030$. The powder patterns of Lovozero and Greenland spodiophyllite are similar (Table 146).

The chemical composition of Lovozero and Greenland spodiophyllite is similar, but the former is characterized by a lower silica, alkali and fluorine content and a higher magnesium and water content (Table 147).

According to Semenov the chemical formula of spodiophyllite has the following form: K(Mg, Fe)$_{2.5}$Li$_{0.5}$[Al$_{0.5}$Si$_{3.5}$O$_{10}$](F, OH)$_2$.

Spodiophyllite forms at the hydrothermal stage of the pegmatitic process. It is closely associated with aegirine, natrolite and chlorites. Under surface conditions it is readily destroyed.

68. Celadonite

K$_{<1}$(Fe,··Mg,Fe···)$_2$[Si$_4$O$_{10}$](OH)$_2$. nH$_2$O; mon.; sp.gr. 2·77 H. 1

Celadonite was first detected and studied in the Lovozero massif by Semenov (1957$_2$) in the altered zones on Karnasurt. The present description is based on his data.

This mineral forms pseudomorphs after aegirine II and independent circular segregations up to 0·5 cm in diameter, of a greenish-azure colour. In places where it is widely developed the rocks in the altered zone have a greenish-azure tint. Under the electron microscope celadonite can be seen to have the form of scales with irregular outlines.

The mineral is optically biaxial, negative, with a small optic axial angle. Refractive indices: $Ng = 1·640$; $Np = 1·626$; $Ng - Np = 0·014$. Intense pleochroism is characteristic: from azure-green along Ng to yellowish, almost colourless along Np; absorption scheme $Ng > Np$.

It has been found from X-ray structural and electron diffraction study that celadonite belongs to the mica group. Its Debye powder patterns are indistinct,

TABLE 148 Interplanar spacings of celadonite

Line no.	I	d	Line no.	I	d	Line no.	I	d
1	1	4·43	5	6	2·57	8	8	1·511
2	10	3·84	6	4	2·40	9	2	1·306
3	5	3·32	7	3	1·655	10	2	1·209
4	5	3·05						

with a small number of lines, similar to those of the standard powder pattern (Table 148).

Celadonite is a secondary mineral formed by replacement of aegirine in fracture zones, probably under the influence of hydrothermal solutions.

69. Chabazite

(Ca,Na) [$AlSi_2O_6$]$_2$. $6H_2O$; trig.; sp.gr. 2·1; H. 4.5

Chabazite occurs in small amounts. In the form of white crusts up to 4 mm thick, it lines the walls of miarolitic cavities in the zeolitic zones of the pegmatites or the zeolitized parts of the rocks. These crusts are made up of small crystals, usually up to 0·5 mm, rarely 3 mm in diameter. The form of the crystals is rhombo-hedral. Lustre vitreous. Cleavage distinct along the rhombohedron. In thin sections white, transparent. Between crossed nicols zoning parallel to the rhombo-hedron is clearly visible. Birefringence very low. Interference colour grey to light grey of the first order. Optically uniaxial, positive. Refractive indices: $Ne =$ 1·479—1·478; $No = 1·476$—1·472; $Ne - No = 0·003$—0·006.

X-ray study of chabazite by Sludskaya showed that the Debye powder pattern of this mineral (Table 149) was identical with the standard chabazite powder pattern.

Recalculation of the chemical analysis (Table 150) shows that the composition of Lovozero chabazite is expressed by the formula (Ca, Na)[$AlSi_2O_6$]$_2$. $5·3H_2O$ and differs from the theoretical composition in the low water-content.

Apart from the elements shown by chemical analysis, zinc, gallium, strontium, titanium, beryllium, copper, niobium and manganese have been detected in chabazite by spectrographic analysis.

In the rocks chabazite has been found in foyaites at the contact with the pegmatitic vein on Kuftn'yun, where it forms crusts on spreusteinized nepheline and on altered eudialyte in the zeolitized parts.

In the pegmatites chabazite is present in considerable quantity in the central zones of the complex replacement bodies on the north-eastern slope of Karnasurt, where it lines the walls of miarolitic cavities in hackmanite, prismatic natrolite and

TABLE 149 Interplanar spacings of chabazite

Line no.	I	d	Line no.	I	d	Line no.	I	d
1	7	5·54	14	5	1·859	26	4	1·306
2	7	4·81	15	8	1·802	27	7	1·284
3	10	4·30	16	8	1·727	28	7	1·266
4	9	3·87	17	1	1·690	29	4	1·225
5	9	3·50	18	8	1·637	30	2	1·208
6	9	3·19	19	7	1·553	31	5	1·198
7	10	2·83	20	7	1·514	32	1 double	1·170
8	6	2·60	21	3 broad line	1·492	33	5	1·154
9	6	2·48			1·449	34	5	1·122
10	5	2·30	22	7	1·420	35	2	1·092
11	6	2·09	23	7	1·398	36	6	1·068
12	3	1·985	24	6	1·363	37	6	1·051
13	2	1·911	25	8	1·329	38	7	1·033

late microcline in the form of small crystals or outgrowths of these. Mixed with other zeolites and clay minerals chabazite, in the form of a fine-grained aggregate, fills up cracks in hackmanite and prismatic natrolite and is an important component of the replacement complexes.

In time of separation chabazite belongs to the latest minerals and probably crystallized from late hydrothermal solutions.

TABLE 150 Chemical composition of chabazite from Karnasurt hackmanitic stock

Constituent	Content, per cent	Atomic proportions	Calculation of atomic ratios		
SiO_2	50·87	0·8470	0·8470	4·15	—4
TiO_2	nil	—		—	
Al_2O_3	18·63	0·3656 ⎫			
Fe_2O_3	0·23	0·0028 ⎬ 0·4264	2·09	—2	
MnO	nil	— ⎭			
MgO	2·34	0·0580 ⎭			
CaO	4·87	0·0868 ⎫			
Na_2O	1·24	0·0400 ⎬ 0·1820	0·89	—1	
K_2O	2·60	0·0552 ⎭			
H_2O^+	9·25	2·1824	2·1824	10·69	—10·7
H_2O^-	10·41	—	—		
		O = 3·5302	3·5302	17·30	—17·3
Total	100·44	—	—		
Analyst		Nikolaeva, 1953			

70. Thomsonite

$Ca_2Na[AlSiO_4]_5 . 6H_2O$; orthorhomb.; sp.gr. 2·3—2·4; H. 5

Thomsonite occurs very rarely in the Lovozero massif. It was observed microscopically by Eliseev in the lujavrites and foyaites of the differentiated complex (Eliseev et al., 1939). Borodin detected this mineral in considerable amounts in the central zone of a pegmatite in the Koklukhtiuai valley and the following description is based on his data.

Thomsonite forms after nepheline and sodalite. It is represented by sheaf-like aggregates of small acicular white crystals (Fig. 237). Colourless in thin sections. Optically biaxial, positive. $2V = 60°$. Birefringence, as in natrolite, low. Differs from natrolite in having higher refractive indices ($Ng = 1·515$).

Thomsonite fills up miarolitic cavities in natrolite. It is usually later than natrolite, on which it develops. Sometimes it is found in intimate intergrowth with fine-grained natrolite. More rarely it is found replacing nepheline and sodalite.

71. Apophyllite

$KCa_4[Si_4O_{10}]F . 8H_2O$; tetr.; sp.gr. 2·3; H. 4·5—5

Apophyllite was detected by Semenov in 1953 in one of the Lepkhe-Nel'm pegmatites. The following description is based on his data.

Apophyllite forms colourless and white, granular and also acicular and spherulitic segregations up to 1·5 cm in diameter. Occasionally tetragonal crystals up to 0·3 cm long are found. Optically uniaxial, positive. Refractive indices: $Ne = 1·535$; $No = 1·532$. Interference colours low, sometimes anomalous.

Apart from the principal constituents, spectrographic analysis has shown the presence of strontium, lanthanum, cerium, titanium, beryllium, manganese and yttrium. The high tenor of manganese, rare earths and strontium, which seem to replace calcium isomorphously, is striking.

FIG. 237. Thomsonite vugs (T) in natrolite (N). Natural size

72. Hemimorphite*

$Zn_4[Si_2O_7](OH)_2 . H_2O$; orthorhomb.; sp.gr. 3·40—3·50; H. 4—5

Hemimorphite was first detected and studied in the Lovozero massif by Semenov and the following description is based on his data.

The mineral occurs in the central zone of the orthoclase-natrolite pegmatite with apatite (Lepkhe-Nel'm) in the form of small elongated crystals measuring up to $3 \times 1 \times 0·5$ mm, in the cavities of natrolite druses, in close association with oxidized sphalerite.

Hemimorphite is colourless, transparent, with a vitreous lustre. Optically biaxial, positive. Extinction straight. Elongation positive. Refractive indices: $Ng = 1·636$; $Np = 1·615$; $Ng - Np = 0·021$. Apart from the principal constituents,

* [The Russian authors use the obsolescent name calamine—Eds.]

iron, manganese, magnesium, beryllium, calcium, lead, aluminium and copper have been detected by spectrographic analysis.

Hemimorphite is a product of alteration of sphalerite under surface conditions.

73. Allophane

$mAl_2O_3 . nSiO_2 . pH_2O$; amorph.; sp.gr. 1·85—1·89; H. 3

A mineral similar to allophane was found in the Lovozero massif by Semenov in the cavities of pegmatitic blocks on Alluaiv, in the form of crustified, compact segregations, white, with conchoidal fracture. Optically isotropic. Refractive index about 1·490. Apart from the principal constituents, the presence of zirconium, strontium, calcium, magnesium, iron, niobium, sodium, barium, manganese, titanium and vanadium has been established by spectrographic analysis. The mineral occurs extremely rarely in the massif and has not yet been studied. It may be a zirconium-enriched allophane.

74. Minerals of the chlorite family

$(Fe,Mg,Mn)_5(Fe,Al)[AlSi_3O_{10}](OH)_8 . nH_2O$; mon.; sp.gr. 2·5—3; H. 2

Minerals similar in physical and chemical properties to magnesium-iron and magnesium chlorites occur in small amount in the Lovozero pegmatites.

Fig. 238. Manganese-bearing variety of chlorite (dark), developing on spherulite of aegirine II (Ae)

Magnesium-iron varieties of the chlorite family were observed by Semenov in the Kuivchorr, Lepkhe-Nel'm, Mannepakhk and Koklukhtiuai valley pegmatites. These minerals form pseudomorphs after aegirine, or round segregations up to 1 cm in diameter. Sometimes they form incrustations lining the walls of cavities in albite or are closely associated with minerals of the replacement complex in the central parts of pegmatite bodies. The colour of the minerals varies from greenish-yellow to azure-green and green. All the magnesium-iron varieties of the chlorite-like minerals are secondary, formed in the process of replacement of aegirine, arfvedsonite or biotite.

Manganese-bearing varieties of minerals belonging to the chlorite family are

TABLE 151 Interplanar spacings of chlorite-like minerals from Karnasurt pegmatite

Line no.	Unaltered variety		Oxidized variety		Line no.	Unaltered variety		Oxidized variety	
	I	d	I	d		I	d	I	d
1	—	—	1	4·61	9	1	1·73	—	—
2	9	4·45	—	—	10	1	1·714	—	—
3	8	4·10	—	—	11	1	1·665	—	—
4	10	3·27	—	—	12	1	1·605	—	—
5	9	2·62	—	—	13	1	1·547	1	1·542
6	9	2·49	2	2·40	14	1	1·500	—	—
7	3	2·33	—	—	15	—	—	1	1·410
8	2	2·18	1	2·19	16	1	1·200	—	—

TABLE 152 Chemical composition of dark-brown variety of manganese chlorite

Constituent	Content, per cent	Recalculation to 100% after deduction of oxidized manganese	Atomic proportions	Calculation of atomic ratios		
SiO_2	10·98	11·92	0·1983	0·3897	3·71	—4
Al_2O_3	8·99	9·76	0·1914			
TiO_2	0·90	0·98	0·0124			
Nb_2O_5	2·50	2·71	0·0204			
Fe_2O_3	5·62	6·10	0·0764			
FeO	—	—	—	0·2131	2·03	—2
MgO	1·22	1·32	0·0327			
CaO	3·12	3·39	0·0604			
BaO	1·53	1·66	0·0108			
MnO_2	46·08	—	—			
MnO	—	41·03	0·5784			
Na_2O	1·32	1·43	0·0460	0·6362	6·06	—6
K_2O	0·52	0·56	0·0118			
H_2O^+	9·00	9·77	2·1236	2·1236	20·2	—20
H_2O^-	8·60	9·36				
			O = 2·6471	2·6471	25·2	—25
Total	100·38	99·99				
Specific gravity	2·83					
Analyst		Kazakova, 1949				

widely distributed in the Karnasurt pegmatites and also in those of Kedykvyrpakhk, Kuivchorr and Kitkn'yun. These minerals form radiate-fibrous segregations from 0·1 to 3 cm in diameter or irregular individuals measuring $3 \times 2 \times 0.5$ cm, filling cavities in aegirine II, natrolite and albite (Fig. 238).

Colour light-brown, brown, dark-brown to black. Streak brown. Lustre silky in the brown varieties and pitch-like in the black. Soft. Specific gravity of brown varieties 2·618; of dark varieties 2·83. Structure random to radiate-fibrous; in black varieties, massive.

In thin sections the colour varies from yellow through yellowish-brown and brown to black. Pleochroism from black (along Ng) to yellow (along Np). Elongation positive. Optically biaxial, negative. Refractive index of brown varieties about 1·690, rising to 1·749 in the dark oxidized varieties.

Interplanar spacings of two manganese-bearing varieties of chlorite minerals are shown in Table 151.

Recalculation of the chemical analysis (Table 152) shows that the composition of the oxidized variety is given by the formula $(Mn, Fe)_8 (Al, Si)_4 O_{10}(OH)_{12} . 4H_2O$ Beryllium (0·1 per cent), copper (0·01 per cent), molybdenum ($n \cdot 10^{-3}$ [per cent]), zinc, zirconium, vanadium, strontium, lanthanum, yttrium and gallium have also been detected by spectrographic analysis.

The minerals described are nearest in chemical composition and physical properties to pennantite, but differ from it in having a higher tenor of manganese, oxygen and water, probably because of their high degree of oxidation.

The manganese varieties of the chlorite-like minerals most frequently occur in large pegmatite bodies in which the late hydrothermal stage of replacement is much in evidence. These minerals form in the process of replacement of aegirine II and fill up cavities in natrolite and albite, sometimes penetrating these through cracks. They are often associated with montmorillonite.

The manganese chlorites are unstable under surface conditions; divalent manganese is oxidized into tetravalent form. At the first stages of alteration the refractive indices rise and the minerals become brown. The end-product is brownish-black opaque manganese hydroxides.

75. Montmorillonite

$(Al,Mg,Fe)_2 [Si_4O_{10}] (OH)_2 . nH_2O$; mon.; sp.gr. 2·152; H. 1

Montmorillonite is one of the most widespread clay minerals in the Lovozero massif. It was first studied by Semenov (1958) and the following description is based on his data.

Montmorillonite forms irregularly-shaped segregations up to 10 cm in diameter, or replaces nepheline, to the extent of forming pseudomorphs. Colour pink, yellow, green and white. Swells greatly in water, the volume increasing by 56·3 per cent; on drying out, it disintegrates into small irregularly-shaped fragment.

In thin sections montmorillonite is seen to have an aggregate, fine scaly structure. Refractive indices: $Ng = 1·515$; $Np = 1·503$. Elongation positive. The powder pattern of Lovozero montmorillonite is similar to the standard (Table 153).

The chemical analysis data (Table 154) show that the Lovozero montmorillonite is represented by the formula: $(Al, Mg, Fe)_2(Si, Al)_4O_{10}(OH)_2 . 4.5H_2O$.

The presence of 0·005 per cent BeO in montmorillonite has also been established by chemical methods and titanium, copper, zinc, gallium, barium and zirconium have been detected by spectrographic analysis. A tenor of about 0·06 per cent La_2O_3 and 0·11 per cent Y_2O_3 has been established by quantitative spectrographic analysis.

The thermal analysis curve (Fig. 239) shows three endothermic effects and one

TABLE 153 Interplanar spacings of montmorillonite

Line no.	Montmorillonite (standard) after Johansen		Lovozero montmorillonite		Line no.	Montmorillonite (standard) after Johansen		Lovozero montmorillonite	
	I	d	I	d		I	d	I	d
1	10	11·5	s	13·85	15	2	2·249	—	—
2	2	7·44	—	—	16	1	2·175	—	—
3	4	6·67	—	—	17	1	1·877	—	—
4	1	5·79	—	—	18	—	—	—	—
5	3	4·89	w	4·85	19	5	1·652	w	1·635
6	3	4·45	m	4·43	20	5	1·697	w	1·68
7	1	4·28	—	—	21	10	1·492	m	1·48
8	1	3·87	—	—	22	2	1·427	—	—
9	1	3·45	—	—	23	1	1·375	—	—
10	2	3·113	—	—	24	6	1·292	w	1·28
11	4	3·034	w	3·00	25	4	1·247	w	1·24
12	3	2·812	w	2·72	26	2	1·124	—	—
13	7	2·576	m	2·55	27	1	1·074	—	—
14	2	2·404	—	—	28	—	—	—	—

TABLE 154 Chemical composition of montmorillonite
(Koklukhtiuai valley)

Constituent	Analysis 1		Analysis 2	
	per cent	Molecular proportions	per cent	Molecular proportions
SiO_2	48·99	0·817	46·12	0·769
Al_2O_3	22·30	0·219	27·86	0·273
Fe_2O_3	0·36	0·002	1·72	0·011
MgO	3·01	0·075	0·48	0·012
MnO	0·01	—	—	—
CaO	2·87	0·051	} 0·79	0·032
SrO	0·33	0·003		
Na_2O	0·84	0·014	—	—
K_2O	0·84	0·009	—	—
H_2O^+	6·67	1·184	22·15	1·230
H_2O^-	14·64			
Total	100·86	—	99·12	—
Analyst	Semenov		Kazakova	
Reference	Semenov (1958)			

exothermic effect at 990°. The first endothermic break, in the 80-150° interval, is apparently connected with the liberation of hygroscopic water. Semenov (1958) explains the further break at 220-240° as due to the elimination of water connected with adsorbed cations. The third endothermic reaction at temperatures of 615-710° corresponds to the liberation of bound hydroxyl water.

Montmorillonite has been found in the alteration zone on Karnasurt and in the Karnasurt, Kuftn'yun, Kuivchorr and Lepkhe-Nel'm pegmatites. In the major pegmatitic bodies, where late replacement processes are strongly developed, it sometimes forms monomineralic segregations of irregular shape in the central

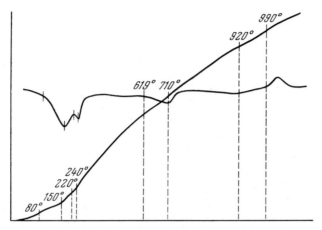

Fig. 239. Thermal analysis curve for montmorillonite

zeolitic zones. In some pegmatites and rocks it is found in the form of pseudomorphs replacing nepheline and may have formed under supergene conditions, whereas the montmorillonite in the central parts of the pegmatites seems to be of late-hydrothermal origin.

76. Zinc montmorillonite

$ZnMgAl_2Si_4O_{10}(OH)_6 . 3·5H_2O$; orthorhomb. (?); sp.gr. 2·312; soft

In 1951 Kuz'menko found montmorillonite containing a large amount of zinc in the Lovozero pegmatites. The zinc montmorillonite forms large monomineralic accumulations up to 20 cm in diameter and veinlets of fine-grained to colloidal structure in prismatic natrolite. The mineral absorbs a great deal of water, so that under natural conditions it is usually a soft, greasy-textured mass. On drying out it disintegrates into small irregularly-shaped fragments. Colour white, more rarely pink, blue, yellowish and greenish. Lustre waxy.

Zinc montmorillonite is seen under the microscope to be cryptocrystalline, with greatly varying refractive indices (from 1·515 to 1·540); this is apparently due to variations in composition of the mineral.

The Debye powder patterns of the four varieties of zinc montmorillonite (white, yellow, green and azure) obtained by Sludskaya (Table 155) showed that all had identical structure and contained lines both of montmorillonite and of sauconite.

Recalculation of the chemical analysis data shows that the composition of zinc montmorillonite (Table 156) is expressed by the formula: $(Zn, Mg)Al_2Si_4O_{10}(OH)_6 . 3.5H_2O$. The mineral seems to be intermediate between montmorillonite and sauconite. The presence of beryllium, copper, strontium, manganese, rare earths, iron and titanium in zinc montmorillonite has been established by the spectrographic method. In the coloured varieties a higher tenor of iron can be noticed. In the green and yellow varieties chromium and niobium are present as

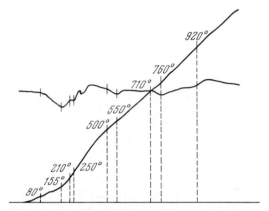

FIG. 240. Thermal analysis curve for zincian montmorillonite

admixtures. Dudykin determined 0.002-0.03 per cent of beryllium in montmorillonites by quantitative spectrographic analysis.

The thermal analysis curve (Fig. 240) is similar to that of montmorillonite, There are four endothermic effects at intervals 80-150° (elimination of hygroscopic water), 210-250° (elimination of water connected with adsorbed cations), 500-550° and 710-760° (elimination of bound water) and an indistinct exothermic effect at 980°. Zinc montmorillonite is present in large amount in the major complex-

TABLE 155　Interplanar spacings of white zinc montmorillonite

Line no.	Sauconite (standard)		Zinc montmorillonite		Montmorillonite (standard)	
	I	d	I	d	I	d
1	7	4·59	5	4·43	m	4·43
2	2	3·68	1	3·63	—	—
3	—	—	—	—	w	3·00
4	4	2·92	1	2·90	w	2·72
5	7	2·64	5	2·58	m	2·55
6	5	1·686	2	1·692	w	1·68
7	—	—	—	—	w	1·635
8	9	1·533	5	1·527	—	—
9	—	—	—	—	m	1·48
10	—	—	—	—	w	1·28
11	—	—	—	—	vw	1·24
12	—	—	—	—	—	—

differentiated bodies of the poikilitic syenite complex (Karnasurt), in which late hydrothermal replacement processes are strongly evident. It fills up cavities and cracks in prismatic natrolite, hackmanite and other minerals of the central zones and is also an important component part of the replacement zones or complexes.

The finely-dispersed (to colloidal) structure of zinc montmorillonite indicates that it was deposited from cold, possibly colloidal, solutions. It is hard to tell whether these were solutions of hydrothermal origin—that is, whether they formed at the final stage of the pegmatitic process—or were surface waters leaching out various minerals. On the other hand, the intimate association of the zinc montmorillonite with minerals of the replacement complex formed at the late hydrothermal stage of the pegmatitic process, together with the fact that this mineral has a high tenor of zinc, whereas zinc minerals occur in very small amounts, or not at all, in the pegmatite bodies concerned, and in the massif as a whole, preclude us from regarding this mineral as a supergene product. In all probability it formed from residual low-temperature pegmatitic solutions.

TABLE 156 Chemical composition of white zinc montmorillonite

Constituent	Content, per cent	Atomic proportions	Calculation of atomic ratios		
SiO_2	41·84	0·6966	0·6966	3·97	— 4
TiO_2	trace	—	—		
Al_2O_3	19·23	0·3772	0·3772	2·15	— 2
Fe_2O_3	0·64	0·0080			
FeO	—	—			
MnO	—	—	0·1584	0·90	— 1
ZnO	10·83	0·1354			
MgO	5·39	0·0150			
CaO	1·72	0·1187			
Na_2O	} 0·3	0·0307	0·1590	0·91	— 1
K_2O		0·0096			
H_2O^+	7·5	} 2·2758	2·2758	12·97	—13
H_2O^-	13·00				
F	0·17	0·0089	3·4179	19·48	—19·5
		O = 3·4090			
Total	100·62	—	—		
Analyst	Nissenbaum, 1952				

77. Sauconite

$Zn_3[Si_4O_{10}](OH)_2 . nH_2O$; mon.; sp.gr. 2·61; H. 1

Sauconite was first detected and studied in the Lovozero massif by Semenov (1953₂). It forms almost monomineralic segregations of finely-aggregated structure measuring up to 50×30 cm. The colour is usually white, sometimes with a blue or brown tinge. In water it swells, the volume increasing by 46·7 per cent. Under ultra-violet rays it glows with a bright bluish-white light.

Optically biaxial, negative. Refractive indices $Ng = 1·551$; $Np = 1·530$. Extinction of flakes near to straight. Elongation positive. Debye powder pattern of Lovozero sauconite similar to standard (Table 157).

Sauconite is readily soluble in HCl, precipitating flocculent SiO_2, while all the zinc passes into solution.

In chemical composition (Table 158) sauconite is the zinc end-member of the montmorillonite-sauconite series, in which zinc is a structural part of the mineral. Recalculation of the analysis of Lovozero sauconite by Semenov showed that its composition was given by the formula: $(Zn, Mg)_3(Al, Si)_4O_{10}(OH)_2 . 4·5H_2O$.

Apart from the elements detected chemically, the presence of lead, copper, gallium, titanium and cadmium has been spectroscopically detected in sauconite;

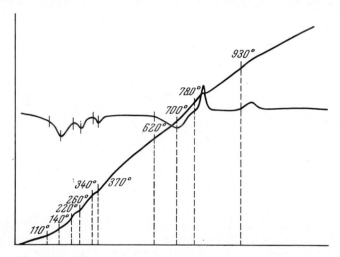

FIG. 241. Thermal analysis curve for Lovozero sauconite

0·008 per cent BeO and 0·022 per cent La_2O_3 were determined by quantitative spectrographic analysis.

The thermal analysis curve of Lovozero sauconite (Fig. 241) is similar to the standard curve (Faust, 1951). Of the four endothermic effects in the intervals 110-140°, 220-260°, 340-370° and 620-700° the first three are probably due to the separation of low-temperature water, partially connected with adsorbed cations, while the last is due to the removal of hydroxyl water and, possibly, to loss of energy on destruction of the crystalline lattice.

Sauconite usually occurs in large complex replacement pegmatite bodies in the

TABLE 157 Interplanar spacings of sauconite

Line no.	Lovozero sauconite		Sauconite (standard)		Line no.	Lovozero sauconite		Sauconite (standard)	
	I	d	I	d		I	d	I	d
1	10	16·1	s	15·4	7	—	—	w	1·748
2	1	7·22	m	7·77	8	1	1·699	vw	1·718
3	4	4·61	,,	4·60	9	7	1·535	s	1·544
4	2	3·69	w	3·87	10	—	—	m	1·334
5	4	2·92	,,	3·09	11	—	—	w	1·005
6	4	2·66	s	2·67	12	—	—	,,	0·890

central part of the massif, genetically connected with the poikilitic syenites. It is usually intimately associated with sphalerite, sometimes forming tree-like intergrowths with orthoclase. In this case the sauconite apparently forms during the replacement of orthoclase under the action of solutions enriched with products of sphalerite oxidation.

In some of the Lepkhe-Nel'm and Kuivchorr pegmatites, in which sphalerite is lacking, large segregations of sauconite are observed in natrolite drusy cavities isolated on all sides. This sauconite seems to have formed from late zinc-rich hydrothermal solutions.

TABLE 158 Chemical composition of sauconite

| Constituent | Lovozero, from orthoclase natrolite pegmatitic body, Lepkhe-Nel'm | | Arkansas |
	per cent	Atomic proportions	per cent
SiO_2	35·10	0·595	33·59
Al_2O_3	6·40	0·126	6·01
Fe_2O_3	0·04	—	0·78
ZnO	35·74	0·441	39·33
MgO	2·38	0·059	0·70
MnO	trace	—	0·12
CaO	2·03	0·036	1·90
SrO	0·20	0·003	—
Na_2O	0·25	0·008	0·13
K_2O	0·14	0·004	0·07
CuO	—	—	0·10
TiO_2	—	—	0·03
H_2O^+	6·20	0·688	6·98
H_2O^-	10·77	1·196	10·68
Total	99·25	—	100·42
Analyst	Semenov, 1952		Kerron
Reference	Semenov (1953)		C. Ross (1945-1946)

78. Halloysite

$Al_4[Si_4O_{10}](OH)_8 . 4H_2O$; mon.; H. 2

Minerals of the halloysite family occur in considerable quantities in the Lovozero massif, along with minerals of the montmorillonite family. They were first detected and studied by Semenov and the following description is based on his data.

Halloysite forms compact or porous segregations of irregular shape, measuring up to 10×10 cm, of a light pink, greenish-grey, grey and azure-blue colour. In thin sections their finely-aggregated structure is revealed. Slightly anisotropic. Refractive indices vary within the range 1·53−1·55.

A primary and a secondary halloysite are distinguished. Primary halloysite occurs in the central part of the orthoclase-natrolite pegmatitic body with apatite on Lepkhe-Nel'm, at the orthoclase-natrolite zone contact, in the form of compact and porous segregations of irregular shape, brownish-cream in colour, measuring up to 10×10 cm, filling cavities and cracks in natrolite. This halloysite seems to have crystallized from late hydrothermal solutions. Secondary halloysite is observed in the central parts of spreustein pseudomorphs after nepheline in the Lepkhe-Nel'm pegmatites and also in the altered zone in the First Eastern stream on Karnasurt, where it is closely associated with the hydromuscovite replacing nepheline, and probably forms in the process of their supergene alteration.

Semenov discovered also halloysite varieties enriched in iron and rare elements.

79. Kaolinite

$Al_4[Si_4O_{10}](OH)_8$; mon.; sp.gr. 2·58; H. 1

Kaolinite was first detected in the Lovozero massif by Gerasimovskii, in the contaminated poikilitic syenites, where it formed in the process of orthoclase replacement. In recent years it has been found in large amount by Semenov in the Kuftn'yun pegmatites, in intimate association with albite in the form of white, irregularly-shaped segregations, measuring up to $5 \times 6 \times 7$ cm, of finely-aggregated structure. Under the microscope it can be seen that the kaolinite particles have a vermiform curved shape. Extinction near to straight. Refractive indices: $Ng = 1·564$; $Np = 1·559$ (Semenov's data).

The fact that kaolinite is associated with only one type of rock, rich in volatile compounds, in which the hydrothermal stage is most advanced, together with its close association with albite in the pegmatites, gives reason for assuming that this mineral is of hydrothermal origin.

TABLE 159 Chemical composition of nontronite from Vavnbed feldspathic rocks
(After Gerasimovskii)

Constituent	Content, per cent	Atomic proportions	Calculation of atomic ratios		
SiO_2	42·60	0·709	}0·805	3·85	— 4
Al_2O_3	4·91	0·096			
Fe_2O_3	24·10	0·302			
TiO_2	1·29	0·016			
Nb_2O_5	0·01	—			
CaO	2·24	0·050	}0·500	2·40	— 2
MgO	3·80	0·094			
K_2O	1·34	0·028			
Na_2O	0·30	0·010			
H_2O^+	5·58	0·620	}2·120	10·18	—10
H_2O^-	13·50	1·500			
Cl	0·22	0·066			
F	0·50	0·026	}3·322	15·96	—16
		$O = 3·230$			
Total	100·39	—		—	
$-O = (F, Cl)_2$	$-0·26$				
—	100·13	—		—	
Analyst		Tumilovich			

80. Nontronite

$Fe_2[Si_4O_{10}](OH)_2 . nH_2O$; mon.; sp.gr. 1·73—1·84

Nontronite was first detected in the Lovozero massif by Gerasimovskii, in altered feldspathic rock on Vavnbed, in the form of earthy masses of green colour. In recent years Semenov has established that it is fairly widespread in the pegmatites, in particular those of Kuivchorr, Lepkhe-Nel'm, Kitkn'yun and other mountains. In the pegmatites it forms round segregations up to 0·5 cm in diameter, apple-green, with conchoidal fracture.

Recalculation of the chemical analysis data (Table 159) shows that its composition is in general represented by the formula $(Fe, Mg)_2(Si, Al)_4O_{10}(OH)_2 . 4H_2O$ with some oxygen deficiency.

Beryllium, manganese, titanium, zirconium, strontium, barium and copper have been detected in nontronite by spectrographic analysis.

Nontronite is usually localized in albitized metasomatic zones and in the marginal zones of pegmatite bodies, in close association with aegirine I and arfvedsonite, on which it forms. More rarely it fills up drusy cavities in natrolite in the central parts of the Lepkhe-Nel'm pegmatites, along with sauconite. It has apparently crystallized from low-temperature late hydrothermal solutions.

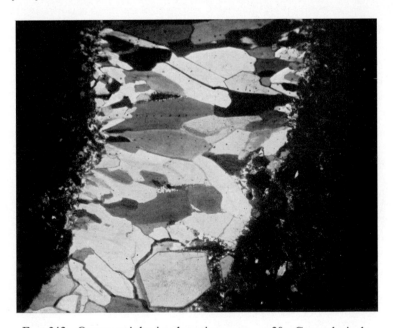

FIG. 242. Quartz veinlet in alteration zone. ×20. Crossed nicols

81. Quartz

SiO_2; trig.; sp.gr. 2·5—2·8; H. 7

Lovozero quartz is here described for the first time. It was found in 1949 by Shilin in the altered zone under a thick horizon of ijolite-urtites in the First Eastern stream on Karnasurt, and was subsequently studied by Tikhonenkov, who detected it in 1950 in exposures of the pegmatite horizon on Alluaiv. In 1952 Semenov found it in the orthoclase-natrolite pegmatite body on Lepkhe-Nel'm.

The altered zone under the ijolite-urtite horizon on Karnasurt is made up of blue, yellow, grey and other coloured clay minerals with relicts of aegirine II, microcline and, more rarely, apatite. The whole of this aggregate is permeated by fine quartz veinlets (Fig. 242), up to 1-2 cm thick. The swells of these veinlets contain cavities whose walls are covered with druses of pure quartz. The size of the quartz crystals reaches $1.3 \times 0.3 \times 0.2$ cm.

In the Alluaiv exposure of the pegmatite horizon quartz occurs in the form of very small grains visible only under the microscope and closely associated with late pink albite (see Fig. 51). In relation to albite quartz is xenomorphic.

In the orthoclase-natrolite pegmatite body with apatite on the northern slope of Lepkhe-Nel'm, Semenov found segregations (measuring up to 2×1 m) of a fine-grained greenish-yellow ochreous rock in the central zone, consisting almost entirely of very small (up to 0.1 mm) round quartz grains. Despite the unusual shape of the segregations the powder pattern of this quartz does not differ from that of ordinary quartz.

In thin sections quartz is colourless, often contaminated with a brown dusty substance. Optically uniaxial, positive. Refractive indices: $Ne = 1.544$; $No = 1.551$ (Tikhonenkov's data). Spectrographic analysis revealed the presence of aluminium, iron, beryllium, gallium, magnesium, manganese and titanium in addition to the silicon.

The fact that this quartz is a member of an albitic mineral association is evidence of its late hydrothermal origin.

82. Chalcedony
SiO_2; cryptocrystalline; sp. gr. 2.59—2.64; H. 7

Chalcedony occurs very rarely in the Lovozero massif and in very small quantity. Earlier investigators took cryptocrystalline varieties of natrolite, feldspar and other minerals for chalcedony and flint.

Chalcedony was found by Tikhonenkov in a pegmatite horizon underlying the ijolite-urtites on Alluaiv, and also by Semenov in a pegmatite vein intersecting the malignite horizon on Kuftn'yun. In the Alluaiv pegmatite horizon it forms greenish-grey, semi-transparent segregations of irregular shape, measuring up to 5×5 cm. It sometimes occurs in the form of accumulations of small spherulites up to 1 mm in diameter, of radiate-fibrous structure. In the Kuftn'yun pegmatite vein it is represented by compact solid white crusts, up to 0.5 cm thick, on albite.

Under the microscope wavy extinction can be detected. Elongation negative. Refractive indices: $Ng = 1.538$—1.540; $Np = 1.531$—1.535; $Ng - Np = 0.005$—0.007 (Tikhonenkov's and Semenov's data). The Debye powder patterns of Lovozero chalcedony are identical with standard.

In the Kuftn'yun chalcedony, apart from silicon, spectroscopical analysis has revealed the presence of calcium, iron, zirconium, beryllium, copper, aluminium, magnesium, manganese and titanium.

Chalcedony is usually intimately associated with aegirine III and fine-grained albite. It probably separated from late hydrothermal solutions of the replacement stage in the central parts of pegmatite bodies.

83. Opal

$SiO_2 . nH_2O$; amorphous; sp.gr. 1·9—2·5; H. 5—6

Opal is fairly widespread in the Lovozero massif. It was first detected and studied by Semenov and the following brief description is based on his data.

Opal occurs in the form of white crusts with pearly lustre, and films on the weathered surfaces of pegmatites and rocks. The thickness of the crusts does not exceed 0·2 cm. Occasionally opal forms irregularly-shaped segregations in pegmatite cavities.

Optically isotropic. Refractive indices 1·443 – 1·452. Spectrographic analysis of the Kedykvyrpakhk pegmatite opal showed the presence of iron, magnesium, aluminium, calcium, zirconium, titanium, beryllium, strontium and manganese.

Opal films have been found in the pegmatites of Kedykvyrpakhk, Mannepakhk, Lepkhe-Nel'm, Kuivchorr, Kuftn'yun and Kitkn'yun. The opal seems to have been deposited from surface alkaline solutions carrying considerable amounts of silicic acid.

84. Natro-opal

$Na_2O . 8SiO_2 . 7H_2O$; amorph.; sp.gr. 1·94 (to 2·19)

Natro-opal was discovered in the Lovozero massif by Gerasimovskii, who studied it in detail, in 1936. Some additional information on its distribution in the massif, its chemical character and genesis was later provided by members of the Kola Expedition. The following description is based mainly on Gerasimovskii's data (1940₃).

TABLE 160 Interplanar spacings of natro-opal

Line no.	Natro-opal, unheated		Natro-opal, heated to 700°		Quartz		Line no.	Natro-opal, unheated		Natro-opal, heated to 700°		Quartz	
	I	d	I	d	I	d		I	d	I	d	I	d
1	—	—	w	4·25	0·25	4·25	17	—	—	w	1·49	0·02	1·45
2	—	—	m	4·01	—	—	18	—	—	w	1·43	—	—
3	—	—	m	3·33	1·00	3·35	19	—	—	m	1·37	0·25	1·375
4	—	—	w	3·14	—	—	20	w	1·33	w	1·30	0·04	1·299
5	—	—	w	2·85	—	—	21	—	—	w	1·29	—	—
6	—	—	m	2·48	0·15	2·45	22	—	—	w	1·26	0·03	1·256
7	m	2·30	vw	2·29	0·1	2·29	23	—	—	w	1·23	0·03	1·228
8	—	—	vw	2·23	0·06	2·23	24	—	—	w	1·20	0·06	1·200
9	—	—	w	2·12	0·09	2·12	25	—	—	m	1·99	0·08	1·180
10	—	—	w	2·00	0·08	1·97	26	vw	1·15	w	1·15	0·01	1·115
11	—	—	w	1·93	—	—	27	—	—	m	1·10	—	—
12	—	—	w	1·87	—	—	28	—	—	m	1·08	0·04	1·080
13	—	—	m	1·82	0·25	1·82	29	—	—	w	1·05	0·02	1·048
14	—	—	w	1·70	0·08	1·66	30	w	1·03	w	1·03	0·01	1·035
15	m	1·63	w	1·61	—	—	31	—	—	—	—	0·01	1·015
16	—	—	m	1·54	0·20	1·54							

The mineral is widely distributed in the massif, where it occurs in the form of thin films and crusts up to 2-3 cm thick and also as coral-like segregations or formations resembling icicles, stalactites and stalagmites, often intergrowing with one another, up to 25 cm long and up to 3 cm in diameter (Figs. 243 and 244).

The colour is white, sometimes with a light-grey, yellowish or pinkish tinge. Lustre from vitreous to dull. Cleavage lacking. Fracture uneven to earthy. Porous. Brittle. Opaque. In thin sections light-grey to dirty-grey. Refractive index varies between 1·440 and 1·448.

Debye powder patterns of natro-opal, (a) unheated, (b) heated to 200° and (c) ignited at a temperature of about 700° were produced in the Crystallographic Institute of the USSR Academy of Sciences (E. P. Meshcheryakova under the direction of Belov). It was found that the powder patterns of the first two samples were identical and contained only five lines, whereas that of the sample heated to 700° was identical with that of quartz (Table 160).

Apart from the low-temperature quartz lines, lines of cristobalite were observed

FIG. 243. Form of natro-opal segregation (after Gerasimovskii)

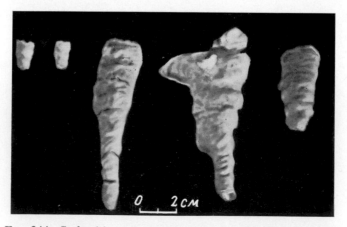

FIG. 244. Stalactitic natro-opal formations (after Gerasimovskii)

in the sample heated to 700°. Gerasimovskii therefore believes that natro-opal heated to 700° turns into a mixture of quartz and cristobalite.

Natro-opal is not soluble in HCl, HNO_3 or H_2SO_4. Its chemical composition varies (Table 161). The silica content varies from 70·68 to 79·93 per cent, the sodium oxide content from 4·17 to 9·11 per cent and the water content from 7·8 to 17·55 per cent.

Natro-opal seems to have the following empirical formula: $m\text{Na}_2\text{O} \cdot n\text{SiO}_2 \cdot p\text{H}_2\text{O}$, where $m=1$, $n=5\text{-}8$, $p=4\text{-}7$. As X-ray investigation shows, part of the fluorine in it occurs in the form of NaF.

Gerasimovskii estimated that of the general total of 5·29 per cent Na_2O (analysis 3), only 2·92 per cent was bonded with fluorine in the form of NaF, while the rest of the sodium remained in another form of bond. Some varieties of natro-opal discovered by Es'kova in the Karnasurt foyaites in 1949 contain almost no fluorine.

Apart from constituents determined by the chemical method the presence of beryllium, lead, copper, zirconium, barium, manganese and titanium in natro-opal has been established by spectrographic analysis.

TABLE 161 Chemical composition of natro-opal

Constituent	Analysis 1 per cent	Analysis 1 Molecular proportions	Analysis 2 per cent	Analysis 3 per cent	Analysis 3 Molecular proportions	Analysis 4 per cent	Analysis 5 per cent	Analysis 6 per cent
SiO_2	76·93	1·281	—	79·93	1·333	—	—	70·68
TiO_2	—	—	—	—	—	—	—	trace
R_2O_3	0·41	—	—	0·20	—	—	—	—
Al_2O_3	—	—	—	—	—	—	—	2·16
Fe_2O_3	—	—	—	—	—	—	—	0·03
CaO	0·04	—	—	0·04	—	—	—	0·17
FeO	—	—	—	—	—	—	—	—
MgO	0·04	—	—	0·08	—	—	—	0·09
MnO	—	—	—	—	—	—	—	trace
Na_2O	7·95	0·123	—	5·29	0·085	4·17	4·19	9·14
K_2O	—	—	—	0·14	0·001	0·12	0·26	0·60
H_2O^+	—	—	3·09	4·20	0·233	—	—	5·35
H_2O^-	9·03	0·502	8·50	3·60	0·478	—	—	12·20
Loss on ignition	5·53	0·308	—	—	—	—	—	—
F	—	—	1·27	0·89	0·047	0·12	0·21	0·08*
Cl	—	—	nil	—	—	nil	—	—
S	—	—	trace	—	—	—	—	—
CO_2	—	—	nil	—	—	—	—	—
Total	99·93	—	—	—	—	—	—	100·50
Analyst	Vladimirova		Arest-Yaku-bovich	Nekrasova		Sokova		Kazakova
Reference				Gerasimovskii (1940₃)				—

* F determined by Danilova

The thermal analysis curve for natro-opal produced by V. Ivanova at the Central Scientific Research Institute for Geological Survey (TsNIGRI) shows one endothermic effect at 130°, apparently connected with the separation of water, and one exothermic effect at 640°, probably due to recrystallization of the mineral (Fig. 245).

Natro-opal occurs in the Lovozero massif in the Chinglusuai valley, on Karna-surt, Sengischorr and Angvundaschorr, in the first Raslak cirque and in other regions. It is found exclusively on the weathered surfaces of rocks containing villiaumite that have been exposed to rain or running water. Recent study of core material has shown that all rocks (poikilitic syenites, eudialytic lujavrites, foyaites,

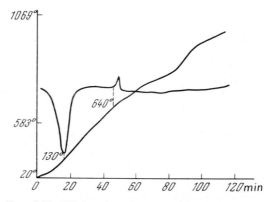

FIG. 245. Thermal analysis curve for natro-opal

aegirine- and hornblende-lujavrites and malignites) containing villiaumite on ex-posure at the surface are soon covered with a crust of natro-opal (in one to two years). The greater the amount of villiaumite in the rock the more rapidly forma-tion of natro-opal proceeds.

The formation of natro-opal is probably due to the dissolution of villiaumite and the action of solutions enriched in sodium fluoride on aluminosilicates (nephe-line, sodalite and others), as was first mentioned by Gerasimovskii.

85. Hydrogoethite
$HFeO_2$; orthorhomb; sp.gr. 3·87; H. 4

Iron hydroxides are fairly widespread in the Lovozero massif. Gerasimovskii and other investigators noted them in the rocks as secondary minerals after pyrrho-tite and pyrite in parts of Punkaruaiv, Ninchurt and the Muruai and Koklukhtiuai valleys.

Iron hydroxides are found also in large amounts in the pegmatites, as reddish-brown coatings, films, crusts and pseudomorphs after iron-bearing minerals. They are probably products of supergene alteration of sphalerite, ilmenite, aenig-matite, astrophyllite, and sometimes of aegirine and arfvedsonite. Segregations of iron hydroxides were found in considerable quantities in the Kuftn'yun pegma-tite vein and were identified by Semenov as hydrogoethite. This mineral does not form pseudomorphs after any ferruginous mineral but is represented by dark brown segregations, of irregular shape, measuring up to $5 \times 2 \times 1$ cm in the central zone albite, where it seems to have formed at the late hydrothermal stage.

86. Psilomelane

$m\text{MnO} . n\text{MnO}_2 . p\text{H}_2\text{O}$; orthorhomb.; sp.gr. 4·4—4·7; H. 4—6

Minerals of the psilomelane group are fairly widespread in the alkali pegmatites. They occur in the Karnasurt, Kuftn'yun, Lepkhe-Nel'm, Mannepakhk and other pegmatites.

The largest accumulations of psilomelane have been observed in the Karnasurt hackmanite-natrolite pegmatite stock, where it forms round or irregularly-shaped nodules and concretions, 10 cm in diameter, and also films and coatings on radiate-fibrous concretions of late aegirine (aegirine 'suns'). In the minerals of the replacement complex psilomelane forms fine dendritic films in cracks.

Colour black. Lustre submetallic, dull in loose varieties. Streak black. In thin sections black, opaque. Sometimes filled with acicular crystals of aegirine II. Recalculation of the chemical analysis (Table 162) of Lovozero psilomelane leads to the formula $\text{MnO} . 6\text{MnO}_2 . 2\text{H}_2\text{O}$. The Lovozero variety differs from normal psilomelane in having a higher potassium content (2·22 per cent K_2O) and in containing lithium (0·05 per cent Li_2O), but the tenor of these elements is insufficient to justify classifying the mineral as cryptomelane or lithiophorite.

The considerable potassium, calcium, barium and lithium content in Lovozero psilomelane indicates that we may expect to find not only cryptomelane in the massif (see description below) but also other minerals of the psilomelane group: ranciéite (Ca), romanèchite (Ba), lithiophorite (Li), as well as strontium-rich varieties.

In addition to the chemical analysis data, strontium, zinc, beryllium, titanium and arsenic have been identified spectroscopically in psilomelane. The thermal

TABLE 162 Chemical composition of psilomelane
from Karnasurt hackmanite-natrolite stock

Constituent	Content, per cent	Recalculation to 100 per cent omitting SiO_2 and R_2O_3	Molecular proportions	Calculation of molecular ratios		
SiO_2	1·57	—	—	—		
R_2O_3	1·50	—	—	—		
MnO_2	81·20	83·28	0·9580	0·9580	6·13	—6
MnO	6·10	6·26	0·0882			
MgO	0·42	0·43	0·0107			
CaO	1·54	1·58	0·0281	0·1587	1·02	—1
BaO	0·97	0·99	0·0064			
Li_2O	0·05	0·05	0·0011			
K_2O	2·22	2·28	0·0242			
H_2O	5·00	5·13	0·2847	0·2847	1·82	—2
Total	100·57	100·00	—	—		
Analyst	Pokrovskaya, 1952					

analysis curve for psilomelane (Fig. 246) shows three endothermic effects at temperatures of 100-250° (elimination of water), 630° and 970° (the last two apparently due to phase transformations).

Psilomelane occurs chiefly in the major multiple-replacement pegmatites of the poikilitic syenite complex. In time of separation it is one of the latest minerals, formed from low-temperature solutions rich in manganese, at the late hydro-thermal stage of replacement, as is indicated by its intimate association with minerals of the replacement complex.

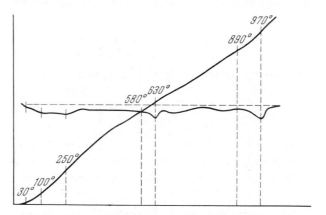

FIG. 246. Thermal analysis curve for psilomelane

87. Cryptomelane
$K_2O . MnO . 15MnO_2 . nH_2O$.; tetrag.; sp.gr. 4·3; H. 6

This mineral was first found in the Lovozero massif by Semenov, in the Kuftn'yun pegmatite vein and in the alteration zone of the Kitkuai valley.

It occurs in the form of veinlets and irregularly-shaped segregations measuring up to $2 \times 1 \times 0.5$ cm and also fills up drusy cavities in albite, in the form of charac-teristic colloform encrusting formations. In the Kuftn'yun pegmatite body it is localized in the central zeolitic zone and closely associated with albite and hydrogoethite.

The formation of cryptomelane is probably connected with processes of hydro-thermal alteration of schizolite, as is indicated by the absence of schizolite in the central zone of the pegmatite body where cryptomelane has developed. Under supergene conditions cryptomelane is covered by black films and powdery masses of manganese hydroxides (including pyrolusite).

88. Vernadite
$MnO_2 . H_2O$; sp.gr. 2·37; H. 2—3

Vernadite was found by Semenov in the central zones of certain pegmatite bodies on Lepkhe-Nel'm where it fills up cavities in natrolite druses or forms segregations measuring up to $20 \times 20 \times 10$ cm. In addition, it has been observed as a secondary mineral after schizolite. Its intimate association with natrolite in the central zones of pegmatites indicates a hydrothermal origin. In the process of alteration it becomes covered superficially with black films and powdery coatings of manganese hydroxides.

89. Hydrargillite

$Al(OH)_3$; mon.; sp.gr. 2·43; H. 3

This mineral is widely distributed in the Lovozero rocks and pegmatites and is an important component of the fine-grained aggregates of natrolite and hydrargillite (bergmannite and spreustein) formed in the process of hackmanite and nepheline replacement.

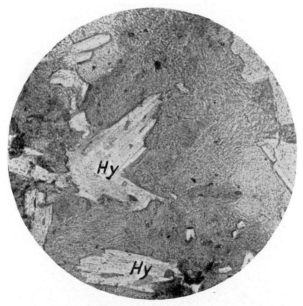

FIG. 247. Hydrargillite scales (Hy) in fine-grained natrolite. × 290. Without analyser

FIG. 248. Hydrargillite (Hy) in poikilitic syenite. Natural size

It occurs as small irregularly-shaped scales, measured in fractions of a milli-metre (Fig. 247), and forms microscopic streaks in fine-grained natrolite replacing hackmanite. In the pegmatites tabular crystals of hydrargillite can be seen in miarolitic cavities in natrolite, measuring some fractions of a millimetre to 2×2 cm in diameter and up to 5 mm in thickness. In the Kuivchorr poikilitic nepheline-syenites almost monomineralic streaks of hydrargillite, up to 2 cm thick, can be found (Fig. 248).

Hydrargillite crystals have a hexagonal-tabular habit, with the basal plane (001) most developed. Highly perfect 'micaceous' cleavage coincides with this direction.

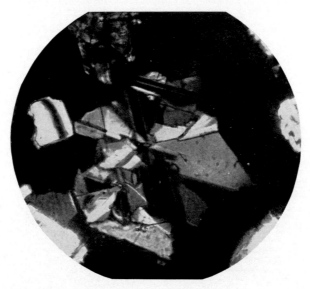

FIG. 249. Stellate outgrowth of hydrargillite. Immer-sion preparation. $\times 90$. Crossed nicols

The mineral often forms twins on (100), sometimes polysynthetic. Under the microscope the hexactinal, stellar structure of the mineral is occasionally visible (Fig. 249).

Hydrargillite crystals are usually colourless, water-clear. Sometimes a yellowish tinge is observable, probably due to the presence of iron (Karnasurt pegmatite hydrargillite). Lustre vitreous, pearly on cleavage planes. Brittle.

In thin sections, transparent. Optically biaxial, positive. Differs from natrolite in having a higher relief and twinned structure and from albite in having a smaller optic axial angle (almost uniaxial). Refractive indices: $Ng = 1.586$—1.593; $Nm = 1.578$—1.581; $Np = 1.577$—1.579; $Ng - Np = 0.004$—0.009.

The Debye powder patterns of Lovozero hydrargillite produced by Sludskaya are identical with the standard (Table 163).

Apart from aluminium, qualitative spectrographic analysis has revealed iron, magnesium, manganese, beryllium, copper, gallium, sodium, calcium and titanium in the hydrargillite from the Karnasurt pegmatites.

In time of separation hydrargillite is one of the late hydrothermal minerals and has formed as a result of the liberation of alumina during the process of replacement of hackmanite and nepheline by natrolite.

TABLE 163 Interplanar spacings of hydrargillite

Line no.	Hydrargillite from Karnasurt pegmatite		Standard hydrargillite		Line no.	Hydrargillite from Karnasurt pegmatite		Standard hydrargillite	
	I	d	I	d		I	d	I	d
1	10	4·85	10	4·82	15	6	1·690	8	1·686
2	9	4·35	6	4·34	16	1	1·661	2	1·657
3	7	3·36	—	—	17	4	1·594	2	1·589
4	6	3·19	2	3·18	18	7	1·465	8	1·458
5	4	2·66	2	2·64	19	5	1·451	4	1·441
6	8	2·46	8	2·45	20	6	1·410	4	1·408
7	8	2·40	10	2·37	21	3	1·366	4	1·360
8	6	2·27	1	2·28	22	2 double	1·322	2	1·316
9	6	2·18	6	2·15	23	1	1·262	2	1·248
10	7	2·06	8	2·04	24	5	1·213	4	1·215
11	7	2·00	8	1·99	25	1	1·200	3	1·195
12	6	2·922	6	1·92	26	1	1·183	2	1·183
13	7	1·810	8	1·798	27	2	1·148	3	1·145
14	7	1·752	8	1·747	28	3	1·126	3	1·124

90. Boehmite

AlOOH; orthorhomb.; sp. gr. 3·02; H. 3·5

Boehmite was first found in the Lovozero massif by Semenov and has not yet been definitively studied. According to Semenov a mineral similar to boehmite was found in close association with natrolite, hydrargillite and montmorillonite formed in the process of alteration of nepheline in the Kitkn'yun pegmatite vein. It is represented by very small lenticular crystals measuring up to 0·5 mm along the long axis. In optical properties and paragenesis it is similar to the Vishnev boehmite.

91. Cuprite

Cu$_2$O; cub.; sp.gr. 5·85—6·15; H. 3·5—4

Lovozero cuprite was first described by Gerasimovskii, whose data we use here. It occurs in very small amount as a secondary mineral after chalcopyrite, in which it forms fine streaks and fringes. It is present also in pegmatitic hybrid veinlets made up of zeolitized nepheline and aegirine with a small amount of sphene, manganilmenite and chalcopyrite. Under reflected light it is bluish-grey. Isotropic.

92. Villiaumite

NaF; cub.; sp.gr. 2·8; H. 3·5

Villiaumite was first detected by Gerasimovskii (1941$_3$) in the poikilitic sodalite-syenites of the Chinglusuai valley. In recent years it has been discovered that this mineral is widely distributed in the rocks and to a smaller extent in the pegmatites of the massif. It occurs as fine grains and irregularly-shaped segregations up to 1 cm in diameter. The larger sizes of segregation are characteristic of the poikilitic syenites and foyaites in the differentiated complex. The colour is carmine red. Lustre vitreous. Semi-transparent. Cleavage perfect along the cube. In thin sections pale pink to pink. Optically isotropic. Refractive index $N = 1\cdot325 - 1\cdot327$ (Gerasimovskii's data).

According to Gerasimovskii the Debye powder pattern is similar to that of artificial sodium fluoride.

Villiaumite is readily soluble in cold water, forming a colourless solution. Table 164 shows that the chemical composition is similar to the theoretical composition of sodium fluoride. Spectroscopically, silicon, aluminium, manganese, titanium, calcium, barium, copper, strontium, iron and magnesium have been detected in it, in addition to the elements identified chemically.

It has now been established that villiaumite is most widespread in rocks with a high tenor of volatile compounds and sodium. In the differentiated complex it is present in the foyaites, juvites, aegirine- and hornblende-lujavrites, malignites, urtites and ijolite-urtites. Its amount in these rocks sometimes reaches 5 per cent or, rarely, more. The maximum content is found in the foyaites, the smallest content in the urtites and ijolite-urtites. It is noteworthy that in all the rocks villiaumite occurs only at depth, where the natrolitization process is not manifested. In the surface parts of the massif it is absent. In the foyaitic horizons the maximum amounts coincide with the central parts, the foyaites of the well-differentiated parts of the complex invariably containing more of this mineral than those of the poorly-differentiated middle part. In the hornblende- and aegirine-lujavrite horizons and also in the urtites, villiaumite is most widespread in the transitional parts between these rocks and the foyaites. In the eudialytic lujavrite complex it was noted by Gerasimovskii (1941₃) only in the mesocratic eudialytic lujavrites of the Chinglusuai valley, while in the rocks of the poikilitic syenite complex it is found in the Chinglusuai valley and on Karnasurt. In the poikilitic syenites villiaumite is most widespread in the sodalitic and hackmanitic varieties, where its tenor amounts to 2-5 per cent in certain places.

TABLE 164 Chemical analysis of villiaumite (per cent)

Constituent	Lovozero	Los Island	Theoretical composition (according to formula)
F	45·28	44·2	45·24
Na	53·83	53·4	54·76
K	0·32	trace	—
Ca	—	1·2	—
Mg	—	trace	—
ZrO_2	—	1·5	—
Insoluble residue	0·84	—	—
Total	100·27	100·3	100·00
Analyst	Sokova	Pisani	—
Reference	Gerasimovskii (1941₃)	A. Lacroix (1908)	—

In the pegmatites villiaumite is present only in the undifferentiated bodies genetically connected with the foyaites of the differentiated complex and with the poikilitic syenites enriched in villiaumite in which hydrothermal replacement processes are not evident.

Both in the rocks and in the pegmatites villiaumite is a late mineral. Its segregations fill up spaces between rock-forming minerals (nepheline, microcline,

FIG. 250. Interrelationship between villiaumite (dark) and nepheline (light). ×46. Without analyser

aegirine, arfvedsonite, primary sodalite; Fig. 250) and rare-metal minerals; more rarely, it is included in late sodalite segregations.

Villiaumite is characteristically found with sodalite, lomonosovite, sphalerite, galena and molybdenite; the absence of zeolites in this paragenesis is also characteristic. These facts indicate that the mineral formed in rocks enriched in mineralizers (particularly sulphur, chlorine and fluorine), the rôle of water among these being negligible.

Under surface conditions villiaumite is leached.

93. Fluorite
CaF_2; cub.; sp.gr. 3·1—3·25; H. 4

Fluorite has been detected in the foyaites of the lower part of the differentiated complex on Karnasurt, in the poikilitic nepheline-syenites on Ninchurt, Mannepakhk and in the Ankisuai and Situai valleys and also in the Lepkhe-Nel'm, Kuivchorr and Suoluai valley pegmatites. It occurs in the form of small equant segregations or individuals of irregular shape, measuring up to 2×1 cm, more rarely as poorly-formed crystals up to 1 cm in diameter. Colour pale violet, violet, more rarely bluish-green. Sometimes colourless. Lustre vitreous. Semi-transparent to transparent. Cleavage perfect cubic. Fracture conchoidal. Brittle. Refractive index $N = 1.434$ (Gerasimovskii's data). In thin sections fluorite is colourless or pale violet. Isotropic.

The fluorite has not been chemically analysed. Apart from calcium and fluorine, the presence of strontium, aluminium, magnesium, manganese, iron, titanium and silicon has been detected spectroscopically.

Fluorite is characteristic of the contaminated rocks and pegmatites in the central and south-eastern parts of the massif, in which calcium mineralization is observable (apatite, sphene, manganilmenite, biotite and others). In the pegmatites it is usually found in the central natrolitic zones or in zeolitized parts of the outer fine-grained zones. Its association with apatite, natrolite and other zeolites indicates a hydrothermal origin.

94. Molybdenite
MoS_2; hex.; sp.gr. 4.7—4.8; H. 1

Molybdenite occurs fairly often in the Lovozero massif but in very small amount both in the rocks and in the pegmatites. It forms platy or irregularly-shaped segregations measuring up to $0.7 \times 0.5 \times 0.2$ cm or individual scales up to 5 mm in diameter. Colour blue-grey. Lustre metallic. Cleavage perfect. White under reflected light.

The mineral occurs in almost all the rocks but is most widely developed in sulphur-rich rocks in the foyaites of the differentiated complex and the poikilitic sodalite-syenites and their associated pegmatites in the Chinglusuai, Muruai, Tyul'bn'yunuai and Motchisuai valleys, in the Mannepakhk and Raslak cirques and on Punkaruaiv. It is usually closely associated with galena, sphalerite, sodalite, hackmanite, lomonosovite, and chinglusuite.

95. Galena
PbS; cub.; sp.gr. 7.4—7.6; H. 2—3

Galena occurs fairly frequently in the Lovozero rocks and pegmatites, usually forming equant 1-cm blocks or individuals, which may be up to 12 mm long and about 5 mm wide or, more rarely, cubes up to 7 mm in diameter. Cleavage perfect parallel to the cube faces. Colour grey, lustre metallic. White under reflected light. Isotropic. Spectrographic analysis shows galena from the Lepkhe-Nel'm and Malyi Punkaruaiv pegmatites to contain bismuth, silver, zinc, copper, molybdenum, barium, tellurium, thallium, gold, beryllium, magnesium, antimony, cadmium, cobalt, gallium, vanadium, strontium and titanium.

Galena is most characteristic of the foyaites of the differentiated complex and the poikilitic sodalite-syenites, where it is usually closely associated with late sodalite and natrolite. It is found in the pegmatites on Karnasurt, Lepkhe-Nel'm, Malyi Punkaruaiv and in the upper reaches of the river Suoluai. It is characteristic of large pegmatite bodies in which hydrothermal processes are far advanced, where it is localized in the central natrolitic zones, or in natrolitized parts of the outer fine-grained zones.

The close association of galena with natrolite indicates that it is of hydrothermal origin. Under surface conditions galena is sometimes replaced by cerussite (Lepkhe-Nel'm orthoclase-natrolite pegmatitic stock with apatite).

96. Sphalerite
ZnS; cub.; sp.gr. 3·5—4·2; H. 3—4

Sphalerite occurs in very small amounts in both the rocks and the pegmatites. It is represented by irregularly-shaped segregations up to 3 cm long, more rarely by poorly-formed tetrahedra up to 8 mm along the long axis. Colour yellow, yellowish-green, bluish-green, brown to black. Streak in black variety dark-brown, in brown varieties orange-yellow, in remaining varieties white. Lustre submetallic in black variety, adamantine in brown and vitreous in light varieties. The light varieties are transparent, the dark opaque. Cleavage perfect cubic, perfect octahedral in yellow varieties. Fracture uneven. Brittle. Refractive index of yellowish-green sphalerite 2·36 – 2·39. The mineral is light-grey under reflected light. Isotropic (Gerasimovskii's data).

Sphalerite dissolves in hydrochloric and nitric acids. Table 165 shows the results of chemical analysis of the green-yellow variety from the Raslak II cirque pegmatites.

In addition to the chemical analysis data the presence of manganese, silicon, cobalt, calcium, barium, silver, aluminium, beryllium, lead, magnesium, titanium, copper, cadmium, nickel, tin and gallium in sphalerite from various parts of the massif (7 samples) has been detected by spectrographic analysis.

It is noteworthy that the dark-coloured varieties contain more iron, magnesium, manganese, calcium and barium. Gallium has been found only in yellow sphalerite from the Karnasurt pegmatites.

In the non-pegmatitic rocks a yellowish-green variety of sphalerite occurs in the foyaites and urtites of the well-layered part of the differentiated complex and the poikilitic sodalite-syenites on Karnasurt and in the Chinglusuai valley.

In the pegmatites sphalerite is most widespread on Karnasurt, Lepkhe-Nel'm, Punkaruaiv and Mannepakhk, in the Second Raslak cirque and in the Chinglusuai, Tyul'bn'yunuai, Muruai and Suoluai valleys. It occurs in the pegmatitic bodies, predominantly those of the poikilitic syenite complex, in which late-hydrothermal replacement processes are strongly developed. Close association with sodalite, natrolite, analcite, ussingite, and sulphides is characteristic of sphalerite.

TABLE 165 Chemical composition of sphalerite
(Gerasimovskii's data)

Constituent	Content, per cent	Constituent	Content, per cent
Zn	66·97	Mn	trace
Fe	0·22	S	32·65
Pb	nil	Insoluble residue	0·15
Cu	,,		
Cd	,,	Total	99·99
		Analyst	Vladimirova

In time of separation the dark varieties are roughly contemporaneous with orthoclase, as can be seen from the mutual intergrowth of these minerals (Fig. 251). The light varieties are later. These occupy cracks in hackmanite, and occur in the zeolitized parts in the fine-grained zones of the pegmatites and in zeolitic zones. The light varieties of sphalerite seem to have crystallized during the hydrothermal stage at the same time as zeolites.

In the process of alteration sphalerite readily oxidizes into limonite, sauconite, calamine [hemimorphite] and other minerals.

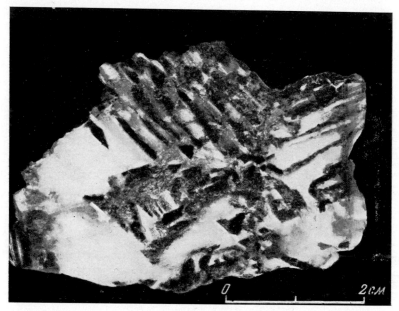

FIG. 251. Fir-tree intergrowths of sphalerite (dark) and sauconite (light) [see also p. 469-Eds]

97. Pyrite

FeS$_2$; cub.; sp.gr. 4·9—5·1; H. 6—6·5

According to Gerasimovskii, pyrite occurs in the Lovozero massif only in the non-pegmatitic rocks. It has been found in the Punkaruaiv foyaites, the Ninchurt lujavrites, the Sengischorr urtites, the poikilitic syenites with hydrosodalite in the Motchisuai and Muruai valleys and also in the eudialytites. Pyrite usually forms segregations of irregular shape and light bronze-yellow colour, up to 2 mm in diameter. Under reflected light it is yellow, with a characteristic shagreen surface. Isotropic.

98. Marcasite

FeS$_2$; orthorhomb.; sp. gr. 4·85—4.90; H. 6—6·5

Marcasite occurs rarely in the Lovozero massif and in small amounts. It is visible only under the microscope, chiefly in the non-pegmatitic rocks, as a secondary mineral after pyrrhotite, pyrite and, more rarely, chalcopyrite.

Gerasimovskii found it in the equigranular nepheline-aegirine-syenites on Punkaruaiv and Ninchurt, in the eudialytites at the head of the Chivruai valley, in the poikilitic hydrosodalite-syenites of the Motchisuai, Vel'kuai and Muruai valleys and in the amphibole- and micaceous-syenites of the Koklukhtiuai valley, where it forms xenomorphic grains measuring up to 0·8 mm and also veinlets and fringes of colloform structure in pyrrhotite.

Under reflected light its colour is creamy-white or yellowish-cream. Anisotropic.

99. Chalcopyrite

CuFeS$_2$; tetrag.; sp. gr. 4·1—4·3; H. 3·5—4

Chalcopyrite was observed by Gerasimovskii in thin sections of the lujavrites and medium-grained nepheline-syenites on Ninchurt, in the porphyritic lujavrites of Flora and in the eudalytites, in the form of xenomorphic grains measuring up to 0·5 mm. Bronze-yellow under reflected light. Isotropic. In the process of alteration it is replaced by marcasite, more rarely by covellite and cuprite.

100. Pyrrhotite

Fe$_n$S$_{n+1}$; hex.; sp.gr. 4·58—4·64; H. 4

Pyrrhotite, the commonest of the sulphide minerals in the Lovozero massif, occurs exclusively in the non-pegmatitic rocks, forming irregularly-shaped segregations measuring up to $0·5 \times 0·2 \times 0·1$ cm and, more rarely, granular aggregates measuring up to 3 cm. The colour is bronze or bronze-yellow. Streak brownish-black. Powder magnetic. Lustre metallic. Fracture uneven. Creamy-pink under reflected light. Anisotropic. The presence of cobalt, nickel, calcium, manganese, beryllium, copper and titanium has been established by spectrographic analysis.

Pyrrhotite has often been noticed in rocks rich in iron (hornblende- and aegirine-lujavrites, malignites and eudialytic lujavrites) in the differentiated and eudialytic complexes. In the poikilitic syenite complex it is found in the nepheline and hydrosodalitic varieties on Lepkhe-Nel'm, Punkaruaiv, Suoluai and elsewhere, and more rarely in the sodalitic varieties (upper reaches of the Chivruai and elsewhere). It is closely associated with other sulphides, as well as with arfvedsonite, aegirine and manganilmenite. It is replaced by marcasite and, more rarely, by limonite.

101. Covellite

CuS; hex.; sp.gr. 4·68; H. 1·5—2

Gerasimovskii observed covellite as a secondary mineral after chalcopyrite, in which it forms streaks and fringes, in one of the thin sections of the Ninchurt medium-grained nepheline-syenite.

102. Löllingite (?)

A mineral resembling löllingite was first detected by Semenov in an ussingitic pegmatitic body on the south-eastern slope of Malyi Punkaruaiv, in the form of platy crystals of a silvery white colour measuring up to $1 \times 2 \times 0.3$ cm. Opaque. Optically anisotropic. Reflective capacity greater than that of galena. After ignition becomes magnetic. Apart from the main elements—cobalt, iron and arsenic—silicon, lead, zinc, nickel, beryllium, calcium, aluminium, copper, gallium, barium, magnesium and titanium have been detected in it by spectrographic analysis.

103. Staffelite (francolite)

$(Ca, Sr)_{10}(P,C)_6O_{23}(F,OH,O)_3$; hex.; (?); sp.gr. 2·94—3·13; H. 1—4

Carbonate-apatite (staffelite) occurs fairly often in the Lovozero massif. The first indications of recognition of a white cryptocrystalline phosphate mineral, effervescent in acids, occur in Sakharov's works on the Lovozero massif. The mineral is at present being studied by Semenov and the following brief description is based on his data.

Staffelite is represented by two varieties in the Lovozero massif, one cryptocrystalline and one spherulitic. The former occurs in an orthoclase-natrolite pegmatitic stock with apatite on Lepkhe-Nel'm, where it forms compact light yellow crusts on the surface of sauconite segregations, and thin (1-3 mm) streaks in a fine-grained quartz aggregate, and also in the central zone of an orthoclase-analcite pegmatite vein on Kuivchorr as irregularly-shaped colloform segregations measuring up to $4 \times 1 \times 1$ cm, of a yellowish-white and bluish colour. Spherulitic staffelite has been found in many pegmatites on Karnasurt, Kuivchorr, Lepkhe-Nel'm, Kedykvyrpakhk and Mannepakhk, forming small radiate-fibrous spherical segregations 0·5-5 mm in diameter, of white, dark-red or light-brown colour. A concentrically zoned structure is sometimes observed in the spherulites, light-brown radiate-fibrous staffelite occurring in the centre and a white compact, sometimes columnar variety at the surface. The light-brown staffelite is weakly pleochroic from light-brown along Np to colourless along Ng. Absorption scheme: $Np > Ng$. Lustre silky or pearly, dull in cryptocrystalline varieties. Fracture conchoidal.

Staffelite is widespread in the large pegmatite bodies genetically connected with the poikilitic nepheline-sodalite-syenites of the central part of the massif. It usually occurs in the central natrolitic zones as crusts and coatings on natrolite crystals or columnar radiate-fibrous segregations in the cavities between these crystals.

Staffelite forms at the late hydrothermal stage, after natrolite, but it is not impossible that some varieties formed also under supergene conditions.

Apart from ordinary staffelite, Semenov has found strontian and magnesian varieties of this mineral in the pegmatites, and is at present studying these.

104. Calcite

$CaCO_3$; trig.; sp.gr. 2·6—2·8; H. 3

Calcite is extremely rare in the Lovozero massif, occurring exclusively in the contaminated rocks near xenoliths of Devonian augite-porphyrites (Koklukhtiuai valley). It has been observed only in thin sections in the form of a fine-grained aggregate in intimate association with cancrinite. There is a characteristic paragenesis with orthoclase, sphene, zircon, ilmenite and apatite.

105. Cerussite

$PbCO_3$; orthorhomb.; sp.gr. 6·46—6·57; H. 3—3·5

Cerussite occurs in very small amount in the Lovozero massif as a secondary mineral after galena, in the form of white ochreous crusts and coatings on the surface and in cleavage cracks in galena.

106. Ancylite

A hydrous carbonate of Sr,Ca and rare earths; rhomb.; sp.gr. 3·82—3·92, H. about 4

Ancylite was discovered by Gerasimovskii in the form of a single irregularly-shaped segregation measuring $2 \times 1·5 \times 1$ cm in area, in the pegmatites of the upper reaches of the Suoluai, in close association with catapleiite and zeolites. Colour light greenish-yellow. Porous. Easily soluble in hydrochloric acid, evolving carbon dioxide.

107. Natron

$Na_2CO_3 . H_2O$; mon.; sp.gr. 1·42—1·47; H. 1—1·5

A mineral resembling sodium carbonate (natron) was first detected in the Lovozero massif by Semenov, who is now studying it. It forms powdery masses, coatings and crusts on the surface of foyaite blocks. Effervesces violently in hydrochloric acid. According to Semenov's data the Debye powder patterns of Lovozero natron are similar to those of synthetic thermonatron.

Sodium, calcium, barium, strontium, aluminium, magnesium, manganese, iron, titanium and silicon have been detected spectroscopically in Lovozero natron. V. V. Danilova has determined 6·41 per cent of fluorine in it.

108. Jarosite

$KFe_3(SO_4)_2(OH)_6$; trig.; sp.gr. 3·15—3·26

Jarosite was first found in the Lovozero massif by Semenov, in coarse-grained, strongly ferruginous and bleached foyaites on the northern slope of Ninchurt, in the form of irregularly-shaped segregations of orange-yellow colour up to $0·5 \times 0·3$ cm in area, filling up cavities between microcline crystals.

*   *   *   *

Apart from the minerals described above, Semenov has detected in the Lovozero massif epistolite, pyrophanite, ulvöspinel, thuringite, chlorophaeite, beidellite, natrodavyne, hisingerite, polysphaerite, thorite, calcioferrite and a number of other minerals, including some new ones that are now under study.

CHARACTERISTIC FEATURES OF THE MINERALOGICAL COMPOSITION AND MINERAL-FORMING PROCESSES IN THE MASSIF

A HIGHLY characteristic feature, distinguishing the Lovozero from most other alkali massifs, is the large number and variety of mineral species occurring in it. Silicates and aluminosilicates are widely distributed in the rocks and pegmatites and make up more than 90 per cent of the volume of the massif; but of the 59 minerals belonging to these groups only 7 (nepheline, microcline, aegirine, arfvedsonite, sodalite, natrolite and albite) play an important part in its structure. The next commonest are the zirconium silicates, mainly minerals of the eudialyte-eucolite group which make up more than 4 per cent of the volume of the massif. The zirconium silicates occur in greatest quantity in the rocks and pegmatites of the eudialytic lujavrite complex. Titanium-niobium silicates, niobium-titanates, titanates and niobates make up roughly 2 per cent by volume of the massif and are concentrated in the rocks and pegmatites of the differentiated complex. The remaining mineral families—fluorides, sulphides, phosphates, oxides and the rest, play a very small part in the structure of the massif, accounting together for about 4 per cent of it. They are present in very small amount and are peculiar to certain types of rocks and pegmatites. Phosphates, fluorides and sulphides, for example, occur mainly in the non-pegmatitic rocks, whereas oxides and carbonates predominate quantitatively in the pegmatites of the poikilitic syenite complex.

A second characteristic feature of the mineralogical composition is the extremely uneven distribution of minerals in the massif. As can be seen from Table 166, the rocks of the eudialytic lujavrite complex differ from those of the differentiated complex by their higher tenor of aegirine and eudialyte and the lower tenor of feldspars. The differentiated complex is characterized by a higher tenor of apatite (0·7 per cent), which is seven times greater than the amount of this mineral in the eudialytic lujavrites, and of loparite and other niobium minerals. The poikilitic syenites differ markedly in composition from all the other rocks and from the average mineralogical composition of the massif, having a lower tenor of feldspars (21 per cent) and aegirine (14·5 per cent), and a very high tenor of sodalite (18 per cent) and hydrosodalite (18 per cent). The high content of volatile matter (water, sulphur, chlorine) in the magma of the poikilitic syenites has influenced the mineralogical composition of the rocks formed.

Table 166 shows also the maximum amounts of the principal and of some secondary and rare-metal minerals found in certain rocks of the massif. The minerals are extremely unevenly distributed throughout the massif as a whole; concentrations well above the average for the massif are to be found in certain rocks. The content of secondary and rare-metal minerals shows particularly marked fluctuations.

In addition to differences in the mineralogical composition of the principal types of rock, the proportions of the principal rock-forming minerals in particular rocks vary from one horizon to another and even within a single horizon, particularly with thickness.

A third characteristic feature of the mineralogical composition of the massif is the abundance of rare-metal minerals. Of the hundred and thirty minerals roughly half contain rare elements as their main constituents. The tenor of zirconium minerals (eudialyte-eucolite, lovozerite and others), of titanium and niobium minerals (murmanite, lomonosovite, ramsayite, lamprophyllite and others) and of rare-earth minerals (loparite, apatite and others) in certain rocks and pegmatites is sometimes considerable. In addition, accessory minerals containing thorium, beryllium and lithium (steenstrupine, hydrocerite, karnasurtite, epididymite, chkalovite, polylithionite, tainiolite and others) are found in the pegmatites.

A fourth feature of the mineralogical composition of the massif is the large

TABLE 166 Average mineralogical composition* of the Lovozero massif (per cent)

Mineral	Eudialytic lujavrite complex	Differentiated complex	Poikilitic syenite complex	Entire massif	Maximum content in rocks (per cent)	Degree of concentration
Feldspars	34	43	21	39	85	2
Nepheline	22	24	18	22	95	4
Aegirine	27	16	14·5	19	50	3
Arfvedsonite	1·7	2	1·0	2	42	42
Natrolite	4·8	6	4·3	5·5	90	18
Sodalite	1	3	18	4·0	72	18
Hydrosodalite	—	—	18	0·5	70	140
Eudialyte	8	1·9	2	4	25	6
Lomonosovite-murmanite	—	1	0·5	0·6	5	8
Lamprophyllite	0·7	0·6	0·4	0·6	2·7	4
Apatite	0·1	0·7	0·2	0·5	35	70
Villiaumite	—	0·4	0·15	0·3	5	15
Ussingite	—	0·1	0·6	0·2	10	50
Ramsayite	0·1	0·1	0·3	0·1	1	10
Pectolite	0·1	0·1	—	0·1	2	20
Rinkolite	—	0·1	—	—	3	—
Sphene	0·1	—	0·4	—	2	—
Cancrinite	—	0·1	—	—	10	—
Ilmenite	—	—	0·3	—	3	—
Other minerals	0·4	0·9	0·35	1·6	—	—
—	100·0	100·0	100·0	100·0	—	—

* Approximate, based on calculating the proportions of minerals in thin sections and allowing for the volumes of the different rock complexes.

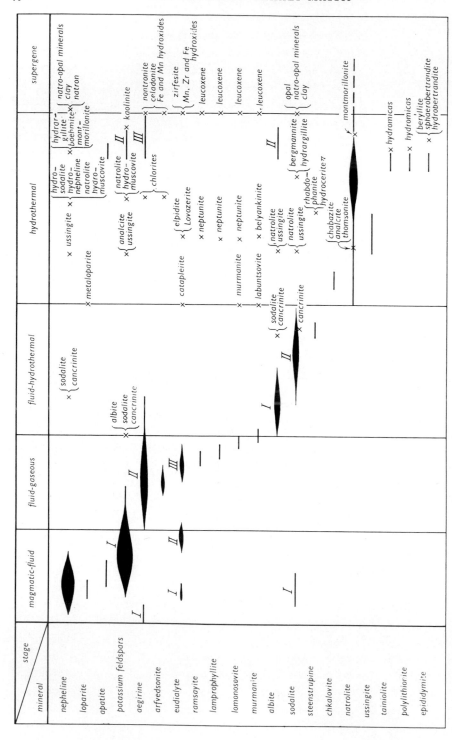

FIG. 252. Sequence of formation of principal and characteristic rare-metal minerals and replacement processes in the Lovozero massif. Crosses indicate the beginning of replacement processes; I-III: mineral generations

number of minerals containing volatile compounds (Cl, F, S and H_2O). Such minerals as sodalite, hackmanite, hydrosodalite, natrolite and ussingite are the principal rock-forming components in certain rocks and pegmatites.

The peculiarities of the chemical-mineralogical composition of the Lovozero massif are clearly evident from the existence of distinct paragenetic associations of the principal rock-forming and rare-metal minerals.

The variety of mineral species and paragenetic associations of minerals in the massif, and the sequence of mineral formation in the rocks and pegmatites are due to four main factors: (1) the chemical composition of the original magma, (2) emanation-differentiation processes, (3) the crystallization-differentiation process and (4) the influence of the country rocks (assimilation). The nature of these factors will be described below, in the chapters on geochemistry and genesis.

We have already mentioned that the formation of the Lovozero massif occupied four main, relatively clearly-marked stages: a magmatic-fluid stage, a fluid-gaseous stage, a fluid-hydrothermal stage and a hydrothermal stage (Fig. 252).

The mineralogical composition of the massif shows that these stages have been manifested in varying degrees in the different rocks and pegmatites, depending on the amount of volatile compounds in the magma at a particular period in the history of the massif: the greater the amount of these compounds, the more advanced are the later stages, as we can see from the mineral associations in the poikilitic sodalite-syenites and their pegmatites.

During *the magmatic-fluid stage* of formation of the massif the principal leucocratic rock-forming minerals—nepheline, microcline, orthoclase and, more rarely, sodalite—were the principal phases to crystallize. These minerals make up the bulk of the rocks. In certain types of rocks that crystallized from a magma with a high tenor of rare elements (zirconium, niobium, rare earths etc.), calcium and phosphorus, complex zirconium silicates (minerals of the eudialyte group), loparite and phosphates (rare-earth apatite) formed at this stage. The sequence in which these minerals separated out varies in the different complexes and types of rocks. A high alkali content in the magma and a notable predominance of sodium over potassium lead to the crystallization of sodium aluminosilicate —nepheline—followed by the formation of microcline, in the majority of the rocks. In the potassium and silica-enriched foyaites, microcline was the first to crystallize and nepheline appeared later.

In the poikilitic sodalite-syenites, which were rich in water and chlorine, sodalite crystallized during the first stage along with nepheline. In the eudialytites and eudialytic lujavrites, which are very rich in zirconium, minerals of the eudialyte group crystallized during the first stage, their formation preceding that of nepheline and microcline in the eudialytites and following that of the principal leucocratic minerals in the eudialytic lujavrites, though preceding that of aegirine II, which crystallized during the second stage.

In the floors of the urtite and the roofs of the underlying lujavrite horizons, where the crystallization of monomineralic nepheline horizons caused all components not forming part of nepheline to be concentrated downwards and produced a concentration of rare earths, titanium, niobium, calcium and phosphorus, the mineral loparite, and apatite as well, formed during the magmatic-fluid stage.

In the pegmatitic process the first stage manifested itself in the formation of reaction borders and of the outer fine-grained zones of the pegmatite bodies, and also in the crystallization of the bulk of the high-temperature potassium feldspars. In the pegmatites genetically associated with the contaminated rocks an excess of assimilated iron separated during the first stage in the form of aegirine I.

During *the fluid-gaseous stage* of the evolution of the massif the bulk of the dark-coloured and rare-metal minerals crystallized—aegirine II, arfvedsonite, eudialyte, mesodialyte, lomonosovite, ramsayite and other titanium-niobium, zirconium and rare-earth minerals, the dark minerals (aegirine II and arfvedsonite) crystallizing before the rare-metal minerals in most of the rocks. The eudialytic lujavrites, the loparite-bearing rock types, the eudialytites and the pegmatites were exceptions to this rule. The reason for the high zirconium concentration in the eudialytic lujavrites is that the eudialyte minerals formed earlier than aegirine II and arfvedsonite. In the pegmatites, the bulk of the titanium, zirconium and niobium minerals crystallized before aegirine II.

At this stage in the evolution of the massif volatile compounds begin to play an important part. Processes of replacement of aegirine by arfvedsonite begin and in certain rock horizons rich in volatile components (the hornblende-lujavrites) arfvedsonite forms instead of aegirine. The replacement of manganilmenite and aenigmatite by ramsayite and astrophyllite and of ramsayite by murmanite probably occurred at this stage.

In the urtite horizons the bulk of the rare-metal minerals crystallized during the first stage; in the foyaite and lujavrite horizons, on the other hand, where the calcium content was lower and the silica content a good deal higher, they crystallized mainly during the second stage in the form of complex sodium titano-niobium silicates—lomonosovite, lamprophyllite, ramsayite and others.

In the lujavrites of the middle poorly-layered part of the differentiated complex, where the division between the calcium and sodium mineral associations is not so pronounced as in the upper part of the complex, rinkolite, a complex titano-silicate of rare earths, calcium and sodium, has often formed instead of lomonosovite minerals.

In the eudialytic lujavrites, where because of the high zirconium content minerals of the eudialyte group crystallized during the first stage, rare-metal minerals formed during the second stage in very small amount, since the bulk of the titanium, niobium and rare earths entered into the crystalline structure of the eudialyte minerals.

In the rocks of the differentiated complex the minerals of the eudialyte group formed during the second stage side-by-side with titanium and niobium minerals, the amount of mesodialyte among the minerals of the eudialyte group increasing with depth, proportionately to the calcium tenor in the rocks.

In the contaminated rocks and their associated pegmatites and also in the hybrid pegmatites, simple zirconium silicates (zircon) and the calcium minerals of titanium, niobium and rare earths (ilmenite, sphene, pyrochlore, apatite and others) formed at this stage instead of loparite and complex zirconium and titanium silicates.

In the large pegmatite bodies high-temperature potassium feldspars continued to crystallize during the second stage and at the end of the period of their formation, titanium, zirconium and niobium minerals (eudialyte, ramsayite, murmanite, lamprophyllite and others) separated; this stage was followed by the crystallization of aegirine II.

In *the fluid-hydrothermal stage* of development of the massif volatile compounds, particularly chlorine, sulphur, fluorine, and carbon dioxide, played an immense part and replacement processes began. In the pegmatites, hackmanite crystallized in the form of large monomineralic segregations and the formation of aegirine II and high-temperature rare-earth and titanium minerals continued (steenstrupine, manganosteenstrupine, nordite, chinglusuite and others). In the non-pegmatitic rocks albite, sodalite, villiaumite and cancrinite crystallized out.

Albitization developed extensively both in the rocks and in the pegmatites, appearing at an earlier stage in the rocks (the fluid hydrothermal stage), while in the pegmatites the formation of albite was delayed till the low-temperature stage (hydrothermal).

Sodalitization is extensive in the rocks, and to a lesser extent in the pegmatites, of the poikilitic syenite complex. The highest tenor of sodalite is observable in the poikilitic-sodalite syenites. In the rocks of the differentiated and eudialytic lujavrite complexes sodalitization increases as the rocks become more leucocratic. Sodalite develops most importantly after nepheline, more rarely after potassium feldspars and albite. Replacement of potassium feldspars by albite and sodalite is accompanied by the liberation of considerable amounts of silica and potassium, which then enter into the composition of natrolite and hydromuscovite.

Cancrinitization is little evident in the Lovozero massif. It is characteristic of the nepheline varieties of rocks with a high content of calcium. Cancrinite is most widely found in the poikilitic nepheline-syenites and to a smaller extent in the urtites and ijolite-urtites, in which it develops after nepheline. More rarely it replaces albite and late sodalite. The essential prerequisite for cancrinite formation is the presence in solution of high concentrations of calcium and carbon dioxide or of sulphur compounds. These conditions occur when the country rocks are assimilated by an alkali magma, or in the floors of urtite horizons, where calcium, phosphorus and volatile compounds including carbon dioxide and sulphur compounds accumulate along with rare elements as a result of crystallization differentiation and emanation processes. Cancrinitization normally coincides with such regions.

The hydrothermal stage, one of the most important in the history of the massif, has left a deep impress on its chemical-mineralogical composition. It was at this stage that a whole series of mineralogical associations formed from elements liberated by the decomposition of early minerals together with those of late residual solutions. In the large complex replacement pegmatite bodies the crystallization of minerals from residual solutions continued during this stage, and natrolitic zones as well as albite, ussingite and analcite replacement zones were formed. In the pegmatites of the poikilitic syenite complex (Table 169, p. 514) rare-earth and thorium minerals (belovite, karnasurtite, hydrocerite, rhabdophanite etc.) formed, along with lithium minerals (tainiolite, polylithionite, hydrotainiolite and others) and beryllium minerals (epididymite, eudidymite, chkalovite, beryllite etc.).

A characteristic feature of the hydrothermal process is the formation from early aluminosilicates (nepheline, microcline, sodalite etc.) of a complex of minerals with a high tenor of silica, water and aluminium. Intensive zeolitization, ussingitization, hydromuscovitization, kaolinization and the formation of late rare-metal minerals occurred.

Zeolitization is widespread both in the rocks and in the pegmatites. The commonest zeolites are natrolite and hydrosodalite; analcite, hydronepheline, thomsonite and chabazite occur more rarely. In the differentiated complex the natrolitization process is most extensively developed in the upper part. In each three-component stratal group natrolitization is most intensive in the floors of the urtite horizons. In the rocks of the eudialytic lujavrite and differentiated complexes intensive natrolitization has developed also at the contacts with poikilitic syenite intrusions and with the pegmatites, that is, in parts where water and other volatile compounds are concentrated. In the non-pegmatitic rocks of the massif natrolite has formed mainly in the process of replacement of higher-temperature leucocratic minerals, such as nepheline, sodalite and feldspars, by hydrothermal solutions.

Hydrosodalite formation is widespread in the poikilitic nepheline-syenites. The mineral does not occur in the other rocks and pegmatites. Analcite forms in both the rocks and the pegmatites mainly in the course of sodalite zeolitization. Hydronepheline is extremely rare, occurring in the midst of spreustein formed after nepheline.

The most favourable conditions for chabazite and particularly for thomsonite formation occur in the contaminated pegmatites of the poikilitic syenite complex, as a result of their enrichment in calcium in the process of assimilation of the Devonian rocks. These minerals develop in the course of natrolite replacement.

Ussingitization is most intensive in the poikilitic sodalite-syenites and their associated pegmatites and also in the sodalitized foyaites of the upper part of the differentiated complex. In the rocks the greatest amounts of ussingite regularly coincide with sections where natrolite is poorly developed. Ussingite forms in the process of sodalite, microcline, albite and, more rarely, nepheline replacement.

In the complex replacement pegmatites of the poikilitic syenite complex ussingite replaces sodalite and prismatic natrolite and is in turn replaced by a fine-grained aggregate of natrolite and analcite.

In the process of zeolitization and ussingitization of potassium feldspars, and also in the process of albitization, large amounts of potassium were liberated, and partially entered into the composition of hydromuscovite, neptunite, late potassium feldspar, lithium micas, hydrosodalite, aegirine III, cancrinite and a great many other minerals (see Table 169, p. 514).

Hydromuscovitization has developed most intensively in the foyaite horizons of the upper part and in some urtite and lujavrite horizons in the lower part of the differentiated complex. In the upper foyaites the greatest amounts of hydro-muscovite coincide with the central parts of the horizons, while in their roofs and floors natrolite replacement processes have developed. Hydromuscovite develops in the foyaite horizons after both microcline and nepheline, but chiefly after nepheline in the lujavrites and urtites in the lower part of the massif. Its formation is probably due to the influence of low-temperature hydrothermal solutions enriched in potassium as a result of the albitization and zeolitization of feldspars, and also of nepheline, which sometimes contains up to 5 per cent K_2O.

Kaolinization is evident to a very small extent in the contaminated poikilitic syenites with hydrosodalite, in which the kaolinite has developed after orthoclase. Kaolinite occasionally occurs in the pegmatites in close association with albite formed at the replacement stage.

Another common phenomenon during the hydrothermal stage was the replacement of rare-metal minerals. Minerals of the eudialyte group, for example, were replaced by lovozerite, catapleiite and elpidite, while loparite was replaced by metaloparite, these processes being accompanied by loss of alkalis and addition of water, and by the concentration of zirconium and titanium in the newly-formed minerals. The replacement by lovozerite of minerals of the eudialyte group occurred most intensively in the deeper parts of the massif, where there had been little zeolitization. In regions of intensive zeolitization and in surface outcrop zirfesite forms after eudialyte, and lovozerite is oxidized and decomposes. Catapleiite and elpidite develop after eudialyte chiefly in the pegmatites.

The formation of murmanite after lomonosovite is widely developed in the rocks and closely connected with zeolitization processes (see description of lomonosovite, murmanite and natrolite). Under the action of hydrothermal solutions and, possibly of surface waters, the sodium phosphate that had been partially fixed in the minerals of the hydrothermal stage (silicophosphates) was leached out of lomonosovite. In the pegmatites replacement of lomonosovite by murmanite is rare. The low tenor of phosphorus and the high tenor of volatile compounds, including water, in the pegmatitic melt caused murmanite to crystallize instead of lomonosovite.

The replacement of murmanite by belyankinite and labuntsovite is observed only in the pegmatites. Under the influence of hydrothermal solutions murmanite oxidizes and breaks down into a series of oxides, with formation of belyankinite; more rarely, labuntsovite forms after it.

The formation of minerals in the rhabdophanite and hydrocerite group after rare-earth minerals is observed only in the complex replacement pegmatites of the poikilitic syenite complex and occurs under the influence of hydrous solutions with the participation of phosphorus partially borrowed from decomposed rare-earth minerals of the steenstrupine, apatite, belovite etc. group. The replacement

LAM 2K

of minerals in the steenstrupine group is accompanied by the formation of rhabdophanite, hydrocerite and leucoxene mixtures which cannot easily be separated.

The formation of neptunite after titanium minerals is widespread in the
pegmatites but rare in the non-pegmatitic rocks. Neptunite replaces ramsayite,
lamprophyllite and murmanite. It forms most frequently after ramsayite by the
agency of solutions enriched in manganese and potassium. Manganese, apart
from occurring in solutions, also appears as a result of the breakdown of schizolite
and of titano-niobium silicates.

The lithium minerals tainiolite and polylithionite are converted into hydromicas under the action of low-temperature hydrothermal solutions. The beryllium
minerals chkalovite, epididymite and eudidymite are replaced by beryllite, sphaerobertrandite and gel-bertrandite, sodium and possibly silica being lost from the
early beryllium minerals in the process. The replacement of lithium and beryllium
minerals is observed only in the complex replacement pegmatites of the poikilitic
syenite complex.

At the end of the hydrothermal stage chlorites formed after aegirine and
arfvedsonite; marcasite, covellite, cuprite and hydrogoethite formed after the
higher-temperature sulphides pyrite, pyrrhotite, sphalerite etc., and sauconite
formed after sphalerite.

During the hydrothermal stage, then, various minerals formed in the different
rocks, depending on their chemical-mineralogical composition and the composition
of the solutions. Under some conditions this process meant the formation of
natrolite; under others, of hydrosodalite and, under still others, of hydromuscovite,
ussingite and other minerals.

Weathering processes, which are not much in evidence in the Lovozero massif,
entail loss of alkalis, calcium, strontium, chlorine and silica from the minerals,
with concomitant concentration of oxides and hydroxides of elements such as
aluminium, iron, titanium, zirconium and manganese, whose compounds readily
hydrolyse. The sodium, chlorine and silicon leached in the supergene process
partially enter into reaction with other compounds and combine as opal, natro-
opal, natron, nontronite and other minerals.

During the supergene stage the main minerals to form are zirfesite, after
minerals of the eudialyte group, and leucoxene after titanium minerals (ramsayite,
lamprophyllite, murmanite, belyankinite, nenadkevichite, labuntsovite, vinogradovite, neptunite and others). Such minerals as lovozerite, schizolite, chlorite
and vernadite decompose in the process into a series of manganese, iron and
zirconium hydroxides. Hydrogoethite forms after the ferruginous minerals—
pyrite, pyrrhotite, ilmenite, aenigmatite, astrophyllite, aegirine and arfvedsonite.
Psilomelane and cryptomelane are converted into pyrolusite. Sphalerite is replaced by calamine. In the process of decomposition of nepheline, hydromuscovite
and aegirine a complex of clay minerals is formed (montmorillonite, nontronite,
celadonite, halloysite and others). Leaching of villiaumite, with the formation of
large amounts of natro-opal and also of opal and natron, covering the alkali rock
surfaces, is characteristic.

The relative importance of the different stages in the evolution of the massif varies. The first stage accounted for the crystallization of minerals forming about 60 per cent of its volume, the second stage for roughly 25 per cent and the third and fourth stages for about 15 per cent. Minerals formed during the supergene stage play a very small part in the make-up of the massif.

The number of mineral species and varieties has conspicuously increased from the first to the fourth stages. During the first stage only 10 minerals formed; during the second, 14; during the third, 15 and during the fourth more than 80. Each stage was characterized by its own peculiar chemical-mineralogical features. During the first stage sodium and potassium aluminosilicates formed, along with sodium calcium and rare-earth titanoniobates and calcium and rare-earth phosphates. In the second stage, on the other hand, Na, Fe and Mg, as well as Ti, Nb and Zr silicates formed. Sodium aluminosilicates (sodalite, hackmanite, cancrinite) and sodium fluoride—villiaumite—containing large amounts of volatile compounds (F, Cl, S, CO_2, SO_3) belong to the third stage. The fourth stage was marked by the crystallization mainly of hydrous sodium and, more rarely, calcium (in the pegmatites) aluminosilicates.

The bulk of the rare elements—niobium, tantalum, rare earths, zirconium, titanium and thorium—in the massif was connected with the first two stages in the form of loparite, apatite, eudialyte and minerals of the lomonosovite-murmanite group.

In the pegmatites, in contrast to the non-pegmatitic rocks, rare-earth and thorium minerals did not crystallize in the first stages, but the concentration of these elements increased towards the third stage, in which they combined to form steenstrupine, manganosteenstrupine, nordite, chinglusuite and other minerals. In addition, with the crystallization differentiation of the pegmatitic melt, the concentration of lithium and beryllium increased towards the fourth stage, leading to the formation of polylithionite, tainiolite, epididymite and other rare-metal accessory minerals.

The increase in the rôle of volatile compounds, particularly water, from the early to the late stages of the mineral-formation process is exceptionally clear in the Lovozero massif. In the third, and especially in the fourth stage, these compounds reach concentrations sufficient to form minerals in their own right. The abundance of mineral species, especially of rare-metal minerals, formed during the hydrothermal stage, is due to the increase in the concentration of rare elements and volatile components in the late solutions and to the interaction of these solutions with all the minerals formed earlier. As a result, the number of components of the system taking part at this stage of the mineral formation process was incomparably greater than at earlier stages.

PART FOUR

GEOCHEMISTRY AND GENESIS

INTRODUCTION

THE genesis of any intrusion, its geology, mineralogy and geochemistry are determined by the intricate geological and physico-chemical factors operative throughout a long period in the history of the earth's crust. A study of the geochemistry and genesis of intrusions therefore reduces itself, in the main, to establishing the factors governing the spatial and temporal distribution of minerals and rocks and to explaining the behaviour and combination of the chemical elements in the processes of mineral formation. From an analysis of the data we have been able to establish the features of the chemical composition of the Lovozero massif, to trace the geochemistry of individual elements, to reveal the reasons for their concentration, dispersion and redistribution in space and time and to indicate the associations of chemical elements conducive to the formation of the various mineralogical parageneses typical of the genesis of the massif.

The behaviour of elements in magmatic processes largely depends on the chemical composition of the magma and their initial concentration and relationship in the magma. A study of the chemical composition of the Lovozero massif enables us to understand the sequence in which the minerals have separated. When this study is combined with analysis of the physico-chemical situation it reveals the features that govern the distribution of the elements, minerals and rocks. Each chemical element has many diverse properties, but it is only in association with other elements and under various physico-chemical conditions that a given element can reveal certain properties. This fact is very important for an understanding of the geochemistry and genesis of the massif.

The geochemical fate of the elements, their concentration, dispersion and redistribution, leading to the formation of different partial magmas and mineralogical parageneses are determined in the main by the following principal factors operative in the formation of the massif: (1) the initial concentration of the elements in the magma, (2) alteration in the composition of the magma through assimilation of the country rocks, (3) emanation processes, (4) crystallization differentiation, (5) isomorphism and (6) transport by hydrothermal solutions.

The chemical composition of the magma, i.e. the initial concentration of chemical elements in it, determines the behaviour of the elements, governs their incorporation in various mineral structures in different quantitative ratios and thus determines the sequence of separation of the minerals. When we speak of the main rock-forming, rare or trace elements, we mainly have in mind their quantitative relationship in the earth's crust. In geochemical analyses of the various rocks of the crust the concept of main rock-forming and rare elements becomes relative, since the same chemical elements may be main, secondary, rare or trace elements in different rocks. In this context the time when they enter the solid phase and their position in the crystalline structures will be quite different.

The behaviour of a given element will not be the same in the mineral-forming processes of different magmas. Thus, for example, beryllium scarcely replaces silicon at all in the granitic process because of excess of silicic acid and is concentrated in the late stages of the process in pegmatitic and greisen parageneses, mainly as beryl. The behaviour of this element is different in the alkaline process, where it replaces silicon in aluminosilicate structures owing to silica deficiency in the alkali magma. In the granitic process titanium forms oxides, either independently or in company with iron (brookite, ilmenite etc.). In an alkali magma it forms various titanosilicates of sodium, iron etc. and niobotitanosilicates and complex oxides with niobium and rare earths. Owing to the low content of aluminium in the magma that element does not form part of the rock-forming minerals in ultrabasic rocks and is concentrated in the late stages of the crystallization process as various chrome-spinellids.

The initial concentration of the chemical elements thus determines the time at which they enter the solid phase, thereby affecting the geochemical fate of other elements remaining in the melt and controlling the processes of their isomorphism. This is all indicative of the great part played by the law of mass action in the geochemical history of the formation of intrusions. This law has left its mark on the geochemistry of mineral-formation processes in the Lovozero alkali massif and has largely determined the fate of the individual elements of which it is composed.

As well as the law of mass action, the interrelations of the main rock-forming and rare elements and their minerals have also been of importance in the formation of the massif.

Assimilation of the country rocks leads to enrichment of the magma with elements not initially present. This affects the balance of the chemical elements and leads to the appearance of different paragenetic mineral associations. When magma is injected into rocks of greatly differing composition its own composition is sometimes greatly affected and hybrid rocks are formed. The assimilation by the magma of rocks of similar composition does not play an important part in the geochemistry of the intrusion. The country rocks of the Lovozero massif differ fundamentally from alkali rocks and their assimilation by the alkali magma has therefore had some effect on the geochemistry of individual elements.

Emanation processes have played a very important part in the formation of the Lovozero massif. The fact that a whole series of chemical elements concentrated in the apical parts of intrusions or in certain areas are transported in the volatile state leads to the formation of special paragenetic complexes of minerals and rocks and to the generation of pegmatitic foci. An element can pass into the volatile state only if other elements, capable of combining with it to form readily volatile compounds, are simultaneously present in the melt. Moreover, a given chemical element will not always pass into a volatile state, even if it forms volatile compounds. Thus, in the presence of water vapour at a given temperature and pressure some compounds may be hydrolyzed and may lose the capacity to pass into a volatile state. In the Lovozero alkali massif emanation processes led to the formation of volatile-enriched rocks—eudialytic lujavrites, poikilitic syenites and pegmatites.

Crystallization differentiation is one of the leading factors in the development of geochemical processes. The Lovozero alkali massif is the clearest example of a well-differentiated massif. In their degree of differentiation all other intrusions, whatever their chemico-mineralogical composition, are intermediate between non-crystalline and well-differentiated massifs of the Lovozero type.

In nature there are two extremes in the filling of space, which are related to the way in which the magma solidifies. The magma sometimes solidifies as a vitreous rock, but on other occasions the process of crystallization proceeds slowly so that separate minerals and, in some cases, monomineralic rocks are formed.

Under these conditions the history of the chemical elements will naturally differ. In the first case they are more or less evenly distributed throughout the rock, reflecting their distribution in the magma, and there are no local concentrations. With crystallization differentiation the chemical elements are grouped and differentiated from one another to form separate minerals or monomineralic rocks. The formation of the rock-forming minerals and their regular distribution in the Lovozero massif determines the geochemistry of all the other elements and their position in time and space.

This makes clear the extremely important part played by the isomorphous substitution processes that determine the place of a given rare or trace element in a mineral and in the massif as a whole. The capacity of chemical elements to replace each other isomorphously in the crystalline structures of minerals because of the similarity of their crystallochemical properties leads to dispersion of a number of elements and facilitates the formation of special associations of chemical elements. Description of the isomorphism of individual elements reveals the major rôle of a small group of elements. These serve as the nuclei of isomorphous associations that form independent families owing to their common physico-chemical and crystallochemical properties. These associations are normally based on the main rock forming elements (sodium, potassium, silicon, aluminium, iron, less frequently niobium, rare earths, titanium and zirconium). The formation of the Lovozero alkali massif in all the complexity of its chemico-mineralogical and chemical processes is revealed by the varying combinations of elements in associations, and the combinations of the associations with one another.

Hydrothermal processes play a considerable part in the redistribution of chemical elements. Hydrothermal solutions decompose previously-formed minerals and rocks, dissolve combined chemical elements and transport them for considerable distances and even outside the intrusions in some cases. In other cases, alteration in the chemical composition and thermodynamic properties of these solutions leads to the refixing of water-soluble compounds in the solid phase by transition to an insoluble state. This alters the previously-formed paragenetic complexes.

All these interacting and mutually conditioning factors determine the nature of mineral development in the formation of intrusions.

CHAPTER ONE

CHEMICAL COMPOSITION OF THE MASSIF

CHEMICAL, spectroscopic, X-ray spectrographic, radiochemical and polarographic analysis have established the presence of 67 chemical elements in the Lovozero alkali massif, 14 of which are elements of the rare-earth group.

Table 167 gives the mean chemical composition of the massif as calculated from 39 complete chemical analyses of average samples of different rocks and from special determinations of a number of elements. In calculation of the composition of the massif allowance was made for the mean chemical composition of all the main varieties of nepheline-syenite: urtites, foyaites, aegirine- and hornblende-lujavrites, malignites, eudialytic lujavrites, porphyritic lujavrites, poikilitic syenites, etc. The mean chemical composition of the complexes was arrived at by consideration of the volume of these types of rock within each complex. The mean composition of the massif was then determined by taking into consideration the volume of each rock complex.

The mean chemical composition of the Lovozero massif differs from the mean composition of the nepheline syenites (given by Daly, 1936) in having a slightly lower content of silicon, aluminium, potassium, calcium and phosphorus and a greater content of iron, sodium, titanium and magnesium, apparently owing to the presence of more aegirine and less orthoclase in the massif. Unfortunately, there is no information on the content of S, F, Cl or of the rarer elements (Zr, Nb, R.E., Li, Be, etc.) either in Daly or in the other reviews of nepheline-syenites and rocks in general.

The Lovozero massif differs from massifs of acid, intermediate and ultrabasic rocks in having a high content of sodium, potassium, ferric iron, titanium and manganese and in being poor in calcium, magnesium and ferrous iron. Its content of Si and Al is midway between that of granites and basic rocks. The chemical composition of the Lovozero massif is closest to that of granites, from which it differs in having a higher content of Ti, Al, Fe^{3+}, Mn, Na, K, H_2O and a considerably lower content of Si. These points are illustrated by Fig. 253.

Table 168 compares the mean content of 29 chemical elements in the Lovozero massif with the clarkes of igneous rocks (as given by Rankama, 1949) and gives the clarkes of the chemical elements in the Lovozero massif calculated by the authors. In this massif the figures show an increased content of strontium, sodium, potassium, manganese, the rare earths, niobium, zirconium, beryllium, lithium, gallium, radium, thorium, uranium, fluorine, sulphur and chlorine and a greatly

TABLE 167　Mean chemical composition of main rock complexes and of the Lovozero massif as a whole

Constituent	Differentiated complex	Eudialytic lujavrite complex	Poikilitic-syenite complex	Massif as a whole	Nepheline-syenites	Granites[1]	Gabbros[2]	Amphibolitic peridotites[3]
SiO_2	53.44	51.79	47.46	52.57	54.63	69.21	48.24	40.91
TiO_2	0.90	1.89	0.60	1.19	0.86	0.41	0.97	0.65
ZrO_2	0.26	1.84	0.19	0.75	—	—	—	—
$(Nb,Ta)_2O_5$	0.13	0.12	0.12	0.13	—	—	—	—
RE_2O_3	0.18	0.10	not determined	0.15	—	—	—	—
Ra	3.2×10^{-10}	6.8×10^{-10}	2.6×10^{-10}	4.25×10^{-10}	—	—	—	—
Th	7×10^{-3}	5×10^{-3}	9.45×10^{-3}	6.53×10^{-3}	—	—	—	—
U	1.25×10^{-3}	2×10^{-3}	0.76×10^{-3}	1.47×10^{-3}	—	—	—	—
Al_2O_3	19.59	13.70	21.46	17.88	19.89	14.41	17.88	5.00
Ga_2O_3	0.0104	0.0052	0.039	0.0096	—	—	—	—
Fe_2O_3	5.04	7.25	4.24	5.68	3.37	1.98	3.16	4.64
FeO	1.30	1.79	1.05	1.44	2.20	1.67	5.95	7.97
MnO	0.22	0.62	0.26	0.35	0.35	0.12	0.13	0.17
MgO	0.96	1.79	0.70	1.20	0.87	1.15	7.51	30.82
CaO	1.52	3.25	1.60	2.06	2.51	2.19	10.99	4.41
SrO	0.15	0.06	not determined	0.11	—	—	—	—
BaO	0.12	0.11	"	0.11	—	—	—	—
BeO	0.0031	0.0050	0.0028	0.0039	—	—	—	—
Na_2O	9.08	9.41	12.56	9.39	8.26	3.48	2.55	0.58
K_2O	5.61	3.68	4.63	4.95	5.46	4.23	0.89	0.36
Li_2O	0.05	0.06	not determined	0.05	—	—	—	—
P_2O_5	0.13	0.30	0.36	0.20	0.25	0.30	0.28	0.03
V_2O_5	0.004	0.008	not determined	0.005	—	—	—	—
SO_3	0.25	0.58	"	0.34	—	—	—	—
S	—	—	0.54	0.03	—	—	—	—
Cl	0.13	0.18	1.02	0.20	—	—	—	—
F	0.14	0.22	0.08	0.16	—	—	—	—
H_2O	0.97	1.22	3.21	1.18	1.35	0.85	1.45	4.56
Total	100.13	99.97	100.13	100.12	100.00	100.00	100.00	100.10
Volume of massif, per cent	63	31	6	—	—	—	—	—
Number of analyses	24	5	10	39	43	—	—	—

[1,2,3] taken from Daly (1936)

reduced content of calcium, magnesium, silicon, oxygen, vanadium, nickel and copper.

If the chemical elements of the massif are divided [on the basis of concentration] into decades (in which the amount present differs by a factor of 10) and compared with the clarkes of igneous rocks, the following picture is found. In the first decade (which comprises elements with clarkes of 10 per cent or above)

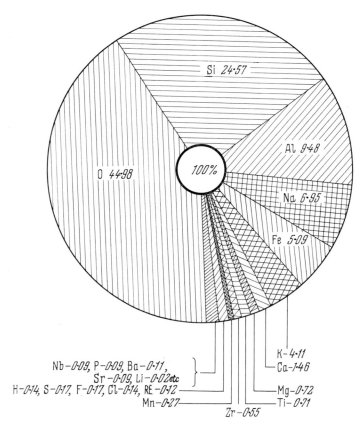

FIG. 253. Diagram of proportions of the chemical elements in the rocks of the Lovozero massif

come O and Si, which are the same as in the first decade of clarkes of the earth's crust; but their amount is somewhat less in the Lovozero massif. The second decade for the Lovozero massif includes chemical elements whose content is between 1 and 10 per cent (Al, Fe, Na, K and Ca). An element missing from this group in the Lovozero massif by comparison with igneous rocks is magnesium. The third decade includes chemical elements present in tenths of one per cent: H, Mg, Ti, Zr, Mn, R.E., S, Cl, and F. This group differs from the third decade for igneous rocks in that it includes magnesium from the previous group and a number of elements from groups lower down the scale: Zr, R.E., Cl, S and F. The fourth decade, consisting of chemical elements with clarkes measured in hundredths of a per cent, contains Nb, P, Ba, Sr and Li. This group differs from that for igneous rocks in containing Li and Nb from groups lower down the scale, and in not containing V and Cu.

The fifth decade of clarkes for the Lovozero massif contains Be, Ta, V, U, Th, Ga and Cu, which are present in thousandths of one per cent. This group differs from the groups for igneous rocks in containing elements that are mainly found in the next (sixth) group. Cu is an exception, since its content in the massif is lower than the clarke. We did not calculate the mean content for other elements present in the massif in ten thousandths of one per cent or less.

Thus the chemical composition of the magma of the Lovozero alkali massif has the following main features to distinguish it from the mean composition of igneous rocks (see Table 168):

(1) a high content of alkalis which are considerably more plentiful than aluminium, coupled with a lack of silicon;

(2) a marked predominance of sodium over potassium;

(3) a marked predominance of sodium over calcium;

TABLE 168 Comparison of the mean content of chemical elements in the Lovozero massif with the clarkes of the earth's crust

Elements	Differentiated complex	Eudialytic lujavrite complex	Poikilitic syenite complex	Lovozero massif	Clarke for igneous rocks according to Rankama and Sahama (1949)	Abundance ratio for massif
Hydrogen	0·11	0·15	0·39	0·14	0·13	1·08
Lithium	0·02	0·03	not det.	0·02	$6·5 \times 10^{-3}$	3·08
Beryllium	0·0011	0·0018	0·0010	0·0014	6×10^{-4}	2·33
Oxygen	45·27	44·37	45·05	44·98	46·60	0·97
Fluorine	0·14	0·22	0·18	0·17	0·060	2·83
Sodium	6·72	6·97	9·30	6·95	2·83	2·46
Magnesium	0·58	1·07	0·42	0·72	2·09	0·34
Aluminium	10·39	7·26	11·38	9·48	8·13	1·16
Silicon	24·98	24·21	22·19	24·57	27·72	0·89
Phosphorus	0·06	0·13	0·16	0·09	0·12	0·75
Sulphur	0·10	0·23	0·54	0·17	0·052	3·27
Chlorine	0·13	0·18	1·02	0·20	0·0314	6·37
Potassium	4·66	3·05	3·84	4·11	2·59	1·59
Calcium	1·08	2·31	1·14	1·46	3·63	0·40
Titanium	0·54	1·13	0·36	0·71	0·44	1·61
Vanadium	0·002	0·004	not det.	0·003	0·015	0·20
Manganese	0·17	0·48	0·20	0·27	0·10	2·7
Iron	4·54	6·47	3·79	5·09	5·00	1·02
Strontium	0·13	0·05	not det.	0·09	0·03	3·00
Nickel	0·0004	0·0003	,, ,,	0·0003	0·008	0·04
Copper	0·0017	0·0014	,, ,,	0·0016	0·007	0·23
Gallium	0·008	0·004	0·027	0·0074	$1·5 \times 10^{-3}$	4·93
Zirconium	0·19	1·36	0·14	0·55	0·022	25·0
Niobium	0·09	0·08	0·08	0·09	0·0024	37·5
Barium	0·11	0·10	not det.	0·11	0·0250	4·4
Rare earths	0·15	0·09	,, ,,	0·12	$1·48 \times 10^{-2}$	8·1
Radium	$3·2 \times 10^{-10}$	$6·8 \times 10^{-10}$	$2·6 \times 10^{-10}$	$4·25 \times 10^{-10}$	8×10^{-11}	5·31
Thorium	7×10^{-3}	5×10^{-3}	$9·45 \times 10^{-3}$	$6·53 \times 10^{-3}$	$1·15 \times 10^{-3}$	5·7
Uranium	$1·25 \times 10^{-3}$	2×10^{-3}	$0·76 \times 10^{-3}$	$1·47 \times 10^{-3}$	4×10^{-4}	3·67
Total	100·17	99·95	100·20	100·11	—	—

(4) increased content of the rare elements, including Zr, Nb, R.E., Ti, Li, Be and Ga;

(5) increased content of Mn, Sr and Ba;

(6) high content of volatiles—Cl, F, S and H_2O.

The molecular ratio of $Na_2O + K_2O$ to Al_2O_3, normally known as the agpaitic ratio, averages 1·16 for the Lovozero massif. Rocks with an agpaitic ratio of less than 1 are very rare and can be classified as miaskitic varieties of nepheline-syenites formed by the assimilation of the country rocks.

The high content of alkalis in the magma and their considerable predominance over aluminium led to the crystallization mainly of sodium-potassium alumino-silicates (microcline, orthoclase, nepheline, sodalite, albite, natrolite etc.), which account for approximately 75 per cent of the volume of the massif. During the crystallization of the magma deficiency of silica and aluminium oxide relative to the alkalis was made good by ferric oxide and a number of rare elements (titanium, niobium, zirconium etc.) and this led to the formation of iron-containing alkaline minerals (aegirine, arfvedsonite) and a whole series of titanosilicates and titano-niobosilicates (loparite, murmanite, lomonosovite, lamprophyllite, ramsayite etc.) and also to the wide development of zirconium silicates (eudialyte, mesodialyte, lovozerite, catapleiite etc.).

The presence of more Na than K led to wider development of sodic alumino-silicates (nepheline, albite, natrolite, sodalite, hydrosodalite, ussingite, analcite etc.) than of potassic aluminosilicates (microcline, orthoclase, micas and clay minerals).

The marked predominance of sodium over calcium caused the wider develop-ment of sodic than calcic minerals in the Lovozero massif both among the main rock-forming minerals (nepheline, aegirine, arfvedsonite, sodalite, natrolite, albite etc.) and among the rare-metal minerals (loparite, murmanite, lomonosovite, lamprophyllite, ramsayite etc.) and the secondary and accessory minerals. The sodium content of the massif is approximately seven times the calcium content and this was responsible particularly for the formation of practically pure albite.

There are very few independent calcic minerals in the massif (apatite, sphene, etc.). This element is usually incorporated in sodic minerals in various ratios, mainly in zirconium silicates, titanosilicates and a number of secondary and accessory minerals.

The increased content of rare elements (titanium, zirconium, rare earths, niobium, lithium, beryllium and gallium) in the magma led to the formation of a large number of accessory rare-metal minerals and also to the incorporation of these elements as isomorphous substituents in the crystal lattices of other minerals.

The increased content of manganese, strontium and barium in the magma led, in addition to incorporation of these elements into the crystalline structures of the rock-forming minerals, to the formation of a considerable quantity of the minerals of these elements at certain stages in the formation of the massif (lamprophyllite, nordite, belovite, labuntsovite, apatite etc.).

The high content of volatiles in the massif (Cl, F, SO_3, S, CO_2 and H_2O) led to slower cooling of the magma, to better differentiation and to the formation of minerals including these compounds. Water, chlorine, fluorine and sulphur are also included in the composition of the main rock-forming minerals (natrolite, sodalite, hydrosodalite, ussingite etc.), the rare-metal minerals (rinkolite, lamprophyllite, eudialyte etc.) and some of the secondary and accessory minerals (villiaumite, fluorite, cancrinite etc.).

CHAPTER TWO

THE GEOCHEMISTRY OF INDIVIDUAL ELEMENTS

ISOMORPHOUS replacements play an extensive part in the geochemistry of a mineral-forming process as intricate as that which occurred in the formation of the Lovozero massif. Almost every chemical element isomorphously replaces several others and is, in its turn, replaced by a number of others. Thus, sodium replaces potassium, calcium and lithium within certain ranges and is in its turn replaced by these elements in other minerals. Titanium and zirconium are replaced by niobium and tantalum, calcium by the rare earths and sodium, and so on. To avoid duplication in the geochemical treatment of a given element we shall therefore concentrate on aspects of the replacement of other elements by the element under consideration.

Geochemical analysis of individual elements is complicated by the lack of structural formulae for the majority of the rare-metal minerals.

All the chemical elements of which the Lovozero alkali massif is made up can be provisionally divided into four groups: (1) major (rock-forming), (2) secondary and volatile, (3) rare and (4) accessory (see Fig. 254). The distribution of the chemical elements in the minerals of the massif is shown in Table 169.

I. MAJOR ELEMENTS

The major elements (Na, K, Al, Si, Fe and O) account for 90-95 per cent of every rock type in the massif (94·21 per cent on average for the massif) and are the main components of the rock-forming minerals and of the majority of the secondary, rare-metal and accessory minerals.

Sodium (11)

Sodium played an important part at all stages in the formation of the massif. The overwhelming majority of the main rock-forming minerals (nepheline, aegirine, arfvedsonite, albite, natrolite, sodalite, analcite and ussingite) are aluminosilicates and sodium silicates. Sodium is present in considerable quantities in the potassic aluminosilicates—microcline and orthoclase. In conjunction with the other features of the chemical composition of the magma, the high content of this element led to the incorporation of sodium as a major element in most of the rare-metal and secondary minerals (eudialyte, ramsayite, lamprophyllite, lomonosovite, murmanite, chinglusuite etc.) in addition to the formation of the aluminosilicates proper.

From chemical and spectrographic analysis data Na is present in more than 70 minerals, in 40 of which it is the main component (see Table 169). The sodium content of the minerals in the massif varies between fractions of one per cent and 53 per cent. It is present in a considerable number of minerals in isomorphous substitution for calcium and potassium. The mean sodium content of the massif is 6·95 per cent, which is approximately 2·5 times its clarke for igneous rocks. The mean content of this element is approximately the same in the rocks of the differentiated complex and the eudialytic lujavrite complex (6·72-6·97 per cent) and is close to its mean content in the massif. Its content is increased (9·30 per cent) in the rocks of the poikilitic syenite complex. There are considerable variations in the sodium content of different rocks in each complex (Table 170). The general pattern of sodium distribution in the rocks of the massif naturally coincides in the main with the distribution of the rock-forming minerals (see Fig. 24).

The sodium content of the pegmatites is similar to that of the parent rocks. Thus, for example, in the hackmanite-natrolite stock on Karnasurt mineralogical calculations show that Na_2O is 14·43 per cent, which is slightly higher than the figure for the sodalitic poikilitic syenites (12·78 per cent).

The greater part of the sodium in the massif was incorporated in the first and second stages of the process of mineral formation, mainly as nepheline and aegirine. Its highest concentration in the solution was probably typical of the third stage, when the history of a considerable part of the sodium atoms was intimately connected with the history of chlorine, sulphur and fluorine. Sodium fluoride separated as villiaumite, while sodium chloride and sodium sulphide were incorporated in the crystal structure of hackmanite.

There were fundamental changes in the history of sodium during the hydrothermal stage of the mineral-forming process when the hydrothermal solutions reacted with the minerals of earlier phases (nepheline, microcline etc.) to return considerable quantities of sodium to the solution for incorporation into the newly-formed minerals of the hydrothermal process (natrolite, hydrosodalite, albite, ussingite, lovozerite etc.).

In the hypergene stage the sodium minerals, including sodalite, hackmanite and villiaumite, were decomposed and such minerals as natro-opal, natron and nontronite, among others, were formed.

In the mineral formation of the Lovozero massif the isomorphism of sodium is isovalent for potassium and lithium and heterovalent for calcium. All the sodic minerals of the massif contain small quantities of potassium and calcium and all the potassium, calcium and lithium minerals contain a small amount of sodium. Isomorphous replacement of calcium by sodium is most typical for a number of rare-metal minerals (loparite, apatite etc.). In loparite, in which the Na_2O content varies between 8·08 and 8·53 per cent (CaO, 3·7-5·6; SrO, 1·76-3·35; $R.E._2O_3$, 30-35·29; Nb_2O_5—7·09-12·81 and TiO_2, 38·86-41·45 per cent) sodium is incorporated in the crystal lattice to compensate for the valency deficiencies that arise

TABLE 170 Sodium content in the rocks of the massif

Differentiated complex	Na$_2$O content, per cent	Eudialytic lujavrite complex	Na$_2$O content, per cent	Poikilitic syenite complex	Na$_2$O content, per cent
Foyaites	8·53-9·70	Eudialytic lujavrites:		Poikilitic sodalite-syenites	12·78
Juvites	13·79	Melanocratic	10-24	Poikilitic nepheline-syenites	6·94-12·36
Urtites	10·95-16·57	Leucocratic	9·00	Poikilitic hydrosodalite-syenites	11·49-12·36
Aegirine-lujavrites:		Porphyritic lujavrites	9·09-9·32	Tawites	15·21-16·28
Melanocratic	8·65-11·64	Porphyritic juvites	10·36-14·9		
Mesocratic	7·01-8·97				
Leucocratic	7·07				
Hornblende-lujavrites	8·28-12·50				
Malignites	7·94-11·42				

TABLE 171 Potassium content in the rocks of the massif

Eudialytic lujavrite complex	K$_2$O content, per cent	Differentiated complex	K$_2$O content, per cent	Poikilitic syenite complex	K$_2$O content, per cent
Eudialytic lujavrites	3·74-6·03	Foyaites	6·23-7·61	Poikilitic sodalite-syenites	5·58
Melanocratic eudialytic lujavrites	1·86	Juvites	3·67	Poikilitic nepheline-syenites	4·08-7·44
Leucocratic eudialytic lujavrites	3·60	Urtites and ijolite-urtites	2·40-5·47	Poikilitic hydrosodalite-syenites	3·80-4·77
Eudialytites	1·35-2·56	Aegirine-lujavrites:		Tawites	1·34-1·62
Porphyritic lujavrites	3·85-6·56	Melanocratic	2·50-3·26		
Porphyritic juvites	2·90-5·80	Mesocratic	6·23		
		Leucocratic	6·70		
		Hornblende-lujavrites	5·30-5·31		
		Malignites	1·11-2·17		

in the replacement of calcium by rare earths and titanium by niobium (see 'Niobium and the rare earths'). Chemical analyses of loparite from different rocks show that increasing contents of sodium, niobium, and the rare earths entail a reduction in its calcium content. The recently-discovered niobian variety of loparite (Tikhonenkov, 1957) that contains 26·26 per cent $(Nb, Ta)_2O_5$ and 10·56 per cent Na_2O, shows that there exist varieties of loparite in which titanium is even more extensively replaced by niobium with a corresponding increase in the sodium content.

The replacement of calcium by sodium in apatite is effected with its simultaneous replacement by rare earths. A similar picture is found with a number of other rare-metal minerals at later stages—rinkolite, nordite, karnasurtite, pyrochlore, belovite etc.

The history of sodium is most intricate in the minerals of the eudialyte-eucolite group. The greater part is to be found in eudialyte as a major constituent. The variable amount of it in the minerals of this group and the existence of calcic members point to isomorphism between these elements. Small quantities of sodium are apparently incorporated in these minerals to compensate valencies on replacement of calcium by rare earths and of zirconium by niobium.

The isomorphism of $Na \rightleftarrows Ca$ is also widely evident in the zeolites formed in the fourth stage of mineral formation, in which there is direct replacement of calcium by sodium following the pattern $Ca^{2+} \rightleftarrows 2Na^{1+}$.

Potassium (19)

Potassium has played an important rôle, although less significant than that of sodium, in the formation of the massif. Its content in the massif is only slightly more than half that of sodium.

There are varying amounts of potassium in more than 70 minerals of the Lovozero massif (see Table 169). It is the main constituent of microcline, orthoclase, biotite, kupletskite, mangan-neptunite, astrophyllite, tainiolite, polylithionite, hydromica, cryptomelane, jarosite, celadonite and other minerals. Considerable quantities of potassium are also present in a number of other rock-forming and rare-metal minerals—nepheline (up to 5 per cent K_2O), aegirine (up to 1·13 per cent), arfvedsonite (up to 3 per cent), eudialyte (up to 1·2 per cent), lamprophyllite (up to 1·5 per cent) etc.

The mean content of potassium in the massif is 4·11 per cent, i.e. approximately 1·5 times the clarke for potassium in igneous rocks. Potassium content is highest in the differentiated complex (4·66 per cent), average in the poikilitic syenite complex (3·84 per cent) and minimum in the eudialytic lujavrite complex (3·05 per cent). This distribution of potassium in the rock complexes is conditioned mainly by the content in the rocks of orthoclase and nepheline, which are the main carriers of potassium. There are considerable variations in the mean content of potassium in different types of rock. It can be seen from Table 171 that there is an increase in potassium content in the rocks of the eudialytic lujavrite complex and the differentiated complex as between melanocratic and leucocratic varieties.

In the poikilitic syenites the highest content of this element is typically found in nepheline and sodalite varieties and the lowest content in tawites, which are very poor in potassium feldspar.

The potassium content of the pegmatites is probably no lower than that of the corresponding parent rocks, owing to the abundance in them of potassium feldspars, which are always main minerals. It should be noted that the potassium content of microcline from the pegmatites is higher than that in microcline from the rocks.

The main mass of the potassium was taken up in the first stage of mineral formation by the crystallization of potassium feldspars and nepheline. According to approximate mineralogical calculations more than 95 per cent of the total amount of potassium was taken up at this time. In the second stage of mineral formation small amounts of potassium were incorporated in aegirine, arfvedsonite, eudialyte, astrophyllite and other minerals. In the fluid-hydrothermal stage it did not form its own minerals but was incorporated by isomorphous substitution in other minerals.

Potassium had an interesting geochemical history in the hydrothermal stage, when considerable quantities passed into solution with sodium and other elements owing to intensive decomposition of potassium feldspars and nepheline. Crystallization of these solutions led to the formation of a whole series of late potassic and potassium-containing minerals (hydromica, hydrosodalite, lovozerite, mangan-neptunite, catapleiite etc.).

Considerable amounts of late microcline, tainiolite, polylithionite and other minerals were formed in the fully-differentiated pegmatites at this stage (see Table 169). At late periods in the hydrothermal stage there was movement of potassium and sodium, especially in poikilitic syenites and the pegmatites associated with them, in connexion with the development of kaolinization processes and with the formation of minerals of the montmorillonite and halloysite group.

In the hypergene stage endogenous minerals were destroyed and hypergene minerals, including potassium-containing minerals (jarosite, celadonite, nontronite etc.), were formed. Most of the minerals that contain small quantities of potassium are sodic, and the potassium in them replaces sodium isomorphously. The K_2O content of nepheline reaches 5 per cent with a corresponding reduction in Na_2O. In the structure of this mineral there are spaces between the silica tetrahedra of sufficient size to take potassium atoms without impairing the stability of the crystalline structure. Since nepheline is usually formed earlier than potassium feldspars its crystalline structure may also be built at the expense of potassium, since the latter is still in an uncombined state.

Isomorphous replacement of small quantities of sodium by potassium is also widespread in arfvedsonite, aegirine, albite, sodalite, natrolite, ussingite, analcite, hydrosodalite and other minerals. Isomorphous inter-replacement of potassium and sodium over wider ranges is found in mangan-neptunite. The K_2O content of this mineral may reach 6·3 per cent for an Na_2O content of up to 8·78 per cent.

In addition to the isovalent isomorphism of K and Na, heterovalent isomorphism of potassium with calcium, strontium and barium is also of common occurrence in minerals of the massif. Replacement of calcium by potassium is typical of the calcic rare-metal minerals, in which potassium and sodium atoms partly replace calcium atoms to maintain the electrostatic equilibrium destroyed on replacement of calcium by rare earths or of titanium and zirconium by niobium (see 'Niobium and the rare earths'). This type of isomorphism is typical of loparite, apatite, belovite, eudialyte, nenadkevichite, sphene and other minerals. In calcic zeolites (apophyllite, chabazite and thomsonite, potassium is apparently incorporated on the pattern $K^{1+} + Na^{1+} \rightarrow Ca^{2+}$.

It is interesting to note the replacement of strontium and barium by potassium in lamprophyllite and labuntsovite. Compensation of valencies is here affected by simultaneous replacement of titanium by niobium on the pattern $K^{1+} + Nb^{5+} \rightarrow Ba^{2+} + Ti^{4+}$; $K^{1+} + Nb^{5+} \rightarrow Sr^{2+} + Ti^{4+}$.

Aluminium (13)

It is a special feature of the geochemistry of aluminium in the massif that in quantity it is extremely deficient in relation to the alkalis. The behaviour of aluminium (4-fold or 6-fold co-ordination) is here decided in favour of the acid properties owing to the general silica deficiency; Al atoms replace Si atoms in silica tetrahedra to form the skeletons of such minerals as potassium feldspars, nepheline and sodalite. It is only in the late stages in the formation of the massif, when the aluminosilicates and silicates are being decomposed and the relationship between the alkalis, silica and aluminium is undergoing change, that aluminium begins to function as a cation and to form a number of hydroxides, micas and clay minerals, in the structures of which it is in 6-fold co-ordination.

Varying amounts of aluminium are found in almost all the minerals of the massif, but it is only a major constituent in 28; these include nepheline (32·29 per cent Al_2O_3), microcline (18·38-19·75 per cent), orthoclase (19·02-20·98 per cent), sodalite (29·32-32·42 per cent), albite (20 per cent), hydrosodalite (28·36 per cent), natrolite (26·51-27·92 per cent), ussingite (17·15-17·67 per cent) and analcite (24·77 per cent) (see Table 169). Apart from aluminosilicates, aluminium forms hydroxides in the Lovozero massif (boehmite and hydrargillite, which arise in the replacement of nepheline and sodalite by natrolite). In pegmatites these minerals sometimes crystallize directly out of the solutions in the replacement stage.

In addition to the formation of its own minerals, various quantities of aluminium are present in nearly all the silicates, zirconosilicates and titanoniobosilicates, as well as in titanoniobates and the oxides and hydroxides of iron, titanium and manganese and in phosphates.

The mean content of aluminium in the massif is 9·48 per cent, which is somewhat higher than its clarke in igneous rocks. It is unevenly distributed among the various rock complexes of the massif. The highest content is typical of the poikilitic syenite complex (averaging 11·38 per cent) and the lowest of the eudialytic lujavrite complex (7·26 per cent). The mean content of aluminium in the differentiated complex is 10·39 per cent, i.e. similar to that in the poikilitic syenites.

The reduced content of aluminium in the rocks of the eudialytic lujavrite complex is associated with the presence in these rocks of large quantities of minerals of the eudialyte-mesodialyte group, which contain scarcely any aluminium. The distribution of aluminium among different types of rock is uneven within each complex (Table 172) owing to the nature of the distribution of minerals rich and poor in aluminium throughout the massif. This applies particularly to nepheline, potassium feldspars, sodalite, natrolite and aegirine (see Fig. 24, p. 57).

The Al_2O_3 content of the hackmanite-natrolite stock on Karnasurt is 22·52 per cent, which is close to its content in the poikilitic sodalite-syenites (21·90 per cent) with which this pegmatitic body is genetically associated. This illustrates the similarity between the aluminium content of the pegmatites and the corresponding parent rocks.

The greater part of the aluminium was taken up in the first stage of mineral formation in nepheline and potassium feldspars. Mineralogical calculations show that approximately 90 per cent of all the aluminium was combined in minerals during the first stage. During the fluid-gaseous stage aluminium did not play a significant part in mineral-forming processes. Small quantities were incorporated in aegirine and arfvedsonite and in rare-metal minerals. In the third stage in the formation of the massif the importance of aluminium increased, as is shown by the wide development of albitization, sodalitization and cancrinitization. In the fourth (hydrothermal) stage there was some upheaval in the geochemistry of aluminium, as in that of the other main elements. Decomposition of previously-formed aluminosilicates led to the entry into solution of additional amounts of aluminium and to the formation of such aluminium minerals as hydrosodalite, natrolite, boehmite, hydrargillite and others. In addition to natrolite a large amount of late microcline, albite, analcite, ussingite and a number of micas and clay minerals were formed in the pegmatites at this stage.

It has already been mentioned that the isomorphism of aluminium and silicon is prevalent in the minerals of the massif and can be observed in all silicates and aluminosilicates at all stages in the process of mineral formation. The ratio of aluminium to silicon in the aluminosilicates varies between 1 : 1 and 1 : 3, in the silicates it does not exceed 1 : 10. Compensation of valencies on replacement of silicon by aluminium is effected by simultaneous uptake of calcium by these minerals on the pattern $Al^{3+} + Ca^{2+} \rightarrow Si^{4+} + (Na, K)^{1+}$.

In the hydrothermal stage aluminium is also incorporated in the crystalline lattices of silicophosphates (karnasurtite and hydrocerite) in place of silicon to maintain the electrostatic equilibrium destroyed on replacement of silicon by phosphorus (see 'Phosphorus'). At this stage there is also pronounced isomorphous inter-replacement of aluminium by magnesium, trivalent iron and titanium. Isomorphous replacement of magnesium by aluminium is typical of lithium micas (tainiolite and polylithionite) and clay minerals of the montmorillonite group. In these cases compensation of valencies is effected by simultaneous replacement of the second magnesium atom by sodium and lithium on the pattern $Al^{3+} + (Na, Li)^{1+} \rightarrow 2Mg^{2+}$.

Replacement of trivalent iron by aluminium is found in goethite. Insignificant amounts of aluminium are incorporated in the crystalline lattices of titanium oxides (rutile, brookite and anatase) in which it probably replaces titanium isomorphously together with trivalent iron and niobium (see 'Niobium') or creates bands of $(Fe, Al)_2O_3$ of varying thickness in the crystalline structure of TiO_2.

Silicon (14)

The typical geochemical feature of silicon in the Lovozero massif is its extreme deficiency in relation to the other main rock-forming elements, which largely determines its geochemistry and fundamentally affects the distribution of both main and rare elements in the minerals.

The mean silicon content in the Lovozero massif is 24·57 per cent whereas in other alkali massifs its content is 25·13 per cent, in granites 33·20 per cent and in the earth's crust 27·6 per cent. The great deficiency of silicon along with that of aluminium and the excess of alkalis leads to the formation of minerals incompletely saturated with silica, such as nepheline, sodalite, hydrosodalite, cancrinite and the complex rare-metal minerals—eudialyte, ramsayite, lamprophyllite, murmanite and others. A higher content of silicon in alkali massifs gives rise to a quite different paragenetic mineral complex: biotite, sphene, pyrochlore, apatite, ilmenite, zircon and others, in which nepheline is reduced, sometimes to the point of disappearance, and there is increased content of potassium feldspars. A similar mineral paragenesis is also created on assimilation of rocks richer in silica by an alkali magma.

Despite the great deficiency of silica, silicon is a fundamental constituent of 70 minerals in the Lovozero massif owing to the surplus of alkalis and the deficiency of aluminium, and is in a dispersed state in 26 minerals (see Table 169). Except for the main rock-forming minerals (nepheline, microcline, aegirine, arfvedsonite, albite, sodalite, natrolite and eudialyte), however, most of the silicon minerals play an insignificant part in the composition of the massif.

Mean silicon content in the massif (24·57 per cent) is 3·15 per cent lower than the silicon clarke for igneous rocks. Silicon content falls slightly between the differentiated complex and the poikilitic syenites (from 24·98 to 22·19 per cent). In the eudialytic lujavrite complex it is 24·21 per cent.

Silicon is unevenly distributed in each rock complex. SiO_2 content in the rocks of the differentiated complex fluctuates between 57·41 and 34·98 per cent, the highest content being found in the aegirine-lujavrites (51·39-57·41 per cent SiO_2), the foyaites (51·55-56·09 per cent) and the hornblende-lujavrites (52·48-54·08 per cent), with the lowest in the malignites (34·98-40·54 per cent) and the urtites (37-44·4 per cent). Thus, silica content in the rocks of the differentiated complex is highest in rocks rich in microcline and aegirine and lower in nepheline-bearing varieties.

Silica content in the rock varieties of the eudialytic lujavrite complex varies between 47·13 and 55·36 per cent; a gradual increase as the varieties become more leucocratic is a typical feature. In the rocks of the poikilitic syenite complex

TABLE 172 Aluminium content in the rocks of the massif

Eudialytic lujavrite complex	Al₂O₃ content, per cent	Differentiated complex	Al₂O₃ content, per cent	Poikilitic syenite complex	Al₂O₃ content, per cent
Eudialytic lujavrites	12·88-18·42	Foyaites	19·69-25·31	Poikilitic sodalite-syenites	21·90
Melanocratic eudialytic lujavrites	11·30	Juvites	27·76	Poikilitic nepheline-syenites	19·83-24·45
Leucocratic eudialytic lujavrites	13·84	Urtites and ijolite-urtites	20·94-39·28	Poikilitic hydrosodalite-syenites	19·94-22·73
Porphyritic lujavrites	15·95-17·41	Aegirine-lujavrites:		Tawites	21·74-22·31
Porphyritic juvites	14·44-17·93	Melanocratic	13·96-17·94		
		Mesocratic	14·41-17·22		
		Leucocratic	20·85		
		Hornblende-lujavrites	13·50-15·91		
		Malignites	7·35-11·20		

TABLE 173 Iron content in the rocks of the massif

Eudialytic lujavrite complex	Content, per cent		Differentiated complex	Content, per cent		Poikilitic syenite complex	Content, per cent	
	FeO	Fe₂O₃		FeO	Fe₂O₃		FeO	Fe₂O₃
Eudialytic lujavrites:			Foyaites	0·47-0·71	2·45-4·12	Poikilitic sodalite-syenites	0·85	5·18
Melanocratic	2·02	9·38	Juvites	0·93	2·78			
Leucocratic	2·47	6·06	Ijolite-urtites	0·28-1·02	2·70-4·64	Poikilitic nepheline-syenites	0·30-1·73	2·27-5·19
Mesocratic	2·01-3·44	5·0-9·8	Urtites	0·11-0·47	2·07-5·36			
Porphyritic lujavrites	0·76-1·6	6·64-8·04	Aegirine-lujavrites:			Poikilitic hydrosodalite-syenites	1·12-1·73	2·19-4·26
Porphyritic juvites	1·36-1·45	4·49-6·64	Melanocratic	0·58-3·03	6·86-10·16	Tawites	1·20-1·33	6·69-6·80
Eudialytites	1·46-4·69	4·04-6·08	Mesocratic	1·48-3·36	4·17-8·60			
			Leucocratic	0·88	3·03			
			Hornblende-lujavrites	2·90-4·53	2·86-5·10			
			Malignites	0·70-1·41	4·23-10·78			

silicon content varies between 44·30 and 50·54 per cent and decreases as the sodalite content increases.

It is apparent that silicon content is slightly higher in the pegmatites of the massif than in the parent rocks, as is shown by their mineralogical composition. There are only small amounts of nepheline in the pegmatites, which are mainly composed of potassium feldspar and aegirine. The increase in SiO_2 concentration in the large fully-differentiated pegmatites towards the end of the process is shown by the formation of high-silicon minerals (albite, microcline, micas, epididymite etc.) in the hydrothermal stage, proceeding as far as the separation of free silica (quartz and chalcedony).

The major part of the silicon in the massif (60 per cent) passed out of solution in the first stage, on the crystallization of nepheline and potassium feldspar. Approximately 25 per cent of the SiO_2 passed out of solution in the second stage, during the crystallization of aegirine II, arfvedsonite and titanium, zirconium, niobium and other minerals. Approximately 15 per cent of the SiO_2 was accounted for in the third and fourth stages, in the crystallization of albite, sodalite, hydro-sodalite, natrolite and other minerals (10 per cent in the third stage and approximately 5 per cent in the fourth).

Apart from its rôle as a major constituent in most of the minerals, silicon is found as isomorphous substituent in certain minerals. Thus, small amounts are incorporated in the crystal lattices of loparite and apatite in the first stage of mineral formation, where they probably replace titanium and phosphorus iso-morphously. On replacement of pentavalent phosphorus by tetravalent silicon in apatite the reduction of positive valencies in the cation group is probably compen-sated by a simultaneous reduction of negative valencies in the anion group by replacement of part of the oxygen by hydroxyl, as can be seen from chemical analyses of apatite.

In the third and fourth stages silicon probably isomorphously replaces alu-minium in hydrargillite in addition to its incorporation in small quantities in titanium minerals (metaloparite, brookite, rutile etc.) and isomorphous replace-ment of phosphorus (in belovite, staffelite [francolite] etc.). Here the valencies are compensated by the simultaneous incorporation of lower-valency cations (such as magnesium and iron, which are present as admixtures in hydrargillite) with silicon in the crystal lattice of the mineral.

The presence of silicon in villiaumite, fluorite, and the sulphides and hydroxides of iron and manganese is clearly due to mechanical admixtures.

Iron (26)

The marked predominance of ferric over ferrous iron is a most important feature of the geochemistry of iron in the Lovozero massif, which distinguishes it from other iron-enriched igneous rocks. The preponderance of alkalis over aluminium and the silica deficiency led to the incorporation of the greater part of the iron in aluminosilicates and silicates in trivalent form to compensate for the deficiency of aluminium.

Some iron is to be found in practically every mineral of the massif (see Table 169). It is a major constituent (more than 5 per cent) of more than 25 minerals: aegirine (21·02-28·58 per cent Fe_2O_3 and 1·35-8·14 per cent FeO), arfvedsonite (10·85-13·85 per cent FeO and 5·01-8·61 per cent Fe_2O_3), astrophyllite (21·27-26·71 per cent FeO and 2·76-6·66 per cent Fe_2O_3), aenigmatite (31·50 per cent Fe) and 6·28 per cent Fe_2O_3) etc. The main mass of the iron in the massif is concentrated in aegirine and arfvedsonite, and only small quantities are found in the other minerals.

The mean content of iron in the massif is 5·09 per cent, which is near its clarke for igneous rocks. The element is unevenly distributed between the different rock complexes. Its content is highest in the rocks of the eudialytic lujavrite complex (6·47 per cent), average in the rocks of the differentiated complex (4·54 per cent) and least in the poikilitic syenites (3·79 per cent). The iron is also unevenly distributed between the different rock types in each complex (Table 173). There is a regular increase in iron content from leucocratic to melanocratic varieties in each rock complex and in each rock-type.

The mean content of iron in the pegmatites is approximately the same as its average content in the parent rocks. Mineralogical calculations show that the mean content of iron in the swell of the hackmanite-natrolite stock is 3·15 per cent, which is slightly lower than its content in the poikilitic syenites.

During the first stage in the formation of the massif, small quantities of iron were dispersed in the main leucocratic minerals (nepheline and potassium feldspars and in loparite). The actual ferruginous minerals to be formed in this stage were aegirine I, titan-låvenite and manganilmenite, which do not play a special part in the composition of the massif. Most of the iron was incorporated in the second stage in aegirine II, arfvedsonite, aenigmatite, eudialyte and other rare-metal minerals. In the third stage the iron was concentrated in the minerals of titanium (chinglusuite and narsarsukite) and the rare earths (steenstrupine, nordite etc.), but small quantities were incorporated in the crystal lattices of aluminosilicates (albite and sodalite) and on rare occasions formed actual sulphide minerals (pyrrhotite). Certain amounts of iron were included in almost all the minerals in the hydrothermal stage and 7 actual ferruginous minerals were formed (aegirine III, hydrogoethite, löllingite, chlorite, pyrite, marcasite and chalcopyrite). Only small quantities of these 7 minerals are found and they do not play a special rôle in the structure of the massif.

Isomorphous replacement of aluminium, titanium, zirconium, manganese, magnesium and zinc by iron is to be found in the minerals of the Lovozero alkali massif. Isomorphous replacement of aluminium by trivalent iron is apparent in all the aluminosilicates and aluminium hydroxides from both early and late stages in the formation of the massif. This is indicated by the constant presence of ferric oxide in nepheline, microcline, orthoclase, albite, sodalite, hydrosodalite, ussingite, natrolite, halloysite, hydromica, hydrargillite etc. in quantities between 0·10 and 2 per cent.

Isomorphous replacement of titanium and zirconium by iron is typical of most of the titanium and zirconium minerals, and it is probable that in this case one titanium or zirconium atom was replaced by ferrous iron and the other two atoms by niobium (see 'Niobium'). This type of isomorphism is found in ramsayite, titan-lǎvenite, lamprophyllite, narsarsukite, eudialyte and other minerals, and is probably due to the predominance of ferrous over ferric iron in these minerals. When titanium and zirconium are replaced by ferric iron (loparite, labuntsovite, murmanite, rutile, eudialyte, zircon etc.) niobium is incorporated with iron in the crystal lattices of the minerals. Here isomorphism follows the pattern: $Fe^{3+} + Nb^{5+} \rightarrow 2(Ti, Zr)^{4+}$.

Isomorphous replacement of manganese by iron is widely manifested in genthelvite, the minerals of the astrophyllite group (kupletskite), neptunite, steenstrupine, ilmenite, chlorites, and in schizolite, chinglusuite, nordite and manganese hydroxides. The isomorphism of ferrous iron with magnesium is typical of arfvedsonite and magnesium micas (biotite and tainiolite). Isomorphism of ferrous iron with zinc is found in genthelvite and sphalerite.

Very small quantities of iron are also incorporated in the crystal lattices of beryllium silicates (chkalovite, epididymite, beryllite etc.) probably to compensate valencies in the isomorphous replacement of silicon by beryllium.

Oxygen (8)

Oxygen is the most abundant element in the Lovozero alkali massif. It is a main component of all the silicates and aluminosilicates. None of the oxygen-free minerals (sulphides and fluorides) play a fundamental rôle in the structure of the massif (see Table 169).

Mean oxygen content in the massif is 44·98 per cent, i.e. slightly lower than its clarke in igneous rocks. This is apparently due to the increased content of volatiles (fluorine, chlorine and sulphur) which act as anions in a number of minerals, including some rock-forming minerals. The mean oxygen content is very similar in the different complexes of the massif (45·27 per cent in the differentiated complex, 44·37 per cent in the eudialytic lujavrites and 45·05 per cent in the poikilitic syenites).

The differing state of oxidation of elements with variable valency and the various quantitative ratios of their incorporation into given minerals at different stages in the process provide an important indication of the rôle of oxygen in the processes of mineral formation. Marked predominance of ferric iron (5·68 per cent Fe_2O_3) over ferrous (1·44 per cent FeO) and the corresponding presence of a large number of minerals in which iron and manganese are present as oxides are typical features of the Lovozero massif.

According to Goldschmidt (1954) the Fe_2O_3 : FeO ratio is increased in the process of magmatic differentiation from ultrabasic to acid and alkaline differentiates. Goldschmidt's view is confirmed by the Fe_2O_3 : FeO ratio in the different types of rock. Thus, our calculations of the ratio of Fe_2O_3 to FeO based on Daly's mean chemical analyses (see Table 167) show the following changes: 0·35-0·58 in peridotites and gabbros, 1·2 in granites and 1·53 in nepheline syenites. In the

Lovozero massif this ratio is 3·94. The Lovozero alkali massif therefore occupies an extreme position in the magnitude of the oxidation potential. The mean Fe_2O_3 : FeO ratios in the different rock complexes are very similar and approximately equal to the ratio for the massif. Thus, in the differentiated complex the ratio is 3·89, in the eudialytic lujavrites it is 4·02 and in the poikilitic syenites 4·04. Within each complex, however, there are wide variations in the ratio between different rock types. In the rocks of the eudialytic lujavrite complex it ranges from 3·18 to 5·46, and is higher in porphyritic varieties. In the eudialyte varieties it is only 1·98, owing to the predominance of ferrous over ferric iron in the minerals of the eudialyte group (up to 4·23 FeO and 1·88 per cent Fe_2O_3).

In the rocks of the differentiated complex the Fe_2O_3 : FeO ratio varies from 1·86 to 7·97 and is typically lowest for hornblende-lujavrites (1·86), average for aegirine-lujavrites (3·61) and ijolitic urtites (3·01), higher for foyaites (5·05) and highest for malignites (7·97) and urtites (6·90). This variation is due in the main to alteration in the ratio between the content in the rocks of aegirine, in which ferric iron predominates over ferrous (up to 3·45 per cent FeO and 23·07 per cent Fe_2O_3) and arfvedsonite, for which the converse is true (up to 13·82 per cent FeO and 8·61 per cent Fe_2O_3).

The Fe_2O_3 : FeO ratio varies in the rocks of the poikilitic syenite complex between 2·26 in hydrosodalite varieties and 5·13-5·24 in sodalite varieties and tawites. Both the ferrous and the ferric forms of iron were involved throughout the process of endogenous mineral formation, but there was marked predominance of trivalent over bivalent iron in most of the minerals (see Table 169). Predominance of ferric over ferrous iron (up to 13·82 per cent FeO and 8·16 per cent Fe_2O_3 in eudialyte, arfvedsonite, lamprophyllite, ramsayite and other minerals) can sometimes be more readily explained by the selective rôle of the crystalline structure of these minerals rather than by alteration in the oxidation-reduction potential conditions. A considerable quantity of ferrous iron was incorporated in the crystalline structure of arfvedsonite, for example, in place of magnesium, which is deficient in the massif.

During mineral formation in the Lovozero massif there was a gradual increase in oxidation potential towards the later stages. This is shown by the increase in the Fe_2O_3 : FeO ratio in the transient minerals* from the first stage to the last. Thus, for example, the ratio varies from 2·58 in aegirine I to 6·57 in aegirine II and 21·17 in aegirine III.

The increased rôle of oxygen is especially noticeable in the hydrothermal stage, in which a number of minerals formed containing iron mainly in ferric form, as well as oxides and hydroxides of iron and manganese with the highest valency of these elements; which include hydrocerite (6·15 per cent Fe_2O_3), manganchlorite (up to 12·10 per cent Fe_2O_3 and 46·08 per cent MnO_2), hydrogoethite (79·90 per cent Fe_2O_3), psilomelane (81·80 per cent MnO_2), cryptomelane (78·86 per cent MnO_2) and vernadite (61·70 per cent MnO_2).

* A transient mineral (Fersman) is a mineral crystallizing throughout a sequence of genetic stages.—Eds.

In the second, third and fourth stages in mineral formation there was partial isomorphous replacement of oxygen by fluorine, chlorine and the hydroxyl group in arfvedsonite, eudialyte, lamprophyllite, rinkolite, apatite, belovite, schizolite, micas and other minerals.

II. Accessory Elements and Volatile Compounds

This group includes Mg, Mn, Ca, Ba, Sr and P, which are present as accessory constituents in the main rock-forming minerals and as major constituents in certain secondary and accessory minerals. The general content of these elements in the Lovozero massif is 2·67 per cent. This group also includes the volatiles (H_2O, F, Cl, S and CO_2), which are found either in the composition of the main (arfvedsonite, aegirine and sodalite) and rare-metal minerals (apatite, rinkolite, lamprophyllite, lomonosovite etc.) or widely distributed in replacement process minerals (sodalite, natrolite, cancrinite and ussingite). The total content of elements that readily form volatile compounds in the massif is approximately 2 per cent.

Hydrogen (1)

Hydrogen is quite widely distributed. Its mean content in the massif is 0·14 per cent, which is close to the hydrogen clarke in igneous rocks. Although the hydrogen content in the massif is not above the clarke, it has played an enormous rôle in the processes of mineral formation.

The geochemical history of hydrogen in the Lovozero massif is essentially determined by the geochemical and mineral-forming rôle of water and the hydroxyl group. Small amounts of hydrogen are also bonded to sulphur, as is shown by the liberation of H_2S when lumps of hackmanite are split.

Hydrogen is present as water or as hydroxyl groups in a large majority of the minerals of the massif (more than 80 minerals). The water content of individual minerals ranges from 0·10 to 44 per cent (see Table 169). It is a major constituent (3-44 per cent) of the following minerals: murmanite (4·17-6·46 per cent H_2O^+ and 6·03-6·13 per cent H_2O^-), nenadkevichite (8·84-8·98 per cent H_2O^+ and 2·00-2·36 per cent H_2O^-), kupletskite (3·83 per cent H_2O^+ and 1·08 per cent H_2O^-), chinglusuite (6·78 per cent H_2O^+ and 16·96 per cent H_2O^-), cancrinite (3·9 per cent H_2O^+ and 7·6 per cent H_2O^-), minerals of the steenstrupine group, pyrochlore, hydrosodalite (5·40 per cent H_2O^+ and 1·25 per cent H_2O^-), zeolites (up to 9·5 per cent H_2O^+ and 10·41 per cent H_2O^-), lovozerite, catapleiite, belyankinite, metaloparite, pectolite, ussingite (3·40 per cent H_2O^+ and 0·3 per cent H_2O^-), elpidite, karnasurtite, erikite, hydrocerite, and micas (up to 5·55 per cent H_2O^+ and 3·08 per cent H_2O^-), epididymite, beryllite, chlorites and clay minerals (up to 12·50 per cent H_2O^+ and 14·5 per cent H_2O^-), and the hydroxides of iron, manganese, aluminium and silicon (up to 31·06 per cent H_2O^+ and 4·0 per cent H_2O^-).

The main mass of the water in the massif is bonded in natrolite and hydro-sodalite. Other water-containing minerals play a secondary rôle. The highest hydrogen content, which is found in the rocks of the poikilitic syenite complex (0·39 per cent), is approximately three times the figure for the massif as a whole. The mean hydrogen content in the rocks of the differentiated complex and the eudialytic lujavrite complex is close to the mean content in the massif (0·11-0·15 per cent).

There are considerable variations in the water content of different rocks in each complex (Table 174).

In the rocks of the eudialytic lujavrite complex water content is highest in the eudialytites and the eudialytic lujavrites and lowest in the porphyritic juvites. In the rocks of the differentiated complex water content is highest at the lower surfaces of horizons of urtite, ijolitic urtites and malignites intensively replaced by natrolite and decreases gradually through aegirine-lujavrites to foyaites. In the rocks of the poikilitic syenite complex water content is highest in nepheline and hydrosodalite varieties and lowest in sodalite varieties.

The water content is higher in the pegmatites than in the enclosing rocks. Thus, it is 5·88 per cent in the hackmanite-natrolite stock of Karnasurt, that is, approximately five times its content in the poikilitic sodalite-syenites, with which it is genetically associated.

During the first stage in the crystallization of the massif water was not in-corporated in the fundamental crystalline structure of the minerals. Its slight content (0·13-1·27 per cent) in nepheline, microcline, orthoclase and other min-erals is probably due either to isomorphous replacement of oxygen by the (OH) group or to partial removal of the alkalis from these minerals and their replace-ment by water in the later (hydrothermal) stages and in the process of hyper-genesis. The second stage of mineral formation saw the appearance, in addition to anhydrous minerals, of minerals containing a hydroxyl group (arfvedsonite, lamprophyllite, kupletskite, rinkolite, biotite etc.) and minerals containing mole-cular water (murmanite, nenadkevichite, chinglusuite etc.). The third and fourth stages are marked by the crystallization of minerals, most of which contain mole-

TABLE 174 Water content in the rocks of the massif (per cent)

Rocks	H_2O^+	H_2O^-
Eudialytic lujavrites	0·96-2·86	0·02-1·31
Eudialytites	2·35-5·02	0·35-0·81
Porphyritic lujavrites	1·68	0·28
Porphyritic juvites	0·14-1·20	0·10-0·50
Foyaites	0·20-1·24	0·08-0·38
Urtites and ijolite-urtites	0·42-2·50	0·12-0·78
Aegirine-lujavrites	0·12-1·82	0·01-0·17
Hornblende-lujavrites	0·31-0·90	0·05-0·17
Malignites	0·50	4·45
Poikilitic sodalite-syenites	0·11	0·94
Poikilitic nepheline-syenites	1·21-6·11	0·60-0·85
Poikilitic hydrosodalite-syenites	3·20	0·57
Tawites	3·17	0·96

cular water (zeolites, hydromicas, minerals of the clay group and hydroxides). The H_2O content is slightly higher in the fourth-stage minerals (up to 39 per cent). Thus, hydrogen concentration increases between the first and last stages in mineral formation.

Isomorphous replacement of fluorine, chlorine and, in part, oxygen by the hydroxyl group is often found in the minerals of the Lovozero alkali massif. This process was most widely developed in the second and third stages of mineral formation. The hydroxyl group isomorphously replaces fluorine in aegirine II, arfvedsonite, lamprophyllite, rinkolite and kupletskite and chlorine in eudialyte, kupletskite, hydrosodalite, ussingite and elpidite. The fourth stage in mineral formation is marked by the isomorphous inter-replacement of the hydroxyl group exclusively with fluorine (in tainiolite, polylithionite, staffelite [francolite], epididymite and other minerals).

Magnesium (12)

The mean magnesium content in the Lovozero alkali massif is 0·72 per cent, which is approximately a third of its clarke in igneous rocks. Since there was little magnesium in the magma and the iron content was high, scarcely any true magnesium minerals were formed in the massif. Such minerals (biotite, phlogopite and lepidomelane) are typical of alkali massifs in which the magnesium content is higher and the alkali content lower. The amphibole and pyroxene crystallizing under these conditions are arfvedsonite, in which iron greatly predominates over magnesium, and aegirine, which is a true ferruginous pyroxene with a slight admixture of magnesium (up to 2·32 per cent MgO).

The greater part of the magnesium was dispersed and incorporated in small quantities in almost all the minerals, though its content is highest in ferruginous minerals (see Table 169). It occurs as a major constituent in only five minerals: arfvedsonite (6·98-9·35 per cent MgO), biotite (up to 20·31 per cent), tainiolite (up to 19·26 per cent), Zn-montmorillonite (5·39 per cent) and celadonite (2·4-4·5 per cent); it is found only in isomorphous substitution in the other minerals.

Of the minerals mentioned, only arfvedsonite is widely distributed; the others are found rarely and under special conditions. Biotite appears exclusively in those regions of the massif where there has been assimilation of magnesium-bearing country rocks. Tainiolite and Zn-montmorillonite are typical only of the intensively replaced pegmatites of the poikilitic syenite complex, while celadonite forms after arfvedsonite in the conditions of hypergenesis.

The distribution of magnesium between the different rock complexes of the massif is uneven. Its content is highest in the rocks of the eudialytic lujavrite complex (1·07 per cent) and half that amount in the differentiated complex and in the poikilitic syenites (mean content 0·58 and 0·52 per cent). Magnesium is also distributed unevenly in the different rock types of each complex (Table 175).

The magnesium content is typically highest in the hornblende-lujavrites of the differentiated complex, owing to the presence of a large amount of arfvedsonite in

TABLE 175 Magnesium content in the rocks of the massif

Eudialytic lujavrite complex	MgO content, per cent	Differentiated complex	MgO content, per cent	Poikilitic syenite complex	MgO content, per cent
Melanocratic eudialytic lujavrites	1·32	Foyaites	0·28-0·53	Poikilitic sodalite-syenites	0·34
Leucocratic eudialytic lujavrites	2·35	Juvites	0·23	Poikilitic nepheline-syenites	0·35-1·03
Eudialytic lujavrites	0·88-3·54	Urtites and ijolite-urtites	0·14-0·90	Poikilitic hydrosodalite-syenites	0·82-1·43
Porphyritic lujavrites	0·44-1·71	Aegirine-lujavrites:		Tawites	0·31-0·55
Porphyritic juvites	0·19-2·90	Melanocratic	2·34		
		Mesocratic	0·92-3·09		
		Leucocratic	0·48		
		Hornblende-lujavrites	2·90-4·26		
		Malignites	0·99-1·73		

TABLE 176 Manganese content in the rocks of the massif

Eudialytic lujavrite complex	MnO content, per cent	Differentiated complex	MnO content, per cent	Poikilitic syenite complex	MnO content, per cent
Eudialytic lujavrites	0·11-1·09	Foyaites	0·17-0·19	Poikilitic sodalite-syenites	0·38
Melanocratic eudialytic lujavrites	1·05	Juvites	0·14	Poikilitic nepheline-syenites	0·10-0·62
Leucocratic eudialytic lujavrites	0·62	Urtites, ijolite-urtites	0·01-0·58	Poikilitic hydrosodalite-syenites	0·14-0·15
Porphyritic lujavrites	0·44-0·69	Aegirine-lujavrites:		Tawites	0·13-0·23
Porphyritic juvites	0·28-0·56	Melanocratic	0·16-0·38		
Eudialytites	1·30-2·16	Mesocratic	0·08-0·37		
		Leucocratic	0·16		
		Hornblende-lujavrites	0·37-0·51		
		Malignites	0·12-0·26		

these rocks. In this complex the Mg content increases from leucocratic to melano-cratic rocks, owing to the presence of considerable quantities of magnesium in aegirine (1·47-2·32 per cent), where it isomorphously replaces divalent iron. In the poikilitic syenites the magnesium content is typically highest in nepheline and hydrosodalite varieties.

The magnesium content of the pegmatites is evidently similar to that of the parent rocks. Thus, the MgO content of the hackmanite-natrolite pegmatitic stock on Karnasurt is 0·48 per cent, which is close to its content in the poikilitic sodalite-syenites (0·34 per cent MgO) with which this pegmatitic body is genetically associated.

The greater part of the magnesium in the massif (approximately 80 per cent) was combined in the second stage of mineral formation when aegirine and arfved-sonite crystallized. Of the remainder approximately 3 per cent separated in the first stage and approximately 17 per cent in the third and fourth stages.

In the very last part of the hydrothermal stage the pegmatite-forming solutions were enriched in magnesium and formed such magnesium minerals as tainiolite and the montmorillonite group. It is probable that part of the magnesium entered these solutions by the decomposition of previously formed magnesium-bearing minerals.

Isomorphous inter-replacement of magnesium and divalent iron typical of arfvedsonite, aegirine, biotite and aenigmatite was widely developed in the mineral formation of the Lovozero alkali massif. Some Mg is found in practically every iron-containing mineral. Isomorphous replacement of aluminium by magnesium in the minerals of the montmorillonite group, formed at the close of the hydro-thermal stage, is less widely developed. Very small amounts of magnesium are also dispersed in all the aluminosilicates (nepheline, microcline, sodalite, albite, natrolite etc.), where its content does not normally exceed 0·5 per cent.

When trivalent aluminium was replaced by divalent magnesium in the minerals of the montmorillonite group two Al atoms were probably replaced by three Mg atoms to maintain electrostatic equilibrium, or by two Mg atoms and one Zn atom, or by one Mg atom and two Zn atoms on the pattern: $2Al^{3+} \leftarrow 3Mg^{2+}$; $2Al^{3+} \leftarrow 2Mg^{2+} + Zn^{2+}$; $2Al^{3+} \leftarrow Mg^{2+} + 2Zn^{2+}$. The two last variants are typical for zincian montmorillonite and sauconite. Aluminium was probably replaced by magnesium in the aluminosilicates of sodium and potassium. In the hydrothermal stage of pegmatite formation there was isomorphous replacement of calcium by magnesium in chabazite and thomsonite.

Manganese (25)

Manganese is a typical element of the Lovozero alkali massif, which differs from most of the other alkali massifs in that its rocks and pegmatites contain a great many manganese minerals and manganic varieties of ferruginous minerals. Mean Mn content in the massif is 0·27 per cent, i.e. three times the clarke for igneous rocks.

The increased manganese content of the massif and its incorporation in insignificant amounts in the crystalline structures of the leucocratic rock-forming minerals (nepheline, potassium feldspars, albite, sodalite and natrolite) which account for 85 per cent of the volume of the massif, led to the formation in the last stages of 15 minerals in which Mn is one of the main mineral-forming elements. These minerals are titan-låvenite (10·34 per cent MnO), manganilmenite (13·06-16·05 per cent), pyrochlore (5 per cent), schizolite (15·92 per cent MnO and 9·35 per cent MnO_2), kupletskite (27·65 per cent MnO), steenstrupine (9·06 per cent), manganosteenstrupine (17·98 per cent), nordite (6·04 per cent), genthelvite (10·21 per cent), mangan-neptunite (8·87-12·94 per cent), Mn-chlorite (up to 41·03 per cent), psilomelane (6·26 per cent MnO and 83·28 per cent MnO_2), cryptomelane (5·15 per cent MnO and 78·8 per cent MnO_2), chinglusuite (13·54 per cent MnO_2) and mangan-belyankinite (14·03 per cent). The greater part of these minerals is confined to the pegmatites. Manganese is present as an accessory constituent (from 0·01 to 3 per cent) in almost all the dark and rare-metal minerals (see Table 169).

Manganese is unevenly distributed in the massif: its mean content is 0·17 per cent in the differentiated complex, 0·48 per cent in the eudialytic lujavrite complex and 0·2 per cent in the poikilitic syenites. There are also considerable variations in manganese content in the rocks of each complex (Table 176).

The highest manganese content in eudialytic lujavrite and eudialytite is due to the presence in them of considerable quantities of minerals of the eudialyte group, in which the MnO content frequently attains 2·5 per cent. In the rocks of all complexes in the Lovozero massif the manganese oxide content is higher in melanocratic than in leucocratic varieties owing to the increased content of aegirine and arfvedsonite, in which the manganese content is also high (up to 1·7 per cent MnO).

In the first stage of formation, when the main leucocratic minerals crystallized, manganese accumulated in the uncrystallized portions of the magma and was only incorporated by isomorphous substitution in aegirine I and in insignificant quantities in apatite and loparite.

The second stage was decisive in the geochemistry of manganese: the greater part of the dark (aegirine II and arfvedsonite) and of the rare-metal minerals (eudialyte, lamprophyllite, lomonosovite, ramsayite etc.), which contain considerable amounts of Mn, crystallized then. By the end of this stage practically all the Mn was bonded in crystalline structures. The formation of late mangan-neptunite in the rocks is due to manganese migration in the decomposition of manganese-containing titanium minerals of the early stages by hydrothermal solutions.

In most undifferentiated and unreplaced pegmatites the geochemical behaviour of manganese follows the same general features as its behaviour in the rocks. The only differences are a wider distribution of mangan-neptunite, the greater part of which crystallized directly from hydrothermal solutions. In the most developed, completely differentiated and intensively replaced pegmatites of the poikilitic syenite complex the behaviour of manganese was somewhat different, probably because of its higher concentration in the pegmatitic melt solution. In such pegmatites a true manganese mineral (schizolite) sometimes crystallized in the first stage of mineral formation. In the fluid-gaseous stage manganese, as in the rocks, was incorporated in dark and rare-metal minerals: kupletskite, which is the manganese end-member of minerals of the astrophyllite group, was formed at this stage. In the third (fluid-hydrothermal) stage manganese was incorporated as a main constituent in such minerals as chinglusuite, steenstrupine, mangano-steenstrupine and nordite. In the hydrothermal stage, in addition to the incorporation of manganese in magnesium-iron and titanium minerals and in micas and phosphates, considerable quantities of mangan-neptunite, Mn-chlorite, psilomelane and cryptomelane were formed. The increase in manganese concentration in the pegmatitic solutions towards the end of the hydrothermal stage was probably due both to crystallization-differentiation and to its extraction from higher-temperature manganese minerals in the process of their replacement (schizolite, steenstrupine, neptunite etc.). Thus, not all the manganese was combined in such pegmatites in the second stage of mineral formation. Most of its minerals were crystallized in the third and fourth stages. Manganese was not accumulated in the minerals in the hypergene stage and was normally carried away by the solutions.

Isomorphous inter-replacement of manganese and divalent iron is very widely manifested in the minerals of the Lovozero alkali massif and associated with the formation of manganian varieties of such minerals as astrophyllite, ilmenite, neptunite and chlorite. Kupletskite is a mineral of the astrophyllite group that is formed when manganese content is increased. Isomorphous replacement of iron by manganese is also found in all the other iron-containing minerals: aegirine, arfvedsonite, biotite, eudialyte, aenigmatite, lamprophyllite, narsarsukite etc.

The isomorphous substitution of manganese for calcium is less clearly shown in such minerals as schizolite, pyrochlore and apatite (up to 1·31 per cent MnO), staffelite [francolite] (up to 3·3 per cent), pectolite (up to 2·1 per cent), mangano-steenstrupine, steenstrupine and nordite. The possibility that manganese replaces titanium and niobium in addition to calcium in pyrochlore is not excluded. Manganese isomorphously replaces magnesium in arfvedsonite, biotite, tainiolite and polylithionite. The MnO content of these minerals varies between 0·20 and 1·70 per cent.

In hybrid pegmatites manganese is often isomorphous with zinc; this leads to the formation of genthelvite with an increased manganese content (10·21 per cent MnO).

The presence of Mn in some titanium minerals (lomonosovite, murmanite, nenadkevichite, ramsayite, brookite etc.) is apparently due to its incorporation into the crystalline structures of these minerals with niobium as a replacement of titanium.

At all stages in mineral formation manganese is involved mainly in the divalent form, and it is only at the end of the hydrothermal stage that minerals containing tetravalent manganese (psilomelane, cryptomelane etc.) appear in the pegmatites of the poikilitic syenite complex. It is probable that at this period manganese was oxidized to a tetravalent state in a number of minerals (schizolite, chinglusuite, chlorites etc.) during their decomposition.

Calcium (20)

The extremely low calcium content is one of the most distinctive features of the Lovozero alkali massif. The mean calcium content in the massif is 1·46 per cent, i.e. less than half the normal figure for igneous rocks. The behaviour of calcium in the massif was largely determined by the reduced calcium content, taken in conjunction with the high content of sodium, zirconium and the rare earths and the low content of phosphorus. The greater part of the calcium is incorporated as an isomorphous substituent in sodi-potassic and rare-earth minerals. The calcium mineral apatite was formed mainly in those regions of the massif where the calcium content of the magma had been increased either by crystallization differentiation (beneath urtite horizons) or by assimilation of the calcium-enriched rocks of the roof. The apatite contains increased quantities of R.E., Sr, Ba, Mn and other elements that isomorphously replace calcium. Calcium is present in about 90 minerals in the massif. There are considerable amounts in 23 minerals and isomorphous admixtures in the others (see Table 169). Calcium oxide is a main constituent of the following minerals: loparite (3-6·32 per cent), titan-låvenite (10·92-13·61 per cent), pyrochlore (13·45 per cent), apatite (43·81-51·93 per cent), eudialyte and mesodialyte (7·01-11·6 per cent), sphene (25·01 per cent), rinkolite (26·68 per cent), manganosteenstrupine (4·66 per cent), nordite (4·46 per cent), fluorite (51·2 per cent), pectolite (32·04-32·46 per cent), schizolite (12·72 per cent), metaloparite (5·25 per cent), belovite (5·23 per cent), leucophane (23·65 per cent), belyankinite (5·8-6·8 per cent), apophyllite (25 per cent), staffelite [francolite] (53·8 per cent) etc. Most of these minerals are found in very small quantities in the massif or are mineralogical rarities. Eudialyte and mesodialyte, also apatite and loparite, are more widely distributed than the others.

Calcium content is highest in the eudialytic lujavrite complex (2·31 per cent), twice as high as in the differentiated complex (1·08 per cent) and the poikilitic syenite complex (1·14 per cent). This uneven distribution is due to the relatively large amount of this element in minerals of the eudialytc group (eucolite, which is widely distributed in the rocks of the eudialytic lujavrite complex); this is probably due to assimilation by the alkalic magma of the calcium-rich rocks of the roof, in which the calcium oxide content varies between 8 and 15 per cent.

There is also considerable fluctuation to the calcium content in the different rock-types of the massif (Table 177). In the eudialytic lujavrite complex its amount increases from the leucocratic to the melanocratic varieties and especially in the eudialytites. In the rocks of the differentiated complex the content of this element is highest in urtites, ijolitic urtites, apatite-urtites and malignites, and lowest in foyaites and leucocratic aegirine-lujavrites. In each three-component stratal group the maximum calcium content is concentrated in the lower surfaces of the urtite horizons and the roofs of aegirine-lujavrite horizons. In the rocks of the poikilitic syenite complex contaminated nepheline and hydrosodalite varieties are richest in calcium.

The content of calcium in the pegmatites is apparently near its content in the parent rocks. Thus, for example, the amount of CaO in the hackmanite stock on Karnasurt is 0·97 per cent, slightly higher than its content in the parent poikilitic sodalite-syenites (0·66 per cent of CaO).

Mineralogical calculations show that 20 per cent of the total amount of calcium in the magma came out of solution in the first stage of mineral formation, 50 per cent in the second stage and approximately 30 per cent in the third and fourth stages combined. Thus, the greater part of the calcium was combined in the first two stages of mineral formation in loparite, apatite, eudialyte and mesodialyte, and as isomorphous admixtures in the main rock-forming and rare-metal minerals.

At all stages in the process of mineral formation there was widely manifested isomorphism of calcium with sodium and the rare earths and, to a lesser extent, with potassium. The isomorphism of calcium with potassium is most clearly seen in loparite, eudialyte, eucolite, rinkolite, titan-låvenite, schizolite, leucophane, thomsonite, chabazite etc. Considerable quantities of calcium are also incorporated as an isomorphous admixture in nepheline (0·20 per cent CaO), aegirine (up to 4·02 per cent CaO), arfvedsonite (up to 2·08 per cent CaO), lomonosovite (up to 1·25 per cent CaO), murmanite (up to 3·16 per cent CaO), nenadkevichite (up to 4·3 per cent CaO), lamprophyllite (up to 4·85 per cent CaO), albite (up to 0·15 per cent CaO), sodalite (up to 1·07 per cent CaO), natrolite (0·48 per cent CaO), hydrosodalite (0·60 per cent CaO) and other minerals, mainly to compensate valencies in isomorphous replacement of silicon by aluminium (nepheline, albite, sodalite, hydrosodalite, natrolite etc.), trivalent iron by manganese (aegirine) and titanium by niobium (in titanoniobosilicates). The pattern of the preservation of electrostatic equilibrium in replacement of iron by manganese is $Fe^{3+} + Na^{1+} \leftarrow Mn^{2+} + Ca^{2+}$. Valency compensation in the replacement of silicon by aluminium and titanium by niobium is dealt with when these elements are described.

Isomorphous replacement of potassium by calcium is represented in potassium feldspars (up to 0·78 per cent CaO), kupletskite (3·6 per cent CaO), polylithionite (1·17 per cent CaO) and other minerals.

In the minerals of the third and especially the fourth stage there is widespread isomorphous replacement by calcium of the rare earths in steenstrupine (1·85 per cent CaO), manganosteenstrupine (4·66 per cent CaO), hydrocerite (2·83 per cent CaO), karnasurtite (up to 2·23 per cent CaO), erikite (up to 1·9 per cent CaO) and other minerals. There may possibly be isomorphous replacement by calcium of divalent manganese, divalent iron and magnesium in genthelvite, chlorites, montmorillonite (zincian), psilomelane, cryptomelane and hydrogoethite.

Strontium (38)

Strontium is a typical element of alkali rocks. Sr content is known to increase in igneous rocks from ultrabasic to acid and especially alkali rocks. Its maximum

TABLE 177 Calcium content in the rocks of the massif

Eudialytic lujavrite complex	CaO content, per cent	Differentiated complex	CaO content, per cent	Poikilitic syenite complex	CaO content, per cent
Eudialytic lujavrites	1·24–5·15	Foyaites	0·54–1·81	Poikilitic sodalite-syenites	0·66
Melanocratic eudialytic lujavrites	3·93	Juvites	1·87	Poikilitic nepheline-syenites	0·61–5·08
Leucocratic eudialytic lujavrites	3·70	Urtites and ijolite-urtites	1·56–11·51	Poikilitic hydrosodalite-syenites	1·68–2·68
Eudialytites	4·75–7·36	Aegirine-lujavrites:		Tawites	0·80–0·81
Porphyritic lujavrites	1·10–2·64	Melanocratic	1·73–4·71		
Porphyritic juvites	1·62–2·86	Mesocratic	1·10		
		Leucocratic	0·46		
		Hornblende-lujavrites	1·71–2·24		
		Malignites	2·28–6·04		

TABLE 178 Strontium oxide content in the rocks

Complex	Rocks	SrO content, per cent
Eudialytic lujavrite	Eudialytic lujavrites	up to 0·04
	Eudialytites	0·38–1·18
	Porphyritic lujavrites	0·26
Differentiated	Foyaites	0·22
	Juvites	0·10
	Aegirine-lujavrites	up to 0·22

content in nepheline-syenites is 0·12 per cent (Rankama, 1949). Because of the similarity of the ionic radii of Sr^{2+} (1·20 Å), Ca^{2+} (1·04 Å) and K^{1+} (1·33 Å) the greater part of the strontium is dispersed in the minerals of these elements, and more readily enters the crystalline structures of calcic minerals. The reduced content of calcium and the increased content of strontium in the Lovozero alkali massif led to the formation of strontium minerals in the pneumatolytic and hydrothermal stages in the formation of the massif.

The presence of strontium has now been established in more than 60 minerals of the Lovozero massif (see Table 169), only three of which are true strontium minerals (lamprophyllite (16·76 per cent SrO), nordite (7·4 per cent SrO) and belovite (33·6 per cent SrO)). The highest strontium oxide content in calcic minerals is found in apatite (2·43-6·24 per cent), loparite (0·62-4·38 per cent), pyrochlore (4·5 per cent), fluorite (3 per cent) and staffelite [francolite] (2·59 per cent). There are also significant quantities in schizolite (0·28 per cent), minerals of the eudialyte group (0·13-1·49 per cent), rinkolite (0·4 per cent), catapleiite (0·5 per cent), erikite (0·6-0·9 per cent), montmorillonite (0·33 per cent), sauconite (0·2 per cent), cryptomelane (0·7 per cent), zirfesite (0·2 per cent) and other minerals.

At 0·09 per cent the mean strontium content in the massif is three times the clarke for igneous rocks. Sr is unevenly distributed between the different rock complexes. Its mean content in the rocks of the differentiated complex (0·13 per cent) is approximately $2\frac{1}{2}$ times that in the rocks of the eudialytic lujavrite complex (0·05 per cent). The higher strontium content in the rocks of the differentiated complex is due to the presence of considerable quantities of lamprophyllite and the increased content of strontium oxide in loparite and apatite.

The strontium oxide content in the rocks of the massif varies from 0 to 0·26 per cent (Table 178) and reaches 1·18 per cent only in the eudialytites, because of the considerable strontium content in the minerals of the eudialyte group.

Strontium content is probably higher in the pegmatites than in the rocks, as is shown by the abundance of lamprophyllite in them and the presence of such minerals as nordite, belovite, staffelite [francolite] and apatite.

Strontium was incorporated in the crystalline structures of other minerals at all stages in the formation of the massif, but the greater part was combined in the first and second stages. In the first stage strontium was dispersed in potassic and calcic minerals—potassium feldspars (up to 0·08 per cent SrO), loparite, apatite and schizolite, in which it isomorphously replaced potassium and calcium. Isomorphous replacement of calcium by strontium is well revealed in the minerals of the apatite group, where there is an increase in strontium content from normal apatite (1-2 per cent SrO) through saamite (14 per cent SrO) to belovite (33·6 per cent SrO) involving a reduction in calcium content from 52 to 5·2 per cent CaO. Strontium is probably involved in the crystalline structure of orthoclase, replacing part of the potassium.

The strontium minerals—lamprophyllite, nordite and belovite—crystallized in the second, third and fourth stages of mineral formation. Lamprophyllite, the most widely distributed, is typical of the second stage of mineral formation for both the rocks and the pegmatites of the massif. Nordite and belovite have been discovered only in the pegmatites of the poikilitic syenite complex. Besides forming strontium minerals, strontium isomorphously replaced calcium during this stage in eudialyte, eucolite, rinkolite, pyrochlore, lovozerite, apatite (late), catapleiite, staffelite [francolite] and other minerals. In the intensively replaced pegmatites of the poikilitic syenite complex considerable quantities of strontium are found in the magnesian and manganian minerals formed at the end of the hydrothermal stage: montmorillonite (0·33 per cent SrO), sauconite (0·2 per cent SrO), crypto-melane (0·7 per cent SrO), psilomelane etc. In these minerals strontium probably replaces Mg and divalent manganese jointly with calcium.

Barium (56)

The barium content of the Lovozero massif, like that of strontium, is higher than the clarke for igneous rocks. At 0·11 per cent its mean content in the massif is almost 4½ times the barium clarke for igneous rocks. Unlike strontium, however, barium more readily replaces potassium, besides being incorporated in calcic minerals, owing to the similarity of their ionic radii (potassium—1·33 Å, barium 1·38 Å). There is scarcely any formation of barium minerals as such.

Chemical and spectrographic analyses have so far revealed barium in more than 50 minerals of the Lovozero massif (see Table 169). It is however only in labuntsovite that it appears as a main constituent (8·61 per cent BaO). Barium is concentrated in the minerals of potassium, strontium, calcium, sodium and, less frequently, manganese: in microcline (0·05 per cent BaO), orthoclase (0·21 per cent BaO), eudialyte (0·65 per cent BaO), lomonosovite (up to 0·15 per cent BaO), lamprophyllite (up to 3·49 per cent BaO), belovite (0·96 per cent BaO), karna-surtite (0·68 per cent BaO), erikite (0·37 per cent BaO), chlorites (1·66 per cent BaO) and psilomelane (0·99 per cent BaO). Small amounts are also present in aegirine and arfvedsonite, where it probably also replaces potassium.

The barium is unevenly distributed among the different rock complexes; thus its mean content in the differentiated complex is 0·05 per cent, in the eudialytic

TABLE 179 Barium content in the rocks

Complex	Rocks	BaO content, per cent
Eudialytic lujavrite	Eudialytic lujavrites Eudialytites Porphyritic lujavrites	0·11-0·14 0·13-0·37 0·07-0·08
Differentiated	Foyaites Aegirine-lujavrites Hornblende-lujavrites	up to 0·10 up to 0·13 0·12
Poikilitic syenite	Poikilitic nepheline- syenites	up to 0·03

lujavrite complex 0·08 per cent. The barium oxide content varies in different rock types between 0·03 and 0·37 per cent (Table 179).

The increased content of barium in eudialytites and eudialytic lujavrites is due to the presence in them of considerable quantities of the minerals of the eudialyte group and lamprophyllite.

Barium was involved in all stages of the process of mineral formation in the Lovozero massif, but most was combined in the first two stages. In the first stage barium was dispersed in potassium feldspars (microcline and orthoclase) and nepheline, in which it was incorporated with potassium. The isomorphism of K and Ba is shown by the existence of potassium-barium feldspars (hyalophane and celsian) in nature. In the Lovozero massif the isomorphism of these elements was also helped by a silicon deficiency in the alkali magma that promoted isomorphous replacement of silicon by aluminium, in which the electroneutrality of the crystalline structures of the minerals was preserved by simultaneous replacement of the monovalent cations by divalent cations (Ca, Ba, Sr) on the pattern: $Si^{4+} + (K, Na)^{1+} \leftarrow Al^{3+} + (Ca, Sr, Ba)^{2+}$.

In the fluid-gaseous stage barium was incorporated mainly in the structures of strontium- and calcium-bearing titano-, niobo- and zirconosilicates, in which it isomorphously replaces strontium, calcium and, in some cases, potassium (lamprophyllite, eudialyte, lomonosovite, nenadkevichite etc.).

In the third stage of mineral formation barium did not play a fundamental rôle. At this stage it was only in the pegmatites of the poikilitic syenite complex that small amounts were incorporated with calcium in the lattices of rare-earth minerals (steenstrupine, manganosteenstrupine etc.).

In the hydrothermal stage barium was incorporated into the structure of belovite in the intensively replaced pegmatites of the poikilitic syenite complex, where it isomorphously replaced strontium and also formed its own mineral—labuntsovite. It was also incorporated with calcium in rare-earth and manganese minerals (karnasurtite, erikite, Mn-chlorites, psilomelane, cryptomelane etc.). The presence of considerable quantities of barium in many of the minerals of the hydrothermal stage is due to an increase in its concentration in the pegmatitic melt solutions brought about both by crystallization differentiation and by extraction from higher-temperature minerals.

Phosphorus (15)

Phosphorus played a fundamental rôle in the processes of mineral formation in the Lovozero alkali massif, although it is present in relatively small amounts. Its average content in the massif is 0·09 per cent, which is slightly lower than its clarke for igneous rocks. During crystallization differentiation of the alkali magma the concentration was greatly increased in many cases, and apatite-enriched rocks, which are not found in acid and basic intrusions, were crystallized.

Phosphorus enters into 23 minerals of the Lovozero massif, in 8 of which it is a main constituent: apatite (37·47-41·26 per cent P_2O_5), lomonosovite (12·84-

14·62 per cent), steenstrupine (3·74 per cent), hydrocerite (5·76 per cent), belovite (28·88 per cent), karnasurtite (2·42-6·81 per cent), erikite (20·06-24·31 per cent) and staffelite [francolite] (39·59 per cent). Small quantities (0·08-1·3 per cent P_2O_5) are also present in arfvedsonite from the pegmatites and in mangano-steenstrupine, natrolite, catapleiite, manganobelyankinite and allophane. Moreover, spectrographic analysis has revealed phosphorus in microcline and albite from the pegmatites and in beryllite, hydromica, cerussite and jarosite (see Table 169).

Of these minerals only apatite and lomonosovite are widely distributed in the rocks of the massif, the remainder being typical mainly of the pegmatites of the poikilitic syenite complex. Phosphorus content is highest in the poikilitic syenite complex (0·16 per cent), average in the eudialytic lujavrite complex (0·13 per cent) and lowest in the differentiated complex (0·06 per cent). The phosphorus content of the various rock types varies from traces to 4·44 per cent (Table 180). An increased phosphorus content is typical of leucocratic rocks: foyaites, urtites, poikilitic syenites and leucocratic eudialytic lujavrites. Its content is highest in urtites, which contain considerable quantities of apatite. In the other leucocratic rocks its increased content is due mainly to the presence of minerals of the lomono-sovite-murmanite group.

The phosphorus content of the pegmatites is clearly well below that of the rocks. Thus, the mean content of this element in the hackmanite-natrolite stock on Karnasurt is 0·01 per cent, but 0·71 per cent in the poikilitic sodalite-syenites with which this pegmatitic body is genetically associated.

Phosphorus is a characteristic element of the early stages in the crystallization of the massif. Nearly all the phosphorus in the massif was combined as apatite and lomonosovite in the first and second stages of mineral formation. In the fluid-hydrothermal stage it was not structurally incorporated in any mineral. In the hydrothermal stage and in conditions of hypergenesis phosphorus was leached from minerals of the lomonosovite group and transported by the solutions as hydrous sodium phosphate. A very small part of the phosphorus entered the crystalline structures of later hydrothermal minerals, including natrolite and hydromica.

The geochemical history of phosphorus in the pegmatites of the Lovozero alkali massif differed somewhat from its history in the rocks. During the initial stages in the formation of the pegmatites phosphorus concentration was very low and it did not form phosphorus minerals but was partly dispersed and incorporated in small amounts in aluminosilicates and silicates (microcline, arfvedsonite, ramsayite etc.). Towards the end of the pegmatitic process phosphorus concentration in the solutions had probably increased. Thus, in the fluid-hydrothermal stage considerable quantities were incorporated in minerals of the steenstrupine group, while in the hydrothermal stage, besides being dispersed in silicates, it formed phosphorus minerals—phosphates and silicophosphates (late apatite, belovite, staffelite [francolite], erikite, karnasurtite and hydrocerite).

The mutual isomorphism of silicon and phosphorus is widely manifested in

the minerals of the massif. Small quantities of P frequently replace silicon isomorphously in silicates, while silicon is incorporated in the crystalline structures
of phosphates, where it replaces phosphorus. In the hydrothermal stage of pegmatite formation there is practically no restriction to the isomorphism of phosphorus and silicon, as is shown by the formation of silicophosphates with a variable
phosphorus and silicon content (karnasurtite, hydrocerite and erikite), in which
an increase in silicon content from 3·42 to 30·27 per cent SiO_2 is accompanied by
a corresponding decrease in P_2O_5 from 24·31 to 2·42 per cent.

In isomorphous replacement of tetravalent silicon by pentavalent phosphorus,
electrostatic neutrality is attained by the incorporation of aluminium and iron into
the crystalline structures of the minerals on the following pattern: $2Si^{4+} \leftarrow P^{5+} +$
$(Al, Fe)^{3+}$.

Isomorphous replacement of silicon by phosphorus, which is widely manifested
in the Lovozero massif, is facilitated both by the similar size of the ionic radii
($Si^{4+} = 0·39$ Å and $P^{5+} = 0·35$ Å) and by silica deficiency in the alkali magma.

Sulphur (16)

At 0·17 per cent the mean sulphur content of the Lovozero alkali massif is
more than three times its clarke for igneous rocks.

Sulphur has been chemically determined in 21 minerals of the Lovozero
massif (see Table 169). It is a main constituent of only 11 minerals—molybdenite
(40 per cent), pyrrhotine (39·6 per cent), galena (13·4 per cent), sphalerite (32·65
per cent), pyrite (53·4 per cent), marcasite (53·4 per cent), chalcopyrite (3·5 per
cent), covellite (33·6 per cent), genthelvite (5·74 per cent), cancrinite (4·6-6·2 per
cent SO_3) and jarosite (31·9 per cent). Since very small quantities of these minerals
are found in the massif they do not play a fundamental part in the general sulphur
balance. Most of the sulphur is concentrated in sodalite (0·02-1·13 per cent),
hydrosodalite (1·38 per cent), ussingite (0·08-0·09 per cent) and lomonosovite
(0·16 per cent). Sulphur is not usually part of the main formula of these minerals,
but forms a subsidiary addition.

Sulphur is very unevenly distributed among the different rock complexes of
the massif. Its content is highest in the poikilitic syenites (0·54 per cent), average
in the eudialytic lujavrite complex (0·23 per cent) and lowest in the rocks of the
differentiated complex (0·1 per cent). The increase in the sulphur content of the
poikilitic syenites and eudialytic lujavrites is associated with the presence of large
quantities of sodalite (hackmanite) and hydrosodalite in these rocks. The distribution of sulphur among the different rock varieties in each complex is shown in
Table 181.

The sulphur content of the pegmatites probably does not exceed that of the
parent rocks and may even be lower. According to mineralogical calculations
sulphur content in the hackmanite-natrolite stock on Karnasurt is 0·17 per cent,
which is a third of its content in the poikilitic sodalitic syenites (0·51 per cent).

At early stages in the processes of mineral formation S did not play a special

TABLE 180 Phosphorus content in the rocks of the massif

Eudialytic lujavrite complex	P_2O_5 content, per cent
Eudialytic lujavrites	0·20
Melanocratic eudialytic lujavrites	0·06
Leucocratic eudialytic lujavrites	0·57
Eudialytites	0·22
Porphyritic lujavrites	0·03
Porphyritic juvites	0·03-0·06

Differentiated complex	P_2O_5 content, per cent
Foyaites	0·27-0·50
Urtites and ijolite-urtites	1·56-4·44
Aegirine-lujavrites	0·09
Melanocratic aegirine-lujavrites	0·01
Mesocratic aegirine-lujavrites	0·08
Leucocratic aegirine-lujavrites	0·03
Hornblende-lujavrites	0·26-0·37
Malignites	0·01-0·52

Poikilitic syenite complex	P_2O_5 content, per cent
Poikilitic sodalite-syenites	0·71
Poikilitic nepheline-syenites	0·36-0·67
Poikilitic hydrosodalite-syenites	0·15
Tawites	trace

TABLE 181 Sulphur content in the rocks of the massif (per cent)

Eudialytic lujavrite complex	SO_3	S
Eudialytic lujavrites	0·21	not det.
Melanocratic eudialytic lujavrites	0·15	,, ,,
Leucocratic eudialytic lujavrites	0·99	,, ,,
Eudialytites	0·15	,, ,,
Porphyritic lujavrites	0·50	,, ,,
Porphyritic juvites	0·06-0·10	0·04

Differentiated complex	SO_3	S
Foyaites	0·21-0·23	not det.
Juvites	0·72	,, ,,
Urtites and ijolite-urtites	0·03-0·10	0·03-0·16
Aegirine-lujavrites	0·1-0·40	not det.
Hornblende-lujavrites	0·14-0·17	,, ,,

Poikilitic syenite complex	SO_3	S
Poikilitic sodalite-syenites	not det.	0·51-0·53
Poikilitic nepheline-syenites	,, ,,	0-0·56
Poikilitic hydrosodalite-syenites	,, ,,	0·43-1·70
Tawites	,, ,,	0·32-0·54

rôle and was incorporated only by isomorphous substitution in apatite and lomono-sovite; at these stages it apparently replaced the complex anion PO_4^{3-} as a complex anion SO_4^{2-}. The electroneutrality of the crystalline structure was ensured by simultaneous incorporation of the requisite amounts of hydroxyl or fluorine.

The greater part of the sulphur in the massif separated in the third and fourth stages of mineral formation. In the fluid-hydrothermal stage it formed sulphur minerals—sulphides (pyrrhotine and molybdenite) or isomorphously replaced chlorine in sodalite and hackmanite. It was incorporated to a lesser extent as a complex anion in the crystalline structure of cancrinite, in which it isomorphously replaced the CO_3^{-2} group. At this stage S isomorphously replaced oxygen in genthelvite in hybrid pegmatites.

In the fourth stage small amounts of sulphur were incorporated in such minerals as ussingite and chkalovite. Sulphides (pyrite, galena, chalcopyrite, sphalerite and covellite) were also formed at this stage and there was isomorphous replacement of phosphorus by sulphur in belovite and of arsenic in löllingite.

Fluorine (19)

The mean fluorine content of the massif, calculated from chemical analyses of the rocks, is 0·17 per cent, approximately three times its clarke for igneous rocks. This figure is clearly too low. Suffice it to say that the fluorine content of the massif is approximately 0·17 per cent purely on the basis of such main fluorine-containing minerals as villiaumite and apatite and that there is also fluorine in aegirine, arfvedsonite and a number of other minerals. The increased content of fluorine in the massif led to the formation of many fluorine-containing minerals, especially villiaumite, which is widely distributed in almost all the alkali rock varieties.

Fluorine has been detected in 24 minerals in the Lovozero massif (see Table 169). It is a main constituent of the following minerals: villiaumite (45·28 per cent), fluorite (48·9 per cent), apatite (up to 3·49 per cent), pyrochlore (3·7 per cent), rinkolite (4·4 per cent), tainiolite (5·36 per cent), polylithionite (up to 5·6 per cent), staffelite [francolite] (2·55 per cent) and leucophane (7·04 per cent). Small quantities (0·08-2·23 per cent) have been detected in aegirine, arfvedsonite, murmanite, lamprophyllite, kupletskite, titan-låvenite, karnasurtite, epididymite, apophyllite, Zn-montmorillonite, elpidite, nontronite and natro-opal. Of these minerals villiaumite, apatite, aegirine, arfvedsonite and natro-opal are widely distributed in the rocks of the massif; the others are found mainly in the pegmatites of the poikilitic syenite complex.

Fluorine content varies in the different rock complexes of the massif. Thus its mean content is 0·14 per cent in the differentiated complex, 0·22 per cent in the eudialytic lujavrite complex and 0·18 per cent in the poikilitic syenites. The amount of fluorine in the different rock types varies between 0·02 and 0·36 per cent (Table 182). Fluorine content increases from below upwards in the rocks of the eudialytic lujavrite complex, i.e. from porphyritic varieties to melanocratic eudialytic lujavrites, parallel with an increase in the amount of aegirine.

In the differentiated complex the fluorine content is highest in the well-layered (upper and lower) sectors, and in each three-component stratal group concentration of this element is confined to the central parts of the foyaite horizons, where there is a large amount of villiaumite and lamprophyllite. There is then a gradual decrease in the amount of fluorine towards the underlying urtites, reaching its lowest point in the central parts of the urtite horizons. Below this, the fluorine content once again increases towards the lower walls of the urtite horizons on account of the apatite and aegirine and reaches its maximum at the upper surfaces of the melanocratic aegirine-lujavrite horizons before once again declining. There is an increase in fluorine content due to aegirine and arfvedsonite between leucocratic and melanocratic lujavrite varieties. Fluorine content is typically higher in the foyaites of well-layered three-component stratal groups than in those that are poorly layered, owing to an increase in villiaumite content. Fluorine content increases with depth in the urtite horizons of the differentiated complex through enrichment in apatite.

A single chemical determination gave a fluorine content of 0·12 per cent for the thin undifferentiated pegmatites of the differentiated complex. That the amount of fluorine in the larger pegmatitic bodies is higher than in the rocks is shown by the abundance in them of fluorine-containing minerals and by the higher fluorine content of minerals in pegmatites by comparison with the same minerals in rocks. Thus, the fluorine content of lamprophyllite from pegmatites is 1·83 per cent and from rocks 1·1 per cent.

Fluorine-containing minerals crystallized at all stages in the process of mineral formation, but those formed in the fourth stage are scarce and, being exclusively confined to intensively-replaced pegmatites, do not make any particular contribution to the general body of the massif. There are considerable quantities of most of the fluorine-containing minerals that crystallized in the first, second and third stages, and some of them are main minerals (aegirine, apatite, villiaumite and arfvedsonite). Most of the fluorine was combined in the third stage as villiaumite. Fluorine entered supergene minerals from high-temperature fluorine-containing minerals on their decomposition by surface waters.

Because of the similarity of the ionic radii of fluorine (1·33 Å), oxygen (1·36 Å) and hydroxyl (1·36 Å), there was isomorphous inter-replacement among them. The isomorphous replacement of oxygen by fluorine and mutual isomorphism between fluorine and the hydroxyl group are widely manifested in the minerals of the first and especially the second stage in the formation of the massif (in apatite, titan-låvenite, arfvedsonite, aegirine, lamprophyllite, astrophyllite, rinkolite, kupletskite and murmanite). Fluorine was not incorporated in the structures of other minerals in the third stage and formed its own minerals—villiaumite and fluorite. In the hydrothermal and supergene stages it was leached from previously-formed minerals by aqueous solutions and carried into surface waters, as is shown by its increased content in the lakes and rivers of the massif.

Fluorine continued to play an active rôle during the hydrothermal stage in the intensively-replaced pegmatites of the poikilitic syenite complex (which it did not do in the rocks and poorly-differentiated pegmatites) and was incorporated in the crystalline structures of a great many minerals, in which it isomorphously replaced oxygen or hydroxyl (karnasurtite, tainiolite, polylithionite, epididymite, apophyllite, leucophane, elpidite and Zn-montmorillonite). The enhanced importance of fluorine in the hydrothermal stage of the pegmatitic process was probably due to an increase in its concentration in the solutions as a result of both crystallization differentiation and of leaching from the higher-temperature fluorine-containing minerals.

Chlorine (17)

Chlorine is widely distributed in the Lovozero alkali massif. At 0·2 per cent its mean content is more than six times the Cl clarke for igneous rocks. The high chlorine content ensured its incorporation in considerable quantities in such widely distributed minerals as arfvedsonite and eudialyte, and the formation of its own mineral, sodalite, which is one of the main rock-forming minerals of the massif.

Chlorine has now been determined in 15 minerals in the Lovozero massif: sodalite (4·88-6·44 per cent), arfvedsonite (0·08-0·41 per cent), eudialyte (0·74-2·19 per cent), lomonosovite (0·1 per cent), lamprophyllite (0·08-0·62 per cent), sphene (0·26 per cent), hydrosodalite (0·16 per cent), apatite (0·04 per cent), pyrochlore (2 per cent), ussingite (0·04-0·05 per cent), elpidite (0·18 per cent), nontronite (0·25 per cent) etc. (see Table 169).

Chlorine content is highest (1·02 per cent) in the poikilitic syenite complex, 0·18 per cent in the eudialytic lujavrite complex and 0·13 per cent in the differentiated complex. There are wide variations in chlorine content in the different rocks of the massif (Table 183).

In the rocks of the poikilitic syenite complex Cl content is typically highest in sodalitic varieties and in tawites, and very small in nepheline and hydrosodalite varieties. In the differentiated and eudialytic lujavrite complexes the content of this element is highest in lujavrites and decreases from melanocratic to leucocratic varieties. These features of the distribution of chlorine in the rocks of the massif are broadly conditioned by the distribution of such widely-distributed chlorine-containing minerals as sodalite, eudialyte and arfvedsonite.

Analysis of the data shows that significant amounts of chlorine are incorporated mainly in minerals that do not contain fluorine (see Table 169). This is because of the difference in the ionic radii of chlorine (1·81 Å) and fluorine (1·33 Å). The minerals of the astrophyllite, pyrochlore and elpidite groups are exceptions. Thus, for example, chlorine is practically absent from fluorine-containing minerals early apatite, titan-làvenite, aegirine, murmanite, rinkolite, villiaumite, karnasurtite, tainiolite, polylithionite, staffelite [francolite] etc. In the same way fluorine is absent from chlorine-containing minerals (lomonosovite, sphene, sodalite, hydrosodalite and ussingite).

Rankama and Sahama (1949) consider that isomorphism between chlorine

TABLE 182 Fluorine content in the rocks

Eudialytic lujavrite complex	F content, per cent	Differentiated complex	F content, per cent	Poikilitic syenite complex	F content, per cent
Melanocratic eudialytic lujavrites	0·36	Foyaites	0·026–0·30	Poikilitic sodalite-syenites	0·12–0·25
Leucocratic eudialytic lujavrites	0·12–0·16	Urtites	0·05–0·12		
Porphyritic eudialytic lujavrites	0·07	Ijolite-urtites	0·13–0·20		
Eudialytytes	0·04–0·11	Juvites	0·26		
		Malignites	0·30		
		Aegirine-lujavrites:			
		Leucocratic	0·05–0·07		
		Mesocratic	0·06–0·26		
		Melanocratic	0·02–0·30		
		Hornblende-lujavrites	0·18–0·30		

TABLE 183 Chlorine content in the rocks

Eudialytic lujavrite complex	Cl content, per cent	Differentiated complex	Cl content, per cent	Poikilitic syenite complex	Cl content, per cent
Melanocratic eudialytic lujavrites	0·33	Juvites	not found	Poikilitic sodalite-syenites	2·69
Leucocratic eudialytic lujavrites	0·21	Urtites and ijolite-urtites	0·03–0·07	Poikilitic nepheline-syenites	0·05–0·1
Eudialytytes	0·34–0·73	Aegirine-lujavrites	0·10–0·14	Poikilitic hydrosodalite-syenites	0·08
Porphyritic lujavrites	0·18	Melanocratic aegirine-lujavrites	0·27	Tawites	1·02–2·56
Porphyritic juvites	0·43	Mesocratic aegirine-lujavrites	0·03		
		Leucocratic aegirine-lujavrites	0·02		
		Hornblende-lujavrites	0·12		
		Malignites	0·02–0·12		

and fluorine is confined to apatite. The data for the Lovozero massif does not confirm this suggestion. Fluorine-containing apatite from the rocks, which is widely distributed, does not normally contain chlorine and very small amounts only (up to 0·04 per cent) are present in late fluor-apatites from the pegmatites. At the same time there is isomorphous replacement of fluorine by chlorine in minerals of the lamprophyllite group, pyrochlore and elpidite, in which the fluorine content varies from 0·12 to 3·7 per cent for a chlorine content of 0·08-2 per cent. In a number of minerals (arfvedsonite, eudialyte, astrophyllite, kuplet-skite, elpidite and nontronite) that contain considerable quantities of (OH), F and Cl, it is difficult to decide whether fluorine is replaced by chlorine or whether, as is more likely, they both replace (OH). The presence of chlorine in sphene is apparently due to isomorphous replacement of oxygen by chlorine.

It can be seen from the distribution of F and Cl in the minerals of the massif that considerable quantities of these elements are combined in the form of villiaum-ite and sodalite.

In addition to sodium fluoride it is clear that potassium fluoride, sodium chloride and potassium chloride were also formed in the Lovozero massif, but because of their high solubility, they were removed by aqueous solutions (Table 184).

The information given shows that the content of F and Cl was considerably higher in the primary magma but that, because of the ready solubility of the com-pounds of these elements, considerable quantities were removed from the massif by hydrothermal solutions. Only sodium fluoride (villiaumite), which is not very readily soluble, formed in large quantities.

TABLE 184 Solubility of the fluorine and chlorine compounds of
Na and K in grams per 100 grams of water at
various temperatures

F and Cl compounds	20°	100°
NaCl	36·0	39·1
NaF	4·2	5·0
KCl	34·0	56·7
KF	95·0	150·0 (80°)

Carbon (6)

The Lovozero massif is extremely poor in carbon. It is a main constituent of only four minerals, of which calcite (44 per cent CO_2), cerussite (16·5 per cent CO_2) and ancylite (22·7-28·38 per cent CO_2) are mineralogical rarities, while cancrinite (0·3-6·3 per cent CO_2) is more widely distributed. Its mean content in the massif is approximately 0·06 per cent. Small quantities of CO_2 are also found (see Table 169) in erikite (1·16 per cent CO_2) and staffelite [francolite] (1·52 per cent CO_2).

All these minerals were late-forming and crystallized in the third and fourth stages in the formation of the massif. It follows that carbon concentration was highest during these stages. CO_2 is also found in the supergene minerals natron (15·4 per cent) and allophane (up to 1·2 per cent).

The carbon in cancrinite, erikite, allophane and staffelite [francolite], probably in the form CO_3^{2-}, isomorphously replaces PO_4^{3-}, SO_4^{2-}, fluorine or the hydroxyl group.

III. Rare Elements

There are more than 30 rare elements in the Lovozero alkali massif including Li, Rb, Cs, Be, Ra, Sc, Ga, Y, R.E., Tl, Ti, Ge, Zr, Hf, Th, Nb, Ta and Te. Titanium is provisionally included in the group because of its major rôle in the geochemistry of a number of rare elements. Taken together these elements account for approximately only 1·5 per cent of the volume of the massif. Seven of them (Li, Be, R.E., Ti, Th, Zr and Nb) form their own rare-metal minerals that are specific to the massif—loparite, murmanite, lomonosovite, ramsayite, lamprophyllite, eudialyte, mesodialyte, lovozerite, rinkolite, lovchorrite, nordite, steenstrupine, chkalovite, epididymite, tainiolite, polylithionite etc., while the remaining rare elements are incorporated in small quantities in the crystalline structures of the minerals of other elements and do not form their own minerals.

Lithium (3)

The mean lithium content of the Lovozero massif (0·02 per cent) is approximately three times its clarke for igneous rocks. Most of the Li in the massif has been dispersed in the rock-forming minerals because of the similarity of its ionic radius to that of magnesium ($Li^{1+} - 0.68$ Å and $Mg^{2+} - 0.74$ Å) and the similarity of a number of its properties to sodium. Independent lithium minerals are found only in the most differentiated highly-replaced pegmatites of the poikilitic syenite complex.

At present only two lithium minerals are known in the Lovozero massif: tainiolite (2·44-3·21 per cent Li_2O) and polylithionite (3·66-6·23 per cent Li_2O). Chemical analyses have revealed the presence of Li in the following minerals from the pegmatites: late albite (0·02 per cent Li_2O), hackmanite (0·1 per cent), neptunite (1·08 per cent), biotite (1·1 per cent), psilomelane (0·05 per cent), silicophosphates (0·09 per cent) and natrolite (0·1 per cent). Spectrographic analysis reveals its presence in nepheline, microcline, aegirine (0·005 per cent), arfvedsonite (0·05-0·5 per cent), ussingite, schizolite (0·5 per cent), sauconite (0·5 per cent and under), halloysite (0·5 per cent) etc. (see Table 169). Mean lithium content is 0·02 per cent in the differentiated complex and 0·03 per cent in the eudialytic lujavrite complex. Its mean content has not been calculated in the poikilitic syenite complex, but it can be assumed to be higher than in the first two in view of the comparatively high lithium content of sodalite and hackmanite (0·1 per cent Li_2O), which are main minerals in the rocks of the poikilitic syenite complex. The Li_2O

content in different rocks of the massif varies from traces to 0·09 per cent (analyst Yu. S. Nesterova). Li_2O content is 0·09 per cent in foyaites, 0·04 per cent in hornblende-lujavrites, 0·0-0·06 per cent in aegirine-lujavrites, 0·04-0·09 per cent in eudialytic lujavrites, 0·07 per cent in porphyritic lujavrites and 0·04 per cent in eudialytites. Thus, lithium content is higher in varieties rich in albite, sodalite and aegirine. Li is practically absent from nepheline rocks (urtites and juvites).

The lithium content in the large pegmatitic bodies of the poikilitic syenite complex is probably higher than in the parent rocks, as is indicated by the presence of independent lithium minerals and larger quantities in the main minerals.

There are certain differences in the geochemical history of Li in the rocks and in the pegmatites. It is found only in a dispersed state in the rocks, whereas in the pegmatites, though it is also found there dispersed, considerable concentrations of lithium are typical in many cases. Both in the rocks and in the pegmatites Li was dispersed in the first three stages of mineral formation and incorporated in the main minerals (aegirine, arfvedsonite, biotite and sodalite), the greater part being combined in arfvedsonite during the second stage. The general features of the geochemistry of lithium were determined by the similarity of the ionic radii to that of magnesium, which is more widely distributed in the massif (0·72 per cent), and it was mainly incorporated in the crystalline structures of magnesium-containing minerals on the pattern: $2Mg^{2+} \leftarrow Li^{1+} + (Fe, Al)^{3+}$.

Because of the lower lithium content in the alkali magma compared with its content in pegmatitic melt-solutions, particularly those associated with poikilitic syenites, and because of its dispersion in the rock-forming minerals of the first three stages, lithium failed to play any significant part during the hydrothermal stage in the formation of the rocks and the majority of the undifferentiated pegmatites, and did not form its own minerals. During the formation of the completely-differentiated pegmatites of the poikilitic syenite complex the concentration of lithium increased towards the end of the process, owing to the higher lithium content in the melt solution and to crystallization differentiation, and was sufficient in the hydrothermal stage for the formation of tainiolite and polylithionite. It should be noted that tainiolite, which is an earlier mineral of the replacement stage, contains less Li_2O than later polylithionite. It therefore follows that the lithium concentration increased towards the end of the events of the replacement stage.

In addition to the formation of independent minerals, small quantities of lithium were incorporated in albite, natrolite, neptunite, psilomelane and other minerals during the hydrothermal stage in the formation of the pegmatites. Mutual isomorphism of Li^{1+} and Mg^{2+} on the pattern $Li^{1+} + Si^{4+} \rightleftarrows Mg^{2+} + Al^{3+}$ is widely manifested in lithia micas.

The position of lithium in the aluminosilicates of sodium and in neptunite is not quite clear. Rankama and Sahama (1949) are of the opinion that lithium can replace Al^{+3} in aluminosilicates, but the possibility is not excluded that it may in some cases isomorphously replace sodium, as is indicated by the constant presence of Li in sodic minerals, the similarity of their chemical properties and the intimate association of these elements in natural processes.

Rubidium (37)

The rubidium content of the massif varies between 0·001 and 0·005 per cent, i.e. considerably less than its clarke for igneous rocks (0·031 per cent). So far Rb has been determined in only four minerals by the X-ray spectrographic method: orthoclase (0·001 per cent), kupletskite (0·2 per cent), labuntsovite (0·3 per cent) and tainiolite (0·3 per cent). These minerals are found in the slightly contaminated pegmatites of the poikilitic syenite complex.

Very small amounts of rubidium are found in all the rocks of the massif. Its content is usually highest in rocks rich in potassium feldspar—foyaites, aegirine-, hornblende- and eudialytic lujavrites. There is considerably less rubidium in rocks that contain mainly sodic minerals (nepheline, sodalite, and natrolite). These include urtites, ijolitic urtites, malignites, juvites and poikilitic nepheline-sodalite-syenites. This distribution of Rb is in agreement with its geochemical characteristics that determine the intimate connexion between Rb and potassium minerals, in which it replaces K owing to the similarity of the ionic radii and properties of these two elements.

Caesium (55)

Caesium is not typical of the Lovozero massif. Spectrographic analysis has revealed its presence only in the aegirine-lujavrites of the differentiated complex.

Beryllium (4)

At 0·001 per cent the mean beryllium content of the massif, calculated from chemical analyses of the different rock types, is more than double the clarke of this element for igneous rocks. Extremely high dispersion is a typical feature of the geochemistry of beryllium in the Lovozero massif. Almost all the Be is dispersed in the crystalline structures of the main rock-forming minerals and it forms independent minerals only in certain pegmatitic bodies at a late stage in their formation. This behaviour of beryllium in the nepheline-syenites is largely due to the similarity of the ionic radii of Be and Si and the marked deficiency of silicon in the alkali magma. In a highly alkaline medium it is assumed that it forms a complex anion of the type $(BeO_4)^{6-}$ capable of replacing $(SiO_4)^{4-}$ in silicates and aluminosilicates. Isomorphous replacement of tetravalent silicon by divalent beryllium is facilitated by the presence of considerable quantities of high-valency cations (such as Fe, Ti, Zr, Nb, R.E. etc.) in the alkali magma, which compensate for the deficient charges in the respective crystalline structures (Beus, 1956).

Beryllium has been found by spectrographic and chemical analysis to be present in more than 75 minerals of the Lovozero massif, only 8 of which are independent beryllium minerals and these of rare occurrence: genthelvite (12 per cent BeO), chkalovite (11·28-12·63 per cent), epididymite and eudidymite (9·66-12·9 per cent), beryllite (40 per cent), sphaerobertrandite (45·2 per cent), gel-bertrandite (34·16 per cent) and karpinskyite (2·58 per cent). Only the first 4 are primary minerals. All the beryllium minerals are found exclusively in pegmatites, mainly in the poikilitic syenite complex and were formed during the last stage in their formation—the replacement stage.

Beryllium is found in a dispersed state in the following minerals*: nepheline (0·001 per cent BeO), potassium feldspar (0·003-0·023 per cent)*, aegirine (0·0025 per cent), hornblende (0·014 per cent)*, murmanite (up to 0·05 per cent)**, nenadkevichite ($n \times 10^{-2}$ per cent), lamprophyllite (0·001 per cent)**, mangano-steenstrupine (0·003-0·023 per cent)*, chinglusuite (up to 0·01 per cent)**, nordite ($n \times 10^{-4}$ per cent), schizolite (0·003-0·023 per cent)*, hackmanite (0·0006-0·022 per cent), sodalite (0·003-0·023 per cent)*, analcite (0·33 per cent), prismatic natrolite (0·003 per cent), eudialyte (0·01 per cent), catapleiite (0·15 per cent), apatite (0·0014 per cent)*, staffelite [francolite] (0·4 per cent)*, karnasurtite (0·35 per cent), hydrocerite (0·3 per cent), ussingite (0·003-0·023 per cent)*, erikite (0·5 per cent), albite (up to 1 per cent), chlorites (0·1 per cent), psilomelane (up to 0·05 per cent)**, fine-grained natrolite (0·003-0·007 per cent), chalcedonic natrolite (0·138 per cent)*, polylithionite (0·07-0·24 per cent)*, tainiolite (0·05 per cent)*, hydromica (0·0014 per cent)*, hydrargillite (0·0003 per cent), mont-morillonite (0·005 per cent), zincian montmorillonite (0·03 per cent), sauconite (0·008 per cent), halloysite (0·5-0·7 per cent)*, etc. (see Table 169).

The Be content in the separate rock complexes of the massif is approximately of the same order: 0·0011 per cent in the differentiated complex, 0·0018 per cent in the eudialytic lujavrite complex, 0·0019 per cent* in the poikilitic syenites. Beryllium content in average samples of different rocks of the massif varies from 0·0004 to 0·0024 per cent (Table 185). Its content is higher in the poikilitic syenites and eudialytic lujavrites, probably because of its concentration in the magma of these rocks by emanation processes.

The Be content of the undifferentiated pegmatites is of the same order as in the parent rocks. In the well-differentiated and highly-replaced pegmatitic bodies of the poikilitic sodalite-syenite complex beryllium content reaches 0·02 per cent, which is more than 10 times its average content in the massif. One can therefore say that increased beryllium content is confined in the massif to the most highly-differentiated pegmatitic bodies that passed through all stages in the pegmatitic process.

The content of Be in the minerals of the massif increases from the minerals of the first to the last stages. Thus, BeO content is slight in the minerals that crystallized in the first stage and varies between 0·001 and 0·013 per cent, and higher (up to 0·014 per cent) in the second stage; minerals that contain several hundredths of one per cent of BeO (up to 0·022 per cent in hackmanite) appear in the third stage; in the fourth stage the content of dispersed beryllium in other minerals is increased (up to 0·015 per cent and above) and independent minerals of the element also appear. Thus the concentration of beryllium in the melt-solution increased towards the end of the process of formation of the massif.

In isomorphous replacement of silicon by beryllium in the aluminosilicates of

---

* Figures marked with one star have been taken from L. L. Shilin (1957), those marked with two stars are spectrographic analysis data.

TABLE 185 Beryllium content in the rocks*

Eudialytic lujavrite complex	Be content, per cent	Differentiated complex	Be content, per cent	Poikilitic syenite complex	Be content, per cent
Melanocratic eudialytic lujavrites	0·0024	Foyaites	0·001-0·002	Poikilitic syenites	0·0019†
Leucocratic eudialytic lujavrites	0·0015	Juvites	0·0016		
		Urtites	0·0009-0·002		
		Ijolite-urtites	0·0012		
Porphyritic eudialytic lujavrites	0·0008	Melanocratic lujavrites	0·0013		
		Mesocratic lujavrites	0·0005-		
Porphyritic juvites	0·0005		0·0013		
		Hornblende-lujavrites	0·0007		
		Malignites	0·0004		

* Analyst Fedorchuk   † Data of Shilin (1957)

TABLE 186 Gallium content in the rocks*

Complex	Rocks	Ga content, per cent
Eudialytic lujavrite	Eudialytic lujavrites	0·003-0·01
	Eudialytites	0·003-0·01
	Porphyritic lujavrites	0·005
Differentiated	Foyaites	0·01
	Urtites	0·01-0·03
	Aegirine-lujavrites	0·003
	Hornblende-lujavrites	0·004-0·01
	Malignites	0·008
Poikilitic syenite	Poikilitic sodalite-syenites	0·03
	Poikilitic nepheline-syenites	0·025
	Tawites	0·015

* Spectrographic determinations by Lizunov

sodium and potassium (nepheline, albite, sodalite, natrolite etc.) there is simultaneous replacement of the alkalis by calcium and less frequently by rare earths on the pattern: $Si^{4+} + 2(Na, K)^{1+} \leftarrow Be^{2+} + 2Ca^{2+}$; $Si^{4+} + (Na, K)^{1+} \leftarrow Be^{2+} + R.E.^{3+}$.

In such dark minerals as aegirine, arfvedsonite, schizolite and chlorites, and in montmorillonite, zincian montmorillonite and sauconite, electrostatic equilibrium is apparently maintained when silicon is replaced by beryllium by replacement of part of the magnesium, manganese or divalent iron by trivalent iron on the pattern: $Si^{4+} + 2(Fe, Mg, Mn)^{2+} \leftarrow Be^{2+} + 2Fe^{3+}$.

In complex titanoniobosilicates and zirconosilicates (eudialyte, catapleiite, nenadkevichite, murmanite, lamprophyllite etc.) beryllium is probably incorporated in the crystalline structures on replacement of titanium by niobium on the pattern: $2(Zr, Ti)^{4+} + Si^{4+} \leftarrow 2Nb^{5+} + Be^{2+}$.

The enhanced amounts of beryllium in phosphates, silicophosphates and other phosphorus-containing minerals (apatite, staffelite [francolite], steenstrupine, manganosteenstrupine, karnasurtite, erikite, hydrocerite etc.) arise from its incorporation with phosphorus in these minerals on replacement of silicon on the pattern: $3Si^{4+} \leftarrow 2P^{5+} + Be^{2+}$.

In replacement of silicon by beryllium in micas (polylithionite, tainiolite, hydromica etc.) there is simultaneous replacement of a corresponding amount of magnesium by aluminium or of oxygen by fluorine and the hydroxyl group. The possibility is not excluded that beryllium replaces aluminium isomorphously in these micas and that there is simultaneous replacement of a corresponding amount of potassium and sodium by divalent elements.

The increase in the concentration of Be in the melt-solution towards the end of the process of mineral formation, especially in pegmatites, has two causes: its concentration in a volatile state during the formation of the pegmatitic foci and its limited isomorphism with silicon and aluminium. Taken in conjunction with the concentration of silicon towards the end of the process of pegmatite formation, the concentration of beryllium leads to the development of a specific association consisting of the beryllium silicates of sodium, albite, beryllium-containing natrolite, lithia micas and, less frequently, quartz.

Scandium (21)

Scandium is not typical of the Lovozero massif. Spectrographic analyses of a large number of different types of rock and mineral show that scandium is practically absent from them. In the pegmatites it has been detected by the spectroscopic method (up to 0·05 per cent) only in early microcline from the Karnasurt pegmatites that are genetically associated with poikilitic syenites.

Gallium (31)

There is a concentration of gallium in the massif. Its mean content, as calculated from quantitative spectrographic analyses of average rock samples, is

0·0074 per cent, which is approximately five times the clarke of this element for igneous rocks. It is a typical dispersed element and does not form its own minerals. Owing to the similarity of the chemical properties and of the ionic radii of gallium (0·63 Å) and aluminium (0·57 Å) Ga is mainly dispersed in aluminosilicates.

Ga has been detected by spectrographic analysis in more than 40 minerals. It is concentrated in nepheline (0·003-0·01 per cent), microcline (up to 0·001 per cent), orthoclase (0·001 per cent), aenigmatite (0·001 per cent), early albite (up to 0·01 per cent),* hackmanite (0·043 per cent), nordite (0·0001 per cent), biotite (0·005 per cent), late albite (up to 0·02 per cent), ussingite (0·031 per cent), natrolite (0·02-0·04 per cent), polylithionite (0·02-0·026 per cent) etc. (see Table 169).

The Ga content is typically highest in hackmanite, natrolite and ussingite (0·02-0·04 per cent) crystallized in the fluid-hydrothermal and hydrothermal stages of mineral formation, and its content does not exceed hundredths of one per cent in first-stage minerals (nepheline and potassium feldspars). The mean content of gallium in the different rock complexes increases uniformly towards the youngest complex—the poikilitic syenites. The content of this element is 0·004 per cent in the rocks of the eudialytic lujavrite complex, 0·008 per cent in the rocks of the differentiated complex and 0·027 per cent in the rocks of the poikilitic syenite complex. Gallium has been detected by the spectrographic method in the rocks of all the complexes (Table 186).

The gallium content of the rocks does not normally exceed 0·01 per cent, except in rocks consisting mainly of aluminosilicates (urtites and poikilitic syenites) in which it may be as much as 0·03 per cent. It therefore follows that an increase in aluminium content in the rocks of the massif (see Tables 172 and 186) leads to an increase in gallium content. The highest gallium concentration is confined to well-differentiated pegmatites genetically associated with poikilitic sodalite-syenites.

Gallium is known to have both lithophile and chalcophile properties. The deficiency of aluminium relative to alkalis in the magma of the Lovozero massif helped to bring out the lithophile properties of gallium in the main, despite the

TABLE 187 Al:Ga ratio in the minerals of the massif

| Stage | Minerals | Content, per cent | | Al:Ga ratio |
		Al	Ga	
I	Nepheline	17·11	0·003	5703
	Potassium feldspar	10·07	0·001	10070
II	Aenigmatite	0·99	0·001	990
III	Hackmanite	16·84	0·043	392
IV	Natrolite	14·31	up to 0·04	358
	Ussingite	9·17	0·031	296
	Polylithionite	6·95	up to 0·026	267

* Spectrographic data.

significant content of sulphur. This is shown by the quite tiny gallium content of sphalerite and other sulphides.

The ratio of aluminium to gallium did not remain constant in the process of mineral formation but decreased uniformly from the early to late stages (Table 187).

Despite the similarity of crystallochemical and chemical properties of Ga and Al, the former shows a greater capacity to concentrate in the late stages of the process of mineral formation, which is also typical of other rare elements that isomorphously replace the main rock-forming elements.

Yttrium (39)

Despite its enhanced content in the massif, yttrium behaves as a typical dispersed element in the process of mineral formation and does not form its own minerals. At 2.34×10^{-2} per cent, its mean content in the massif is 8.3 times the yttrium clarke for igneous rocks.

The presence of yttrium has been established by chemical and X-ray spectrographic analyses in 9 minerals: loparite (0.01-0.05 per cent Y_2O_3), eudialyte (0.23-0.41 per cent), zircon (1.65 per cent), rinkolite (0.14 per cent), steenstrupine (0.77 per cent), manganosteenstrupine (0.13 per cent), nordite (0.95 per cent) and zirfesite (0.3 per cent). In addition it has been detected by spectrographic analysis in nepheline, aegirine, murmanite, natrolite, elpidite, leucophane, apophyllite, chlorites, Zn-montmorillonite, halloysite, kaolinite, cerussite, apatite (late) and other minerals (see Table 169).

Thus, Y is incorporated as a substituent in the crystalline structures of rare-earth and zirconium minerals, in which it isomorphously replaces elements of the rare-earth group and zirconium. Very small amounts of substitution are also found in calcic and sodic minerals. The yttrium content is highest in the zircon typical of contaminated rocks and pegmatites.

Owing to the similarity of its properties to those of the rare earths and their quantitative predominance, yttrium is intimately associated with the elements of this group, though its behaviour in the process of mineral formation follows somewhat different patterns. The accumulated data indicate that there are fundamental differences between the geochemistry of yttrium and the elements of the rare-earth group, which is fully to be expected, since yttrium occupies an independent place in the periodic system and has properties that differ considerably from those of the rare earths.

In natural processes yttrium sometimes forms its own minerals and deposits, in which rare-earth elements are present in subordinate quantities. This feature is also found in the Lovozero alkali massif, in which yttrium is often separated from the rare earths and concentrated in zirconium minerals. Yttrium differs from the rare earths, especially the cerium subgroup, in being concentrated in minerals formed in a volatile-enriched medium (eudialyte and zircon).

A considerable amount of the Y in the massif is concentrated in eudialyte, probably because of the geochemical affinity of this element with zirconium. On replacement of zirconium by yttrium in zircon and eudialyte electrostatic neutrality is achieved by the simultaneous incorporation in the crystalline structures of these minerals of higher valency cations (niobium and tantalum) or by reduction of the charge in the anionic part: $2Zr^{4+} \leftarrow (Nb, Ta)^{5+} + Y^{3+}$.

The presence of small amounts of yttrium in the aluminosilicates of sodium is apparently due to its incorporation in place of part of the sodium and calcium to maintain electrostatic equilibrium on replacement of silicon by aluminium (see 'The Rare Earths').

The Rare Earths (57-71)

Elements of the rare-earth group are typical of the rocks and pegmatites of the Lovozero massif, and those of the cerium subgroup greatly exceed those of the yttrium subgroup. Apart from being incorporated in the crystal lattices of other minerals, the cerium rare earths sometimes form independent minerals, whereas elements of the yttrium subgroup, like yttrium itself, are distributed in the minerals of the cerium rare earths, zirconium, titanium and niobium and do not form their own minerals.

At 0·12 per cent the mean content of the rare earths in the Lovozero massif is eight times their clarke (0·015 per cent) for igneous rocks. There are marked differences to the content of individual elements of the rare-earth group in the massif: the least content is typical of Lu (3.6×10^{-4}) and the greatest content of Ce (3.78×10^{-2}; Table 188). The clarkes of the individual rare-earth elements are between 5 and 24 times greater than their clarkes for igneous rocks.

Rare earths have been detected by chemical, X-ray spectrographic and spectro-

TABLE 188   Rare-earth content in the Lovozero massif (per cent)*

Elements	Lovozero massif	Igneous rocks according to Rankama (Rankama and Sahama, 1949)	Abundance ratio in the massif
Cerium	3.78×10^{-2}	4.61×10^{-3}	8·2
Lanthanum	1.55×10^{-2}	1.83×10^{-3}	8·5
Praseodymium	5.52×10^{-3}	5.53×10^{-4}	10
Neodymium	1.68×10^{-2}	2.39×10^{-3}	7
Samarium	4.8×10^{-3}	6.47×10^{-4}	7·4
Europium	1.2×10^{-3}	1.06×10^{-4}	11·3
Gadolinium	4.8×10^{-3}	6.36×10^{-4}	7·5
Terbium	6×10^{-4}	9.1×10^{-5}	6·6
Dysprosium	3.72×10^{-3}	4.47×10^{-4}	8·3
Holmium	6×10^{-4}	1.15×10^{-4}	5·2
Erbium	2.64×10^{-3}	2.47×10^{-4}	10·7
Thulium	4.8×10^{-4}	2×10^{-5}	24
Ytterbium	1.8×10^{-3}	2.66×10^{-4}	6·8
Lutecium	3.6×10^{-4}	7.5×10^{-5}	4·8

   * Calculated on the basis of the ratios of the rare-earth elements in loparite, apatite and eudialyte established by Barinskii using the X-ray spectrographic method.

graphic methods in more than 45 minerals (see Table 169). They are a main constituent of 12 minerals—loparite (30-35·29 per cent R.E.$_2$O$_3$), apatite (2-7·71 per cent), rinkolite (18·41 per cent), steenstrupine (24·01 per cent), mangano-steenstrupine (20·06 per cent), nordite (19·25 per cent), metaloparite (34·2 per cent), hydrocerite (17·16 per cent), belovite (24 per cent), karnasurtite (15·78-17·58 per cent), erikite (50·3-55·96 per cent) and ancylite (37·81 per cent). Of these minerals, only loparite, apatite, rinkolite and metaloparite are typical of the rocks of the massif: the others are found exclusively in the pegmatites and mainly in the poikilitic syenite complex.

Small quantities of rare earths are found in schizolite (1 per cent R.E.$_2$O$_3$), minerals of the eudialyte group (0·81-2·43 per cent), nenadkevichite (0·25-0·3 per cent), ramsayite (0·32 per cent), kupletskite (0·2 per cent), pyrochlore (3·38 per cent), chinglusuite (0·94-1·18 per cent), lovozerite (0·56 per cent), catapleiite (0·24-0·39 per cent), montmorillonite (0·06 per cent), sauconite (0·022 per cent), halloysite (0·7 per cent), vernadite (0·92 per cent), zirfesite (2·12 per cent) and jarosite (0·9 per cent). Spectrographic analysis also reveals rare earths in nepheline, microcline, aegirine I, ilmenite, aegirine II, arfvedsonite, murmanite, lampro-phyllite, natrolite, neptunite, leucophane, apophyllite, chlorites, zincian mont-morillonite, kaolinite, galena and cerussite.

The rare earths are unevenly distributed among the rock complexes. Thus, their mean content is 0·15 per cent in the differentiated complex and 0·09 per cent in the eudialytic lujavrite complex. The total content of rare earths in different rock types and within the same rock varies from traces to 0·74 per cent (Table 189).

The highest content of rare earths is typical of the juvites and urtites of the differentiated complex and also of the eudialytic lujavrites.

Analysis of the composition of rare earths in the minerals of the Lovozero massif indicates that cerium usually predominates, followed in descending order by lanthanum, neodymium, praseodymium, samarium, gadolinium, dysprosium etc. (Borovskii, 1946; Semenov and Barinskii, 1958). There are, however, considerable variations in the quantitative ratios of these elements (Table 190) in different minerals, which illustrate the differences as well as the common features

TABLE 189 Total content of rare earths in the rocks

Complex	Rocks	RE$_2$O$_3$ content per cent
Eudialytic lujavrite	Eudialytic lujavrites	up to 0·30
	Porphyritic lujavrites	0·06
Differentiated	Foyaites	0·11
	Juvites	up to 0·74
	Urtites	up to 0·68
	Aegirine-lujavrites	up to 0·28
	Hornblende-lujavrites	trace
Poikilitic syenite	Poikilitic nepheline-syenites	trace
	Poikilitic sodalite-syenites	not det.
	Poikilitic hydrosodalite-syenites	,, ,,

TABLE 190 Content of rare earths in the minerals (weight per cent, taking ΣRE_2O_3 as 100 per cent)*

Minerals	RE_2O_3 content, per cent	La_2O_3	Ce_2O_3	Pr_2O_3	Nd_2O_3	Sm_2O_3	Eu_2O_3	Gd_2O_3	Tb_2O_3	Dy_2O_3	Ho_2O_3	Er_2O_3	Tu_2O_3	Yb_2O_3	Lu_2O_3
Loparite (from the rocks)	30·00–35·29	25	53·25	6	14	0·9	0·08	0·56	0·037	0·12	0·008	0·016	0·003	0·008	0·002
Apatite (from the rocks)	6·78–7·71	22	51	5·9	17	1·7	0·2	1·6	0·2	0·4	—	0·3	—	0·2	—
Apatite (from the pegmatites)		21	45	6·8	21	3·7	0·3	1·2	0·1	0·3	0·8	3·6	0·6	2·6	0·4
Eudialyte (from the rocks)	0·81–2·43	14	37	5·7	17·0	6·0	0·8	6·0	0·8	4·8	—	—	—	—	—
Eudialyte (from the pegmatites of the sodalite-syenites)															
Rinkolite	18·41	11	35	7	22	7·2	1·6	6·7	1	4·4	0·9	1·9	0·4	0·5	0·2
Chinglusuite	0·94	3·1	51	8·0	19	4·0	0·2	0·5	—	0·4	—	0·1	—	—	—
Steenstrupine	24·01	24	21	6·8	25	12	1·4	9·5	1·6	9	1·9	4·1	0·8	2·9	0·6
Nordite	19·25	34	55	7·3	20	0·7	—	—	—	0·1	—	0·1	—	0·2	—
Belovite	35·25	22	52	4·1	7·0	0·5	0·1	—	—	—	—	—	—	—	—
Karnasurtite	16·37	24	58	7·8	18·0	1·6	—	0·5	—	—	—	—	—	—	—
Erikite	50·30–55·96	39	48	4·5	11	0·3	—	—	—	—	—	—	—	—	—
Thorite		22	55	3·4	9·3	1·9	—	0·3	—	4	1	2·4	0·2	1·7	0·3
Apophyllite		17	33	6·1	21	6	0·6	5·8	0·8	—	—	—	—	—	—

* Analyst: Barinskii

TABLE 191 Titanium content in the rocks

Eudialytic lujavrite complex	TiO_2 content, per cent	Differentiated complex	TiO_2 content, per cent
Eudialytic lujavrites	0·95–3·86	Foyaites	0·24–0·64
Melanocratic eudialytic lujavrites	3·12	Juvites	0·52
		Urtites	0·15–5·44
Leucocratic eudialytic lujavrites	2·10	Melanocratic lujavrites	1·66–4·32
		Mesocratic lujavrites	0·42–1·42
Porphyritic lujavrites	0·41–1·60	Leucocratic lujavrites	0·50
Porphyritic juvites	1·24–3·60	Hornblende-lujavrites	0·72–1·04
Eudialytites	0·70–2·08	Malignites	7·28–12·80

Poikilitic syenite complex	TiO_2 content, per cent
Poikilitic sodalite-syenites	0·44
Poikilitic nepheline-syenites	0·27–1·51
Poikilitic hydrosodalite-syenites	0·66–0·72
Tawites	1·51–1·64

in their geochemistry. In some minerals, such as eudialyte, rinkolite, apophyllite and chinglusuite there is more neodymium than lanthanum (chinglusuite, eudialyte, rinkolite and apophyllite) or cerium (chinglusuite).

It is interesting that minerals of the eudialyte group differ from most other minerals containing rare earths in that the importance of yttrium and the rare earths of its subgroup is distinctly increased. The yttrium subgroup accounts for approximately 20 per cent of the rare earths in them, while in loparite these elements account for only 1 per cent. Furthermore, the yttrium content of eudialyte is more than 20 per cent of the total rare earths, whereas in loparite its content is measured in hundredths of one per cent.

The greater part of the rare earths in the rocks of the massif was combined in the first stage of mineral formation on the crystallization of the accessory minerals, apatite and loparite. In the second stage rare earths were incorporated in the crystalline lattices of zirconium, titanium and niobium minerals and did not form their own minerals, with the exception of rinkolite, which is rare. There was almost no formation of rare-earth minerals in the third and fourth stages. Rare earths are present only in minerals that developed after high-temperature rare-earth minerals (metaloparite) or other minerals containing rare earths (lovozerite, catapleiite, zirfesite etc.).

The fate of rare earths in pegmatites is interesting. The pegmatites of the massif differ from the rocks in having a lower content of rare earths, as is shown by the almost total absence of loparite and apatite. Rare-earth minerals developed in the pegmatites of the poikilitic syenite complex only at late stages in their formation. There were two stages to the formation of rare-earth minerals in the pegmatites—at the beginning of the fluid-hydrothermal stage and at the end of the hydrothermal stage. The concentration of the rare earths increased in the early stages of the pegmatitic process during the crystallization of nepheline, feldspar and aegirine and of zirconium, titanium and niobium minerals, in which small quantities of rare earths were incorporated. By the beginning of the fluid-hydrothermal stage this concentration sufficed for the formation of rare-earth minerals: steenstrupine, manganosteenstrupine and nordite. In the third and fourth stages of mineral formation rare-earths accumulated in the residual pegmatitic solution since the greater part of the rock-forming elements had entered the solid phase as hackmanite and prismatic natrolite. They were precipitated from the solutions as phosphates, silicophosphates and silicates of the rare earths and thorium at the end of the fourth stage in mineral formation. It remains possible that the increased concentration of the rare earths towards the end of the hydrothermal stage was also due to decomposition of higher-temperature rare-earth minerals.

Isomorphous inter-replacements between rare earths and calcium are of widespread occurrence in the minerals of the Lovozero alkali massif. Practically all the calcic and calcium-containing minerals also contain rare earths, while the rare-earth minerals, in their turn, contain calcium. The most complete isomorphism of this type is revealed in loparite, metaloparite, apatite, belovite, pyrochlore, rinkolite, eudialyte etc. in which an increase in rare-earth content is usually accompanied by a decrease in the quantity of calcium. Thus, the CaO content falls in loparite from 5·6 to 3·7 per cent and the total content of rare earths shows a corresponding increase from 30·65 to 35·06 per cent $R.E._2O_3$ (see Tables 71 and 72). On replacement of Ca^{2+} by $R.E.^{3+}$ valency compensation is clearly effected by simultaneous incorporation of sodium in place of calcium, silicon in place of phosphorus or hydroxyl and fluorine in the anion section on the pattern: $2Ca^{2+} \leftarrow R.E.^{3+} + (Na, K)^{1+}$; $Ca^{2+} + P^{5+} \leftarrow R.E.^{3+} + Si^{4+}$; $Ca^{2+} \leftarrow R.E.^{3+} (F, OH)^{-1}$.

In the zirconosilicates (eudialyte, mesodialyte, catapleiite and lovozerite) part of the rare earths probably compensates valencies on replacement of zirconium by niobium and tantalum in addition to replacing calcium (see 'Yttrium').

The presence of rare earths in the titanosilicates, silicates and aluminosilicates of sodium and potassium and clay minerals can be explained by their incorporation to compensate valencies on replacement of titanium by niobium and silicon by aluminium by simple patterns: $2Ti^{4+} \leftarrow (Nb, Ta)^{5+} + R.E.^{3+}$; $2Si_4 + (K, Na)^{1+} \leftarrow 2Al^{3+} + R.E.^{3+}$; $Si^{4+} + (Mg, Ca)^{2+} \leftarrow Al^{3+} + R.E.^{3+}$.

Many problems arise during analysis of the data on the distribution of rare earths in rocks and minerals. It would be most interesting to establish the reasons for the dispersion of the rare earths in many minerals and for the different ratios between individual elements of this group in different minerals.

The data indicate that despite similarity in physico-chemical and crystallo-chemical properties, the individual elements of the rare-earth group behave somewhat differently in different mineral-forming processes (see Table 190) and enter the crystalline structures of the minerals in different ratios. This is because each element of this group has specific properties, which are now used in their industrial separation. Although the separation of elements of this group is not complete in natural processes, the tendency for separation is clearly revealed.

The relative concentration of the heaviest rare-earth elements (the Yttrium subgroup) in the eudialyte of the upper part of the massif and in the rare-earth minerals in the pegmatites of the sodalite-syenites, which are the most volatile-enriched, leads one to assume that the elements of this group were separated in the volatile state, probably as chlorides.

Differences in the chemical composition and crystalline structure of minerals into which the rare earths are incorporated is another important factor in the separation of rare-earth elements. Attention should be paid to the considerable differences in the ionic radii, which vary from 0·14 Å for lanthanum to 0·80 Å for lutecium, and to the capacity of some of these elements to alter their valency in a given medium (Ce^{3+} and Ce^{4+}; Pr and Nd can probably be tetravalent, europium is probably quite frequently in a divalent state). The behaviour of the rare earths and their uneven distribution in the minerals and the stages of the crystallization process were also affected by the intricate nature of the chemical composition of the massif: elements such as Ti, Zr, Nb, Ta, Mn and Fe, which change their properties with alteration in the environment, were involved in its formation.

Thallium (81)

Thallium is not typical of the Lovozero massif and has been detected by spectrographic analysis in only four minerals (apatite from the rocks, cryptomelane, galena and cerussite).

Titanium (22)

Titanium is one of the most important elements in the Lovozero massif, and has a considerable effect on the geochemistry of a whole series of elements, the chief being Nb, Ta, R.E., Zr etc. At 0·71 per cent its mean content in the massif is approximately one and a half times the clarke of the element for igneous rocks. The geochemical history of titanium was determined by the excess of alkalis over aluminium and silicon in the alkali magma. Besides complex oxides, it formed many complex sodium titanosilicates and was also incorporated into the crystalline structures of the zirconosilicates and silicates of Fe and Mg.

Some titanium is present in most of the minerals of the massif. Titanium oxide is a main constituent of 24 minerals: titan-låvenite (up to 11·3 per cent), loparite (up to 41·45 per cent), pyrochlore (8·04 per cent), manganilmenite (up to 51·35 per cent), sphene (up to 40·5 per cent), lomonosovite (up to 29·77 per cent), murmanite (up to 30·4 per cent), nenadkevichite (up to 12·12 per cent), ramsayite (up to 47 per cent), lamprophyllite (up to 31·26 per cent), astrophyllite, kuplet-skite (12·04 per cent), aenigmatite (8·16 per cent), chinglusuite (up to 9·62 per cent), rinkolite (8·27 per cent), metaloparite (44·01 per cent), belyankinite (up to 49·32 per cent), mangan-neptunite (up to 17·38 per cent), narsarsukite (19·25 per cent), rutile (94 per cent), brookite (86·89 per cent), anatase (95 per cent), karnasurtite (up to 12·33 per cent) etc. (see Table 169). Nearly all these minerals crystallized directly from the magmatic or pegmatitic melt-solution and only a few (metalo-parite, belyankinite, rutile, brookite and anatase) are secondary minerals formed from primary titanium minerals under the action of hydrothermal solutions in the third and fourth stages of mineral formation. The primary titanium minerals were crystallized mainly in the second stage. Loparite, ilmenite and titan-låvenite crystallized in the first stage; the last two are of extremely rare occurrence in alkali rocks and are then found only in contaminated varieties.

Most of the titanium minerals (lomonosovite, murmanite, lamprophyllite, ramsayite, nenadkevichite etc.), which formed in the second stage, are accessory minerals in the rocks, and it is only in the pegmatites that they sometimes occur in considerable quantities. Mean titanium content is highest in the rocks of the eudialytic lujavrite complex (1·13 per cent), where there is almost twice the content found in the differentiated complex (0·54 per cent).

The titanium content of the poikilitic syenites (0·36 per cent) is lower than that of the differentiated complex. The higher titanium content in the eudialytic lujavrite complex is due to the presence in the rocks of a large amount of aegirine, which contains up to 2-3 per cent of TiO_2, and of minerals of the eudialyte group, which contain 0·3-0·9 per cent TiO_2. There is an increase in titanium content in the rocks of the massif from leucocratic to melanocratic varieties, mainly owing to the increase in aegirine content (Table 191).

The mean titanium content of the pegmatitic melt solution was no lower than that of the magma. This is indicated by the large content of titanium minerals (lamprophyllite, ramsayite, murmanite, aenigmatite etc.) in the pegmatites (higher, in a number of cases, than in the rocks) especially in the pegmatites of the differentiated complex.

Calculations of the mineralogical composition of the massif reveal that approximately 10 per cent of the titanium was precipitated from the melt in the first stage of mineral formation, approximately 80 per cent in the second stage and approximately 10 per cent in the third and fourth stages combined. Thus, titanium concentration was highest in the second stage, when a great many titanium minerals were formed. This behaviour of titanium is due mainly to its very small dispersion in aluminosilicates, most of which were crystallized in the first stage of mineral formation. Such minerals as aegirine and eudialyte, in which large amounts of titanium were incorporated, did not play a fundamental rôle in the first stage.

There are widespread indications in the Lovozero massif of the isomorphous replacement of titanium by the niobium that is always present in titanium minerals; an increase in niobium content is accompanied by a corresponding decrease in titanium content (see 'Niobium').

Titanium is present in a dispersed state in nearly all the minerals, though most of it resides in aegirine and eudialyte.

The isomorphism of Ti to Zr and Fe is most widely developed in the Lovozero massif. Isomorphous replacement of zirconium by titanium is found in titanlåvenite, eudialyte, mesodialyte, catapleiite, lovozerite, zircon and other zirconium minerals. It is most clearly manifested in minerals of the låvenite group, in which decrease in zirconium content from 20·79 to 16·72 per cent ZrO_2 is accompanied by increase in titanium content from 2·35 to 11·30 per cent TiO_2. On replacement of Fe^{3+} by titanium in the silicates of iron (aegirine, arfvedsonite etc.) lower valency cations e.g. Al^{3+} and $(Mn, Mg)^{2+}$ were probably incorporated simultaneously with titanium to compensate valencies. Electroneutrality was effected by the patterns: $2Fe^{3+} \leftarrow Ti^{4+} + Mn^{2+}$; $Fe^{3+} + Si^{4+} \leftarrow Ti^{4+} + Al^{3+}$.

The presence of titanium in lithia micas and clay minerals is clearly due to replacement of Mg^{2+} by titanium on the pattern: $2Mg^{2+} \leftarrow Ti^{3+} + Li^{1+}$.

Very small amounts of titanium are also present in the aluminosilicates of sodium and potassium.

Germanium (32)

Germanium has not been discovered in the rocks of the massif. It is only in the beryllite and brown sphene, found exclusively in the intricately replaced pegmatites of the poikilitic syenite complex and formed at the close of the hydrothermal stage in the pegmatitic process, that spectrographic analysis has revealed traces of germanium.

Zirconium (40)

Zirconium is a widely-distributed element in the Lovozero massif. At 0·55 per cent its mean content in the massif is 25 times the zirconium clarke for igneous rocks. Zr is known to have 6-fold and 8-fold co-ordination in mineral structures. In granite massifs, in which there is a deficiency of large cations by comparison with silicon and aluminium, zirconium forms a simple silicate, zircon, in the structure of which it has 8-fold co-ordination. In nepheline-syenite massifs and, especially in the Lovozero massif, where there is excess of alkalis over aluminium and silicon, zircon is incorporated in crystalline structures mainly in 6-fold co-ordination in place of the missing aluminium, and most of it forms complex zirconosilicates of sodium and calcium. The abundance of zirconium in the massif has led to the formation of many zirconium minerals and to its incorporation as an isomorphous admixture in Ti, Nb and R.E. minerals and, to a lesser extent, in iron silicates.

Zirconium has been detected by chemical and spectrographic analyses in more than 50 minerals of the Lovozero massif (see Table 169) and is a main component of 10: titan-låvenite (16·72-23·20 per cent ZrO_2), seidozerite (23·14 per cent ZrO_2), minerals of the eudialyte group (11-14·37 per cent), zircon (61·42-65·08 per cent), lovozerite (up to 16·54 per cent), catapleiite (23·91-33·24 per cent), elpidite (20·33 per cent) and zirfesite (30·47 per cent).

The most widely-distributed zirconium minerals are those of the eudialyte group, which become major rock-forming minerals in some types of rock and pegmatite. Zircon and titan-låvenite occur only in the hybrid contaminated rocks and pegmatites. Zircon is also typical of metasomatic zones at the contacts of the massif. The other minerals were formed in the alteration of minerals of the eudialyte group.

An enhanced amount of zirconium oxide is also typical of titanium-niobium minerals: lomonosovite (0·91-2·88 per cent), murmanite (up to 2·06 per cent), ramsayite (up to 0·4 per cent), lamprophyllite (0·05-0·42 per cent), kupletskite (up to 1·19 per cent), pyrochlore (0·99 per cent), sphene (0·96 per cent), chinglusuite

TABLE 192 Zirconium content in the rocks

Complex	Rocks	ZrO_2 content, per cent
Eudialytic lujavrite	Eudialytic lujavrites	0·56-3·45
	Eudialytites	6·26-8·68
	Porphyritic lujavrites	0·18
	Porphyritic juvites	0·40-2·28
Differentiated	Foyaites	0·12-0·72
	Juvites	0·23
	Urtites	0·01-0·72
	Aegirine-lujavrites	0·13-1·05
	Hornblende-lujavrites	0·06-0·62
Poikilitic syenite	Poikilitic nepheline-syenites	0·16-0·49
	Poikilitic sodalite-syenites	0·37

(up to 3·02 per cent), belyankinite (3·06-6·64 per cent), brookite (0·5 per cent) etc. and of rare-earth and ferruginous minerals that contain certain amounts of titanium and niobium: arfvedsonite (0·09 per cent), manganosteenstrupine (1·08 per cent), hydrocerite (0·49 per cent), erikite (0·43 per cent) etc.

Zirconium content is highest in the rocks of the eudialytic lujavrite complex (mean content 1·36 per cent); its mean content is 0·19 per cent in the rocks of the differentiated complex and 0·14 per cent in the poikilitic syenites.

The high content of zirconium in the upper part of the massif and the presence of a large amount of chlorine (in eudialyte and sodalite) in this region lead one to assume that the zirconium was concentrated in the apical part of the massif as chlorides that ascended from lower parts of the magmatic hearth at early stages in the formation of the massif. The isomorphism of zirconium with titanium, niobium and the rare earths was due to the almost total absence of titanium, niobium and rare-earth minerals in the rocks of the eudialytic lujavrite complex, where the high zirconium concentration led to the crystallization of a large amount of minerals of the eudialyte group in which there was isomorphous incorporation of titanium, niobium and the rare earths.

The zirconium content of the various rock types varies from 0·01 to 8·68 per cent (Table 192). The abundance of minerals of the eudialyte group in the pegmatites of all complexes and especially in the eudialytic lujavrite complex indicates that the zirconium content of the pegmatitic melts was no lower than that of the parent magmas.

Except in the eudialytites, the greater part of the zirconium in all the rocks and pegmatites was combined as minerals of the eudialyte group during the second stage in the process of mineral formation. Zirconium minerals crystallized in the first stage in eudialytites, in which zirconium concentration was very high.

It has already been mentioned above that the isomorphism of zirconium for titanium and, to a lesser extent, for niobium, the rare earths and iron is widely manifested in the minerals of the Lovozero massif. There are significant amounts of zirconium in nearly all the titanium minerals.

Isomorphous replacement of iron by zirconium is found in the silicates of iron, aegirine and arfvedsonite. In these minerals zirconium probably replaces Fe^{2+} on the pattern: $2Si^{4+} + Fe^{2+} \leftarrow 2Al^{3+} + Zr^{4+}$.

The presence of zirconium in pyrochlore is apparently due to its incorporation in place of niobium to compensate valencies on replacement of calcium by rare earths on the pattern: $Ca^{2+} + Nb^{5+} \leftarrow R.E.^{3+} + Zr^{4+}$.

One can explain the presence of very small amounts of zirconium in aluminosilicates (nepheline, microcline, orthoclase, sodalite, albite etc.) by the replacement of large cations (Na, K, Ca) by zirconium atoms. The presence of considerable amounts of zirconium in clay minerals (halloysite, kaolinite, montmorillonite etc.) can be explained by the open packing of their structure, but most simply by sorption.

Hafnium (72)

There are very small admixtures of hafnium in the Lovozero massif. It is intimately associated with zirconium and accompanies it at all stages in the process of mineral formation. Hafnium is present exclusively in zirconium and zirconium-containing minerals, in which the ratio of zirconium to hafnium varies between 37 and 78 (Table 193).

On the basis of the $ZrO_2 : HfO_2$ ratio in eudialyte (the most widely distributed zirconium mineral of the rocks), which is 57 on average, the mean hafnium content of the massif will be 0·0097 per cent, approximately 22 times its clarke for igneous rocks. It should be noted that the ratio of hafnium and zirconium in the Lovozero massif is close to their ratio in the earth's crust.

TABLE 193   Zirconium and hafnium content in the minerals of the massif
(Gerasimovskii, 1957)

Minerals	Content, per cent		$\dfrac{ZrO_2}{HfO_2}$
	ZrO_2	HfO_2	
Zircon	60-66	1·15-1·40	45-57
Eudialyte:			
From the rocks	8·5-11·0	0·13-0·20	50-65
From the eudialytites	10-11	0·15-0·18	61-73
From the pegmatites	9-13·8	0·17-0·22	50-66
Lovozerite	11-15	0·14-0·20	72-78
Catapleiite	29-30	0·60-0·65	46-48
Titan-låvenite	15·6	0·28	56
Belyankinite	6-8	0·10-0·15	53-60
Zirfesite	32-34	0·87-0·90	37-38

Niobium (41)

The Lovozero massif is enriched in niobium. At 0·09 per cent its mean content in the massif is approximately 37 times the niobium clarke for igneous rocks. The geochemical fate of this element in the processes of mineral formation was determined by the high content of titanium, zirconium and the rare earths in the magma of the Lovozero massif, by the closeness of the physico-chemical properties of titanium and niobium and, especially, by the similarity of their ionic radii. The greater part of the niobium was incorporated in the crystalline structures of titanium, titanium-containing, zirconium and, less frequently, rare-earth minerals, or else formed minerals in common with titanium and the rare earths. Nb is most widely distributed in titanium minerals, is less typical of zirconium minerals (though it is present in all the zirconium minerals of the massif) and is found comparatively rarely in the true rare-earth and thorium minerals.

Niobium is present in 48 minerals of the massif (see Table 169) with wide variations in content (from fractions of one per cent to 52·09 per cent Nb_2O_5). The niobium content is very small in most of the minerals (approximately 40) and rarely exceeds 2-3 per cent. It is a main component of only 10 minerals— loparite (7·09-12·81 per cent Nb_2O_5), metaloparite (10·78 per cent), lomonosovite (up to 8·47 per cent), murmanite (6·56-7·71 per cent), belyankinite (up to 7·86 per cent), gerasimovskite (up to 44·9 per cent), nenadkevichite (24·05-24·61 per cent), pyrochlore (50·09 per cent), anatase (up to 21·61 per cent) and karnasurtite (up to 8·2 per cent). There is more niobium than titanium in pyrochlore, nenadkevichite and gerasimovskite, very small amounts of which are found in the massif. Pyrochlore is typical of contaminated pegmatites, while nenadkevichite and gerasimovskite are found only in the pegmatites of the poikilitic syenites. There are small amounts of niobium in brookite (3·44 per cent Nb_2O_5), ramsayite (up to 3·07 per cent), titan-låvenite (up to 3·01 per cent), rinkolite (2·58 per cent), rutile (up to 3 per cent), chlorites (2·71 per cent), zirfesite (up to 2·40 per cent), steenstrupine (up to 2·13 per cent), hydrocerite (2 per cent), manganosteen-strupine (up to 2 per cent), elpidite (1·43 per cent), manganilmenite (0·26-1·44 per cent), eudialyte (0·54-1·16 per cent), lamprophyllite (0·16-0·62 per cent), kupletskite (0·66-2·48 per cent), seidozerite (0·6 per cent), catapleiite (0·95 per cent), erikite (up to 0·9 per cent), polylithionite (0·4-0·95 per cent) and nontronite (0·01 per cent). It has also been detected in a considerable number of minerals by spectrographic analysis.

It should be noted that of the 48 minerals that contain niobium only 10 are found in the rocks of the massif (loparite, metaloparite, lomonosovite, murmanite, ramsayite, eudialyte, lamprophyllite, rinkolite, zirfesite and nontronite); the others are typical of the pegmatites.

The niobium content is approximately the same in the different rock complexes and ranges from 0·08 per cent in the eudialytic lujavrite and poikilitic syenite complexes to 0·09 per cent in the differentiated complex. Its distribution within each complex is extremely uneven (Table 194). In the rocks of the eudialytic lujavrite complex niobium content is typically highest in porphyritic juvites and eudialytites because of their increased content of eudialyte and loparite.

The mean content of niobium in the upper, middle and lower sectors of the differentiated complex is similar and of the same order as its mean content in the complex and in the massif as a whole. This indicates that the mobility of niobium

TABLE 194 Niobium content in the rocks

Complex	Rocks	(Nb, Ta)$_2$O$_5$ content, per cent
Eudialytic lujavrite	Eudialytic lujavrites	0·06-0·28
	Eudialytites	up to 0·93
	Porphyritic lujavrites	0·03-0·92
Differentiated	Foyaites	0·097-0·16
	Urtites	up to 0·25
	Ijolite-urtites	0·007
	Aegirine-lujavrites	0-0·66
	Hornblende-lujavrites	up to 0·12
Poikilitic syenite complex	Poikilitic nepheline-syenites	0·004-0·13
	Poikilitic sodalite-syenites	up to 0·41
	Tawites	0·03

in the volatile state is slight. Niobium was re-distributed among different rock types during the differentiation of the complex; in the upper and lower parts of the complex, where differentiation is well defined, there are regular features in the distribution of niobium in the three-component stratal groups; these features are obscured in the poorly-differentiated central part. An enhanced niobium concentration is usually found at the floors of urtite horizons, the upper parts of the adjacent aegirine-lujavrite horizons and in the central parts of foyaite horizons. A reduced concentration is found in aegirine-lujavrites and in the central parts and roofs of urtite horizons. The clearness with which this feature of the distribution of niobium is revealed is directly proportional to the extent of the differentiation of the rocks into foyaites, urtites and lujavrites. Nevertheless, despite the different niobium content of the various rocks, its mean content in each three-component stratal group approximately equals the mean content in the complex.

Two niobium-containing mineral associations can be distinguished in the three-component groups. Loparite is typical of the floors of urtite horizons and roofs of the underlying melanocratic lujavrites, minerals of the lomonosovite-murmanite group are typical of foyaite horizons, and in lujavrite horizons loparite is typical of the roofs and mainly lomonosovite or murmanite at the floors.

In the poikilitic syenite complex the content of both niobium and niobium-containing minerals is highest in sodalitic varieties.

It is very difficult to calculate the mean niobium content for the pegmatites as a whole owing to the variability of their composition. Sample calculations of the quantitative mineralogical composition of individual pegmatitic bodies do, however, indicate that figures for the mean content of niobium in them are very close to those for its mean content in the massif and in the respective parent rocks. In other words, the absolute concentration of niobium in the pegmatitic melt-solution cannot have been greatly in excess of its concentration in the parent alkali magma. The greater part of the niobium in alkali pegmatites is concentrated in the feldspar-aegirine zones, where niobium is located in murmanite, lomonosovite, nenadkevichite, belyankinite and other minerals.

Thus, the niobium content of the different rocks is approximately the same, though it occurs in different forms that reflect an alteration in the physico-chemical conditions of the environment.

A large part of the niobium in the massif was combined in loparite in the first stage of mineral formation. In the second stage it formed minerals of the lomonosovite-murmanite group or was incorporated as admixtures in titanium and zirconium minerals. In pegmatites, in which loparite was not formed in the first stage, niobium concentration increased towards the second stage in mineral formation and this led to the development of large quantities of murmanite. In the most developed types of pegmatite true niobium minerals also appeared (nenadkevichite). In the third stage of mineral formation, when the crystallization of the rocks had been largely ended and the processes of albitization and sodalitization had begun, niobium was almost absent from the pneumatolytic solutions.

There was still a significant amount of niobium in the pegmatitic solutions in the third stage. The crystallization during this stage of hackmanite and, partly, of prismatic natrolite, in which niobium is not incorporated, led to its accumulation in the residual pegmatitic solutions, from which it was precipitated during the replacement stage as hydroxides, silicates and silicophosphates of the rare earths, thorium and niobium. Niobium also accumulated in secondary minerals (rutile, brookite, zirfesite, hydrocerite, catapleiite etc.) formed during the decomposition and replacement of earlier titanium-niobium, titanium, zirconium and rare-earth minerals, and was also incorporated in chlorites, micas and clay minerals (poly-lithionite, halloysite, nontronite etc.).

Isomorphism of niobium with titanium and zirconium and, to a lesser extent, with the rare earths and iron is widely manifested in the Lovozero massif.

In isomorphous replacement of titanium by niobium there is usually simul-taneous replacement of Ca^{2+} by Na^{1+} or R.E.$^{3+}$, or else the second titanium atom is replaced by iron on the patterns:

$$\left.\begin{array}{l} Ti^{4+} + Ca^{2+} \leftarrow Nb^{5+} + Na^{1+}; \\ Ti^{4+} + 3Ca^{2+} \leftarrow Nb^{5+} + 2Na^{1+} + Ce^{3+} \end{array}\right\} \text{loparite, metaloparite, rinkolite, etc.;}$$

$$\left.\begin{array}{l} 2Ti^{4+} \leftarrow Nb^{5+} + (Fe, Al)^{3+}; \\ 3Ti^{4+} \leftarrow 2Nb^{5+} + Fe^{2+} \end{array}\right\} \begin{array}{l} \text{ilmenite, ramsayite, lamprophyllite, lomonosovite,} \\ \text{murmanite, kupletskite, karnasurtite, brookite, ru-} \\ \text{tile, etc.} \end{array}$$

In the zirconium minerals (eudialyte, mesodialyte, eucolite, titan-låvenite, catapleiite, elpidite, zirfesite, etc.) isomorphous replacement of zirconium by niobium is accompanied by simultaneous replacement of calcium by sodium or of zirconium by rare earths and bivalent iron: $Zr^{4+} + Ca^{2+} \leftarrow Nb^{5+} + Na^{1+}$; $3Zr^{4+} \leftarrow 2Nb^{5+} + Fe^{2+}$.

The incorporation of niobium into rare-earth minerals (steenstrupine, man-ganosteenstrupine, erikite etc.) was probably due to isomorphous replacement of rare earths by this element with simultaneous replacement of a corresponding amount of manganese or calcium by sodium (to maintain electroneutrality): R.E.$^{3+} + 2(Mn, Ca)^{2+} \leftarrow Nb^{5+} + 2Na^{1+}$.

The presence of small quantities of niobium in chlorites, micas and clay minerals is probably due to its incorporation in the crystalline structures to compensate valencies on replacement of silicon by aluminium on the pattern: $2Si^{4+} + Fe^{3+} \leftarrow 2Al^{3+} + Nb^{5+}$.

Tantalum (73)

The mean tantalum content of the massif is approximately 7×10^{-3} [per cent], approximately 30 times its clarke for igneous rocks. Because of the similarity between the properties of tantalum and those of niobium and titanium (especially the ionic radii) and also because there is far less of it, tantalum does not form its own minerals, but is incorporated with Nb and Ti in almost all the niobium, niobium-containing and titanium minerals.

The tantalum oxide content has been determined for only 7 minerals by chemical, X-ray spectrographic and spectrographic methods: loparite (0·51–0·77 per cent), eudialyte (0·06 per cent),* murmanite (0·5–0·56 per cent), nenadkevichite, ramsayite, pyrochlore (1–2 per cent)† and metaloparite (0·66 per cent); (Table 169).

Ta$_2$O$_5$ content in the rocks of the massif varies between 0·001 and 0·05 per cent (Table 195); it is most plentiful in urtites and eudialytites, owing to the presence in them of loparite and eudialyte. The ratio of tantalum to niobium in the rocks (Table 195) and in the most widely-distributed niobium minerals (loparite, murmanite and metaloparite) is not stable, but varies between 8·4 and 17·5 per cent. The mean Ta : Nb ratio in the Lovozero alkali massif is 1 : 12·8. The ratio of tantalum to niobium in nepheline syenites given by Rankama and Sahama (1949) is 1 : 387·5, which is far from according with data for the Lovozero massif and other massifs in the Soviet Union. Thus, for example, this ratio is 1 : 12 for the nepheline syenite massifs of the Vishnevye mountains (Es'kova et al., 1958). It seems likely that Rankama's data for tantalum are too low and need to be checked.

TABLE 195   Ta$_2$O$_5$ content in the rocks (analyst Kukharchik)

Rocks	Ta$_2$O$_5$ content, per cent	Ta:Nb ratio
Eudialytites	0·03	1:14·5
Eudialytic lujavrites	0·007*–0·01	1:17·5
Foyaites	0·004*–0·01	1:8·4
Aegirine-lujavrites	0·006	1:12·8
Hornblende-lujavrites	0·008	1:12·0
Ijolite-urtites	0·001	—
Urtites	up to 0·05	1:9·6
Poikilitic nepheline-syenites	0·008	1:13·1

* Spectrographic data

Tellurium (52)

Tellurium is almost entirely absent from the Lovozero massif. It has been detected by spectrographic analysis only in the rarely-encountered mineral galena, in which its presence is probably due to isomorphous replacement of sulphur.

Radium (88)

The amount of radium in the Lovozero alkali massif is very small. Nevertheless, at $4·25 \times 10^{-10}$ per cent, its mean content is five times the radium clarke for igneous rocks. Radium content is higher ($6·8 \times 10^{-10}$ per cent) in the rocks of the eudialytic lujavrite complex than in those of the differentiated complex ($3·25 \times 10^{-10}$ per cent) or the poikilitic syenite complex ($2·6 \times 10^{-10}$ per cent). Its content varies in different rocks between $1·32 \times 10^{-10}$ and $1·22 \times 10^{-9}$ per cent (Table 196).

* Data of Gerasimovskii et al., 1957.
† X-ray spectrographic analysis data.

An increased amount of radium is found in eudialytites and in some urtite varieties that contain more of the thorium- and uranium-containing minerals loparite and eudialyte.

TABLE 196 Radium content in the rocks

Rocks	Ra content, per cent
Eudialytic lujavrites	$6·8 \times 10^{-10}$
Foyaites	$(4-6·65) \times 10^{-10}$
Juvites	$2·7 \times 10^{-10}$
Urtites	$1·32 \times 10^{-10}-1·22 \times 10^{-9}$
Aegirine-lujavrites	$(1·54-6·65) \times 10^{-10}$
Hornblende-lujavrites	$(1·96-3·66) \times 10^{-10}$
Poikilitic syenites	$2·6 \times 10^{-10}$

Thorium (90)

There is some thorium in nearly all the rocks and in most of the rare-earth and rare-earth containing minerals. The enhanced content of rare earths in the massif and the similarity of their ionic radii to thorium determined the geochemical history of this element. Most of it is concentrated in rare-earth minerals, in which it isomorphously replaces cerium and lanthanum.

The ThO_2 content has been determined in 10 accessory minerals by chemical analysis (Table 169): loparite (0·39-1·04 per cent), nenadkevichite (0·01 per cent), rinkolite (0·63 per cent), chinglusuite (0·06 per cent), steenstrupine (10·23 per cent), manganosteenstrupine (11·28 per cent), hydrocerite (15·14 per cent), thorite (15·66 per cent), karnasurtite (2·82-6·22 per cent) and erikite (0·32-1·15 per cent). Only two of these minerals (loparite and rinkolite) occur in the rocks of the massif, the others are typical of the pegmatites of the poikilitic syenite complex.

The mean thorium content of the massif is $6·53 \times 10^{-3}$ per cent, almost six times its clarke for igneous rocks. Thorium content in the various rocks of the massif varies between $1·67 \times 10^{-3}$ and $6·23 \times 10^{-2}$ per cent (Table 197). Thorium content is enhanced at the floors of urtite horizons and in the roofs of the underlying lujavrite and eudialytite horizons, probably because of their content of loparite and, possibly, eudialyte.

During the crystallization of the rocks of the massif, thorium was incorporated

TABLE 197 Thorium content in the rocks

Rocks	Th content, per cent
Eudialytic lujavrites	5×10^{-3}
Eudialytites	$1·82 \times 10^{-2}$
Foyaites	$(2·6-9·5) \times 10^{-3}$
Juvites	5×10^{-3}
Urtites	$1·67 \times 10^{-3}-6·23 \times 10^{-2}$
Aegirine-lujavrites	$2·65 \times 10^{-3}-1·57 \times 10^{-2}$
Hornblende-lujavrites	$(2·82-6·36) \times 10^{-3}$
Poikilitic syenites	$9·45 \times 10^{-3}$

mainly in loparite and rinkolite and did not form its own minerals. When early orthoclase and aegirine crystallized in the pegmatites of the poikilitic syenite complex during the early stages of the pegmatitic process thorium was not incorporated in the crystal lattices of these minerals and therefore accumulated in the melt. At the beginning of the fluid-hydrothermal stage most of it came out of solution as minerals of the steenstrupine group.

Thorium once again accumulated in the residual solutions during the crystallization of hackmanite and natrolite, since it was not incorporated in the crystal lattices of these minerals. It was precipitated from the residual solutions in the replacement stage as minerals of rare occurrence (thorite, hydrous silicates, silicophosphates and phosphates of the rare earths and thorium.

In isomorphous replacement of R.E.$^{3+}$ by Th^{4+} in rare-earth minerals, electrostatic equilibrium is maintained by replacement of a corresponding amount of divalent cations (Ca, Mn) by sodium or of part of the silicon by aluminium on the pattern:

$$\left. \begin{array}{l} \text{R.E.}^{3+} + (\text{Ca, Mn})^{2+} \leftarrow \text{Th}^{4+} + \text{Na}^{1+} \\ \text{R.E.}^{3+} + \text{Si}^{4+} \leftarrow \text{Th}^{4+} + \text{Al}^{3+} \end{array} \right\} \text{hydrocerite, karnasurtite and erikite.}$$

Uranium (92)

Uranium is present in the Lovozero alkali massif as very small admixtures and does not form its own minerals. Its content in the rocks varies between 0.38×10^{-3} and 3.60×10^{-3} per cent (Table 198).

The mean content of uranium in the massif is 1.47×10^{-3}, i.e. approximately four times its clarke for igneous rocks. Its content is highest in the eudialytic lujavrite complex (2×10^{-3} per cent); the figure for the differentiated complex is 1.25×10^{-3} per cent and for the poikilitic syenites 0.76×10^{-3} per cent.

The ratio of thorium to uranium varies in the rocks of the Lovozero massif from 1.7 to 12. The range is from 1.7 to 7.2 in the rocks of the eudialytic lujavrite and differentiated complexes and reaches 12 only in the poikilitic syenites (Tables 197 and 198).

Uranium oxide has so far been determined in eight minerals by chemical analysis: loparite (0.0024 per cent), eudialyte (0.01 per cent), nenadkevichite (0.11-0.13 per cent), kupletskite (0.1 per cent), chinglusuite (0.46 per cent),

TABLE 198 Uranium content in the rocks

Rocks	U content, per cent
Eudialytic lujavrites	2×10^{-3}
Foyaites	$(1.16-1.95) \times 10^{-3}$
Juvites	0.79×10^{-3}
Urtites	$(0.38-3.60) \times 10^{-3}$
Aegirine-lujavrites	$(0.45-1.95) \times 10^{-3}$
Hornblende-lujavrites	$(0.57-1.07) \times 10^{-3}$
Poikilitic-syenites	0.76×10^{-3}

manganosteenstrupine (0·2 per cent), pyrochlore (0·97 per cent) and lovozerite (0·042 per cent), in which it isomorphously replaces thorium and possibly zirconium and rare earths.

No direct connexion can be traced between the thorium and uranium content of the minerals. Uranium content is usually very small in minerals with a high thorium content, but there are some minerals containing small amounts of thorium and rare earths in which there is sometimes more uranium than thorium (nenadkevichite and chinglusuite). An enhanced uranium content is typical of rare-metal minerals from the late stages of formation (manganosteenstrupine, chinglusuite and pyrochlore).

IV. Accessory Elements

We have classified He, Cu, Ag, Au, Zn, Cd, Sn, Pb, V, As, Sb, Bi, Cr, Mo, Co and Ni as accessory elements of the massif. Their content is measured in thousandths and ten-thousandths of one per cent or less. Of these elements Mo, Cu, Zn, Pb, Co and As form their own minerals in some rock varieties and in the pegmatites (molybdenite, pyrite, chalcopyrite, pyrrhotite, sphalerite, galena, löllingite etc.), while the others can be detected only by spectrographic analysis and are present mainly in sulphides.

Helium (2)

The distribution of helium in the Lovozero massif has not been studied. According to Gerling (1941) the content of this element in loparite from the Alluaiv pegmatitic vein is 0·0567 mg per gram of the mineral. Helium is probably present in other thorium- and uranium-containing minerals.

Copper (29)

At 0·0016 per cent the mean content of copper in the massif is less than a quarter of its clarke for igneous rocks.

The presence of copper has been detected spectrographically in 63 minerals, in three of which (chalcopyrite, covellite and cuprite), which are mineralogical rarities in the massif, it is a main constituent (Table 169).

By polarographic and spectrographic analysis the copper content of the rocks is measured in thousandths of one per cent and reaches hundredths of one per cent only in malignites (Table 199).

Very small amounts of copper are present in the minerals of all stages of mineral formation. Spectrographic analysis puts its content at not more than 0·005 per cent in most of the minerals. Copper gives average lines only in lamprophyllite, epididymite, halloysite and galena, and its content is further enhanced in chlorites (0·01 per cent) and allophane (up to 1·6 per cent). The copper-containing minerals (chalcopyrite, cuprite and covellite) occur in very small quantities mainly in hybrid contaminated rocks and pegmatites and in reworked Devonian xenoliths of basic rocks (known as medium-grained nepheline syenites) and less frequently in malignites and other rocks. These features of the distribution of copper minerals indicate that copper probably entered the alkali magma by the assimilation of the enclosing basic rocks.

TABLE 199   Copper content in the rocks

Complex	Rocks	Cu content, per cent
Eudialytic lujavrite	Eudialytic lujavrites Eudialytites Porphyritic juvites	0·0014 0·006 up to 0·01*
Differentiated	Foyaites Juvites Urtites Aegirine-lujavrites Hornblende-lujavrites Malignites	0·0022 0·003 0·0014 0·001-0·002 up to 0·005* 0·025
Poikilitic syenite	Poikilitic syenites	up to 0·001*

* Spectrographic data

Silver (47)

There is a very small quantity of silver in the Lovozero massif as a trace element. It does not form its own minerals. It has been detected by spectrographic analysis in 8 minerals—nenadkevichite, late microcline, albite, natrolite, galena, sphalerite, cerussite and halloysite (Table 169). These minerals were formed during the hydrothermal stage of the pegmatitic process and are all confined to the pegmatites of the poikilitic syenite complex. The most notable admixtures of silver have been detected in sphalerite and cerussite from the Lepkhe-Nel'm pegmatites. This indicates the intimate geochemical association between silver and zinc and lead in the alkalic process.

Gold (79)

Galena is the only mineral in the massif in which gold has been detected by spectrographic analysis.

Zinc (30)

Zinc has so far been established in 44 minerals of the Lovozero massif, in most of which it is present in hundredths and thousandths of one per cent (Table 169). The most important admixtures of zinc are found in schizolite, nenadkevichite, sphene, hydrocerite, karnasurtite, chabazite, chlorites, psilomelane, galena and löllingite, i.e. mainly in the minerals of pegmatites from the poikilitic syenite complex. Zinc has been determined by chemical analysis in mangano-steenstrupine (approximately 3 per cent ZnO), genthelvite (40·22 per cent), zincian montmorillonite (10·83 per cent), sauconite (35·74 per cent), halloysite (0·11 per cent), sphalerite (66·97 per cent), calamine (67·5 per cent), nontronite (4·85 per cent) and karpinskyite (3·26 per cent). Except for genthelvite, which occurs only in hybrid pegmatites, all these minerals are confined to the pegmatites of the poikilitic syenite complex.

Zinc was partly dispersed at early stages in the process of mineral formation and accumulated only in the residual hydrothermal solutions. Sphalerite, which is present in minute quantities mainly in leucocratic rock varieties, was formed in the rocks during the hydrothermal stage. In the most developed pegmatites of the poikilitic syenite complex, in which the hydrothermal stage was particularly strongly manifested, the concentration of zinc became sufficient for the formation of zincian montmorillonite and sauconite, which are typical of lower temperatures, in addition to sphalerite. The formation of zincian montmorillonite together with sauconite and montmorillonite and the enhanced zinc content of halloysite point to the isomorphism of zinc for Mg and Al at late stages in the process of mineral formation. Zinc is isomorphous with manganese and iron (genthelvite) in hybrid pegmatites.

Cadmium (48)

There is only a very small amount of cadmium. It has been detected by spectrographic analysis in three minerals only: sauconite, galena and sphalerite, and has not been detected in the other minerals and rocks of the massif. The fact that cadmium is confined to zinc minerals suggests isomorphous replacement of zinc at the end of the hydrothermal stage.

Tin (50)

Tin has been detected by spectrographic analysis in the foyaites, aegirine-lujavrites and hornblende-lujavrites of the differentiated complex and in 11 minerals: aegirine, loparite, titan-låvenite, arfvedsonite, eudialyte, lomonosovite, ramsayite, genthelvite, natrolite, sphalerite and rutile. Thus, very small admixtures of tin are usually confined to iron-magnesium-titanium, zirconium and zinc minerals. The dispersion of tin in the minerals and rocks was determined both by its slight content and by the similarity of its ionic radii to those of Fe, Ti and Nb, which play a fundamental rôle in the geochemistry of the massif.

Lead (82)

Lead (up to 0·01 per cent) has been detected by spectrographic analysis in all types of rock and in 32 minerals formed at all stages in the formation of the massif.

It is only in manganosteenstrupine (0·1 per cent), brookite (0·1 per cent), löllingite (up to 0·1 per cent) and erikite (up to 0·5 per cent)* that its content is slightly enhanced (Table 169). In addition to its dispersion in the minerals of the massif, lead forms two minerals, galena and cerussite, which occur comparatively rarely (especially cerussite) and in very small amounts. Both these minerals are intimately associated with the minerals of the hydrothermal stage of the pegmatitic process.

The wide dispersion of lead in the minerals of all stages of the process can be explained by its isomorphous replacement of potassium, which has been pointed out by Belov (1957). The enhanced lead content of thorium minerals is apparently due mainly to decay of the thorium.

Vanadium (23)

Vanadium is a typical trace element of the Lovozero massif. At 0·003 per cent its mean content in the massif is a fifth of the vanadium clarke for igneous rocks.

Extremely small amounts of vanadium (up to 0·01 per cent) have been detected by spectrographic analysis in the composition of 18 minerals. The content of vanadium oxide is enhanced in aegirine (0·24 per cent), arfvedsonite (0·03 per cent), biotite (up to 0·05 per cent) and in the minerals of the chlorite group (up to 0·05 per cent),† i.e. in minerals rich in iron.

The mean vanadium content based on chemical analysis has been calculated for only two of the rock complexes in the massif, the differentiated complex (0·002 per cent) and the eudialytic lujavrite complex (0·004 per cent). It has been detected by chemical and spectrographic methods in all the rock types of the massif (Table 200).

The observed increase in vanadium content from leucocratic to melanocratic rock varieties is due to the higher aegirine content of melanocratic varieties, since vanadium concentration is at its highest in aegirine. The geochemical history of vanadium in the massif is intimately associated with the geochemistry of trivalent iron, which it replaces owing to the similarity in their chemical properties and especially in their ionic radii.

Arsenic (33)

Löllingite (72 per cent) is the only mineral in which arsenic is a main constituent (Table 169). It has been detected by spectrographic analysis in 6 minerals: natrolite, hydrocerite, karnasurtite, hydrogoethite, psilomelane and jarosite (up to 0·5 per cent). Its presence has not been established in the rocks of the massif.

All these minerals were formed in the late hydrothermal stage of the pegmatitic process or are the products of hypergenesis (jarosite). At earlier stages in mineral formation arsenic, owing to its low content in the magma, was dispersed in amounts

* Spectrographic analysis data are given for erikite and löllingite.
† Spectrographic data are given for biotite and chlorites.

TABLE 200 Vanadium content in the rocks

Eudialytic lujavrite complex	V₂O₅ content, per cent	Differentiated complex	V₂O₅ content, per cent	Poikilitic syenite complex	V₂O₅ content, per cent
Eudialytic lujavrites	0·009-0·012	Foyaites	up to 0·05	Poikilitic sodalite-syenites	up to 0·01
Eudialytites	not found	Urtites, ijolite-urtites	0·01	Poikilitic nepheline-syenites	nil
Porphyritic eudialytic lujavrites	0·008	Melanocratic and mesocratic aegirine-lujavrites	0·003-0·015		
Porphyritic juvites	up to 0·05	Leucocratic aegirine-lujavrites	up to 0·05		
		Hornblende-lujavrites	up to 0·05		

TABLE 201 Nickel content in the rocks

Eudialytic lujavrite complex	Ni content, per cent	Differentiated complex	Ni content, per cent	Poikilitic syenite complex	Ni content, per cent
Eudialytic lujavrites	0·0003	Foyaites	0·0004	Poikilitic syenites	trace
Eudialytites	0·0014	Juvites	0·0008		
Porphyritic juvites	trace	Aegirine-lujavrites	0·0003		
		Hornblende-lujavrites	trace		

below the sensitivity threshold of the methods used in analysis. Its concentration in the late stages of the process exhibits the general behaviour of the dispersed elements in the process of mineral formation.

Antimony (51)

There is scarcely any antimony in the Lovozero alkali massif. It has been detected by spectrographic analysis only in galena (up to 0·1 per cent).

Bismuth (83)

Bismuth has been detected by spectrographic analysis only in the lead minerals galena (up to 1 per cent) and cerussite (up to 0·05 per cent), which indicates that it is intimately associated with the chalcophile group of elements.

Chromium (24)

Chromium (up to 0·1 per cent) has been detected by the spectrographic method only in rocks enriched in aegirine and hornblende, i.e. in rocks rich in iron, and in 6 minerals: aegirine, arfvedsonite, biotite, natrolite, epididymite and zincian montmorillonite (Table 169). The presence of chromium in aegirine, arfvedsonite and biotite is probably due to its isomorphous replacement of iron in these minerals. Chromium was incorporated in these minerals mainly in the second and fourth stages of mineral formation and was dispersed because of its very small content in the massif.

Molybdenum (42)

Molybdenum has been detected by spectrographic analysis in the foyaites of the differentiated complex (up to 0·05 per cent) and in 8 minerals: aegirine II (0·005 per cent), arfvedsonite (0·01 per cent), natrolite (0·1 per cent), late microcline (up to 0·1 per cent), polylithionite (up to 0·5 per cent), chlorites ($n \times 10^{-3}$ per cent), galena (up to 0·5 per cent) and cerussite (up to 0·1 per cent); (Table 169). It also forms its own mineral, molybdenite, which occurs quite frequently in both the rocks and the pegmatites, though in very small amounts. The molybdenite content is highest in rocks rich in sulphur: sodalitized foyaites and poikilitic syenites, and also in the pegmatites associated with them. Most of the Mo was dispersed in ferruginous minerals (aegirine and arfvedsonite) in the second stage of mineral formation. In the pegmatites of the poikilitic syenite complex it was also incorporated in minerals formed in the hydrothermal stage, mainly aluminosilicates, and less frequently in lead sulphides and carbonates (galena and cerussite).

Tungsten (74)

There is scarcely any tungsten in the Lovozero alkali massif. Traces have been detected by spectrographic analysis only in the loparite and eudialyte from the pegmatites of the differentiated complex.

Cobalt (27)

Cobalt occurs very rarely as minute traces, which can be determined only by spectrographic analysis. It has been detected in porphyritic juvites and in eight minerals: manganilmenite, aegirine II, genthelvite, pyrrhotite, chalcedonic natrolite, galena, sphalerite and löllingite (approximately 2 per cent)*, mainly in the sulphides and arsenides.

Nickel (28)

Nickel has been detected in ten-thousandths of one per cent in almost all the rocks (Table 201) by polarographic and spectrographic methods.

At 0·0003 per cent the mean Ni content is approximately 1/27th of its clarke for igneous rocks. Minute quantities are present in the ferruginous, manganian, rare-earth, sulphurous and arsenious minerals, mainly of the contaminated rocks and pegmatites, but also of the pegmatites in the poikilitic syenite complex. It does not form its own minerals. Ni has been detected by the spectrographic method in 11 minerals: aegirine, schizolite, arfvedsonite, ramsayite, steenstrupine, manganosteenstrupine, biotite, pyrrhotite, ussingite, sphalerite and löllingite. It probably replaces iron in these minerals and, less frequently, manganese and titanium. The fact that most of the nickel, like the cobalt, is confined to the contaminated rocks and pegmatites indicates that, at least in part, these elements probably entered the alkali magma in the assimilation of basic Devonian rocks.

V. Associations of Chemical Elements

To sum up, 67 chemical elements, which play various rôles in the structure of the massif, have now been detected. The chemico-mineralogical composition of the massif in all its diversity is determined by the various combinations and ratios of these elements.

The behaviour of each element in the different mineral-forming processes is largely dependent on the changes in the physico-chemical properties of the medium and, in the first instance, on the concentration of the element and of the other main elements and dominant rare elements. Changes in the medium are due mainly to emanation processes, crystallization differentiation and assimilation of the country rocks. The geochemistry of the individual elements makes it evident that isomorphism plays an immense part in their distribution in the massif. The capacity of elements for isomorphous replacement of each other leads in some cases to their concentration and in others to dispersion. Thus, for example, Li and Be are dispersed in alumino- and ferrosilicates during the early stages in the formation of the massif and do not form their own minerals. At late stages in the pegmatitic process their concentration proceeds as far as the formation of their own minerals. Nb and R.E. are largely dispersed in Zr minerals in the rocks of

* Determined by the radiochemical method.

the eudialytic lujavrite complex and do not form their own minerals. These elements are concentrated mainly in the differentiated complex and there do form minerals.

Both isovalent and heterovalent isomorphous replacement of chemical elements were widely manifested in the process of the formation of the Lovozero alkali massif.

Isovalent isomorphism is typical of elements in all groups of Mendeleev's periodic system. K and Na are monovalent elements extensively involved in isomorphous replacements in the massif at all stages in the processes of mineral formation (see the sections dealing with the geochemistry of K and Na). Despite the great difference in the ionic radii of K and Na they still replaced each other in minerals when their concentrations were high. The ratio of Na_2O to K_2O in the main minerals varies from 0·04 to 1 in potassic minerals and 1 to 30 in sodic minerals.

Among the monovalent elements there is also isomorphous replacement of sodium by lithium. The incorporation of lithium, which has smaller ionic dimensions, in place of Na in the crystal lattices of sodic minerals is energetically advantageous, and Li was therefore incorporated in the crystal lattices of all rock-forming and other minerals containing Na, despite its low concentration in the magma.

There is slight isomorphous replacement of potassium by rubidium in the potassic minerals of the massif (in orthoclase, kupletskite and tainiolite) and by thallium (in cryptomelane). Among the monovalent anions there is widespread mutual isomorphism between F and OH. On rare occasions there is isomorphous replacement of fluorine and the hydroxyl group by chlorine.

The divalent elements most subject to isomorphism are Mg, Fe and Mn. These three elements accompany each other in all ferriferous, magnesian, manganian and titanium-niobium minerals, because of the similarity of their chemical properties and ionic radii. There is also isomorphism of Ca, Sr and Ba, which always accompany and supplement each other in the minerals of these elements. Less frequently there is isomorphous replacement of calcium and magnesium by manganese (in apatite, staffelite [francolite], steenstrupine, nordite etc.), of manganese by calcium (in chinglusuite, schizolite, manganosteenstrupine, manganilmenite, genthelvite, chlorites, psilomelane etc.) of magnesium by strontium (in montmorillonite and sauconite), of manganese by strontium (in schizolite and cryptomelane) and by barium (in chlorites, psilomelane, cryptomelane and vernadite). There is unrestricted isomorphism between manganese and zinc during the formation of genthelvite in hybrid pegmatites.

There are some signs of the isomorphous replacement of divalent iron by cobalt, nickel and zinc in the minerals of the massif. Sphalerite, sauconite, galena and cerussite normally contain traces of cadmium, owing to the similarity of the chemical properties and ionic radii of cadmium, lead and zinc.

Amongst the trivalent elements there is widespread isomorphous replacement of aluminium by gallium. The incorporation of gallium in the crystal lattices of all aluminosilicates and other aluminium-containing minerals was facilitated by the similar chemical properties of gallium and aluminium and their similar ionic radii. There is also isomorphism between rare-earth elements of the cerium and yttrium subgroups. Since elements of the cerium subgroup were much more plentiful than those of the yttrium subgroup in the magma, cerium and lanthanum are dominant elements in all the rare-earth minerals of the massif and members of the yttrium subgroup are incorporated in the crystal lattices as small isomorphous admixtures.

Among the trivalent elements isomorphism of aluminium with iron is quite widespread. There is some trivalent iron in practically all the aluminosilicates and admixtures of aluminium are similarly found in iron-containing titanoniobo-silicates and in the hydroxides of iron.

Very small traces of vanadium and chromium are also present in iron-containing minerals (in aegirine, arfvedsonite, biotite and chlorites). In this case there is probably isomorphous replacement of Fe^{3+} by trivalent vanadium and chromium, owing to the similarity of their ionic radii.

Zirconium and hafnium are tetravalent elements that exhibit isomorphism. Minute traces of hafnium are present in almost all zirconium minerals, because of the similarity in the chemical properties of zirconium and hafnium and in their ionic radii.

Isomorphous interreplacement between Ti and Zr is widely manifested. The titanium and titanium-containing minerals of the massif contain small quantities of zirconium and, on the other hand, titanium is present in all the zirconium minerals. The isomorphism between Ti and Zr is usually partial, i.e. one element is dominant in the mineral and only small quantities of the other are present, probably because of the considerable difference between their ionic radii. An exception is provided by titan-låvenite and seidozerite, in which the $TiO_2 : ZrO_2$ ratio is nearly $1 : 2$; these minerals, are however, rare in the Lovozero massif.

Isomorphism of Th^{4+} and U^{4+} is also found in the thorium minerals. Small quantities of U are incorporated in the crystal structures of thorium minerals, probably because of the low U/Th ratio in the magma. In addition to the types of isomorphism already mentioned, amongst the tetravalent group of elements is found also incorporation of very small amounts of Ge^{4+} in silicates, where it probably isomorphously replaces Si^{4+}.

Nb and Ta are pentavalent elements that commonly exhibit isomorphism in the minerals of the Lovozero massif. Since they have similar chemical properties and identical atomic radii, and since there was much more Nb than Ta in the magma, Ta was incorporated in the crystal lattices of niobium minerals and could not concentrate to the point where it formed its own minerals.

Heterovalent isomorphism, which apparently joins chemical elements of different groups into links in the unified chain of processes in mineral formation, is of particular interest in the geochemistry of the massif. Thus, there is isomorphous interreplacement of calcium, strontium, barium and magnesium with Na, K and Li in a number of minerals. The divalent elements, Ca, Mg, Mn and Fe^{2+} are replaced by trivalent, thus: Ca—Rare Earths; Mg, Mn and Fe^{2+}—Al and Fe^{3+}. The same thing occurs between the groups of trivalent and tetravalent elements. Thus, titanium isomorphously replaces iron in the silicates of sodium and iron; aluminium replaces silicon in aluminosilicates. Titanium, zirconium and silicon, in their turn, isomorphously replace the corresponding elements of Group V: niobium, tantalum and phosphorus. All heterovalent isomorphous replacements are accompanied by simultaneous incorporation of other elements into the crystalline structures to compensate valencies.

The chemical elements of which the Lovozero massif is composed can be grouped into natural associations of isomorphous elements. These associations are based on a few main, accessory or typical rare elements of similar physico-chemical and crystallochemical properties, round which other elements capable of isomorphous interreplacement with them, but playing a less important rôle in given crystallochemical structures, are apparently grouped.

Six main associations of isomorphous elements named after the main elements can be provisionally distinguished in the Lovozero alkali massif: sodium-potassium, calcium-strontium, iron association, calcium-rare earths, aluminium-silicon, titanium-zirconium-niobium.

The sodium-potassium association also includes Ca, Li, Rb, Sr and Ba, which are typically involved in isomorphous interreplacement with Na and K (Fig. 255, *a*). This association of elements is typical of all minerals in which sodium and potassium are main mineral-forming elements.

The calcium-strontium association also includes Ba, Mg, Na and K (Fig. 255, *b*), between which there are isomorphous interreplacements. This association of elements is found in calcium, strontium and barium minerals in which Ca, Sr or Ba are main components and Mg is incorporated as isomorphous admixtures replacing calcium.

The calcium-rare earths association, which includes Th, U, Mn, Nb and Ta (Fig. 255, *c*) in addition to Ca and elements of the rare earth group, is found in the rare earth minerals: loparite, rinkolite, nordite, steenstrupine, mangano-steenstrupine, metaloparite, hydrocerite, karnasurtite, erikite and ancylite. There is isomorphous interreplacement between the rare earths and calcium in the elements of this association, and small amounts of the other elements replace the rare earths or calcium.

The association of elements that are isomorphous with iron is very typical of the Lovozero massif. In addition to Fe^{2+} and Fe^{3+} it includes Mn (Mg, Li), Al, Zn (Ti, Nb, Ta), Zr, V, Cr and Ni (Fig. 255, *d*). This association is found in aegirine, arfvedsonite, ilmenite, astrophyllite, aenigmatite, biotite and other minerals of which iron is a main constituent.

The aluminium-silicon association includes P, Be, Ge and Ga (Fig. 255, *e*) as well as Si and Al, and isomorphous interreplacements occur between Si and Al and between Si and P; there are small isomorphous admixtures of Be, Ga and Ge in aluminosilicates and silicates. This association is peculiar to all the silicates and silicophosphates.

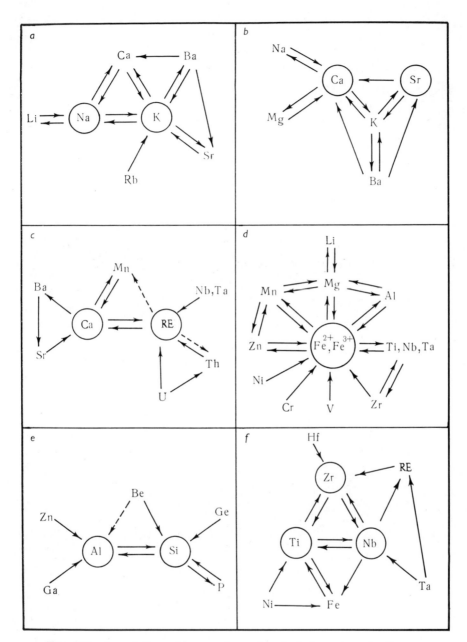

FIG. 255. Associations of isomorphous chemical elements; a-f—diagrams of associations (see text)

The titanium-zirconium-niobium association is also extremely typical of the Lovozero massif. It also includes Hf, Ta, R.E., Fe and Ni (Fig. 255 f). There is isomorphous interreplacement between the main elements of this association, while small amounts of the others are sometimes incorporated in the minerals of the main elements. This association is specific to all minerals of which Ti, Zr or Nb are main constituents.

One can also distinguish a number of smaller isomorphous associations for other elements in the Lovozero massif, but they are not decisive in the processes of mineral formation and are mainly included as secondary constituents in the associations that have been described.

The associations of isomorphous elements are component parts of the minerals and in combinations with each other in various proportions they account for the diversity in mineralogical composition and paragenetic associations of the minerals of the massif.

Each chemical element that is a main member of an association will introduce the whole range of elements that are isomorphous to it into a mineral if, and only if, it is itself a main constituent of the mineral. If it is incorporated into minerals as an isomorphous admixture that is not structure-forming, it does not introduce all the other members of its association, or introduces only very small amounts of those closest to it, exhibiting very similar physico-chemical properties.

CHAPTER THREE

THE GENESIS OF THE MASSIF

WE have an abundance of data from which to trace the history of the formation of the Lovozero massif after the injection of the alkali magma into the gneissose granites and the Devonian effusive-sedimentary cover beds.

Not enough work has yet been done on the way in which the intrusions were injected and emplaced. This is particularly true for alkali intrusions occurring in platform regions. There are several theories that purport to explain how the alkali magmas were injected. The commonest of these are the assimilation and tectonic theories. In essence the assimilation theory states that the magma reworked the country rocks and occupied their area. However, the available information indicates that although the process of assimilation plays a fundamental rôle in the formation of alkali intrusions it is not a decisive factor in the process of their injection.

Whatever the rôle that they ascribe to assimilation processes, most investigators see tectonic processes as the main cause of the injection of the alkali magmas. The shape and volume of the intrusions that occur in tectonic disturbances and the injection of intrusions are determined by faults, displacements of blocks of the country rocks in different directions, upheavals of the roof and down-warping of the floor.

In 1903 Daly developed a theory of overhead stoping, according to which blocks of the fractured roof, being heavier than the magma, sank deep into the earth's crust, giving place to the ascending magma. This theory was used by Ussing (1890, 1912) to explain the way in which alkali magma had been injected in Southern Greenland, where there are large blocks (xenoliths) of sandstone at great depths (down to 900 m) in the alkali massifs.

Eliseev (1953) also supports the tectonic theory for the Lovozero massif and considers that the alkali magma was injected into a gently dipping system of joints intersected in places by vertical joints confined to the contact zone between the gneissose granites and the overlying Devonian rocks.

The major rôle of tectonics in the injection of the intrusion is demonstrated by the relatively great thickness of the Lovozero massif, the steep contacts with the gneisses and the presence of xenoliths of Devonian rocks from the roof far from the surface of the massif, as well as by the fact that (like the Khibiny massif) it occurs in the region of a major tectonic fault (Polkanov, 1933, 1935).

Eliseev, Vorob'eva, Gerasimovskii and others who have studied the Lovozero alkali massif distinguish four stages in its formation, but do not agree about when each stage developed or about the rocks that represent a given stage (see Part One, Table 2).

One can assert from analysis of the interrelations between the different rock complexes and between the rocks within the complexes that the alkali magma from which the Lovozero massif was subsequently formed was largely injected in a single act. The existence of vein eudialytite and porphyritic lujavrites, pegmatites and other dyke rocks, and the phases of the poikilitic syenites, which together account for not more than 7 per cent of the volume of the massif, and which did not play a fundamental rôle in its structure, are due to the formation, for various reasons, of partial magmas or melts in the body of a large intrusive during its formation and their subsequent injection into crystallized regions of the massif. In our opinion there is insufficient foundation for ascribing the eudialytic lujavrites to a separate phase. Their chemical-mineralogical composition, the absence of intrusive contacts between the eudialytic lujavrites proper and the rocks of the differentiated complex and the large number of xenoliths in the eudialytic lujavrites indicate that they are probably hybridized rocks formed as a result of assimilation of roof rocks by the magma of the apical part of the intrusion, which was enriched in zirconium and volatile compounds in the course of the emanation process.

The fine-grained porphyritic rocks that occur in the lower part of the eudialytic lujavrite complex, apparently cutting through the horizontal layering of the differentiated complex in places, probably also developed from a hybrid magma when the physico-chemical conditions were affected by tectonic disturbances. It can be assumed that porphyritic rocks were formed from small chambers of eudialytic lujavrite magma that had remained uncrystallized after the formation of the main mass of the eudialytic lujavrites and the upper division of the differentiated complex. Tectonic disturbances led to the injection of this already crystallizing magma along the contacts between the eudialytic lujavrite complex and the upper part of the differentiated complex, and this conditioned the geological position of these rocks and the formation of porphyritic lujavrite veins in the eudialytic lujavrites and in the rocks of the differentiated complex. The porphyritic texture of these rocks is due to the segregation of volatile compounds with a high thermal capacity when the development of fissures led to their more rapid crystallization.

The great diversity of rocks in the differentiated complex, which accounts for the greater part of the volume of the massif, is mainly the result of crystallization differentiation of pure alkali magma *in situ* beneath the blanket of country rocks and eudialytic lujavrites.

The poikilitic syenites are a late phase of the massif. Their chemical-mineralogical composition indicates that they were formed as a result of the injection into the rocks of the differentiated complex and of the eudialytic lujavrite complex of melts that originated in the body of the massif itself (like the pegmatitic magmas) by the enrichment of the ordinary alkali magma in volatile compounds of sulphur, chlorine, fluorine and water.

The veining is the last phase in the process of the formation of the massif. The widely distributed veins are pegmatites, which crystallized from melt solutions enriched by volatile compounds and rare elements as a result of emanation and crystallization processes.

The temporal and spatial distribution of six main controls govern the complexity in the structure and chemical-mineralogical composition of the massif, the distribution features of the rocks of which it is composed, paragenetic mineral associations, and geochemistry and genesis. These six controls are: (1) the chemical composition of the parent magma; (2) assimilation of the country rocks; (3) the emanation process; (4) crystallization differentiation; (5) isomorphism; (6) replacement processes in the hydrothermal stage.

We shall consider the rôle of each of these factors in the formation of the massif.

CHEMICAL COMPOSITION OF THE PARENT MAGMA

The initial composition of the magma, i.e. the initial concentration and relationship of the chemical elements in it, is one of the main factors in the formation of the massif. In contrast to the mean composition of igneous rocks (Table 168) the chemical composition of the massif is typified by a higher content of alkalis, volatiles (Cl, S, F and H_2O), rare elements (Zr, Nb, Ti, R.E., Ta, Li, Be etc.) and of Sr, Ba and Mn and a relative deficiency of Si, Al, Ca and Mg. It is difficult to compose a physico-chemical diagram with the abundance of components to be found in the Lovozero alkali massif, especially because there is a marked change in the rôle of the individual components at different stages in its evolution. The rôle of some components in the process of mineral formation declines absolutely at later stages in the formation of the massif, while other chemical elements that do not play a fundamental rôle in the early stages become important components of the system in the late stages. We give below an analysis of the chemical-mineralogical composition of the Lovozero massif that clarifies the rôle of the concentration of individual elements in the mineral-forming processes of the massif.

It is known that in a physico-chemical system in equilibrium the ratios of the chemical elements and their concentration are of decisive importance in the development of the system and in the formation of the various solid phases, as well as in the distribution of the elements in these phases, i.e. the minerals. To demonstrate the rôle of concentration it is sufficient to compare the importance of this factor in the monotypic rocks of the nepheline-syenite group, in which differences in chemical composition, apparently not very significant, nevertheless lead to the formation of different mineral parageneses and to the development of different crystallo-chemical structures, thus determining the fate of both the main rock-forming elements and the rare elements.

When comparing the compositions of alkali massifs one normally uses the agpaitic ratio, i.e. the molecular ratio of the sum of the alkalis and alumina. This ratio alone does not, however, suffice to illustrate the rôle of concentration, since

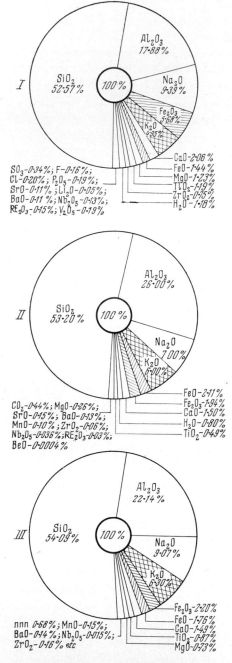

$SO_3-0.34\%$; $F-0.16\%$;
$Cl-0.20\%$; $P_2O_5-0.19\%$;
$SrO-0.11\%$; $Li_2O-0.05\%$;
$BaO-0.11\%$; $Nb_2O_5-0.13\%$;
$RE_2O_3-0.15\%$; $V_2O_5-0.19\%$

$CO_2-0.44\%$; $MgO-0.26\%$;
$SrO-0.15\%$; $BaO-0.13\%$;
$MnO-0.10\%$; $ZrO_2-0.06\%$;
$Nb_2O_5-0.036\%$; $RE_2O_3-0.03\%$;
$BeO-0.0004\%$

nnn 0.68%; $MnO-0.15\%$;
$BaO-0.14\%$; $Nb_2O_5-0.015\%$;
$ZrO_2-0.16\%$ etc

FIG. 256. Diagrams of the mean chemical composition of the Lovozero (I), Vishnevogorsk (II) and Khibiny (III) alkali massifs

alkalis and aluminium can be replaced by other elements in the formation of minerals. Aluminium, for example, is replaced by ferric oxide and magnesium, and itself replaces silicon and magnesium; sodium and potassium replace calcium, manganese, barium, strontium etc. To reveal the distinctions in the chemical compositions of separate intrusions and to clarify the rôle of concentration one must consider the ratio of all the main, accessory and widely-distributed rare chemical elements.

To illustrate the rôle of concentration as a factor we shall compare data for the chemical and mineralogical composition of the Lovozero massif with similar data for two other well-studied nepheline syenite massifs: the Khibiny and Vishnevogorsk massifs (Fig. 256).

The content of Na, Fe^{3+}, Ti, Zr, Nb, R.E., F, Cl, S and H_2O is higher in the Lovozero massif than in these two massifs, while the content of K, Al, Fe^{2+} and Ba is lower. The differences in the chemical composition of these massifs are due partly to the fundamentally differing ratios between the main rock-forming minerals and partly to the formation of different complexes of accessory and rare-metal minerals (Fig. 257).

Thus, microcline and albite are more widely developed in the Vishnevogorsk massif than in the Lovozero massif, and biotite was formed in place of aegirine, which is totally absent. The rare-metal minerals in the nepheline syenites of the Vishnevye mountains are zircon, pyrochlore, sphene and ilmenite instead of loparite, eudialyte, lamprophyllite, ramsayite, murmanite and many others present in the Lovozero massif. Lithium and beryllium minerals are absent from the Vishnevogorsk massif and minerals

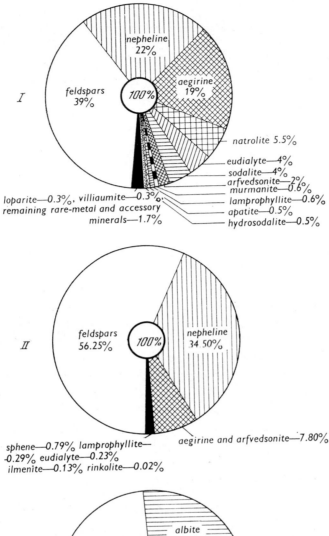

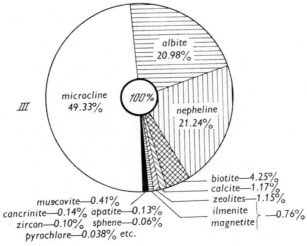

FIG. 257. Diagrams of the mean mineralogical composition of the Lovozero (I), Khibiny (II) and Vishnevogorsk (III) alkali massifs

containing S, Cl, F and H_2O are less widely developed, but cancrinite and calcite are more widely distributed. This indicates a higher CO_2 content (Es'kova *et al.*, 1958).

The enhanced content of sodium and iron in the Lovozero massif and the relative deficiency of Si and Al led to the formation of complex iron-, titanoniobo- and zirconosilicates of sodium, whereas in the Vishnevye mountains the excess of alumina, which fixed all the alkalis, led to the formation of simple silicates (zircon and sphene) by the rare elements (Ti, Nb and Zr) and even to the formation of complex oxides (pyrochlore and ilmenite).

Since the content of Fe, Ti and Zr is higher in the Lovozero massif than in the Vishnevogorsk massif, and since niobium is capable of isomorphous replacement of these elements, the greater part of the niobium was incorporated in the crystalline structures of the minerals of these elements or formed complex minerals with Ti and R.E.; in the Vishnevogorsk massif niobium formed its own mineral —pyrochlore, even although its content was lower, and it was simultaneously dispersed in Fe, Ti and Zr minerals.

In chemical composition the Khibiny alkali massif is intermediate between the Lovozero and Vishnevogorsk massifs. It therefore contains both zircono- and titanoniobosilicates of sodium, potassium, calcium and the rare earths—minerals of the eudialyte group, rinkolite, lovchorrite and astrophyllite, and simple silicates (zircon and sphene) and oxides (ilmenite and pyrochlore). Thus, the difference in the initial concentrations and ratios of the chemical elements in alkali magmas determines the course of the process of crystallization in intrusions, leads to the formation of different mineral parageneses and determines the main features of the behaviour of individual elements. During the development of the Lovozero massif and the other massifs, the concentration of the chemical elements did not, however, remain constant in individual regions owing to a number of factors. It was varied by the mutual interaction of emanation processes and crystallization differentiation.

Assimilation as a Factor Governing the Diversity of the Rocks in the Massif

The alkali magma of the Lovozero massif was injected into rocks of two types of sharply-contrasting chemical composition and the processes of assimilation are therefore revealed in it in a dual fashion. At the steeply-dipping lateral contacts of the massif where it borders on the gneissose granites, assimilation brought about less alteration in the chemical composition of the alkali magma, probably owing to its slight activity because of the low concentrations of volatiles in these regions and the great similarity between its chemical composition and that of the gneissose granites. The alteration in the chemical composition of the alkali magma at the contact with the gneissose granites is shown by some silicon enrichment that gave rise to the crystallization of a large quantity of feldspars in the zones round the contacts and to the formation of such minerals as ilmenite and zircon instead of the titanosilicates and zirconosilicates of sodium. This slight alteration in the ratios between the chemical elements did not, however, disturb the general course of crystallization in the massif.

In the apical region of the intrusion, where the alkali magma was in contact with basic rocks of greatly different composition (Devonian augite-porphyrites, picrite-porphyrites etc.) assimilation had a strong influence on the course of mineral forming processes, which were also affected by the enrichment of the alkali magma in the apical sector of the massif by volatile compounds that increased its activity.

In this case the reworking of the country rocks by the alkali magma led to its quite considerable enrichment with iron, calcium, magnesium and titanium and to the formation of an essentially hybrid magma, which crystallized as eudialytic lujavrites richer in iron (7·25 per cent Fe_2O_3 and 1·79 per cent FeO), calcium (3·25 per cent CaO), magnesium (1·79 per cent MgO) and titanium (1·89 per cent TiO_2) than the rocks of the differentiated complex where the contents are: Fe_2O_3- 5·04 per cent, FeO 1·3 per cent, CaO 1·52 per cent, MgO 0·96 per cent and TiO_2 0·9 per cent (Table 167).

The development of a mineral of the eudialyte group richer in calcium (meso-dialyte) in the upper part of the eudialytic lujavrite complex is a clear example of the effect of assimilation of the country rocks. As the eudialytic lujavrites become less contaminated with increase in depth the mesodialyte is gradually replaced by eudialyte, which is the more sodic member of this series.

The interaction of the alkali magma with the country rocks was halted at different stages in different regions of the massif. In the deeper horizons, poor in volatiles, the interaction with augite-porphyrites was less intensive and the magma was only slightly enriched with iron, magnesium, calcium and titanium; this led subsequently to the formation of contaminated rocks and pegmatites that differ from uncontaminated rocks in having a slightly enhanced content of aegirine and in the appearance of orthoclase, aegirine-augite and the presence of sphene, apatite, ilmenite, biotite and zircon, as well as minerals typical of uncontaminated rocks. Enrichment of the pegmatitic melt with iron caused earlier crystallization of aegirine in the contaminated pegmatites.

The Emanation Factor

The course of crystallization in the massif was affected by the emanation process, which is one of the dominant factors in the redistribution of chemical elements in magma (Vlasov, 1956). This factor led to the accumulation of volatile compounds (chlorine, fluorine, sulphur, hydrogen, sodium and zirconium) and to a lesser extent of other rare elements, in the magma of certain regions of the intrusive. Crystallization of this magma led to the formation of eudialytic lujavrites, eudialytites and poikilitic nepheline-sodalite syenites. Emanation processes also conditioned the extensive development of pegmatites in the massif and especially the formation of pegmatite horizons beneath the urtite horizons, which formed a barrier to the passage of emanations carrying a wide assortment of volatile compounds including rare elements. The concentration of these elements, and especially zirconium, in the upper part of the massif, points to the rôle of the emanation factor in their redistribution.

The higher content of zirconium (1·36 per cent), chlorine (0·18 per cent) and fluorine (0·22 per cent) in the eudialytic lujavrite complex than in the differentiated complex (Zr-0·19 per cent, Cl-0·13 per cent, F-0·14 per cent) suggests that zirconium probably migrated from the lower to the upper parts of the magma as chlorides and fluorides. The great part played by fluorine and chlorine in the formation of eudialytic lujavrites is also indicated by the presence of considerable quantities of chlorine in minerals of the eudialyte-eucolite group and by the fairly extensive distribution of sodalite and arfvedsonite in them.

The high volatile content of the magma fundamentally affected the redistribution of sodium, niobium and rare earths of the yttrium subgroup. It can be seen from Tables 168 and 170 that the sodium and niobium contents of the two main rock complexes are approximately the same (6·72-6·94 per cent Na and 0·08-0·09 per cent Nb), although one would expect that their content would be lower in the rocks of the eudialytic lujavrite complex because of impoverishment of the alkali magma through assimilation of considerable quantities of the country rocks, which contain almost no niobium and only about 2 per cent of Na. The approximately equal content of sodium and niobium in the eudialytic lujavrites and in the uncontaminated rocks indicates that there was a considerable concentration of these elements in the apical region of the intrusion in the form of volatile compounds. Since the fluorides and chlorides of the rare earths of the cerium subgroup are not readily volatile compounds they were not concentrated in the upper part of the massif; their content in the differentiated complex is even higher (0·15 per cent) than in the eudialytic lujavrite complex (0·09 per cent). The increase in the content of rare earths in loparite with increase in depth and their small representation in the pegmatites is clear evidence of the absence of rare earths, especially of the cerium subgroup, in the volatile phase. Chemical analysis shows that the content of rare earths in loparite from the lower urtite horizons of the upper part of the differentiated complex, which are rich in apatite, is higher than in the loparite from the malignites and the upper horizons of the urtites. Loparite is rarely found in pegmatites and then only in very small amounts exclusively in the outer zones, where it is intimately associated with nepheline.

The rare earths of the yttrium subgroup behaved somewhat differently. They are relatively concentrated in minerals of the eudialyte group, in which the content of yttrium oxides and the rare earths of its subgroup is approximately 40 per cent of the total rare earths, and also in a number of minerals from the pegmatites. They are concentrated in the upper part of the massif and in the pegmatites because the chlorides of these elements are more highly volatile than are rare-earth elements of the cerium subgroup.

The rôle of the emanation factor was not so clearly revealed in the formation of the differentiated complex as in the upper part of the massif. Thus, enrichment of the upper part of the complex in sodium led to alteration in the composition of minerals of the eudialyte-eucolite group. Eudialyte, the sodic member of this series, is more extensively developed in the upper part, while the amount of meso-dialyte, which contains more calcium, increases in the direction of the lower parts. Increased concentration of sodium, fluorine and water led to the more extensive development of villiaumite and of the processes of natrolitization and hydro-muscovitization. Natrolite content increases gradually in the rocks of the differentiated complex from its lower to its upper parts. Hydromica is extensively developed in the upper horizons of the foyaites, where it is a late mineral formed after microcline and nepheline.

A number of horizons of hornblende (arfvedsonite)-lujavrites confined to thick foyaite horizons were formed by the concentration of volatiles in certain regions of the differentiated complex, especially in its upper part.

The rôle of emanation processes was most clearly revealed in the formation of the poikilitic syenites. Accumulation of sodium (9·3 per cent), sulphur (0·54 per cent), chlorine (1·02 per cent), fluorine (0·18 per cent) and water (3·21 per cent) in some parts of the magmatic hearth led to the formation of a special magma, from which the poikilitic nepheline-, sodalite- and hydrosodalite-syenites later crystallized. The high content of chlorine, sulphur and water in the magma led to the crystallization of sodalite and hydrosodalite as main rock-forming minerals in these rocks.

The various pegmatites of the Lovozero massif also owe their origin to emanation processes. The diverse pegmatitic bodies and their genetic types, represented by intricate mineral parageneses differing fundamentally from the parent rocks (see Part Two, Chapter 5), were produced by the difference in the concentrations of readily-volatile compounds, including rare-metal compounds, and by other factors. The emanation factor was manifested with particular clarity in the most developed pegmatites, in which large quantities of such minerals as hackmanite, natrolite, ussingite, analcite, late albite and potassium feldspar developed. There was more extensive development of Ti, Nb and Zr minerals containing volatiles than in the rocks, and the replacement stage was clearly revealed in the formation of a complex of lithium and beryllium minerals and other minerals with a high volatile content. The volatile content of the minerals in the pegmatites is higher than that of the same minerals in the rocks. Thus, fluorine content is higher in arfvedsonite from the pegmatites than in arfvedsonite from the rocks.

Apart from their direct influence on the redistribution of chemical elements in the magma, emanation processes facilitated the concentration and dispersion of niobium, the rare earths, titanium, zirconium and other rare elements, by lowering the viscosity of the magma and retarding its rate of cooling, thus leading to more complete stratification of the rocks.

In view of the great rôle of emanation processes in the formation of the Lovozero alkali massif, one can pose the question of the significance of this factor in the origin and development of alkali magmas in general.

Magmas that reach the surface of the earth normally have a temperature of 1000-1200°. One can readily concede that under the conditions existing in some parts of the earth's crust the magmas will reach considerably higher temperatures, of the order of several thousand degrees, and that all the elements and their compounds will be capable of volatility at these temperatures. An intrusion of whatever composition formed under these conditions by tectonic disturbances (pressure reduction) will act as a distillation column in which the vertical distribution of the elements and their compounds will depend on their volatility, i.e. vapour and gas pressures. The more volatile elements and their compounds will, of course, occupy the upper parts of the column, and the less volatile will be confined to the lower parts. According to this view of the process, by which a single magmatic hearth is differentiated into a complex of separate magmas, the alkali magmas in the series will occupy the upper part of the distillation column, since their compounds are the most volatile. Alkali intrusions are formed on the injection of such magmas into the upper layers of the earth's crust.

THE CRYSTALLIZATION FACTOR

In addition to the emanation factor, crystallization differentiation played a great part in the formation of the different paragenetic complexes of minerals and rocks in the massif.

It has already been noted in the final chapter of the first part of the book (see 'Distribution pattern of the minerals in rocks of the Lovozero massif') that the distribution of minerals and chemical elements in the massif follows strictly-defined rules, in which the main rock-forming elements determine the fate of the rare and trace elements in the process of mineral formation. The crystallization of the five main elements (sodium, potassium, silicon, oxygen and iron) as nepheline, aegirine and feldspars, which formed separate thick horizons, led to the exclusion of other, less abundant elements and largely determined their geochemical features (especially the ways in which they combined with other elements).

Crystallization differentiation led to the division of the massif into a regular sequence of groups of rock layers. This process was most clearly manifested in the differentiated complex. All the rocks of this complex are mainly composed of three minerals: nepheline, feldspar and aegirine; the diversity of the rocks arises from the different quantitative ratios of these minerals. The process of stratification led to different spatial and temporal combinations of these minerals and to the formation of three main rock types: foyaites, urtites and lujavrites, horizons of which occur at strictly-defined points in the profile of the massif. That the layered structure of the massif is due to a single process of crystallization of the magma *in situ* is shown by the identical sequence of the rocks in the differentiated complex at different points in the massif, the absence of intrusive contacts between the rocks of which it is composed, gradual transitions between the rock layers in each stratal group and between stratal groups, and the interdependence of the thicknesses of the layers in each group. A theory of rhythmic crystallization differentiation can be based on these facts. The process of this crystallization differentiation can be depicted in the following way.

Crystallization of the alkali magma begins after its injection and the expenditure of its heat in heating and reworking the country rocks. The structure of the massif shows that its cooling, and therefore crystallization, occurred mainly from above downwards. In the course of time the process of crystallization was slowed down because the internal heat was lost more slowly when the country rocks had been heated through by the heat of the melt. At a certain stage in the evolution of the massif the rate of loss of heat by the magma through the country rocks and its own upper crystallized part was so slow that it could be compensated by the heat produced in the crystallization of a single main rock-forming mineral, the components of which were in a supersaturated state under these conditions. It should be remembered that this process occurred in tranquil tectonic conditions and that consequently there was no intensive mixing of the magma and no formation of special gas channels to carry away the heat of compounds with a high heat capacity together with that of readily volatile compounds. It is not by chance that alkali intrusions are well layered only under platform conditions.

The great predominance of sodium over potassium in the magma and the deficiency of silicon led, in the first place, to the crystallization of nepheline, which was sometimes able to grow as a continuous layer when evolution of heat by the intrusion was slow. The differentiation of the massif into clearly-defined three-component urtite-lujavrite-foyaite stratal groups began at this time. The crystallization of a monomineralic nepheline horizon led to the concentration of components not incorporated in this mineral in the underlying magma layer. There were two reasons for this: first, the nepheline horizon extracted its components from the underlying magma layer; secondly, it expelled the components of other minerals downwards. Thus, in the process of the crystallization of nepheline and the formation of an urtite horizon the underlying magma layer was impoverished of sodium and aluminium in particular, and there was a corresponding increase in the concentration of iron, potassium and silicon.

At a certain stage in the process the concentration of nepheline components in the magma layer beneath the urtite horizon was greatly reduced and could not be adjusted by diffusion from the deeper-seated horizons, since a thick magma layer, in which feldspar and aegirine components (iron, potassium and silicon) were in a supersaturated state, formed between the lower boundary of the continuous nepheline layer and the magma layer that was still rich in nepheline components. The nepheline that crystallized from this interlayer consisted of separate grains accompanied by microcline and aegirine, i.e. the formation of the lujavrite horizon had begun and was in progress.

In the crystallization of the lujavrite horizon the greater part of the iron passed into the solid phase and combined with most of the sodium as aegirine, which also extracted its components from the underlying magma horizon. There was thus a reduction in the concentration of sodium and iron in the magma layer beneath the lujavrite horizon and a corresponding increase in the concentration of potassium and silicon, i.e. the conditions created were suitable to the crystallization mainly of microcline and the formation of foyaite horizons, in places consisting almost entirely of microcline. Since the concentration of K, Al and Si was higher in the foyaite horizon, microcline crystallized before nepheline and aegirine, which fill the interstices between its crystals.

With the large-scale crystallization of microcline, sometimes as a practically monomineralic horizon, the immediately underlying magma layer gave up the components of this mineral (K and Si) and was correspondingly enriched with nepheline and aegirine components (Na, Al and Fe). Nevertheless the concentration of iron was not sufficient for the formation of considerable quantities of aegirine. The high concentration of sodium and aluminium and the deficiency of silicic acid led once again to the crystallization of nepheline and the formation of an urtite horizon and so on. This process was repeated with varying degrees of definition many times over.

This is a very simple mineralogical and geochemical outline of rhythmic crystallization differentiation.

The data show that the intensity of the process of rhythmic crystallization differentiation varied in different parts of the massif: monomineralic rock horizons were formed in some places, while in others the process was halted at various intermediate stages and, at some points, in the initial stages.

The temporal and spatial distribution of both the main rock-forming minerals and the rare-metal minerals is intimately dependent on rhythmic crystallization differentiation. The diverse paragenetic associations of rock-forming and rare-metal minerals were produced by alteration in the chemical nature of the magma during crystallization.

The distribution pattern of the rare-metal minerals (see Part One, Chapter 5) in the rocks of the massif indicates that rhythmic crystallization differentiation was a dominant factor in the concentration and dispersion of the rare elements (titanium, the rare earths, niobium and tantalum). There is a direct link between the extent of layering in the rocks and the concentration of rare elements in them. Other conditions being equal, the rare elements usually concentrated where the differentiation of the rocks into three-component stratal groups was most complete.

We shall consider the concentration and dispersion of the rare elements in detail for each rock complex in relation to the level of its differentiation.

The behaviour of the rare elements in the differentiated complex is different in the well-layered and poorly-layered regions. In the well-layered regions the rare elements were redistributed in the three-component stratal groups in the course of differentiation and their content in certain horizons is tens and hundreds of times their mean content in the complex; this is not so in the undifferentiated sectors. It has already been noted that rare elements are normally most plentiful in the differentiated complex at the lower surfaces of urtite horizons and the roofs of the adjacent aegirine-lujavrite horizons.

During the formation of the urtite horizons, these factors led to the concentration of calcium, phosphorus, niobium, tantalum, rare earths, titanium, zirconium, thorium and other elements not incorporated in the crystalline structure of nepheline along with the major elements in the magma of the underlying layer. As the urtite horizon crystallized and its thickness increased, the content of these elements continued to rise. This process led to an increased concentration of rare elements in the lower surfaces of the urtites and the roofs of the aegirine-lujavrite horizons (and malignites) immediately adjacent to the urtites. There is a direct relationship between the content of rare elements in the lower surface of the urtite horizon and the roof of the aegirine-lujavrite horizon. It should be noted that the thicker and more nearly monomineralic the urtite horizon, the higher, other conditions being equal, is its content of rare elements concentrated at its lower wall. The maximum concentrations of niobium, titanium, rare earths and other elements both in the differentiated complex and in the Lovozero massif as a whole are found precisely in these mineralized zones.

The content of calcium and phosphorus and of the rare elements increases gradually between the roof and floor of an urtite horizon. The increased content of these elements, and silicon deficiency, created favourable conditions for the formation of rare-metal minerals rich in calcium and phosphorus and poor in silicon (rare-earth apatite, loparite, mesodialyte etc.).

In the incompletely differentiated and poorly differentiated sectors of the complex the mean content of the rare elements indicated above is of the same order, but there is not such a high concentration of these elements in particular zones as in the completely differentiated regions. In the incompletely differentiated lower part of the complex, from which urtite horizons are usually absent, increased concentrations of rare elements are associated with the lower walls of nepheline-enriched foyaite horizons. In the central poorly-differentiated part of the complex increased accumulations of rare elements are not usually formed. This region consists in the main of melanocratic, mesocratic and leucocratic aegirine-lujavrites, and foyaites and urtites are of rare occurrence.

Thus crystallization differentiation, and especially the formation of urtite horizons, is a dominant factor in the concentration of such rare elements as titanium, niobium, tantalum and the rare earths in the Lovozero massif. In itself this crystallization process would not lead to a high concentration of rare elements if monomineralic rocks had not been formed. The crystallization of aegirine-lujavrites and foyaites in the three-component stratal groups of the differentiated complex did not create conditions favourable to the concentration of rare elements and is more likely to have led to their dispersion. This does not apply to the roofs of the aegirine-lujavrite horizons, at which the formation of monomineralic urtite horizons gave rise to the concentration of rare elements.

Two factors governed the dispersion of rare elements in aegirine- and hornblende-lujavrites. In the first place, on crystallization of the minerals of which these rocks are composed (nepheline, microcline and aegirine or hornblende), which did not take place simultaneously, the rare elements and the residual melt-solutions were repulsed in different directions by the planes of the growing crystals and thus dispersed. Secondly, rare elements can be incorporated as isomorphous admixtures in the crystalline structures of aegirine and hornblende. There are considerable quantities of titanium and zirconium in these minerals (up to 2·7 per cent TiO_2 and up to 0·8 per cent ZrO_2 in aegirine, up to 1·68 per cent TiO_2 and up to 0·09 per cent ZrO_2 in hornblende). There was therefore scarcely any formation of rare-metal minerals in the aegirine- and hornblende-lujavrites and these rocks are poorer in rare-metal minerals than the urtites or even the foyaites.

During the crystallization of the foyaites, niobium, tantalum, the rare earths, zirconium and titanium, elements not incorporated in the crystalline structures of microcline and nepheline, were forced by the growing crystals of these minerals into their interstices, where the relative concentration of the rare elements increased. Since the foyaites contain little iron there was no great dispersion of these rare elements in them as isomorphous admixtures in aegirine, and more rare-metal minerals were therefore formed than in the lujavrites.

The reduced calcium content of the foyaites, and increase in their sodium content owing to the withdrawal of potassium in microcline, led to the formation of what is mainly a sodic association of rare-metal minerals in these rocks (unlike the urtites), and the titanium-niobium minerals in the association are not complex oxides of the type of loparite but sodium silicates (murmanite, lomonosovite, lamprophyllite, eudialyte etc.). There are only small quantities of rare earth calcic minerals in the foyaites (loparite, rare earth apatite), most of the rare earths being incorporated as isomorphous admixtures in minerals of the eudialyte-eucolite group, which are more plentiful in the foyaites than in the urtites.

Thus, the rare elements are concentrated in some horizons and dispersed in others during the differentiation of the rocks into three-component stratal groups, although their mean content in the three-component group is approximately the same as their mean content in the differentiated complex.

Redistribution of the chemical elements as a result of crystallization differentiation of the magma led to the appearance of certain paragenetic mineral associations. Depending on the composition of the rocks and on isomorphism, the rare elements form different minerals in different rocks or are incorporated as isomorphous admixtures in the crystal lattices of the main rock-forming and rare-metal minerals.

Each rock variety of the differentiated complex has its own specific association of rare-metal minerals. Thus, loparite and apatite are typical of the urtites, lomonosovite, murmanite, lamprophyllite and eudialyte of the foyaites, while small quantities of both are found in the lujavrites in addition to ramsayite, which is typical of lujavrites.

There is qualitative alteration in a series of rare-metal minerals in each three-component stratal group between the roofs of the foyaite horizons and the floors of the underlying urtite horizons, and one set is gradually replaced by another. Lomonosovite and murmanite are replaced by loparite and apatite, and eudialyte by mesodialyte. This replacement is due to an increase in the concentration of calcium, phosphorus and the rare earths in the magma and to a decrease in silicon content as a result of the deposition of microcline, and subsequently of nepheline.

Under these conditions titanium and niobium crystallize as titanoniobates instead of silicates, and take up rare earths and phosphorus with calcium, while the rare earths also form apatite.

In each three-component foyaite-lujavrite stratal group, increased contents of rare-metal minerals are typical of: (1) the zone of transition between the urtites and the lujavrites and (2) the upper regions of the foyaite horizon. Each zone has its own specific rare-metal mineralization. This mineralization consists of the calcic minerals of Ti, Nb and R.E. in the first case (loparite and apatite), while the rare-metal minerals of the foyaite zone are sodium silicates of Ti, Nb and Zr (murmanite, lomonosovite, lamprophyllite and eudialyte). The rare earths are dispersed in the foyaite zone and do not form their own minerals.

In the poorly-layered middle region of the differentiated complex minerals of the lomonosovite-murmanite group occur with loparite in aegirine-lujavrites.

One can easily follow the rôle of crystallization differentiation in the formation of the eudialytic lujavrite complex from the behaviour of niobium, the rare earths and titanium in the rocks of this complex. It has been noted above that an increase in the concentration of zirconium in the magma under the influence of emanation processes played a considerable part in the eudialytic lujavrite complex by the dispersion of niobium and the rare earths. Most of the titanium in this complex was also dispersed and incorporated as an isomorphous admixture in the crystal lattices of aegirine and, to a lesser extent, of zirconium minerals.

The dispersion of these rare elements is due both to the high concentration of iron and zirconium in the magma of the eudialytic lujavrites, which was responsible for the absence of large accumulations of niobium, rare-earth and titanium minerals in the rocks of the complex, and to the incomplete nature of the layering. Even at the level of differentiation to be found in the eudialytic lujavrite complex, one can observe the initial stage of local accumulation of titanium, rare-earth and niobium minerals (loparite, murmanite, lomonosovite, lamprophyllite etc.). The content of these minerals is higher in the leucocratic rocks. This is apparently connected with the lower content of aegirine and zirconium minerals in leucocratic varieties, since considerable quantities of niobium, rare earths and titanium remain in the melt after their crystallization. In melanocratic eudialytic lujavrites, or when differentiation is not found, almost all of the niobium and rare earths is incorporated as isomorphous admixtures in aegirine and eudialyte.

Bearing in mind that the content of niobium, titanium and rare-earth minerals is found to increase in the rocks of the eudialytic lujavrite complex as the rocks become more leucocratic, one can assume that when differentiation of eudialytic lujavrites is most complete and there has been formation of rocks with a low content of eudialyte and aegirine such as foyaites and urtites, higher concentrations of rare-metal minerals could be formed in them. This hypothesis is confirmed by the example of the porphyritic juvites. In a partly-defined three-component stratal group including a porphyritic juvite layer the maximum concentration of niobium, rare earths and titanium in the complex is concentrated in these rocks. The content of these elements in the juvites is more than ten times their mean content in the complex. In this group, however, there is only a general tendency for the concentration of rare elements to increase in the direction of the floor of the juvite horizon, and in this respect it differs from well-differentiated stratal groups in which monomineralic urtite horizons are developed.

Layering differentiation is not apparent in the rocks of the poikilitic syenite complex and there are no increased local accumulations of rare-metal minerals and rare elements.

Thus there are strictly regular features in the distribution of rare-metal minerals and rare elements in the massif: the concentrations of rare elements in the rocks increase with the degree of differentiation.

Crystallization differentiation led in the pegmatitic process to the formation of monomineralic zones and to an increase in the concentration of such elements as thorium, gallium, lithium, beryllium and zinc in the residual melt in addition to titanium, niobium, the rare earths and zirconium; this led to the formation of fundamentally distinct new paragenetic associations, which include the minerals of lithium, beryllium, zinc, the rare earths, phosphorus, fluorine etc.

ISOMORPHISM AS A FACTOR IN MINERAL FORMATION

Isomorphism is variously revealed as a factor in mineral formation in the Lovozero massif in relation to change in chemical composition in a given region of the intrusion. In some cases it led to the dispersion of a number of accessory and rare elements and in others to their concentration. Thus, increased concentrations of calcium and zirconium in the apical region of the magmatic hearth (eudialytic lujavrite complex), due to assimilation and emanation processes, determined the geochemistry of niobium, tantalum and the rare earths in the rocks of this complex. The high initial concentration of zirconium in the magma of the eudialytic lujavrites caused earlier crystallization of zirconium minerals (the eudialyte eucolite group). Since niobium and titanium have similar crystallo-chemical properties to zirconium and the rare earths have similar properties to calcium the greater part of the rare earths, niobium, tantalum and especially titanium was isomorphously incorporated in the crystalline structures of minerals of the eudialyte-eucolite group. There are the following quantities of niobium, the rare earths and titanium in the minerals of this group: Nb_2O_5 0·93-1·08 per cent; $R.E._2O_3$ 0·81-1·78 per cent; TiO_2 0·48 0·9 per cent. It is interesting to note that the Zr : R.E. : Nb ratio in the minerals of the eudialyte-eucolite group and in the eudialytic lujavrite complex is approximately the same at 15 : 1 : 1.

The titanium from the parent magma of the eudialytic lujavrites differs from niobium and the rare earths in that only very small amounts were isomorphously incorporated in zirconium minerals (0·06 per cent TiO_2). Most of it remained in the melt after the crystallization of eudialyte and mesodialyte and was isomorphously captured by aegirine in the same way as in the aegirine-lujavrites of the differentiated complex.

Thus, those rocks of the complex that include much eudialyte, mesodialyte and aegirine in their composition (the melanocratic eudialytic lujavrites) contain least niobium, rare-earth and titanium minerals. An excess of rare earths over the amount incorporated in minerals of the eudialyte group is dispersed in apatite. It should be noted that the rare-earth content is lower in the apatite of the eudialytic lujavrite complex than in that of the differentiated complex.

Isomorphism facilitated the concentration of Ca, P, Ti, R.E., Nb and Ta at the lower surfaces of the urtite horizons, where their content had been increased by crystallization differentiation, and they were fixed in loparite and rare-earth apatite. On the other hand, in horizons rich in iron (aegirine-lujavrites), in which the concentration of these elements was lower, isomorphism facilitated their dispersion in aegirine and arfvedsonite.

When there was much more Ti than Nb and Ta and an abundance of iron, the capacity of Nb and Ta to replace Ti and Fe isomorphously led to the almost total absence of independent niobium minerals and to the formation of complex titanium-niobium minerals in the Lovozero massif. The distribution of Ta, which is the least plentiful of these elements in the massif, was most clearly affected by the dispersive rôle of isomorphism. The similarity of its crystallochemical properties to those of Nb and to a lesser extent of Ti and Zr led to the total absence of tantalum minerals from the massif.

There is almost total dispersion of Th in the minerals of the rare earths, owing to its capacity to replace R.E., which are much more abundant and it is only in the pegmatites that its concentration is slightly increased in a number of cases and accessory complex rare earth-thorium minerals are formed. Low-temperature isomorphous interreplacements of Si and P led to the formation of silicophosphates at late stages in the pegmatitic process.

The Rôle of Hydrothermal Processes

Pneumatolytic-hydrothermal and hydrothermal solutions played a great part in the redistribution and fixation of the chemical elements. These solutions, which were operative at a late stage in the formation of the massif, altered the habit and chemical-mineralogical composition of the rocks, and especially the pegmatites. The nature of the alterations expressed in the formation of a new mineral complex was not the same for the different rocks and pegmatites. In the eudialytic lujavrites, for example, this process was revealed as a widespread alteration of eudialyte and its conversion to lovozerite and catapleiite. The process of natrolitization developed widely in urtites, that of hydrosodalitization in poikilitic syenites, hydromuscovitization in foyaites and albitization, natrolitization, ussingitization, analcitization etc. in pegmatites (see Part Three, Chapter 4).

Hydrothermal processes are revealed: (1) in the filling of fissures and cavities in rocks and pegmatites and (2) in the replacement of previously-formed minerals by the addition and subtraction of a series of elements. Replacement processes are most widely developed in the rocks and pegmatites of the Lovozero massif, but the filling of fissures is not often found. This character of the development of hydrothermal activity was conditioned by the tranquil tectonic conditions (insignificant development of tectonic fractures and zones of disturbance). When alkali massifs are formed in regions of folding, i.e. under disturbed tectonic conditions (the Urals) hydrothermal solutions are distributed along systems of faults to produce local autometasomatosis, which is revealed in the albitization, carbonatization and zeolitization of the pegmatite veins and the alkali rocks in fracture zones.

*   *   *   *

Operating in varying degrees and in different combinations with each other, the main factors described above led to the formation of 13 paragenetic mineral associations in the massif, which differed from each other in the quantitative and qualitative ratios of the main rock-forming and rare-metal minerals.

The following paragenetic mineral associations are those that are most apparent in the rocks: (1) eudialytic lujavrite association, (2) urtite, (3) lujavrite, (4) foyaite, (5) poikilitic nepheline-syenite and (6) poikilitic sodalite-syenite.

1. The eudialytic lujavrite association consists of nepheline, aegirine, microcline and the minerals of the eudialyte-eucolite group with subordinate amounts of lamprophyllite and murmanite. There are equal quantities of the main minerals. This association is specific to the upper part of the massif, which is composed of eudialytic lujavrites.

2. The urtite association consists largely of nepheline, and the natrolite that developed after it, with subordinate quantities of microcline and aegirine. The typical rare-metal minerals are loparite and rare-earth apatite. There are subordinate amounts of mesodialyte, eudialyte, murmanite and other minerals. This association is most typical of the differentiated complex.

3. The lujavrite association is represented by almost equal amounts of microcline, nepheline and aegirine. In some lujavrite varieties arfvedsonite is also a main mineral (hornblende-lujavrites). The typical rare-metal minerals are eudialyte, mesodialyte, loparite, ramsayite and rinkolite.

4. The foyaite association consists mainly of microcline with a subordinate amount of nepheline, sodalite and aegirine. The typical rare-metal minerals are murmanite, lomonosovite, lamprophyllite and eudialyte.

5. The poikilitic nepheline-syenite association consists largely of nepheline and microcline with a subordinate amount of aegirine. In some varieties of these rocks the nepheline has been almost entirely replaced by hydrosodalite and the feldspar represented is orthoclase. The accessory minerals are very small amounts of eudialyte, ramsayite, lamprophyllite and murmanite.

6. The poikilitic sodalite-syenite association is represented mainly by sodalite and microcline with a subordinate quantity of aegirine, nepheline and ussingite. The typical rare-metal minerals are eudialyte, murmanite, lomonosovite, lamprophyllite, chinglusuite and nordite.

It was mentioned in Part Two that there are also six fundamental paragenetic mineral associations in the pure pegmatites of the Lovozero massif: (1) nepheline-aegirine I-microcline-eudialyte, (2) nepheline-aegirine I-microcline, (3) sodalite-nepheline-aegirine I-microcline-eudialyte, (4) feldspar-aegirine II, (5) hack-manite-natrolite and (6) natrolite-ussingite-analcite-albite.

1. The nepheline-aegirine I-microcline-eudialyte association is typical of the undifferentiated pegmatites of the eudialytic lujavrite and poikilitic syenite complexes and also of eudialytites. It is very similar in composition to the eudialytic lujavrite association, from which it differs only in having a higher content of minerals of the eudialyte group and in containing mainly first-generation aegirine.

2. The nepheline-aegirine I-microcline paragenetic association is represented mainly by microcline, aegirine I, nepheline and less frequently arfvedsonite. The rare-metal minerals that are always present include eudialyte and sometimes small quantities of murmanite, lamprophyllite and ramsayite. It differs from the lujavrite association in the presence of aegirine I instead of aegirine II and in its higher content of rare-metal minerals. All the small undifferentiated pegmatites and the outer zones of large completely-differentiated pegmatitic bodies in the differentiated complex are fundamentally composed of this paragenetic mineral association.

3. The sodalite-nepheline-aegirine I-microcline-eudialyte association is similar in composition to the poikilitic sodalite-syenite association, but typically contains aegirine I instead of aegirine II and more of the rare-metal minerals—eudialyte, lamprophyllite, lomonosovite, murmanite, chinglusuite and nordite. It is typical of the undifferentiated pegmatites of the poikilitic syenite complex.

4. The feldspar-aegirine II paragenetic association consists mainly of common potash feldspar (microcline or orthoclase) and second-generation aegirine with a subordinate amount of eudialyte, murmanite, lamprophyllite, ramsayite and other zirconium, niobium and titanium minerals, most of which are associated in the pegmatites with this paragenetic mineral association. The central parts of poorly-differentiated pegmatitic bodies usually consist of block zones of this association, which also forms practically monomineralic feldspar and aegirine zones in the large completely-differentiated bodies.

5. The hackmanite-natrolite paragenetic association is exclusively developed in the largest completely-differentiated pegmatitic bodies that are genetically associated only with poikilitic sodalite-syenites. It forms block hackmanite-natrolite or monomineralic hackmanite and natrolite zones in the central parts of these bodies. As well as hackmanite and natrolite this association contains rare-earth and thorium minerals (steenstrupine, manganosteenstrupine, nordite, rare-earth apatite, karnasurtite) as accessory minerals. Hackmanite and most of the rare-earth and thorium minerals are absent from the pegmatites of poikilitic nepheline-syenites and from the rocks of other complexes in the massif and the association is essentially reduced to natrolite with a subordinate amount of apatite.

6. The natrolite-ussingite-analcite-albite paragenetic mineral association consists of albite, ussingite, late potassium feldspar, microcrystalline natrolite and

analcite with subordinate amounts of chabazite, hydrargillite and microcrystalline aggregates of micaceous, mica-like and clay minerals. The accessory minerals are tainiolite, polylithionite, epididymite, montmorillonite etc. Thus the typical rare-metal minerals of this paragenetic association are lithium and beryllium minerals.

The natrolite-ussingite-analcite-albite association and its associated typical rare-metal minerals represent the last stage in the evolution of the Lovozero alkali massif.

7. The hybrid pegmatite association consists of orthoclase and aegirine-augite. The accessory minerals represented are biotite, thomsonite, ilmenite, sphene, apatite, zircon and pyrochlore. This association is seemingly superimposed on the preceding associations as a result of the processes involved in assimilation of the country rocks.

The different spatial combinations of the paragenetic mineral associations given above are responsible for the whole diversity of the rocks and pegmatites of the massif and together account for its general mineralogical paragenesis, controlled by the intricate temporal and spatial combination of the effects of the varied mineral-forming and geochemical factors.

BIBLIOGRAPHY

RUSSIAN LIST

ALEKSEEVA, L. M., KOSTYLEVA, E. E. and KURBATOVA, I. D. 1927. Zirconium. In: *Non-ore minerals, 3.* Akad. Nauk SSSR, Leningrad.

ANTONOV, L. B. 1935. *The mining wealth of the Kola tundras.* Khimteoretizdat, Leningrad.

BELOV, N. V. 1939. Isomorphous substitutions in the apatite group. *Dokl. Akad. Nauk SSSR, 22* (2).

BELOV, N. V. 1957. Crystallochemistry of the basic petrochemical process. Summaries of papers at a symposium on the geochemistry of rare elements in relation to the problem of petrogenesis. Vernadskii Institute of Geochemistry and Analytical Chemistry. Akad. Nauk SSSR, Leningrad.

BELOV, N. V. and BELYAEV, L. M. 1949. The crystalline structure of ramsayite $Na_2Ti_2Si_2O_9$ *Dokl. Akad. Nauk SSSR, 69* (6).

BEUS, A. A. 1956. The geochemistry of beryllium. *Geokhimiya* (5).

BONSHTEDT, E. M. 1923. Neptunite from the Khibiny and Lovozero tundras. In: *The Khibiny massif,* Moscow. (*Tr. Sev. nauchnopromysl. eksped. Inst. po izuch. Severa* 16.

BONSHTEDT, E. M. 1924. The manganic neptunite of the Khibiny and Lovozero tundras. *Izv. Akad. Nauk SSSR,* ser. 6 (18).

BONSHTEDT, E. M. 1925. Ussingite and schizolite from the Lovozero tundras. *Dokl. Akad. Nauk SSSR,* ser. A (3).

BONSHTEDT, E. M. 1930. Lamprophyllite of the Khibiny and Lovozero tundras. *Tr. Min. muzeya Akad. Nauk SSSR* (4).

BONSHTEDT, E. M. 1932. Nepheline deposits within the Union. In: *Khibiny apatites and nephelines, 4,* Goskhimizdat, Leningrad.

BORNEMAN, I. D. 1936. Deduction and verification of chemical formulae for some of the Khibiny titanosilicates. In: *Anniversary volumes for the 50th anniversary of Academician V. I. Vernadskii's research and teaching activity, 2.* Akad. Nauk SSSR, Moscow.

BORNEMAN, I. D. 1946. The chemical nature of murmanite. In: *Problems of mineralogy, geochemistry and petrography.* Akad. Nauk SSSR, Moscow, Leningrad.

BORNEMAN, I. D. 1947. Isomorphous substitutions in certain phosphates and titanosilicates. *Tr. Inst. geol. nauk Akad. Nauk SSSR,* 86, min.-geokhim. ser. (16).

BORODIN, L. S. 1954. Belovite—a new alkalic pegmatite mineral. *Dokl. Akad. Nauk SSSR, 96* (3).

BORODIN, L. S. 1955_1. Mineral indicators of niobium and the nepheline syenites. *Dokl. Akad. Nauk SSSR, 103* (5).

BORODIN, L. S. 1955_2. Certain aspects of niobium concentration in nepheline syenites. *Dokl. Akad. Nauk SSSR, 103* (5).

BORODIN, L. S. and NAZARENKO, I. I. 1957. Eudialyte from the alkalic rocks of Cape Tur'e and the chemical nature of eudialyte. *Dokl. Akad. Nauk SSSR, 112* (2).

BOROVSKII, I. B. 1946. A study of the composition of certain rare-earth minerals. In: *Problems of mineralogy, geochemistry and petrography.* Akad. Nauk SSSR, Moscow, Leningrad.

603

BUROVA, T. A. 1936. Niobium in Khibiny and Lovozero minerals (titanozirconosilicates). In: *Data on the geochemistry of the Khibiny tundras*, 2. Akad. Nauk SSSR, Moscow, Leningrad.

BYKOVA, V. S. 1941. The chemical composition of Lovozero loparite and the method of analysis. *Dokl. Akad. Nauk SSSR, 33* (2).

CHIRVA, E. F. 1937. The results of crystallographic and optical study of loparite from the Khibiny tundras. *Tr. Lomonosovsk. inst. Akad. Nauk SSSR*, ser. min. (10).

CHIRVINSKII, P. N. 1946_1. Quantitative chemical and petrographic description of the eudialytic pegmatites from Mt Vavnbed and the Lovozero tundra. *Tr. Petrograf. inst. Akad. Nauk SSSR* (7/8).

CHIRVINSKII, P. N. 1936_2. New progress on the mineralogy of the Khibiny and Lovozero tundras. *Priroda* (8).

DANILOVA, V. V. 1954. *A method of fluorine determination and its use in geochemical research*, Moscow, Akad. Nauk SSSR (Library of the Department of Geology and Geography).

ELISEEV, N. A. 1936. The geological structures of the Khibiny and Lovozero intrusive massifs. *Problemy sov. geol.* (1).

ELISEEV, N. A. 1937_1. Structures of ore fields in the deep-seated intrusives of the Kola Peninsula. *Izv. Akad. Nauk SSSR*, ser. geol. (6).

ELISEEV, N. A. 1937_2. The Paleozoic in the central region of the Kola Peninsula. *Problemy sov. geol.* (4).

ELISEEV, N. A. 1940. The eudialytes of Luyavrurt. *Zap. Vseros. min. ob-va.* pt. 69 (4).

ELISEEV, N. A. 1941. The origin of primary banding in the Lovozero deep-seated intrusive. *Zap. Vseros. min. ob-va*, pt. 70 (1).

ELISEEV, N. A. 1946. Devonian effusives of the Lovozero tundras. *Zap. Vseros. min. ob-va*, pt. 75 (2).

ELISEEV, N. A. 1948. Features of the connexion between ore shows and the various structural elements of intrusive massifs. *Zap. Vseros. min. ob-va*, pt. 77 (4).

ELISEEV, N. A. 1953. *Structural petrology*. Leningrad univ., Leningrad.

ELISEEV, N. A. *et al.* 1938. Geological structure and petrographic composition of the Lovozero tundras. *Izv. Akad. Nauk SSSR*, ser. geol. (2).

ELISEEV, N. A. *et. al.* 1939. Geological and petrographic outline of the Lovozero tundras. In: *Trans. 17th Session of the 1937 Int. Geol. Congress*, Moscow.

ELISEEV, N. A. and NEFEDOV, N. K. 1940. Loparite deposits of Luyavrurt. *Productive resources of the Kola Peninsula, 1*. Akad. Nauk SSSR, Moscow, Leningrad, 1940.

ELISEEV, N. A. and SVERZHINSKAYA, E. A. 1941. The chemical composition of the Lovozero eudialytes. *Dokl. Akad. Nauk SSSR, 31* (3).

ELISEEV, N. A. and FEDOROV, E. E. 1953. *The Lovozero deep-seated intrusive and its metamorphism.* Akad. Nauk SSSR, Moscow.

ES'KOVA, E. M. 1957. Genthelvite from alkalic pegmatites. *Dokl. Akad. Nauk SSSR, 116* (3).

ES'KOVA, E. M., MUKHITDINOV, G. M. and KHALEZOVA, E. B. 1959. Some typical features of the chemical and mineralogical composition of the alkalic rocks of the Vishnevii mountains. *Tr. Inst. min., geokhim. i kristallokhim. redkikh elementov*, Akad. Nauk SSSR (2).

FERSMAN, A. E. 1922. Results of expeditions in the Khibiny and Lovozero tundras. *Dokl. Akad. Nauk SSSR*, ser. A (Jan.-Dec.).

FERSMAN, A. E. 1923_1. Regular mineral intergrowths in the Khibiny and Lovozero tundras. *Izv. Akad. Nauk SSSR*, ser. 6 (1-18).

FERSMAN, A. E. 1923_2. Mineral associations of the Khibiny and Lovozero tundras. *Izv. Akad. Nauk SSSR*, ser. 6 (1-18).

FERSMAN, A. E., 1923_3. Minerals of the Khibiny and Lovozero tundras. In: *The Khibiny Massif.* Moscow. (*Tr. Sev. nauchno-promysl. ekspeditsii, Inst. po izuch. Severa*, 16.)

FERSMAN, A. E. 1925. The Khibiny and Lovozero tundras, 1, Routes. (*Tr. Inst. izuch. Severa*, 16.)

FERSMAN, A. E. 1928. Description of the Khibiny and Lovozero tundra deposits. *Tr. Inst. izuch. Severa*, 39.

FERSMAN, A. E. 1929. Problems of the Khibiny and Lovozero tundras. *Priroda* (5).

FERSMAN, A. E. 1931. Geochemical diagram of the Lovozero tundras. *Dokl. Akad. Nauk SSSR*, ser. A (4).

FERSMAN, A. E. 1933[1]. Rare elements in the alkali massifs of the Kola Peninsula. In: *Khibiny rare elements and pyrrhotites, 5*. Goskhimtekhizdat, Leningrad.

FERSMAN, A. E. 1933[2]. Rare elements of the Khibiny and Lovozero tundras. In: *Khibiny apatites, 6*, Leningrad.

FERSMAN, A. E. 1935. The geochemistry of alkalic magmas. *Izv. Akad. Nauk SSSR* (10).

FERSMAN, A. E. 1937[1]. Mineralogy and geochemistry of the Khibiny and Lovozero tundras. In: *Trans. 17th Session Int. Geol. Congr. Northern excursion Guide*. Leningrad, Moscow.

FERSMAN, A. E. 1937[2]. General characteristics of the Khibiny minerals. In: *Minerals of the Khibiny and Lovozero tundras*. Akad. Nauk SSSR, Moscow.

GERASIMOVSKII, V. I. 1934. Description of the sodalite in the south-eastern region of the Lovozero tundras. *Tr. Lomonosovsk. inst. Akad. Nauk SSSR*, ser. min. 7.

GERASIMOVSKII, V. I. 1936[1]. On the genesis of the Lovozero tundra loparite and murmanite deposits. *Redkie metally* (5).

GERASIMOVSKII, V. I. 1936[2]. On the mineralogy of the south-eastern region of Luyavrurt. *Tr. Lomonosovsk. inst. Akad. Nauk SSSR*, ser. min. (7).

GERASIMOVSKII, V. I. 1936[3]. Murmanite of the Lovozero tundras. *Redkie metally* (4).

GERASIMOVSKII, V. I. 1936[4]. Ussingite of the Lovozero tundras. In: *Collected scientific papers of members of the Young Communist League of the USSR Academy of Sciences*. Akad. Nauk SSSR, Moscow, Leningrad.

GERASIMOVSKII, V. I. 1937[1]. Ussingite of the Lovozero tundras. *Tr. Lomonosovsk. inst. Akad. Nauk SSSR*, ser. min., 10.

GERASIMOVSKII, V. I. 1937[2]. Erikite from the Lovozero tundras. *Tr. Lomonosovsk. inst. Akad. Nauk SSSR*, ser. min., 10.

GERASIMOVSKII, V. I. 1938. Chinglusuite: a new mineral. *Izv. Akad. Nauk SSSR*, ser. geol. (1).

GERASIMOVSKII, V. I. 1939[1]. Pegmatites of the Lovozero alkalic massif. *Tr. inst. geol. nauk Akad. Nauk SSSR*, 18, ser. min.-geokhim. (5).

GERASIMOVSKII, V. I. 1939[2]. Chkalovite. *Dokl. Akad. Nauk SSSR, 22* (5).

GERASIMOVSKII, V. I. 1940[1]. On the problem of niobium and tantalum in the USSR. *Tr. inst. geol. nauk Akad. Nauk SSSR*, 39, ser. min.-geokhim. (8).

GERASIMOVSKII, V. I. 1940[2]. Mangan-ilmenite from the Lovozero alkali massif. *Tr. inst. geol. nauk Akad. Nauk SSSR*, 31, ser. min.-geokhim. (6).

GERASIMOVSKII, V. I. 1940[3]. New data on the mineralogy of the Lovozero alkali massif. In: *Productive resources of the Kola Peninsula, 1*. Akad. Nauk SSSR, Moscow, Leningrad.

GERASIMOVSKII, V. I. 1940[4]. Lovozerite: a new mineral of the Lovozero tundras. *Tr. inst. geol. nauk Akad. Nauk SSSR*, 31, ser. min.-geokhim. (6).

GERASIMOVSKII, V. I. 1941[1]. Metaloparite—a new mineral of the Lovozero tundras. *Dokl. Akad. Nauk SSSR, 33* (1).

GERASIMOVSKII, V. I. 1941[2]. Nordite: a new mineral of the Lovozero tundras. *Dokl. Akad. Nauk SSSR, 32* (7).

GERASIMOVKII, V. I. 1941[3]. Villiaumite from the Lovozero tundras. *Dokl. Akad. Nauk SSSR, 32* (7).

GERASIMOVSKII, V. I. 1941₄. The rôle of zirconium in the minerals of nepheline-syenite massifs. *Dokl. Akad. Nauk SSSR, 30,* 9.

GERASIMOVSKII, V. I. 1946. The genesis of the eudialyte from the Lovozero alkali massif. *Sov. geol.* (10).

GERASIMOVSKII, V. I. 1947. Structure of the lujavrite rock complex of the Lovozero Massif. *Dokl. Akad. Nauk SSSR, 56* (9).

GERASIMOVSKII, V. I. 1950. Lomonosovite: a new mineral. *Dokl. Akad. Nauk SSSR, 70* (1).

GERASIMOVSKII, V. I. 1956. The geochemistry and mineralogy of nepheline-syenite intrusions. *Geokhimiya* (5).

GERASIMOVSKII, V. I. and KAZAKOVA, M. E. 1950. Beliankinite: a new mineral. *Dokl. Akad. Nauk. SSSR, 71* (5).

GERASIMOVSKII, V. I., KAKHANA, M. M. and RODIONOVA, L. M. 1957. The niobium/ tantalum ratio in the agpaitic rocks of the Lovozero alkalic massif. *Geokhimiya* (5).

GERASIMOVSKII, V. I. and TURANSKAYA, N. V. 1954. High lanthanum and cerium content in the minerals of the agpaitic nepheline-syenites of the Lovozero massif (Kola Peninsula). *Geokhimya* (4).

GERASIMOVSKII, V. I. and SHIVALEEVSKII, I. D. 1957. The zirconium/hafnium ratio in the zirconium minerals of the Lovozero Massif. *Geokhimiya* (8).

GERLING, E. K. *et al.* 1941. The age of the Lovozero tundras. *Dokl. Akad. Nauk SSSR, 31* (2).

GEVESHI, G. 1935. The chemistry and geochemistry of the titanium group. In: *Fundamental ideas in geochemistry* (2). Goskhimtekhizdat, Leningrad.

GEVESHI, E. K., ALEKSANDER, E. and VYURSTLIN, K. 1935. The quantitative ratio of niobium and tantalum in titanium minerals. In: *Fundamental ideas in geochemistry* (2). Goskhimtekhizdat, Leningrad.

GOLDSCHMIDT, V. M. *et al.* 1938. *Collected papers on rare-element geochemistry.* Red. gornotopliv. i geol.-razved. lit., Moscow, Leningrad.

GUTKOVA, N. N. 1924. A brief account of work in the Khibiny and Lovozero tundras in the summer of 1924. *Dokl. Akad. Nauk SSSR,* ser. A.

GUTKOVA, N. N. 1925. Results of mineralogical work in the Lovozero tundras in the summer of 1925. *Dokl. Akad. Nauk SSSR,* ser. A.

GUTKOVA, N. N. 1927. A brief account of mineralogical work in the Lovozero tundras in the summer of 1926. *Dokl. Akad. Nauk SSSR,* ser. A.

GUTKOVA, N. N. 1930. Murmanite: a new titanosilicate from the Lovozero tundras. *Dokl. Akad. Nauk SSSR,* ser. A.

KHAZANOVICH, K. K. 1934. The eudialyte of the Lovozero tundras. *Razvedka nedr* (4).

KHAZANOVICH, K. K. 1936₁. Geological outline and industrial minerals of the north-western region of the Lovozero tundras. *Tr. Leningr. ob-va estestvoisp.* (1).

KHAZANOVICH, K. K. 1936₂. A note on the rare elements of the Kola Peninsula. *Min. syr'e* (3).

Khibiny and Lovozero Tundras. Edit. Acad. A. E. Fersman, *1,* 1925. (*Tr. Inst. po izuch. Severa* (29))

The Khibiny Massif. Edit. Acad. A. E. Fersman, Moscow, 1923. (*Tr. Sev. nauchnopromysl. ekspeditsii. Inst. po isuch. Severa* 16).

KNIPOVICH, YU. N. 1925. The chemical composition of loparite. *Izv. geol. kom., 44* (2).

KOSTYLEVA, E. E. 1923. The new mineral ramsayite from the Khibiny and Lovozero tundras. *Dokl. Akad. Nauk SSSR,* ser. A, July-Dec.

KOSTYLEVA, E. E. 1925. Ramsayite from the Khibiny and Lovozero tundras. *Izv. Akad. Nauk SSSR,* ser. 6, *19* (9-11).

KOSTYLEVA, E. E. 1927. Report on work in the Khibiny tundras in the summer of 1926. *Dokl. Akad. Nauk SSSR.* ser. A (1).

KOSTYLEVA, E. E. 1929. A eudialyte-eucolite isomorphous series from the Khibiny and Lovozero tundras. *Tr. min. muzeya Akad. Nauk SSSR* (3).

KOSTYLEVA, E. E. 1932. Report on the work of the Lovozero group. In: *Khibiny apatites, 2.*

KOSTYLEVA, E. E. 1935. Eudialyte as a zirconium ore in the Khibiny and Lovozero tundras. In: *Khibiny rare elements and pyrrhotites, 5,* Gozkhimtekhizdat, Leningrad.

KOSTYLEVA, E. E. 1937. A mineralogical study of the Khibiny and Lovozero tundras. In: *Minerals of the Khibiny and Lovozero tundras.* Akad. Nauk SSSR, Moscow, Leningrad.

KOSTYLEVA, E. E. 1940_1. Materials on the geochemistry of hafnium. *Tr. Inst. geol. nauk Akad. Nauk SSSR,* ser. 8 (39).

KOSTYLEVA, E. E. 1940_2. The genetic interrelationships of zirconium and zirconosilicates in alkalic rocks. *Izv. Akad. Nauk SSSR* (2).

KOSTYLEVA, E. E. 1944. Zirconosilicates. *Mineralogiya Soyuza,* ser. A, 6.

KOSTYLEVA, E. E. 1945. Zirfesite: a new zirconium mineral of the zone of hypergenesis. *Dokl. Akad. Nauk SSSR, 48* (7).

KOTEL'NIKOV, V. I. 1935. Rare earths of the south-east of the Lovozero tundras (Kola Peninsula). *Razvedka nedr* (15).

KRAVCHENKO, V. T. 1933. A mineralogical survey of Suoluaiv. In: *Khibiny apatites, 6,* Leningrad.

KRAVCHENKO, V. T. 1936. A note on the study of neptunite from the Khibiny and Lovozero tundras. *Tr. Lomonosovsk. inst. Akad. Nauk SSSR,* ser. min., 7.

KRISHTOFOVICH, A. H. 1937. Upper Devonian plants from the north-east of the Lovozero tundras (Kola Peninsula). *Izv. Akad. Nauk SSSR,* ser. geol. (4).

KRYZHANOVSKII, V. I. 1924. Sulphur compounds of the Khibiny and Lovozero tundras. *Tr. Geol. i min. muzeya Akad. Nauk SSSR, 4* (2).

KUPLETSKII, V. M. 1925. The mining wealth of the Kola Peninsula and Karelia. *Vestn. Karelo-Murmanskogo kraya,* (22) and (23/24).

KUPLETSKII, B. M. 1932. *Petrography of the Kola Peninsula.* Akad. Nauk SSSR, Leningrad. (*Petrografiya Soyuza,* ser. 1, *Regional'n. petrogr.,* 1.)

KUPLETSKII, B. M. 1936_1. A geological and petrographic outline of the Khibiny tundras. In: *Memorial volumes for the 50th anniversary of Acad. V. I. Vernadskiy's research and teaching activity, 2.* Akad. Nauk SSSR, Moscow.

KUPLETSKII, B. M. 1936_2. A note on the genesis of alkalic rocks. *Izv. Akad. Nauk SSSR,* ser. geol. (2/3).

KUPLETSKII, B. M. 1937_1. A petrographic outline of the Khibiny tundras. In: *Minerals of the Khibiny and Lovozero tundras.* Akad. Nauk SSSR, Moscow, Leningrad.

KUPLETSKII, B. M. 1937_2. The formation of the nepheline-syenites of the USSR. *Petrografiya SSSR,* ser. 2 (3).

KUTUKOVA, E. I. 1940. The titan-låvenite of the Lovozero tundras. *Tr. Inst. geol. nauk Akad. Nauk SSSR,* 31, ser. min.-geokhim. (6).

KUZ'MENKO, M. V. 1950. Chalcedonic natrolite in the pegmatites of alkalic magmas. *Dokl. Akad. Nauk SSSR, 72* (4).

KUZ'MENKO, M. V. 1954. Beryllite: a new mineral. *Dokl. Akad. Nauk SSSR, 99* (3).

KUZ'MENKO, M. V. 1955. Nenadkevichite: a new mineral. *Dokl. Akad. Nauk SSSR, 100* (6).

KUZ'MENKO, M. V. 1957. A note on the classification and genesis of alkalic pegmatites. *Tr. Inst. min., geokhim. i kristallokhim. redkikh elementov Akad. Nauk SSSR,* 1.

KUZ'MENKO, M. V. 1959. Karnasurtite: a new mineral. *Tr. Inst. min., geokhim. i kristallokhim. redkikh elementov Akad. Nauk SSSR,* 2.

KUZNETSOV, I. G. 1925. Loparite: a new rare-earth mineral of the Khibiny tundras. *Izv. geol. kom., 44* (6).

LABUNTSOV, A. N. 1925. Natrolite from the Khibiny and Lovozero tundras. *Tr. geol. i min. muzeya Akad. Nauk SSSR, 5* (2).

LABUNTSOV, A. N. 1926. Titanium elpidite from the Khibiny tundras and its paragenesis. *Dokl. Akad. Nauk SSSR*, ser. A.

LABUNTSOV, A. N. 1927. Zeolites of the Khibiny and Lovozero tundras. *Tr. Min. muzeya Akad. Nauk SSSR* (2).

MEL'NIKOV, M. P. 1893. Data on the geology of the Kola Peninsula. *Zap. Russk. min. obshch.*, *30*.

MILOVANOV, G. N. 1933. Rare earths and elements of the third and fourth groups. *Redkie metally* (4).

Minerals of the Khibiny and Lovozero tundras. 1937. Collected papers. Akad. Nauk SSSR, Moscow, Leningrad.

NEFEDOV, N. K. 1938. Some new rocks of the Lovozero deep-seated intrusive in the Kola Peninsula. *Zap. Vseros. min. ob-va, 67* (3).

New minerals and rare mineral species of the Khibiny and Lovozero tundras. 1923. In: *The Khibiny massif*, Moscow. (*Tr. Sev. nauchno-promysl. ekspeditsii Inst. po izuch. Severa,* 16.)

PERVUSHIN, S. A. 1935. The Kola Peninsula as a raw-material source of rare metals and its economy. *Redkie metally* (2).

POKROVSKII, S. D. and SAY'YE, E. A. 1933. Eudialyte deposits of the Khibiny and Lovozero tundras. In: *Khibiny apatites, 5*, Leningrad.

POKROVSKII, S. D. and KHAZANOVICH, K. K. 1934. Eudialyte. *Karelo-Murmanskii krai* (3/4).

POLKANOV, A. A. 1933. The geology, metallogenic history and industrial mineral formation of the Kola Peninsula. In: *Problems of the Kola Peninsula*. Georazvedizdat.

POLKANOV, A. A. 1935. *A geological and petrographic study of the north-western region of the Kola Peninsula*, pt. 1. Akad. Nauk SSSR, Leningrad, Moscow.

PYATENKO, YU. A. 1956. Roentgenometric research on the crystalline structure of chkalovite. *Dokl. Akad. Nauk SSSR, 108* (6).

RIMSKAYA-KORSAKOVA, O. M. 1939. A crystallographic study of ramsayite from Punkaruaiv in the Lovozero tundras. *Uch. zap. Leningr. gos. univ.*, 34.

SAL'E, E. A. 1932. The rare earths and thorium. In: *Tr. vses. geol. konf. po tsvetnym metallam*, vol. 5. Tsvetmetizdat, Leningrad.

SAL'E, E. A. 1933. Preliminary results of zirconium ore prospecting in the Lovozero tundras. In: *Khibiny apatites, 6*, Leningrad.

SEMENOV, E. I. 1953[1]. *Mineralogy and geochemistry of secondary processes in the pegmatites of the Lovozero alkali massif*. Thesis, Moscow. (Archives Inst. rare-earth min., geochem. and crystallochem., USSR Academy of Sciences.)

SEMENOV. E. I. 1953[2]. Sauconite in alkalic pegmatites. In: *The weathering crust*, 2. Akad. Nauk SSSR, Moscow.

SEMENOV, E. I. 1956. Kupletskite: a new mineral of the astrophyllite group. *Dokl. Akad. Nauk SSSR, 108* (5).

SEMENOV, E. I. 1957[1]. Leucophane in the alkalic pegmatites of the Kola Peninsula. *Tr. Inst. min. geokhim. i kristallokhim. redkikh elementov Akad. Nauk SSSR*, 1.

SEMENOV, E. I. 1957[2]. Lithia mica and other micas and hydromicas in the alkalic pegmatites of the Kola Peninsula. *Tr. Min. muzeya Akad. Nauk SSSR*, 8.

SEMENOV, E. I. 1957[3]. Gelbertrandite and spherobertrandite: new aqueous silicates of beryllium. *Tr. Inst. min., geokhim. i kristallokhim. redkikh elementov Akad. Nauk SSSR*, 1.

SEMENOV, E. I. 1957[4]. Titanium and niobium oxides and hydroxides in the Lovozero alkali massif. *Tr. Inst. min., geokhim. i kristallokhim. redkikh elementov Akad. Nauk SSSR*, 1.

SEMENOV, E. I. 1957[5]. Minerals of the montmorillionite group in alkali massifs. *Tr. Inst. min., geokhim. i kristallokhim. redkikh elementov Akad. Nauk SSSR*, 2.

SEMENOV, E. I. and BARINSKII, R. L. 1958. Features of the composition of rare earths in minerals. *Geokhimiya* (4).

SEMENOV, E. I. and BUROVA, T. A. 1955. The new mineral labuntsovite and the mineral known as titano-elpidite. *Dokl. Akad. Nauk SSSR*, 101 (6).

SEMENOV, E. I. *et al*. 1956. Vinogradovite: a new mineral. *Dokl. Akad. Nauk SSSR, 109* (3).

SEMENOV, E. I., KAZAKOVA, M. E. and SIMONOV, V. I. 1958. The new zirconium mineral seidozerite and other minerals of the wöhlerite group in alkalic pegmatites. *Zap. Vseros. min. ob-va* 87 (5).

SEMENOV, E. I. and SALTYKOVA, V. S. 1954. Epididymite in the alkalic pegmatites of the Lovozero and Khibiny massifs. *Labor. min., geokh. redkikh elementov Akad. Nauk SSSR*, 5 (1).

SHCHERBINA, V. V. 1933. A petrographic and geochemical study of the rocks of the south-western region of the Lovozero tundras. In: *Materials on the petrography and geochemistry of the Kola Peninsula*, pt. 2, Moscow. (*Tr. Sov. po izuch. proizvod. sil SSSR*, ser. Kol'skaya, 3.)

SHILIN, L. L. 1953. Lithia micas from the pegmatites of alkalic magmas. *Tr. Min. muzeya Akad. Nauk SSSR*, 5.

SHILIN, L. L. 1956. Karpinskyite: a new mineral. *Dokl. Akad. Nauk SSSR, 107* (5).

SHILIN, L. L. and SEMENOV, E. I. 1957. The beryllium minerals epididymite and eudidymite in the alkalic pegmatites of the Kola Peninsula. *Dokl. Akad. Nauk SSSR, 112* (2).

SHILIN, L. L. and TSAREVA, L. P. 1957. The distribution of beryllium in the rocks and minerals of the pegmatite veins of the Lovozero and Khibiny tundras. *Geokhimiya* (1).

TIKHONENKOV, I. P. and KAZAKOVA, M. E. 1957. Nioboloparite: a new mineral from the perovskite group. *Zap. Vseros. min. ob-va*, 86, (6).

TIKHONENKOV, I. P., SEMENOV, E. I. and KAZAKOVA, M. E. 1957. The first discovery of elpidite in the Union. *Dokl. Akad. Nauk SSSR, 114* (5).

VAKAR, V. A. 1932. Perspectives of zirconium raw material for Soviet industry. In: Trans. 4th All-Union geol. conf. on nonferrous metals, 5. Leningrad.

VLASOV, K. A. 1946. Textural and genetic classification of granitic pegmatites. *Dokl. Akad. Nauk SSSR, 53* (9).

VLASOV, K. A. 1951. On the genesis of pegmatites. *Dokl. Akad. Nauk, SSSR, 78* (2).

VLASOV, K. A. 1952. Textural and paragenetic classification of granitic pegmatites. *Izv. Akad. Nauk SSSR, ser. geol.* (2).

VLASOV, K. A. 1953. Pegmatites: classification and genesis. In: *Comptes rendus de la 19e session du Congrès géologique international. 1952*, fasc. 6. Algiers.

VLASOV, K. A. 1956[1]. Factors in the formation of various types of rare-metal granitic pegmatites. *Izv. Akad. Nauk SSSR* (1).

VLASOV, K. A. 1956[2]. The emanation process and crystallization differentiation as principal factors in the formation of a number of rare-element deposits. In: *Problems of geochemistry and mineralogy*, Akad. Nauk SSSR, Moscow.

VLODAVETS, V. I. 1933. Zirconium deposits of the south-west of the Lovozero tundras. In: *Khibiny apatites, 6, Leningrad*.

VLODAVETS, V. I. and KOGAN, B. I. 1937. Industrial use of the Khibiny and Lovozero minerals. In: *Minerals of the Khibiny and Lovozero tundras*. Akad. Nauk SSSR, Moscow, Leningrad.

VOROB'YEVA, O. A. 1933. A petrographic and geochemical survey of the south-eastern region of the Lovozero tundras. In: *Khibiny apatites, 6, Leningrad*.

VOROB'EVA, O. A. 1937[1]. The feldspar group. In: *Minerals of the Khibiny and Lovozero tundras*. Akad. Nauk SSSR, Moscow, Leningrad.

VOROB'EVA, O. A. 1937[2]. A petrographic study of the Lovozero tundras. In: *Minerals of the Khibiny and Lovozero tundras*. Akad. Nauk SSSR, Moscow, Leningrad.

VOROB'EVA, O. A. 1938. On the genesis of the loparite deposits of the Lovozero massif. *Izv. Akad. Nauk SSSR*, ser. geol. (3).

VOROB'EVA, O. A. 1940. Primary banding of the Lovozero alkali massif. In: *Productive resources of the Kola Peninsula, 1.* Akad. Nauk SSSR, Moscow, Leningrad.

VUL'F, T. E. and KHAZANOVICH, K. K. 1935. The lovchorrite, loparite and eudialyte of the Khibiny and Lovozero tundras as a source of rare earths and metals. *Priroda* (3).

NON-RUSSIAN LIST

BARTH, E. B. W., POSNJAK C. 1934. The crystal structure of ilmenite, *Zs. f. Kryst.* (A), *88*.

BERMAN, H. 1937. Constitution and classification of the natural silicates. *Amer. Min. 22*, (5).

BÖGGILD, O. B. 1903. Erikite, a new mineral. *Medd. om Grönland, 26*.

BÖGGILD, O. B. 1903. New examinations of schizolite. *Medd. om Grönland, 26*.

BÖGGILD, O. B. 1905. Mineralogia groenlandica. *Medd. om Grönland, 32*.

BÖGGILD, O. B. 1906. On some minerals from Narsarsuk at Julianehaab, Greenland. *Medd. om Grönland, 33*.

BÖGGILD, O. B. 1914. Ussingit, ein neues Mineral von Kangerdluarsuk. *Zs. f. Kryst., 54*.

BÖGGILD, O. B., WINTER C., 1901. On some minerals from the Nephelite-Syenite at Julianehaab, Greenland. *Medd. om Grönland, 24*.

BORGSTRÖM, L. H. 1901. Mineralogiska Notizer. Hackmanite. *Geol. För. Förh., 23*.

BORGSTRÖM, L. H. 1930. Chemismus der Mineralien der Sodalith-Grupps. *Zs. f. Kryst., 74* (1).

BRADLEY, W. M. 1909. Analyse des Neptunite von San Benite County, Californien. *Zs. f. Kryst., 46*.

BRÖGGER, W. C. 1890. Die Mineralien der Syenitpegmatitegange der Südnorwegischen Augit- und Nephelinsyenite. *Zs. f. Kryst., 46*.

DALY, R. A., 1933. *Igneous rocks and the depths of the earth.* New York.

FAUST, C. T. 1951. Thermal analysis and X-ray studies of sauconite and of some zinc minerals of the same paragenetic association. *Amer. Min., 36* (11-12).

FERSMAN, A. E. 1926a. Die Mineralien der Chibina und Lujawr-Tundren. *Neues Jb. Min., Geol. und Paläontol.*, Abt. A (55).

FERSMAN, A. E. 1926b. Minerals of the Kola Peninsula. *Amer. Min., 11* (11).

FERSMAN, A. E. 1929b. Geochemische Migration der Elemente. Teil 1. *Abk. z. prakt. Geol. u. Bergwirtsch* (18).

FLINK, G. 1901. On the minerals from Narsarsuk. *Medd. om Grönland, 24*.

GAERTNER, H. K. 1930. Die Krystallstrukturen von Loparit und Pyrochlor. *Neues Jb. Min., Geol. u. Paleontol.*, Abt. A, B1, Bd *61*.

GLASS, J. J., JAHNS, R. H., STEVENS, R. E. 1944. Helvite and danalite from New Mexico and the helvite group. *Amer. Min., 29* (5-6).

GOLDSCHMIDT, V. M., 1954. *Geochemistry.* Oxford.

GOSSNER, B. DREXLER, K. 1935. Über Krystallform von Lamprophyllit. *Zs. f. Kryst., 91*.

GOSSNER, B., STRUNZ, H. 1932. Die chemische Zusammensetzung von Narsarsukit. *Zs. f. Kryst., 82*.

GRAHAM, W. A. P. 1935. An occurrence of narsarsukite in Montana. *Amer. Min., 20* (8).

ITO, T., WEST, J. 1932. The structure of bertrandite. *Zs. f. Kryst., 83* (5/6).

LACROIX, A. 1908. Sur l'existence du fluorine de sodium cristallisé comme élément des syénites néphéliniques des îles de Los. *C. R. Acad. Sci. Paris, 146*.

LACROIX, A. 1911. Les syénites néphéliniques de l' archipel de Los. *Nouv. Arch. Mus. Paris, 3*.

RAMSAY, W. 1890. Geologische Beobachtungen auf der Halbinsel Kola. *Fennia, 7*.

RAMSAY, W. 1893. Über den Eudialyt von der Halbinsel Kola. *Neues Jb. f. Min., Geol. u, Paleontol., 8.*

RAMSAY, W. 1897-1899. Das Nephelinsyenitgebiet auf der Halbinsel Kola. *Fennia, 15* (2).

RAMSAY, W., HACKMAN, V. 1894. Das Nephelinsyenitgebiet auf der Halbinsel Kola. *Fennia, 11.*

RANKAMA, K., SAHAMA Th. G. 1949. *Geochemistry.* Chicago.

ROSS, C. S. 1946. Sauconite—a clay mineral of the montmorillonite group. *Amer. Min., 31* (9-10).

ROSS, C. S., HENDRICKS, S. B. 1945. Minerals of the montmorillonite group. *U.S. Geol. Surv., Prof. Pap.* (205 B).

SMITH, W. C., BANNISTER, F. A. 1946. Pennantite, a new manganese-rich chlorite from Benallt mine, Rhiw, Carnarvonshire. *Min. Mag.* (194).

THUNGUTT, S. J. 1894-1895. Zur Chemie einiger Alumosilicate. *N. J. f. Min., Geol. u. Paleontol., 9.*

TILLEY, C. E. 1958. Problems of alkali rock genesis. *Quart. J. geol. Soc. Lond., 113,* pt. 3 (451).

USSING, N. V. 1890. Mineralogisk-petrografiske Undersögelser of Grönlandeske Nefelin syenit. *Medd. om Grönland, 14.*

USSING, N. V. 1912. Geology of the country around Julianehaab, Greenland. *Medd. om Grönland, 38.*

WEIDMAN, S. 1907. Irvingite, a new variety of lithia-mica. *Amer. J. Sci.,* ser. **4,** *23.*

SUBJECT INDEX

Principal references are given in italics